W9-BVH-900

Biological Science

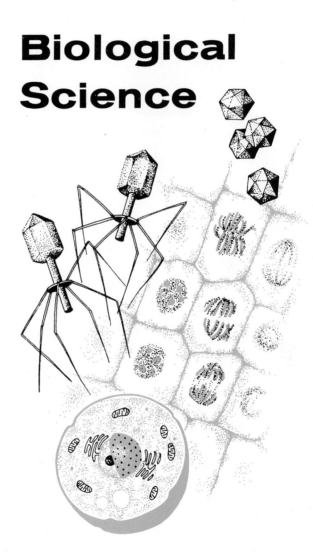

REVISED EDITION

Biological Science

WILLIAM H. GREGORY

EDWARD H. GOLDMAN

GINN AND COMPANY

A XEROX EDUCATION COMPANY

XEROX

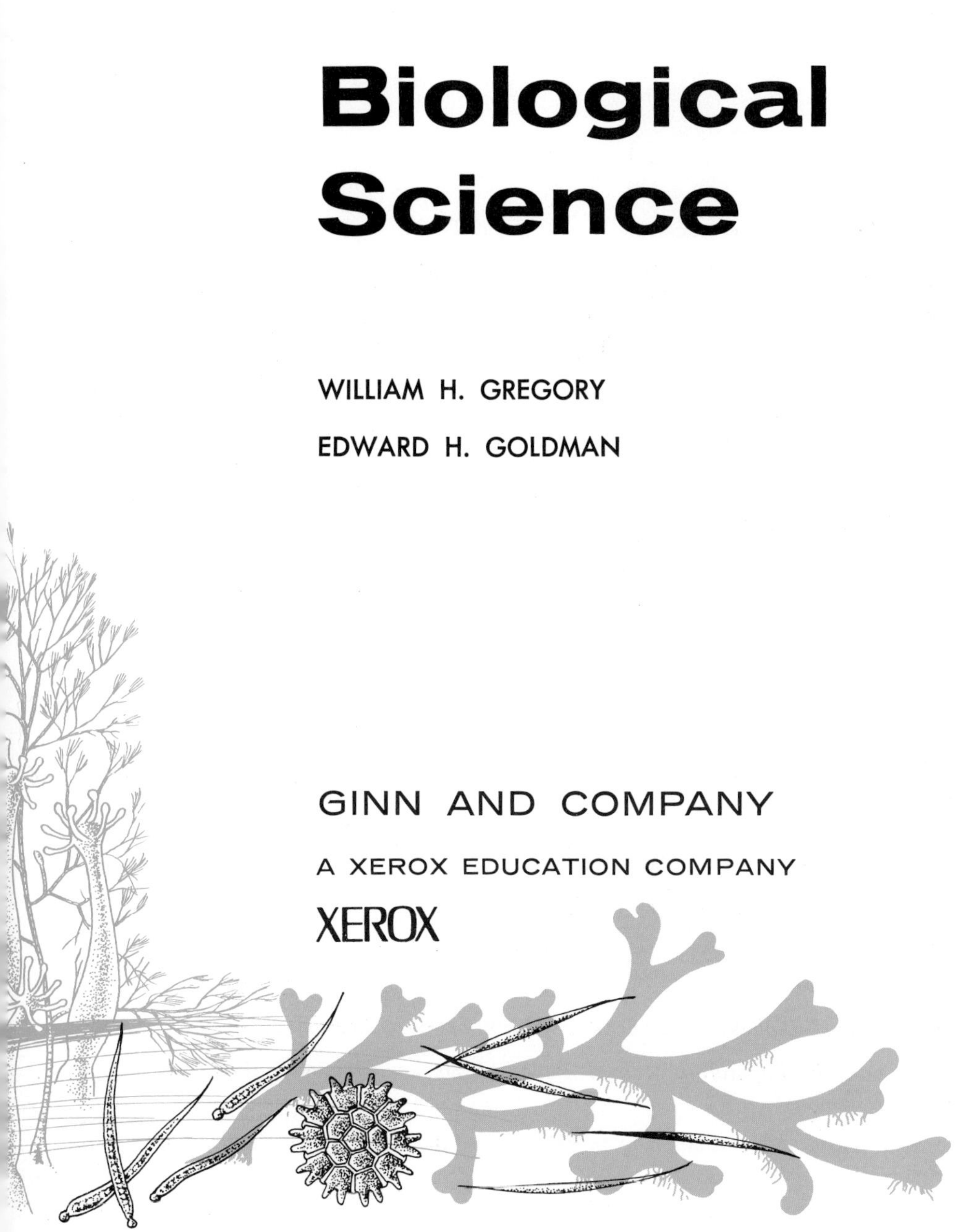

© Copyright, 1971, by Ginn and Company (Xerox Corporation)

© Copyright, 1968, 1965, by Ginn and Company

ALL RIGHTS RESERVED

HOME OFFICE: LEXINGTON, MASSACHUSETTS 02173

0–663–22690–2

William H. Gregory received his B.S. and Ed.M. degrees from Temple University, Philadelphia. As well as being a biology instructor, he has also served as Special Assistant in Science and Assistant Director of Science in the Philadelphia Public Schools. In 1962, Mr. Gregory was named principal of Central High School in Philadelphia.

Edward H. Goldman received his B.S. and M.S. degrees from the University of Pennsylvania, Philadelphia. Also an experienced biology instructor, Mr. Goldman has served as Head of the Science Department at South Philadelphia High School, as an "on camera" biology instructor in the Radio-Television Division of the Philadelphia Public School System, and as a television biology consultant in Dade County, Florida.

ALSO AVAILABLE FROM GINN AND COMPANY

Teachers' Manual: Biological Science, Revised Edition, by William H. Gregory and Edward H. Goldman

Laboratory Manual: Biological Science, Revised Edition, by William H. Gregory

Teachers' Edition of Laboratory Manual: Biological Science, Revised Edition, by William H. Gregory

Achievement Tests and *Answer Key* to accompany *Biological Science, Revised Edition*

Ginn Biological Science Transparencies

Preface

Тне CONTENT of any biology course for young people must take into account the rapid growth of the life sciences. In recent years, biology has advanced with ever-increasing momentum from the mere description of living forms to the threshold of understanding life at the molecular level. The electron microscope has revealed the structure of the hitherto invisible viruses; biochemists have unravelled the secrets of the genetic material; the significance of formerly disputed organelles within the cell has been clarified; the controlling role of enzymes in the metabolism of organisms has been established; the search for life's origins in the distant reaches of space has been undertaken.

Despite this vast increase in knowledge, however, the problem of teaching students is still that of teaching fundamentals. It is this awareness that has guided the authors in the preparation of this revised edition. Although much of the new material included herein has intrinsic value as knowledge for the student, its main contribution is in lending new clarity to the understanding of the fundamentals of biology.

In agreement with current curricular trends, the scope of the present edition has been enlarged, and the sequence somewhat reorganized. The areas of molecular biology, genetics, and evolution have been expanded and, because of their increased prominence in the life sciences, are presented in the earlier units of the book. A new chapter on viruses has been included in which these organisms are examined as the most elementary of replicating systems. An understanding of their structure and reproduction will serve to orient the student toward a molecular view of life and provide him with a grasp of DNA structure and the chemistry of genetics. Another new chapter provides a much more extensive, contemporary treatment of human reproduction.

Other changes in this edition are also noteworthy. A more modern taxonomic system has been adopted. Many primitive organisms formerly classified as either plants or animals are now assigned to the newly established kingdoms Monera and Protista. A separate, illustrated section on classification has been included. We continue to emphasize evolution as a unifying principle, tracing the development of organisms from the simplest to the most complex. By retaining this systematic treatment of organisms throughout the largest portion of the book, the teacher is offered many opportunities to illustrate biological principles through the sequential study of type organisms. Finally, the increasingly important subject of ecology has been amplified into three chapters, one of which treats man's role in nature and his present concerns about overpopulation, deterioration of his environment, and the conservation of his resources.

Our goals in this revised edition remain the same as those stated in the first edition: a text that is reasonably complete in content, up-to-date and accurate in detail, pedagogically sound, and useful to beginning students of varying degrees of interest and ability. All considerations regarding depth of exposition have had as their criteria the needs of both the average and above average student. Given these parameters of student ability and background, certain areas of the text may be studied in detail, or they may be treated in terms of their significance within a broader spectrum of study.

Unit One, *Life and Its Origins,* ranges widely over the basic concepts of modern biology. It presents the wonder and diversity of life, the nature and possible origins of life on earth and elsewhere in the universe, the chemistry of life, and the sources of energy on which living things "run." Its objective is to capture interest at the outset by making biology dramatic and by providing abundant opportunity for laboratory work early in the course.

Prominent in the first unit is the presentation of the structures and the roles of DNA and RNA in life's continuity. The new Chapter 4, *The Threshold of Life: Viruses,* underscores this point. Viruses are presented not primarily as agents of disease, but as simplified bits of life consisting solely of proteins and nucleic acids. Understanding their structure will aid greatly in comprehending later discussions of the cell (Chapter 5) and of modern genetics (Unit Two).

The final chapters of the first unit concern themselves with the physics and chemistry required to understand fundamental biological phenomena. Chapter 6, *The Chemistry of Life,* discusses inorganic molecules with emphasis on the protein macromolecules. A related discussion of the kinetic theory of matter provides the basic explanations necessary to understand diffusion, osmosis, and active transport. Chapter 7, *Energy and Living Things,* heightens the student's understanding of the fundamental energy systems upon which life depends. Photosynthesis is explained as an energy-storing process, respiration as an energy-releasing process, and ATP as the energy "currency" of living things. Thus the entire world of life is viewed here as an energy exchange system.

Unit Two, *The Stream of Life,* is an up-to-date exposition of genetics and evolution. Chapter 8, *Chromosomes and Genes,* discusses early Mendelism, meiosis, non-disjunction of chromosomes, sex-linkage, and certain aspects of human heredity. Chapter 9, *Chemical Genetics,* considers the chemistry of the genetic material, how DNA encodes the traits of organisms, the nature and rate of mutations, and population genetics. The chapters on evolution discuss the evidences and the mechanisms of change. The logic of Darwinian natural selection is fortified through a discussion of the genetic mechanisms that underlie evolution.

Unit Three, *The Primitive Forms of Life,* groups the less advanced forms of life (bacteria, algae, fungi, and protozoa) into four chapters. This grouping places them in a more rational taxonomic framework. Bacteria and blue-green algae are assigned to Kingdom Monera; the various other algae, the fungi, and the protozoa are assigned to Kingdom Protista. Although there is some disagreement among taxonomists, the authors have adopted the four-kingdom system as having fewer inconsistencies than the older, two-kingdom system, which "squeezed" controversial organisms into either the plant or animal kingdom because there was nowhere else to put them.

Unit Four, *The Plant Kingdom,* consists of five chapters that provide a logical basis for understanding the evolution of plants. Chapter 16, *Mosses and Ferns: Primitive Land Plants,* examines the incomplete conquest of land by the mosses and the ferns. Chapters 17, 18, and 19 view the seed plants as highly specialized organisms that have been able to conquer land environments because of their vascular tissue and their water-free reproductive methods. Their structure and physiology are covered in considerable detail. Chapter 20, *Plant Growth and Behavior,* is unusually thorough for an introductory text and provides for a number of laboratory experiences.

Unit Five, *Invertebrate Animals,* Unit Six, *Vertebrate Animals,* and Unit Seven, *The Biology of Man,* trace the development of animal life from the simplest metazoans to the most complex animal forms. An expanded, detailed treatment of the invertebrate animals provides the basis for a continuing developmental-evolutionary approach. The vertebrate classes are treated in a similar fashion.

Unit Seven, *The Biology of Man,* is thoroughly modern in presentation. In Chapter 31, *The Human Pattern Emerges,* an up-to-date anthropological treatment sets the position of *Homo sapiens* and his forerunners in a balanced perspective with the other primates. The electrochemical nature of the nerve impulse furnishes the basic point of departure in Chapter 37, *Nervous Coordination.* In Chapter 38, *The Endocrine Glands and Human Behavior,* the close relationship between the endocrine and the nervous systems is heavily emphasized. The same chapter contains a discussion of smoking and health, which is reinforced by today's statistical evidence. Chapter 39, *Human Reproduction,* is a totally new chapter, containing an extensive coverage of the male and female reproductive systems, pregnancy, and birth. The development of the human fetus is beautifully illustrated by the photography of Lennart Nilsson. Chapter 40, *The Diseases of Man,* discusses both communicable and organic diseases, and accords a contemporary treatment to the nature of the immunity reaction.

The final unit, *The Web of Life,* is an enlarged coverage of ecology. It is perhaps broader in scope than any other unit, for it explores the interrelationships through which the biotic complex achieves unity. After explaining the working concepts of the modern ecologist in Chapters 41 and 42, the discussion proceeds to the ecology of man. The final chapter, *Man and the Balance of Nature,* is a provocative examination of man's place in and effects on the web of life. The application of present and future biological expertise to the problems of world food shortages and the threat of environmental pollution are considered here.

Study aids are provided at the end of each chapter to assist both the teacher and the student. *Important Points* is a concise restatement of the main points of the chapter. *Review Questions* are generally easy and factual, usually requiring short answers. Questions in *Check Your Understanding,* on the other hand, are more thought provoking, requiring a higher degree of mastery. In many instances, the answers depend on understandings not specifically found in the text. *Research Projects and Reports* lists activities and experiments that vary from simple to elaborate. Designed principally for the individual student, they may be used for small groups or, sometimes, for an entire class. Our purpose in suggesting these activities is to stimulate student interest and imagination. The activities range in difficulty from those that can be carried out by all students to those that will offer real challenge to even the most able students.

The authors wish to express grateful acknowledgment for the many suggestions by teachers and students that have been incorporated into the present edition.

WILLIAM H. GREGORY

EDWARD H. GOLDMAN

Acknowledgments

Special appreciation and thanks are expressed to the following persons for reading the manuscript and offering suggestions for its improvement. Introductory science texts are especially vulnerable to criticism by experts, and the authors accept full responsibility for any residual errors of commission and omission.

CAROLYN GIBSON
Biology Teacher
North Hills High School
Pittsburgh, Pennsylvania

SAMUEL S. LEPOW
Director of Science Education
Philadelphia Public Schools
Pennsylvania

PHOEBE H. KNIPLING
Supervisor of Science
Arlington County Public Schools
Virginia

SAMUEL GOLDBERG, M.D.
Albert Einstein Medical Center
Philadelphia, Pennsylvania

Cover Design: Bernard LaCasse
Unit Openings and Classification Section: Josette Gourley
Text Illustrations: Louis Cary, Cheslie D'Andrea, Robert DeCoste, Alex Ebel, Stephen R. Peck, Mildred Waltrip, Graphics/Ken Jones, Magnuson & Larson, Inc.

Acknowledgments for Photographs

2–5 Allan Roberts
2–6 Lick Observatory
2–7 Lick Observatory
2–10 Sidney Fox, University of Miami
2–11 E. S. Barghoorn, Harvard University. From "Microorganisms from the Gunflint Chert," Elso S. Barghoorn and Stanley A. Tyler, *Science*, vol. 147, pp. 563–577, 5 February, 1965.
2–12 Lick Observatory
3–2 Bausch &.Lomb, Inc.
3–3 Hugh Spencer
3–4 Lico, Inc.
4–2 Virus Laboratory, University of California, Berkeley
4–3 R. Francki
4–4 Markham, Smith and Wyckoff (left); Rothamsted Experimental Station, Harpenden, England (center); Virus Laboratory, University of California, Berkeley (right)
4–5 R. W. Horne, John Innes Institute, Norwich, England

4–6 Virus Laboratory, University of California, Berkeley
4–10 Dr. Lee D. Simon, The Institute for Cancer Research, Philadelphia
5–4 Dr. K. R. Porter
6–9 Laboratory of Molecular Biology, Cambridge, England
7–9 T. E. Weier
8–1 Tjio and Puck, *Proceedings of the National Academy of Sciences*, 44. No. 12, 1958
9–1 Wide World Photos
10–1 Walker-Missouri Resources Division
10–2 Gurnee Dyer
10–3 Field Museum of Natural History
10–6 American Museum of Natural History
10–7 American Museum of Natural History
10–8 American Museum of Natural History
10–9 Field Museum of Natural History
10–10 Painting by Charles R. Knight, Field Museum of Natural History

10–11 Painting by Charles R. Knight, Field Museum of Natural History
10–12 American Museum of Natural History
10–13 Peabody Museum of Natural History, Yale University
10–14 Peabody Museum of Natural History, Yale University
10–15 Painting by Charles R. Knight, Field Museum of Natural History
11–1 Peabody Museum of Natural History, Yale University
11–2 Science Service
11–3 The Bettmann Archive
11–4 Historical Pictures Service-Chicago
11–8 United Fresh Fruit and Vegetable Association (left); Abernathy Photo Company (right)
12–4 T. F. Anderson, Institute for Cancer Research, Philadelphia, and E. Wollman and F. Jacob, Institut Pasteur, Paris
12–6 The Nitragin Company, Inc.
12–7 General Electric Company
12–8 Monkmeyer Press Photo Service
12–9 Chas. Pfizer & Co., Inc.
13–8 The Boeing Company
14–4 Hugh Spencer
14–5 Daniel Calderwood
14–6 Daniel Calderwood
14–8 Allan Roberts
15–6 Clinton Misco Corporation
16–3 Hugh Spencer
16–5 Field Museum of Natural History
17–10 The Upjohn Company
18–2 Timothy Plowman
18–3 Timothy Plowman
18–4 Timothy Plowman
18–6 Ward's Natural History Establishment
18–9 Allan Roberts
20–1 Philip Gendreau
20–2 Photos by Joseph O'Donnell
20–4 USDA
20–8 General Biological Supply House
21–2 H. W. Ketchen, National Audubon Society
23–1 Carolina Biological Supply Company
23–2 Daniel Calderwood
23–3 Carolina Biological Supply Company
23–6 Daniel Calderwood
23–12 Daniel Calderwood
24–1 American Museum of Natural History
24–5 General Biological Supply House
24–6 Daniel Calderwood
24–7 Daniel Calderwood
24–8 USDA
25–8 Hugh Spencer
25–10 Hugh Spencer
25–14 Hugh Spencer
26–7 American Museum of Natural History
27–2 U. S. Department of the Interior, Fish and Wildlife Service
27–3 American Museum of Natural History
27–4 Field Museum of Natural History
27–6 Cron from Monkmeyer
27–12 Hugh Spencer
27–13 David T. Hoopes
27–14 W. T. Davidson, National Audubon Society
27–16 U. S. Department of the Interior, Fish and Wildlife Service
27–17 H. A. Williams, Shostal
27–19 Ewing Galloway
27–20 Courtesy J. L. B. Smith, Rhodes University, Grahamstown, South Africa
28–2 American Museum of Natural History
28–6 Hugh Spencer
28–7 Hugh Spencer
29–1 American Museum of Natural History (top and bottom right, paintings by Charles R. Knight)
29–2 Painting by Charles R. Knight, Field Museum of Natural History
29–3 American Museum of Natural History

29–4 U. S. Department of the Interior, Fish and Wildlife Service
29–5 American Museum of Natural History
29–6 U. S. Department of the Interior, Fish and Wildlife Service
29–7 Ewing Galloway
29–9 American Museum of Natural History
29–10 American Museum of Natural History
29–15 Hugh Spencer (top), A. W. Ambler from National Audubon Society (center), John H. Tashjian from National Audubon Society
30–2 American Museum of Natural History
30–3 Australian News & Information Bureau
30–5 American Museum of Natural History
30–6 Australian Consul General
30–7 O. S. Pettingill, Jr., from National Audubon Society
30–8 American Museum of Natural History
30–9 American Museum of Natural History
30–10 Hugh S. Davis
30–11 Allan C. Enders
30–14 American Museum of Natural History
30–16 American Museum of Natural History
30–18 American Museum of Natural History
30–19 American Museum of Natural History
30–20 American Museum of Natural History
30–23 Field Museum of Natural History
30–25 American Museum of Natural History
31–6 American Museum of Natural History
31–7 Editorial Photocolor Archives; American Museum of Natural History (bottom right)
31–8 American Museum of Natural History
32–4 The National Foundation—March of Dimes
32–6 General Biological Supply House
32–7 General Biological Supply House
32–8 Bausch & Lomb, Inc.
33–2 Morris Huberland
33–3 The Upjohn Company
33–4 Science Service
33–5 USDA
33–6 Children's Hospital Medical Center, Boston
33–7 E. R. Squibb & Sons
33–8 Daniel Calderwood
35–3 Chas. Pfizer & Co.
35–13 De Wys, Inc.
35–15 The New York Hospital
38–8 Allan Roberts
38–9 Peter Aaron
38–10 Eugene Anthony, Black Star
39–7 Photos by A. Lennart Nilsson, from *A Child Is Born*, by A. L. Nilsson, Axel Ingelman-Sundberg, and Claes Wirsen. A Seymour Lawrence Book/Delacorte Press, New York, 1966.
39–8 Museum of Science, Boston. Photos by Barry Real.
40–4 Bill Anderson
41–1 Robert Lapin
41–2 Josef Muench
41–4 William M. Johnson, Division of Soil Survey, USDA
41–6 Ernest Libby
41–12 Carl Ostman
42–1 Michael Wynne-Wilson
42–3 Ewing Galloway
42–4 Laurence Lowry
42–5 USDA
42–6 Daniel Calderwood
42–7 Josef Muench
42–8 De Wys, Inc.
42–10 Josef Muench
42–12 Weston Kemp
43–2 UNICEF photo by FAO
43–6 American Museum of Natural History
43–7 National Park Service
43–8 Florida Game and Fresh Water Commission
43–9 Bureau of Reclamation
43–10 United Press International
43–11 Allegheny Conference on Community Development
43–12 Tennessee Valley Authority
43–13 American Forest Products Industries, Inc.
43–14 Daniel Calderwood

Contents

To the Student

W<small>E LIVE</small> in a technological society molded by the products of science. The strength of our society depends upon our ability to adapt the discoveries of pure research to the benefit of all people. What would the world be like without the products of electronics research? What would be the state of medical science without modern drugs, without X rays, or without modern microscopes? All such products of technology are adaptations of discoveries made by the research scientist.

For centuries, the advancing front of knowledge has been extended by the trained minds of scientists. Today, the pace of scientific advance has been accelerated far beyond that of any previous time in history. A reason for this acceleration has been the increasing number of young people, like yourself, who have found their science studies challenging and rewarding. Many of these young people have gone on to advanced studies and have added their contributions to human betterment.

B<small>IOLOGICAL</small> S<small>CIENCE</small>, R<small>EVISED</small> E<small>DITION</small>, teaches the fundamentals of the science of life. We hope that some of you, as a result of studying this book, will make science your life's work. But our purpose is much broader than this. For most of you, we hope that this book will provide an insight into the nature of scientific research, its achievements, and its applications.

You and your fellow students are better off in many ways than were your parents or your grandparents. You have been immunized against many of the diseases that until recently were serious health hazards. You can expect to live, on the average, about twenty-five years longer than a person born in 1900. You benefit from the most advanced techniques for the treatment of human illness the world has ever known. Many of these benefits have resulted from the work of biologists.

From what we have said, you may gather that biologists know everything there is to know about living organisms. Such an idea would be far from the truth. Biology is an exciting search for new knowledge. Many questions are still unanswered. What causes cancer? What causes mental illness? Can hereditary defects be prevented? How can more products of the sea be used to feed the world's ever-growing population? What biological systems can sustain life on a long space voyage? Scientific research has the fascination of an unsolved mystery. Researchers find this aspect of science an intellectual challenge.

More students study biology than any other science. Perhaps the reason for this is that they are more interested in living things than in nonliving things. Biologists have certainly contributed much to our health and welfare. Each new discovery is reported via press, radio, and television. A primary purpose of your biological studies is to give you an understanding of the many biological discoveries that will occur in your lifetime.

You will note that BIOLOGICAL SCIENCE, REVISED EDITION, is divided into eight units. The first two pages of each unit provide a framework for the chapters that follow. The chapters in each unit clothe the framework, giving the major ideas form and substance. Before you read any single chapter of this book, read the introductory pages for each unit in succession. This will give you the flavor of the entire book from the very start.

Important Points

At the end of each chapter, we have provided a listing entitled *Important Points.* After you have read the chapter through once, it is a good idea to read each item under Important Points to identify concepts that are still not clear. Go back to the sections of the chapter that explain these concepts and read them again. If you still have difficulty understanding them, bring them to the attention of your teacher for explanation and class discussion. This will be helpful not only to you, but also to some of your classmates who may be having difficulty with the same concepts.

Review Questions

One of the best ways of mastering science concepts is to answer questions about them. We have provided a number of review questions at the end of each chapter. Most of them require short answers, although some will be more demanding. Generally, questions of this type are often asked as part of an oral review. In some cases, the questions may be assigned as part of a written examination. You should be able to answer most of them without any difficulty after a careful reading of the chapter.

Check Your Understanding

The questions under this heading will frequently require more extensive answers than those listed under *Review Questions.* In a number of cases you may not be able to find exact answers anywhere. These are questions designed to stimulate your ability to reason and think about some of the major problems of biology. If you like to ponder unsolved problems, many items under *Check Your Understanding* will be to your liking. These questions may also lead to interesting class discussions. Controversy is characteristic of the scientific community.

Research Projects and Reports

We hope that you will try your hand at the *Research Projects and Reports,* also listed at the end of each chapter. The materials needed for the projects can generally be obtained easily and inexpensively. For some projects, you will have to borrow equipment from school supplies. The directions given for the projects are not always complete to the last detail. In such cases, we have omitted certain details so that you can solve some of the problems yourself. Although this may be time-consuming, we think you will find it more satisfying in the end. A difficulty faced by even the most advanced research workers is the determination of the proper experimental design to provide the information being sought.

If your interest lies more along literary lines, you may want to write a report on one of the topics listed with the end-of-chapter material. Your school librarian will be glad to assist you in searching for source material. Newspapers and magazines should not be overlooked as accurate sources of timely scientific information.

Scattered throughout the book are short biographical sketches of famous biologists. Entitled *Milestones in Biology,* these sketches may provide you with the incentive for a more extensive report. Whether you write a report or not, the Milestones will bring you into close association with the lives and thoughts of some of the great biologists.

Biology offers many opportunities for establishing lifelong hobbies. Biology appeals to people of diverse skills and aptitudes. For people who like outdoor activities, trapping and identifying wildlife, making collections of plants and animals, and nature photography are a few possible hobbies. For others, microscopy, tropical fish, and soilless gardening are interesting indoor hobbies. Don't confine your study to just reading about biology. Try several of the projects on your own. You may find that it's much more fun than you had expected.

Further Reading

A characteristic of successful science students is their avid interest in reading. We have listed several books and articles at the end of each chapter under the heading *Further Reading.* You may find the *Scientific American* articles quite difficult. However, if you want the most authoritative information, this magazine is highly recommended. *Scientific American* also includes a feature called "The Amateur Scientist," which will suggest projects that you may want to do.

We sincerely hope that you will find the study of biology an enjoyable, profitable experience. Many of our former students discovered their life's work through their introduction to life science. Others have developed an understanding of the world of life that they could have acquired in no other way.

THE AUTHORS

Biological
Science

Life and Its Origin

FOR MANY CENTURIES man has struggled to solve the problem of life. Even the most primitive people recognized the connection between the heart beat and life. Life ceased when the heart stopped. Breathing was also associated with life. Did not the breath leave the body when death occurred?

The animals that man hunted or maintained in his herds also provided information about life. The slaughtering of these beasts was the source of man's earliest ideas about anatomy and physiology. The herd was the source of meat for the tribe. If disease struck the herd, it became a matter of great concern.

Man's early attempts to explain life, disease, and death met with little success. Disease and death were considered supernatural events. They could be controlled only by witch doctors who had supernatural powers. In Babylon and Egypt, religious groups began the first systematic attempts to organize existing knowledge about the life processes and structure of the human body. Much of their information came from the practice of embalming the dead.

Under the influence of the early Greek civilization, a more enlightened view of life developed. Natural science arose and flourished. Man's ideas about life began to emerge from the shadow of the supernatural.

In the centuries that followed, man's curiosity about life led him to explore the surface of the earth and the depths of the sea. And now, as man stands upon the threshold of exploring space, he wonders about the existence of life on other planets. Fred Hoyle, one of Great Britain's outstanding astronomers, thinks there may be billions of planets that support life in the Milky Way alone.

The ideas that man has developed about life and its origin have been changed by the invention of scientific instruments. The whole world of microorganisms was unknown before the optical microscope. Viruses could not be examined before the invention of the electron microscope. Life has been found in the smallest drop of water, the tiniest speck of dust. We may learn still more about the simplest forms of life if we can but invent other instruments to study them. Each new generation has improved existing instruments and devised new ones so that the search for the origin and meaning of life might continue.

1

The Diversity of Life

LIFE EXISTS in amazing abundance upon the earth. Within the depths of the sea all manner of living things are found. The whale, the seal, the porpoise, and the fish all make their home there. In the darkness of the great ocean deeps, whales feed on giant squids. Along the sloping sea shelves that fringe our continents, live vast schools of fish. On these same continental shelves, thousands of plant-like forms thrive.

On the fringe of the sea, life has established itself in pools and along the beaches. Mussels cling to the pier pilings. Clams burrow in the bay bottoms. Crabs, large and small, scurry on the beach. The shells of sea creatures are tossed high upon the shore to dry among the dunes.

THE VARIETY OF LIFE. Millions of years ago, the living things that were nurtured in the sea invaded the land. Gaining a foothold first in the tidal pools, the invaders gradually became adapted to life out of water. New forms of animals developed to crawl and creep on the land and to fly in the air. Large ancestors of the frog, toad, snake, and lizard appeared. These were followed by the flying animals and, still later, by such familiar animals as the cat, dog, tiger, and fox.

There is hardly a place on earth where life is not found. It swarms in the humid rain forests of the tropics. It survives the parched dryness of the desert. It abounds in the prairies and grassy meadows. Living things have been found miles above the the earth and even in the snow-covered polar regions.

BIOLOGY: THE SCIENCE OF LIFE. Biology, the science of living things, is one of the fundamental sciences and probably one of the oldest. Biology has its beginnings in the earliest writings of man. Centuries of human endeavor added so much information about living things that subdivisions of the subject were required. Botany became the science of plant life. Zoology became the science of animal life.

The growth of scientific knowledge in the last few centuries has produced many more subdivisions of biology. Physiology deals with living processes and functions in plants and animals. Anatomy is concerned with the structure of living things as revealed by dissection. Genetics deals with how living things transmit their characteristics from one generation to the next. Ecology is the science of interrelations between living things and their surroundings. One

of the most interesting of all the subdivisions of biology is paleontology, which is the study of ancient forms of life.

THE PHYSICAL SCIENCES. The sciences that deal with the physical world, as opposed to the living world, are called physical sciences. Chemistry is the science of matter and its changes. Physics is the science of energy.

The biological and physical sciences are not separate and distinct. The fundamental ideas of one frequently apply to another. For instance, there is considerable application of chemical ideas to biology. This has established the science known as biochemistry. Similarly, the application of the ideas of physics to biology has established the science of biophysics.

Naming Living Things

Each year biologists discover thousands of new kinds of living things. These are given scientific names, usually Latin, by their discoverers. The names are carefully chosen to identify relationships that may exist between the new forms and the old. More

1–1 Diversity of Life

than one and one-half million organisms have been named and classified since scientific classification began in the middle of the 18th century.

When we attempt to organize living things into groups, we recognize certain patterns that indicate family relationships. The dog, the wolf, and the fox are similar. The clam, the oyster, and the snail are alike in many ways. The careful investigation of the forms of life that is necessary to classify them has revealed broader likenesses. These indicate in many cases that even apparently dissimilar forms may be related.

Biologists believe that the ancient forms of life gradually changed to produce the plants and animals of the present. Before we begin our study of the oldest plants we shall scan the entire world of living things so that you may see the whole picture before concentrating on its parts.

Man began naming living things long before biology was an organized science. The names were often simple descriptions of the animal, like blackbird. But there are many birds that are black—some big, some small. Biologists have learned that they are not all the same. The raven, the crow, and the grackle are just a few birds that might be so called. The common name is not exact or specific.

THE PROBLEM OF COMMON NAMES. Often a common name broadly describes color or function and thus may refer to several kinds of organisms. The biologist hears such names as bug, or worm, or cat commonly used in this way. Any insect that crawls on legs is a bug. If it crawls and has no legs, it's a worm, even though it may be the larva of an insect. The biologist also hears people describe a plant as a moss, or fern, or daisy, although the plant may not be one of these at all.

If all people spoke the same language, common names would still present problems. When we consider the variety of languages, we have greater difficulties. In Germany the name for the animal we call the horse is *das Pferd*. The Frenchman calls the same animal *cheval;* the Italian, *caballo.*

1–2 The name "blackbird" describes a characteristic of all the birds illustrated. Scientists, however, need names that will identify different kinds of black birds.

Boat-tailed Grackle
Cassidix mexicanus

Common Crow
Corvus brachyrhynchos

Black Drongo
Dicrurus macrocercus

European Blackbird
Turdus merula

1–3 All of the leaves illustrated are leaves from maple trees. They all belong to the same genus, but differences in the structure of the leaves distinguish different species.

Add to these the Japanese, Chinese, Russian, Spanish, and all the rest, and we have vast confusion.

SCIENTIFIC NAMES. The use of the modern system for naming organisms began in the 18th century. At that time Latin was the universal language of scholars. Latin bridged the language barrier very nicely. It was an international language. The botanists and zoologists of that time named plants and animals in Latin. Usually the name was a short descriptive paragraph, rather than the brief scientific name we now use. Today, practically all living things have Latin names. In a few cases words of Greek origin are employed, but these are the exception.

In place of short descriptions, biologists use just two Latin words to name living things. *Rosa alba* is the name of the white rose. *Felis domestica* is the domestic cat. *Felis leo* and *Felis tigris* are the scientific names of the lion and tiger respectively.

The system of using two Latin names is called the *binomial system of nomencla-*

ture. The first of these two names is the **genus**. It is the large group to which the plant or animal belongs. In the examples given above, *Rosa* is the genus of roses; *Felis* is the genus of cats. The name following the genus is the **species**. This describes a specific type within the genus. *Rosa alba* is the white rose. *Felis domestica* is the house cat. The important thing to note here is that biologists all over the world use the same scientific name for a particular plant or animal. If you were to visit a zoo in Berlin you would see the name *Felis leo* on the lion's cage, just as in Paris or New York.

Classifying Living Things

Let's switch our attention for a moment from zoos to supermarkets. Suppose you want to buy some canned pineapple. You will find it along with other kinds of canned fruit in a certain section of the market. The items have been grouped or classified into categories for your convenience. The need for classifying the items arose as a result of the large number of them on sale in the store.

In a similar way, the huge number of living things has created the need for classifying them. When the first scientifically prepared list of animals was made in 1758, there were just 4,236 names. One hundred years later the number had grown to 129,000. Today, more than two centuries later, the number of classified animals has risen to about 1,250,000! There are in addition about 350,000 species of other known organisms.

The classification of living things serves at least two useful purposes. First, it enables the biologist to perceive likenesses in structure and function in the world of life. Second, it permits the student to survey the entire living world. Instead of studying a million forms, the student studies a few representative forms of life from the major groups.

BASES FOR CLASSIFICATION. The number of bases that could be used for classifying living things is very great: color, size, appearance, external and internal structure, habitat, method of reproduction. Using just one of these is usually a most unsatisfactory procedure. It is far better to use a combination of many of them so that true relationships can be established. Thus, a bat flies in the air like a bird, but closer examination of it reveals that it is not birdlike in many other ways. A seal might be considered a fish, but it lacks scales and does not have fins. The internal organization of its body is more highly developed than that of a fish. It is not, therefore, classified with fishes.

TAXONOMY. The biologist who attempts to group living things into natural categories is called a *taxonomist*. Taxonomy is scientific classification of living things. When the taxonomist does his job well, he exposes a view of the entire world of living things to the student. He tries to show the natural relationships that exist in plant and animal forms.

The beginnings of scientific classification are found in the writings of the Greek scientists Aristotle and Theophrastus. Aristotle made a crude attempt to classify the animals known to the ancient world. Theophrastus (370–285 B.C.) made a greater contribution by attempting to apply scientific principles to the naming of plants. Sometimes called "The Father of Botany," he was the author of the first known botanical book, *Historia Plantarum* (The History of Plants). Theophrastus studied the structure of the stems and leaves of plants. He grouped plants into families on the basis of the likenesses he recognized in them.

With the spread of Roman civilization and the discovery of caravan routes to the Orient, travelers brought back exotic plants and told tales of strange new animals. Still later, voyagers brought back specimens from the newly discovered islands and mainland to the west. The periods of exploration and conquest greatly increased knowledge of the forms of life.

During the 17th and 18th centuries, scholars began to compile long lists of the known animals and plants. Because Latin was used by all learned men, these descriptive volumes were written in that language. The large reference works containing long descriptions of the animals were called *bestiaries*. Similar volumes describing plants were called *herbals*. Some of these ancient texts are still referred to by biologists.

LINNAEUS AND MODERN CLASSIFICATION. The one man who contributed most to the systematic classification of living things was a Swedish botany professor, Carolus Linnaeus (lih-NEE-us) (1707–1778). To his laboratory at the University of Upsala were sent many kinds of strange plants from all over the world.

Linnaeus had traveled widely and was a confirmed collector. In 1753 he published a

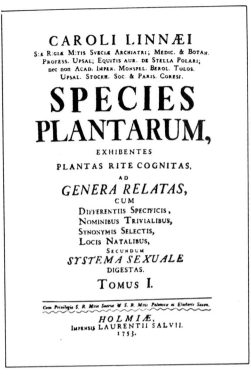

1–4 Title page of *Species Plantarum*

volume entitled *Species Plantarum,* which became a standard reference work for the naming of plants. In 1758 he published the tenth edition of a work titled *Systema Natura,* which contained descriptions of the animals then known in the civilized world. This book is still used as the basic reference for the naming of animals.

These two books began the system of naming all living things by assigning just two Latin names to them, the *genus* name and the *species* name. Linnaeus also tried to arrange all living things in large groups to show the natural relationships that exist among them. Thus, all of the plants having the characteristics of lilies were placed together in the lily family. Similarly, all of the grasses were listed together in another

family. A number of the groups originated by Linnaeus are still useful to botanists.

CHARLES DARWIN. There is no classification in nature. Yet, it would seem that all fish are related. So are birds. Linnaeus had sought a method of relating life forms to each other, but was not very successful. A century passed before an idea was proposed that provided a more logical basis for classification of plants and animals.

In 1859 the English naturalist Charles Darwin (1809–1882) published the *Origin of Species*. His book aroused a great controversy among biologists. In it he suggested that the complex plants and animals living today have developed by a slow process of change from simpler plants and animals that lived millions of years ago. Darwin's theory was bitterly attacked by many people, some of them outstanding leaders in biology. Gradually, however, so much evidence accumulated in support of his theory that it has been accepted as one of the great foundations of modern biology.

Darwin's theory provided a completely logical basis for classifying living things. If we accept the idea that all life came from simpler forms, it is useful to try to discover which forms of life came earlier. This suggests the establishment of family trees, relating present organisms to their probable ancestors. It also leads to the arrangement of organisms into large groups in the order of their probable appearance on earth. Darwin's theory has helped us to develop the most logical basis for classification that we have yet discovered.

Let us go back several pages, where we discussed some members of the genus, *Felis:* the domestic cat, the tiger, and the lion. We might also have mentioned the wildcat, but this animal does not belong to the same genus. Its scientific name is *Lynx rufus*. Several of its characteristics are different from the cat, the lion, and the tiger, a notable one being its short tail. However,

St. Bernard

Chihuahua

Huskie

Coyote

Wolf

Dingo

1–5 The three dogs at the top appear quite different, but they are all classified in the same genus and species (*Canis Familiaris*). Although the other three animals resemble dogs and each other, they each have important differences and are classified as distinctly different species of the same genus (Canis).

since both these genera, *Felis* and *Lynx*, have catlike qualities, they are placed together in a larger group called a **family.** In this case it is the cat family, and it bears the scientific name *Felidae.*

In much the same way, several families of related animals are grouped into an **order.** You are probably well aware of the likenesses that exist between cats and dogs and will not be surprised to learn that taxonomists place them together in the same order, *Carnivora.*

The characteristics that are common to members of different orders of organisms

enable us to establish still larger groups called *classes.* A number of classes is gathered into a still larger group called a **phylum.** All the phyla of animals together, for example, make up the animal **kingdom.**

Now that we have seen how the larger groups are built up, let us reverse the process, and start downward from the top. The largest subdivision is the *kingdom.* The kingdom is divided into *phyla.* Sometimes the phylum is divided into *subphyla.* Each phylum or subphylum is divided into *classes,* the classes into *orders,* the orders into *families,* the families into *genera,* the genera into *species*. Here are the groups to which the tiger would belong.

> **Kingdom:** *Animal*
> **Phylum:** *Chordata*
> **Class:** *Mammalia*
> **Order:** *Carnivora*
> **Family:** *Felidae*
> **Genus:** *Felis*
> **species:** *tigris*

The Moneran Kingdom

If you were asked to name the simplest living thing you know, you would probably name something like a bacterium, a single-celled organism. Your answer would be correct; however, even among single-celled organisms there are degrees of simplicity. Some of the simplest cells lack structures that are present in more complex cells. Many simple cells, for example, do not contain an organized nucleus. For this reason, taxonomists consider the cells that lack an organized nucleus the most primitive of all organisms. These most primitive forms of life are grouped together in the kingdom *Monera*. Many monerans exist separately as single cells, but others form cell clusters, known as colonies, or chains of cells, known as filaments.

The kingdom Monera consists of two phyla: (1) the phylum *Schizophyta* (skiz-AHF-uh-tuh), which consists of the single-celled bacteria, and (2) the phylum *Cyanophyta* (cy-uh-NAHF-uh-tuh), which consists of plant-like organisms that contain a blue-green pigment within their cells.

The Protist Kingdom

For many years, taxonomists divided organisms into two kingdoms, the plant and the animal kingdom. When the microscope brought a whole new world of life into view, biologists found it difficult to classify many of the single-celled organisms as either plants or animals. The science of taxonomy faced a serious problem. How should these single-celled creatures be classified? In 1866 the German biologist Ernst Haeckel suggested that such organisms might be grouped together in the kingdom *Protista*. At the time, the name Protista did not receive wide acceptance. Today, however, many biologists prefer to group all these simple forms of life in this kingdom. Some taxonomists also include the two phyla of monerans in the protist kingdom, but there is no agreement about this.

The ten phyla of protists contain many single-celled forms. Some of these single-celled organisms are plant-like, while others are essentially animal-like. Taxonomists believe that organisms similar to the single-celled, plant-like organisms evolved into many-celled plants. Biologists also believe that the higher animals of the animal kingdom evolved from earlier forms of single-celled, animal-like protists.

Not all of the protists are simple organisms. Some of the members of the phylum *Phaeophyta* (fee-AHF-uh-tuh), for example, are giant brown sea weeds. The red algae, phylum *Rhodophyta* (roh-DAHF-uh-tuh), are also many-celled, complex organisms. The fungi, phylum *Mycophyta* (my-KAHF-uh-tuh), are included in this kingdom also.

The Animal Kingdom

Of the twelve phyla of animals listed on pages 22–30, the less complex forms are listed first. The more complex forms, which evolved later in the history of the development of life on earth, are listed later. Many biologists believe that an organism similar to those in the protist phylum *Mastigophora* (mas-tuh-GAHF-ur-uh) was the forerunner of the many-celled animal phyla. The sequential arrangement of the phyla is not meant to indicate that each phylum produced those that follow, however.

THE INVERTEBRATES. Many forms of life developed from the single cells that first lived on the earth. For the most part they were *invertebrates,* or animals that lacked a backbone. All of the phyla, with the exception of the last, consist of animals of this type. Among them are the sponges, jellyfish, different kinds of worms, starfish, oysters, clams, and insects. Many invertebrates are not very familiar to you because they live in the darkness of the sea, out of sight. Studies of the development and life histories of these animals may reveal ways in which different forms of life have changed through eons of time.

THE CHORDATA. All of the animals that have a backbone belong to the phylum

CLASSIFICATION OF MAN

Division	Name	Some Distinguishing Characteristics
Kingdom	Animal	Cells do not have chlorophyll or cell walls. Has powers of locomotion.
Phylum	Chordata	Persistent or transient notochord, a rod of cartilage, running down back. Gill slits at some time during development.
Subphylum	Vertebrata	Notochord replaced by a "backbone" of vertebrae. Enlarged anterior end of spinal cord (brain). Most have appendages in pairs.
Class	Mammalia	Hair and mammary glands. Four-chambered heart. Diaphragm. Warm blooded.
Order	Primata	Eyes usually front of head. Usually nails instead of claws. Five digits on each limb. Prominent canine teeth.
Family	Hominidae	Manlike qualities. Fossil members of this family were progenitors of man.
Genus	Homo	Human qualities. Highly developed brain. Fashioned tools and used fire. Homo sapiens only living species of this genus.
species	sapiens	Modern Man

Chordata and are known more commonly as *vertebrates*. The simplest of the vertebrates, the fishes and their relatives, swam in the ancient seas. Other vertebrates, such as the amphibians, reptiles, birds, and mammals, appeared more recently on the earth. As far as biologists have been able to discover, man made his appearance last.

The Plant Kingdom

The plant kingdom is divided into two phyla, the phylum *Bryophyta* (bri-AHF-uh-tuh) and the phylum *Tracheophyta* (tray-kee-AHF-uh-tuh). These two phyla are believed to have evolved from organisms similar to those found in the protist phylum *Chlorophyta* (kloh-RAHF-uh-tuh), the green algae. Although most of the forerunners of the modern plants lived in the water, the bryophytes and the tracheophytes are all land-dwellers.

THE BRYOPHYTA. The liverworts and mosses make up the phylum Bryophyta, and are believed to be closely related to the earliest plants that lived on land. Bryophytes do not have special tissues for carrying water throughout the plant body. For this reason, they are sometimes called *nonvascular* plants. Although they are land plants, the life cycle of the bryophytes is dependent upon the presence of water. Consequently, these plants are most often found in a moist, boggy environment.

THE TRACHEOPHYTA. The clubmosses, horsetails, ferns, pines, and flowering plants make up the phylum Tracheophyta. These very successful plants have special conducting tubes, called *trachea,* that carry water through the plant body. Since they contain water-conducting tubes, they are often referred to as vascular plants. *Vascular* means containing tubes or ducts. The tracheophytes compose the largest plant phylum by far. The flowering plants, the most common and best known of all plants, are the most numerous of all the tracheophytes and number more than a quarter of a million species.

IMPORTANT POINTS

The science of biology began as a result of man's interest in the great variety of living things found on earth. Subdivisions of biology were required as the amount of information about life expanded.

Practically all of the million and a half known organisms bear scientific names consisting of two Latin terms: the genus name and the species name. This binomial system was begun by the Swedish botany professor Carolus Linnaeus in the middle of the 18th century.

The present system of grouping plants and animals into larger categories is based upon structural and functional relationships that suggest a common ancestry. The evolutionary principle used in establishing these relationships was proposed by Charles Darwin in 1859. Darwin believed that slow changes had occurred in the ancient forms of life to produce the modern forms.

Many biologists divide organisms into four kingdoms: monerans, protists, animals, and plants. Monerans are the simplest forms of life. Protists appear to have developed from the early monerans. Plants and animals probably developed from specialized protists.

1. What are some of the problems that would be caused by using common names for plants and animals?
2. Why has Latin been used for the scientific names of organisms?
3. What are the two main parts of a scientific name?
4. Besides establishing the binomial system, what contribution did Linnaeus make to scientific classification?
5. Charles Darwin is not usually considered a taxonomist. Explain his contribution to taxonomy.
6. List seven categories into which living things are divided.
7. What are some of the characteristics that might be used for classifying flowers?
8. Compare the Bryophyta and Tracheophyta.
9. List five animals classified as invertebrates.
10. What are the four kingdoms of living things?

CHECK YOUR UNDERSTANDING

11. Compare the need for classifying organisms two centuries ago with the present.
12. What reasons might be given for not classifying the bat as a bird?
13. What function does the taxonomist perform besides simply classifying living things?
14. How does Darwin's theory make taxonomy more logical?
15. From its position in the classification table, which plant phylum would you expect appeared most recently on the earth?
16. What reasons can you give for building a system of classification upon characteristics other than function alone?
17. Compare the number of species of flowering plants with the number of known bacteria.
18. What advantages does an understanding of classification offer to the biology student?

RESEARCH PROJECTS AND REPORTS

1. Obtain information from your school or public library and prepare a report on one of the following topics:

   Theophrastus   **Charles Darwin**

   Carolus Linnaeus   **The Early Herbalists**

2. *Leaf or Flower Collection:* You may have collected leaves or flowers before this and not bothered too much about classifying them completely. This is the time to attempt it. You might also want to expand your collection of plants with some pressed seaweeds, mosses, ferns, and other less commonly collected forms.

3. *Classifying Common Organisms:* Try your hand at working out the complete classification of some of the following:

   Your tropical fish   **Some animals at the zoo**

   Neighborhood pets   **Neighborhood trees**

FURTHER READING

Living Things—How to Know Them. Harry E. Jaques. William C. Brown Company, Dubuque, Iowa. Introduces the student to the methods of scientific classification by use of illustrations.

Green Laurels. Donald C. Peattie. Simon and Schuster, New York, N.Y. Chapters 4, 5, and 6 describe the life and work of Linnaeus.

Parade of the Animal Kingdom. Robert Hegner. Macmillan Company, New York, N.Y. Interesting reading about the various phyla that make up the animal kingdom. Many illustrations help the reader understand some of the obscure forms of life.

A Guide to the Natural World. The Editors of Life. Time Incorporated, New York, N.Y. An illustrated portrayal of the world of life as it is interpreted by the modern taxonomist.

CLASSIFICATION
of Living Things

BIOLOGISTS disagree on the subject of classification. Some recognize a system of classification that includes only two kingdoms of organisms: Plant and Animal. Others prefer a system that includes a third kingdom, Protista, to accommodate certain single-celled organisms that have both plant and animal characteristics. However, as more has been learned about the detailed structure of microscopic life, other biologists have added a fourth kingdom, Monera. The main distinction between the monerans and the protists is that the protists contain organized nuclei and the monerans do not.

On the illustrated pages that follow, you will find organisms grouped into four kingdoms: monerans, protists, plants, and animals. Although the four-kingdom system of classification has certain advantages, it should be noted that it is not the only acceptable one.

The Moneran Kingdom

MONERANS are the simplest organisms known. Their cells possess neither an organized nucleus nor other organelles. Most of them are single-celled, although some form colonies or filaments. They reproduce mostly by asexual cell division (fission). The kingdom Monera consists of two phyla: Schizophyta (the single-celled bacteria) and Cyanophyta (the blue-green algae).

PHYLUM SCHIZOPHYTA
(bacteria)

Greek: *schizein* (cleave) and *phyton* (plant)

Extremely minute single-celled organisms, without a distinct nucleus. Lack chlorophyll. Classified according to shape: *cocci* (spherical), *bacilli* (rod-like), *spirilla* (spirals). May occur singly or grouped into colonies, or as individuals arranged in chains. Many with limited powers of locomotion by flagella. Reproduce by fission. About 2,000 species.

PHYLUM CYANOPHYTA
(blue-green algae)

Greek: *kyanos* (dark blue) and *phyton* (plant)

The simplest algae, mostly aquatic or terrestrial in moist habitats. Single cells, colonies, filaments, or sheets. Reproduce by fission; sexual reproduction unknown. No organized nuclei or chloroplasts present. Blue color due to preponderance of phycocyanin along with chlorophyll *a* and carotenoids. Stored food similar to glycogen. Nutrition is plant-like, involving photosynthesis. About 2,500 species.

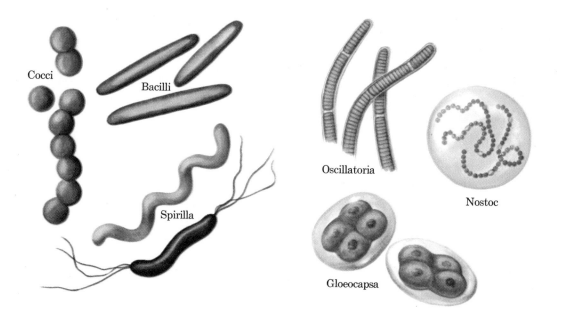

Cocci

Bacilli

Spirilla

Oscillatoria

Nostoc

Gloeocapsa

The Protist Kingdom

THE KINGDOM OF PROTISTS includes a great variety of simple organisms, often single-celled, that are more advanced than the monerans. The nucleus and other organelles are well-developed. The protists include such diverse organisms as the plant-like algae, the fungi, and the animal-like slime molds and flagellates. Some are green autotrophs; others are heterotrophs; still others are parasites upon man and other animals.

PHYLUM MASTIGOPHORA

(flagellates)

Greek: *mastix* (whip) and *phoros* (bearing)

Locomotion by whip-like appendages called flagella. Unicellular or colonial. Many ingest food and are animal-like in their nutrition. Some are free-living; some are parasites; and some form symbiotic relationships with their hosts. Some contain chlorophyll and perform photosynthesis.

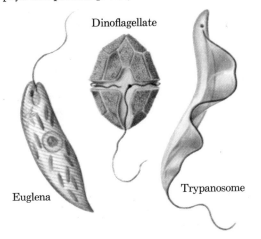

Dinoflagellate

Euglena

Trypanosome

PHYLUM RHIZOPODA

(amebas)

Greek: *rhiza* (root) and *pod* (foot)

Rhizopods are among the simplest of all protists. Locomotion usually by means of irregular, and sometimes changeable, body extensions called pseu-

dopodia. All are heterotrophs; the pseudopodia are often used to engulf food. Many produce intricate shells or other external skeletal structures.

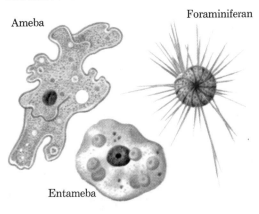

Ameba

Foraminiferan

Entameba

PHYLUM SPOROZOA

(spore formers)

Greek: *spora* (seed) and *zoion* (animal)

Parasitic with complicated life cycles, which include a resistant stage during which the organism is enclosed in a walled capsule or spore. Usually with no locomotor structures (pseudopodia or flagella may be present in certain stages of the life cycles of some). All are heterotrophic. About 2,000 species.

Plasmodium
(Malaria Organism)

PHYLUM CILIOPHORA
(ciliates)

Latin: *cilium* (hair) and Greek: *phoros* (bearing)

Locomotion by means of cilia. Unicellular, but with complex structure. Usually with both a macronucleus and a micronucleus. Reproduction by conjugation or fission. All are heterotrophic. About 6,000 described species.

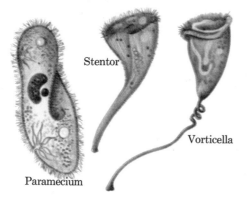

Stentor

Vorticella

Paramecium

PHYLUM MYXOMYCETES
(slime molds)

Greek: *myxa* (mucus or slime) and *mykes* (fungus)

Organisms with complex life cycles that can be plant-like at one stage and animal-like at another. Individuals usually occur as flagellates, but at one stage may combine to form an ameboid mass with hundreds of nuclei and no cell boundaries. This mass moves about and ingests food like a gigantic ameba. At a later stage this mass becomes anchored and produces projections called sporangia. Reproduction is by spores, which in some genera have cellulose walls, produced in the sporangia. Widely distributed, found under damp conditions on decaying vegetation. About 450 species.

PHYLUM MYCOPHYTA
(fungi)

Greek: *mykes* (fungus) and *phyton* (plant)

Plant-like organisms, but without chlorophyll; no true roots, stems, or leaves. Mostly saprophytic, but a few are parasitic on plants or animals. The body is primarily a system of thread-like cell groups called mycelia. About 57,500 species.

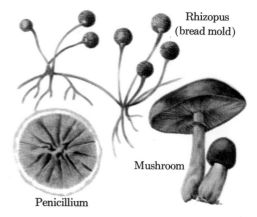

Rhizopus
(bread mold)

Mushroom

Penicillium

PHYLUM CHLOROPHYTA
(green algae)

Greek: *chloros* (green) and *phyton* (plant)

The green algae, mostly freshwater. Single motile and nonmotile cells, motile and nonmotile colonies, filaments, ribbons, and tubular forms. Sexual reproduction often by means of motile gametes, but many other methods, both sexual and asexual, are known. Cells highly organized. Characteristic pigments: chlorophyll *a* and *b*, xanthophylls, and B-carotene. Photosynthetic; food stored as starch. About 6,750 species.

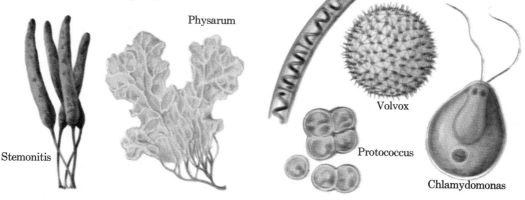

Physarum

Spirogyra

Volvox

Protococcus

Stemonitis

Chlamydomonas

PHYLUM CHRYSOPHYTA

(golden algae, diatoms)

Greek: *chrysos* (gold) and *phyton* (plant)

Simple algae in which carotene and xanthophylls are the dominant pigments. Foods seldom stored as starch, but more often as an oil. Mostly unicellular, but colonial, filamentous and tubular forms are known. About 12,500 species in three classes.

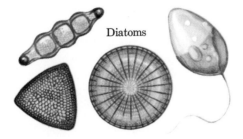

Diatoms

PHYLUM PHAEOPHYTA

(brown algae)

Greek: *phaios* (dusky) and *phyton* (plant)

Cool-water, marine algae, often with rather complex forms. Known as brown seaweed or kelps. Usually brownish or olive-green in color. Characteristic pigments are chlorophylls *a* and *c*, B-carotene, and xanthophylls, especially fucoxanthin. Food stored as a special carbohydrate, laminarin. Cell walls often surrounded with algin, an economically important substance. Alternation of generations with distinct sexual and asexual phases. About 1,750 species.

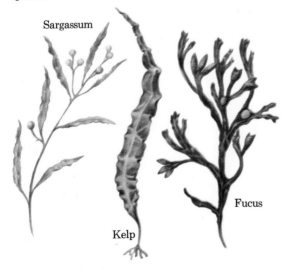

Sargassum

Kelp

Fucus

PHYLUM RHODOPHYTA

(red algae)

Greek: *rhodon* (rose) and *phyton* (plant)

Predominantly warm-water, marine algae, usually red. Many extremely complex life cycle patterns are known, but there are no motile reproductive cells. Characteristic pigments are chlorophylls *a* and *d,* carotenoids, and phycoerythrin. Food stored as a special starch. About 3,750 species known.

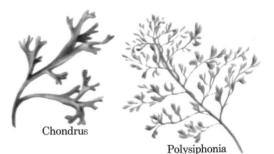

Chondrus

Polysiphonia

The Plant Kingdom

MORE THAN a quarter million species of plants are included in the Plant Kingdom. Most of them are the familiar flowering plants and trees of our woodlands, meadows, and gardens. A few, like the ferns, are not so familiar. Still less familiar are the mosses and liverworts, whose remote ancestors were among the first plants to establish themselves upon the land. The ferns and the flowering plants constitute the phylum Tracheophyta. The mosses and their allies are grouped together in the phylum Bryophyta. The tracheophytes have vascular tissue (vessels for the transport of food and water); bryophytes do not.

PHYLUM BRYOPHYTA
(nonvascular plants)

Greek: *bryon* (moss) and *phyton* (plant)

Small plants without vascular tissue, true roots, stems, or leaves, but often appearing superficially like vascular plants. Reproductive structures multicellular, with an outer sterile jacket of cells. Alternation of generations. Gametophyte the dominant generation. Sporophytes often parasitic on gametophyte. About 24,000 species.

PHYLUM TRACHEOPHYTA
(vascular plants)

Greek: *tracheia* (artery or windpipe) and *phyton* (plant)

Structurally complex, with vascular tissue. Main generation is the sporophyte. Gametophytes often microscopic, parasitic. This phylum is divided into four subphyla, one of which contains the three classes of ferns, conifers, and flowering plants. About 260,700 species.

CLASS FILICINEAE
(ferns)

Stems usually underground, leaves complex. Sporangia numerous, mostly clustered on undersides of leaves. Alternating sporophyte and gametophyte generations are independent. Water required for free-swimming sperm. About 10,000 species.

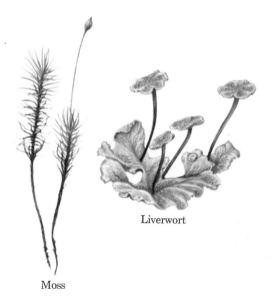

Liverwort

Moss

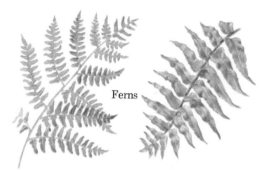

Ferns

CLASS GYMNOSPERMAE

(conifers, cycads, and ginkgoes)

Stems and leaves complex. Many species have needle-like leaves. Seeds not enclosed in a fruit ("naked"), but are attached to the surface of modified leaves called cones. Sperms motile or nonmotile, enclosed in pollen tube. About 700 species.

Fir

Sequoia

Ginko

Pine

CLASS ANGIOSPERMAE

(flowering plants)

Stems and leaves complex, spores produced in a flower. Seeds enclosed in a fruit. Sperm cells nonmotile, enclosed in pollen tube. More species than all other plant species combined. There are two subclasses of angiosperms, together containing over 300 families and over 250,000 species.

Subclass Dicotyledoneae

(dicots)

Flowering plants with two cotyledons (primitive seed leaves) in the embryo. Floral organs usually in groups of fours or fives, leaves netted-veined, stems with a cylinder of vascular tissue; cambium, and pith cells present. About 200,000 species.

Daisy

Magnolia

Phlox

Arrowwood

Subclass Monocotyledoneae

(monocots)

Flowering plants with one cotyledon in the embryo. Floral organs in groups of three; leaves parallel-veined; stems with scattered vascular bundles, cambium absent. About 50,000 species.

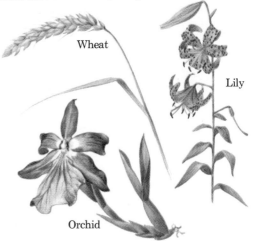

Wheat

Lily

Orchid

The Animal Kingdom

ANIMALS, like plants, are well-known forms of life. Unlike the plants, animals generally move about and respond quickly to stimuli in their environment. Another major difference is that animals generally feed upon other living things, whereas plants are usually autotrophic. Although many species have become adapted to terrestrial life, the sea nurtures most of the animals of the earth. Living in the sea and hidden from view, many animals are strangers to the eyes of man. Biologists divide the Animal Kingdom into as many as twenty-five phyla. Some of the more common phyla are listed here.

PHYLUM PORIFERA

(sponges)

Latin: *porus* (pore) and *ferre* (to bear)

Primitive aquatic animals, mostly marine. Usually stationary as adults. Usually colonial or consisting of many individuals indistinguishably fused. Body wall of two cell layers, inner layer of collar cells. Pores in body wall connected to an internal canal system. Skeleton of spicules or spongin. No tissues or organs. About 5,000 species divided into three classes.

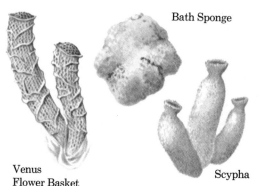

Bath Sponge

Venus Flower Basket

Scypha

PHYLUM COELENTERATA

(coelenterates)

Greek: *koilos* (hollow) and *enteron* (intestine)

Mostly marine animals. Body wall of an outer ectoderm and inner endoderm, enclosing a sac-like digestive cavity with a single opening, the mouth. Radial symmetry. No segmentation. The typical sac-like type of body organization occurs through-

out, but is modified to form either a tubular polyp or a bell-shaped jellyfish. Usually provided with tentacles with highly specialized stinging cells. About 9,000 species divided into three classes.

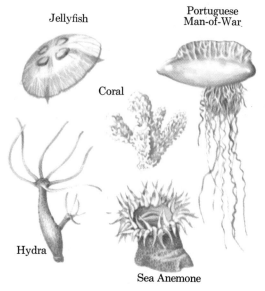

Jellyfish

Portuguese Man-of-War

Coral

Hydra

Sea Anemone

PHYLUM PLATYHELMINTHES

(flatworms)

Greek: *platys* (broad or flat) and *helminthos* (worm)

Worms much flattened dorsoventrally. Bilateral symmetry. Possess a definite third layer of cells, the mesoderm. Central nervous system developed. One body opening. No body cavity. Aquatic and terrestrial species; free-living and parasitic. About 5,500 species divided into three classes.

Tapeworm

PHYLUM NEMERTINEA (ribbon worms)
Greek: *Nemertes* (a Nereid or sea nymph)

A small phylum similar to Platyhelminthes. Mostly marine. Small to very long (one species reaches 90 feet). Ribbon-shaped, flat, and unsegmented. Gut with two openings. No body cavity. About 550 species.

Micrura

PHYLUM NEMATODA (roundworms)
Greek: *nema* (thread)

Parasitic and free-living worms. Bilateral symmetry. Digestive system tubular, with mouth and anus. Body cavity present, but poorly formed. Body elongate, cylindrical and usually pointed at both ends. About 10,000 species.

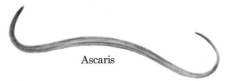
Ascaris

PHYLUM ROTIFERA (rotifers)
Latin: *rota* (wheel) and *ferre* (to bear)

Microscopic freshwater and marine animals with well-developed body cavity and organ systems. Tufts of cilia present, especially around the mouth. About 1,500 species.

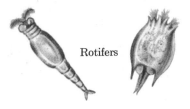
Rotifers

PHYLUM ANNELIDA
(segmented worms)

Latin: *anellus* (ringed)

Bilateral symmetry; relatively complex organ systems; non-jointed appendages (if any); body segments more or less similar. Marine, freshwater or terrestrial. Segmentation and body cavity suggests relationship to the arthropods. About 7,000 species have been described, divided into two minor and three major classes.

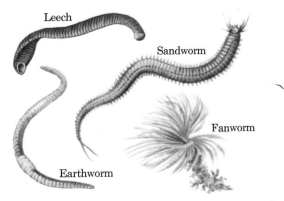
Leech
Sandworm
Fanworm
Earthworm

PHYLUM MOLLUSCA (mollusks)
Latin: *molluscus* (soft)

Soft-bodied, unsegmented animals without jointed appendages. Bilateral symmetry tending to asymmetry (snails). Gut with two openings. Usually a shell is present (absent or rudimentary in some); gills; mantle and mantle cavity; and a muscular foot. Mostly marine but many are freshwater and some (snails) are terrestrial. About 132,000 modern species have been described and fossil forms are numerous. Usually divided into six classes.

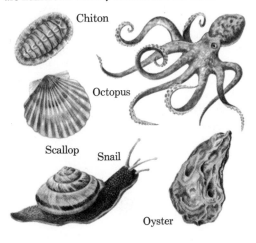
Chiton
Octopus
Scallop
Snail
Oyster

PHYLUM ECHINODERMATA

(echinoderms)

Greek: *echinos* (hedgehog) and *derma* (skin)

All marine. Complex. Adults radially symmetrical (usually on a plan of five repeated parts), larvae bilaterally symmetrical. Skin usually spiny; body wall with calcareous plates (may be reduced); water vascular system; large coelom. About 6,000 modern species divided into five classes.

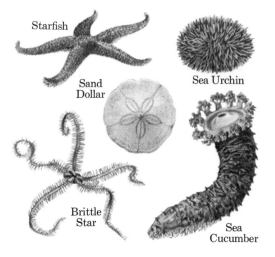

Starfish

Sand Dollar

Sea Urchin

Brittle Star

Sea Cucumber

PHYLUM ARTHROPODA

(arthropods)

Greek: *arthron* (joint) and *pod* (foot)

Complex animals; exoskeleton; jointed appendages; segmentation well-developed with a tendency for segments to fuse or to be grouped into definite body regions. Respiration by gills or tracheae, or by a modification of these. Ventral nerve cord and open circulatory system. Inhabit all environments. There are eight classes, totalling approximately 800,000 species. Seven of the classes are listed here.

CLASS ONYCHOPHORA

Tropical wormlike species having many annelid features. Many paired legs; weak segmentation; respiration by means of tracheae. Sometimes listed as a separate phylum.

Peripatus

CLASS ARACHNIDA

Arthropods with no antennae and with four pairs of legs; respiration by means of tracheae or "book lungs"; segmentation reduced. Mainly terrestrial. About 15,000 species.

Spider

Scorpion

CLASS MEROSTOMATA

Horseshoe crabs. Coastal species. Show structural similarities to spiders and scorpions.

Horseshoe Crab

CLASS CRUSTACEA

Arthropods with two pairs of antennae; respiration by gills. Most occur in aquatic habitats, but a few occur in moist terrestrial situations. Number of legs varies. Usually have hard body covering. About 30,000 species.

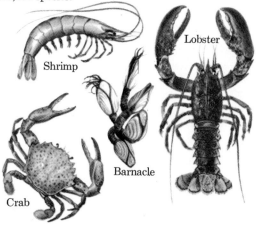

Shrimp

Lobster

Crab

Barnacle

CLASS CHILOPODA

Elongate and superficially worm-like arthropods. Little regional specialization of different segments. One pair of long antennae; one pair of poison claws beneath the head. Body flat with one pair of walking legs on each segment of the abdomen. Terrestrial. About 4,000 species.

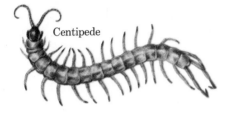

Centipede

CLASS DIPLOPODA

Elongate and superficially worm-like arthropods. Little regional specialization of different segments. One pair of short antennae. Body round with two pairs of walking legs on each segment. Terrestrial. About 8,000 species.

Millipede

CLASS INSECTA

Arthropods with one pair of antennae; three pairs of legs; tracheal respiration. Body usually divided into head, thorax, and abdomen. Many with wings. Primarily terrestrial. There are 29 orders containing more than 700,000 species (more than all other animal species combined). Some of the orders are listed here.

ORDER ODONATA. Fairly large insects with two similar pairs of large, membranous wings that do not fold; antennae short; body long and slender. Immature forms are aquatic. Chewing mouth parts. Incomplete metamorphosis.

Dragonfly

ORDER ORTHOPTERA. Medium to large insects; terrestrial; forewings leathery; hindwings folded fan-like, used for flying. Chewing mouth parts. Incomplete metamorphosis.

Cricket

Grasshopper

ORDER ISOPTERA. Small, soft-bodied, ant-like insects; wings narrow, equal length. Winged and nonwinged forms. Chewing mouth parts. Social. Incomplete metamorphosis.

Termite

ORDER HEMIPTERA. True bugs. No wings or two pairs of wings, with forewings partly thickened. Jointed beak for sucking arises from front of head.

Harlequin Bug

ORDER HOMOPTERA. No wings or two pairs of wings held arched together; wings same thickness. Jointed beak for piercing and sucking attached to base of head. Incomplete metamorphosis.

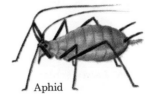

Aphid

ORDER LEPIDOPTERA. Two pairs of scaly wings. Coiled sucking tube for mouth parts. Usually fairly large, showy insects. Complete metamorphosis.

Monarch Butterfly

Cecropia Moth

ORDER DIPTERA. Usually two-winged; hind wings may be reduced to knoblike organs of balance. Small or medium sized. Antennae small; eyes large. Sucking and piercing mouth parts. Complete metamorphosis.

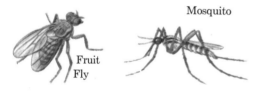

Mosquito

Fruit Fly

ORDER HYMENOPTERA. No wings or two pairs of wings hooked together, hind wings smaller. Chewing or sucking mouth parts. The only insects with "stingers." Complete metamorphosis.

Bee

Ant

Potter's Wasp

ORDER COLEOPTERA. Largest order of insects. No wings or two pairs of wings, the outer pair a hard

sheath beneath which the hind pair is folded. Chewing mouth parts. Short antennae usually. Forewings meet in straight line down back. Metamorphosis complete.

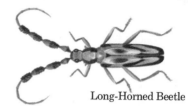

Long-Horned Beetle

PHYLUM HEMICHORDATA
(hemichordates)

Greek: *hemi* (half) and Latin: *chorda* (cord)

Wormlike marine animals. Once classified with the chordates; now classified as a separate phylum. Lack characteristic notochord of chordates. Prominent proboscis for burrowing. Dorsal nerve cord; gill slits; gut with two openings. About 100 species.

Acorn Worm

PHYLUM CHORDATA
(chordates)

Latin: *chorda* (cord)

The vertebrates and their invertebrate kin. Phylum is characterized by the possession, at some stage of development, of a notochord; a hollow, dorsal, nerve cord; and gill slits or pouches. Segmentation and coelom evident. There are about 45,000 existing species divided into three subphyla.

Subphylum Urochordata

Marine animals. Free-swimming larvae and stationary adults. Larvae with notochord and primitive nervous system that disappear or become altered in the adult form. About 2,000 species.

Sea Squirt

Subphylum Cephalochordata

Free-swimming, marine organisms. Tapered at both ends with notochord, gill slits, and mouth with fringed sensory appendages. About 20 species.

Amphioxus

Subphylum Vertebrata

The notochord is replaced by a backbone of vertebrae as the central axis of the endoskeleton. There is an enlarged brain that is protected by a cranium of cartilage or bone. Most have appendages in pairs and nearly all have olfactory organs, ears, and eyes. By far the majority of chordates belong to this subphylum. There are about 40,000 species divided into seven classes.

CLASS AGNATHA

The jawless fishes. Eel-like fishes lacking paired appendages (fins) and having a suction, disc-type mouth. Skeleton of poorly developed cartilage; two-chambered heart; exposed gill slits. No scales.

Hagfish

Lamprey

CLASS CHONDRICHTHYES

The cartilaginous fishes, having a well-developed cartilaginous skeleton. Marine fish with true jaws and paired appendages (fins). Two-chambered heart; uniform vertebrae; exposed gill slits; scales. About 600 species.

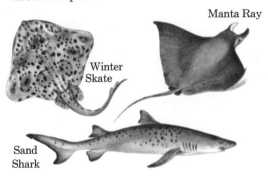

Manta Ray

Winter Skate

Sand Shark

CLASS OSTEICHTHYES

The bony fishes. The majority of modern fishes belong to this group. Possess a bony skeleton, scales, and an air bladder. Two-chambered heart; covered gills; paired fins. About 20,000 species.

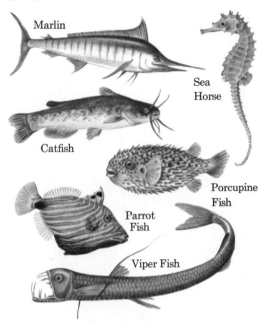

Marlin

Sea Horse

Catfish

Porcupine Fish

Parrot Fish

Viper Fish

CLASS AMPHIBIA

Animals with a moist, smooth, scaleless skin. Larvae usually aquatic, respiring by gills; most adults typically terrestrial and respiring by lungs. Typically a tetrapod (two pairs of appendages), though these may be reduced or lacking in some species; digits without claws. Three-chambered heart. Cold-blooded. About 2,800 species.

Toad

Tree Frog

Pacific Salamander

Green Frog

CLASS REPTILIA

Lung-breathing animals, most of which have scaly, dry skins. Independent of water for breeding purposes; eggs with membranes enclosing fluids and with shell. Includes transition between three- and four-chambered heart. Cold-blooded. About 6,000 species.

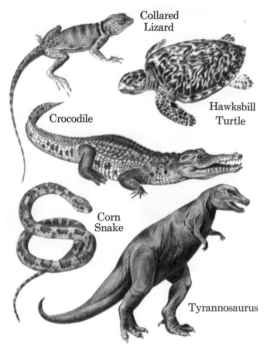

Collared Lizard

Crocodile

Hawksbill Turtle

Corn Snake

Tyrannosaurus

CLASS AVES

Birds. Scales modified as feathers. Skeleton with hollow bones and solidified to form rigid, bony box; no teeth. Two sets of appendages, one modified into wings. Warm-blooded, or homeothermic (maintain constant body temperature). Four-chambered heart. About 8,600 species in 27 orders.

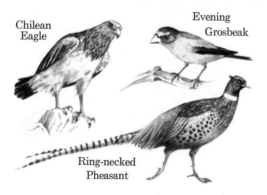

Chilean Eagle

Evening Grosbeak

Ring-necked Pheasant

Toucan

King Penguin

Ostrich

Purple Heron

Wood Duck

CLASS MAMMALIA

Young born alive and fed on milk secreted from mammary glands of the mother. Most possess hair of some kind. Homeothermic (warm-blooded); four-chambered heart. Most possess teeth. There are three subclasses, 18 orders, and approximately 5,000 species.

Subclass Prototheria

Egg-laying mammals.

ORDER MONOTREMATA. Very primitive, reptile-like mammals found in Australian region. Egg-laying, non-placental, and only primitive development of mammary glands. Six species.

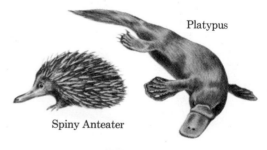

Platypus

Spiny Anteater

Subclass Metatheria

Young born underdeveloped. Develop further in mother's pouch.

ORDER MARSUPIALIA. Mammals whose young are born immature and then carried and nurtured in a pouch in the female. Non-placental. Limited geographical distribution; mainly in Australia. About 250 species.

Koala Bear

Kangaroo

Opossum

Subclass Eutheria

The majority of mammals belong to this subclass. Called placental mammals because they develop to maturity inside the uterus of the female where they are attached by a membrane (placenta). Distribution is world-wide. There are 16 orders in this subclass; seven are described here.

ORDER INSECTIVORA. Small, insect-eating mammals, adapted for burrowing. Usually with very high metabolism and voracious diet. Many species nocturnal. About 400 species.

Shrew

ORDER CHIROPTERA. Only flying mammals. Wings formed by membranes stretched across four greatly elongated fingers and then to legs. Thumb is small and free. World-wide distribution. About 800 species.

Bat

ORDER CETACEA. Marine mammals with forelimbs reduced to flippers and hind limbs absent. Skin naked, eyes small, and head very large. About 95 species.

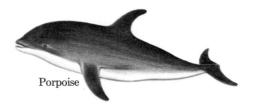

Porpoise

ORDER CARNIVORA. Flesh-eaters, usually with sharp claws and highly specialized teeth for catching and tearing flesh. About 280 species.

Brown Bear

Lion

ORDER PERISSODACTYLA. Plant-eating, hoofed, and grazing mammals. With an odd number of toes; one, three, or five. About 17 species.

Horse

ORDER ARTIODACTYLA. Grazing herbivores with 2 or 4 toes. Most have complex stomach. Many with horns or antlers. About 200 species.

Mule Deer

ORDER RODENTIA. A large, world-wide group of mostly small mammals with teeth adapted for gnawing; four large incisor teeth with sharp cutting edges. Very high reproductive capacity. About 2,030 species.

Beaver

ORDER PRIMATES. Much enlarged cranium, with the eyes rotated to front of head. Usually stand erect; have thumbs opposing the fingers and usually have nails replacing claws. About 190 species.

Tarsier

Uakari Monkey

Chimpanzee

Orangutan

2

The Setting of Life

Man has been an earth-bound creature for a million years or more. He has sought living things in the great depths of the oceans and amid the snowy peaks of mountains. He has explored the polar regions, the vast plains, the deserts, and isolated islands. He has noted similarities and differences among plants and animals. The immediate setting of life is the planet upon which man lives.

Modern astronomy has introduced us to a universe so vast that it is almost beyond the imagination. It is a universe filled with many star systems like our Milky Way. Some of these systems may contain planets like those that revolve about the sun. Thus, other stars may have earthlike planets capable of supporting some form of life.

Like Columbus sailing upon uncharted seas, man will find ways to venture into space. The moon is man's first venture into space. Journeys to Mars and Venus will follow the moon explorations. We may some day discover that the world of life extends far beyond the earth.

Conditions for Sustaining Life

As man studied life, he identified certain conditions necessary to sustain it. These conditions are known to exist only on earth.

That is why scientists believe that the variety of life found on earth is not present on other planets of the solar system.

WATER. Water is of fundamental importance to life. The bodies of all plants and animals contain it in varying amounts. Furthermore, it seems certain that life originated in ancient seas that once covered most of the earth. Today about 70 per cent of the earth's surface is covered by water.

2–1 This view of the Pacific Ocean emphasizes the vast areas covered by water.

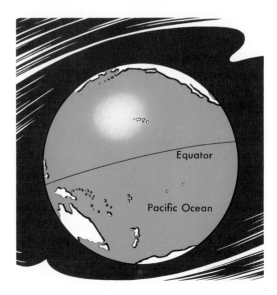

Equator

Pacific Ocean

The earth is the only planet in the solar system that has oceans.

THE ATMOSPHERE. The atmosphere that surrounds the earth provides oxygen, which most living things require. Near the earth's surface the atmosphere is fairly dense. The farther man rises from the surface, the less oxygen is available. That is why high-altitude planes and space vehicles must carry their own supply of oxygen.

The atmosphere also acts as a shield against the searing radiations of the sun. If there were no atmosphere, daytime temperatures would reach 230 degrees Fahrenheit. Night temperatures would drop as low as minus 300 degrees Fahrenheit. The moderation of these temperatures makes life possible.

TEMPERATURE RANGE. Outer space is intolerably cold. Only when sunlight is converted into heat is life possible. If the heat is excessive, life perishes. The temperature range in which life is found is the range bounded by the freezing point and the boiling point of water. This range is from 32° F to 212° F. Between these two temperatures water is generally found in liquid form, although some water exists as a vapor in the atmosphere.

Like the glass cover of a greenhouse, the atmosphere shields the earth from much of the harmful radiation of the sun, but traps enough heat to ease the cold of midnight.

In addition to supplying the energy to warm the earth, sunlight is necessary for the growth of all green plants. It provides energy for the chemical reactions that occur in plants to produce food from water, carbon dioxide, and mineral compounds.

THE CHEMICALS OF LIFE. The basic building materials of the stars, the planets, and of living things are the elements. The

2–2 The atmosphere acts like the glass of a greenhouse. It allows solar radiations to enter, but traps heat radiations.

2–3 Greenhouse Effect. Solar radiations are absorbed and re-radiated as heat waves, which cannot pass through the glass roof.

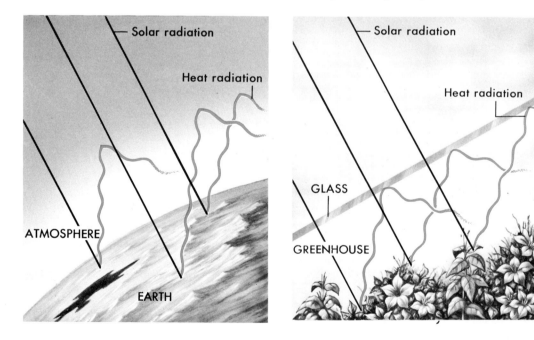

elements hydrogen and helium, which make up over 99 per cent of the sun and stars, are widely distributed in the universe. On earth, however, there are greater concentrations of other elements, such as carbon, oxygen, nitrogen, iron, and magnesium. These are some of the elements that are necessary for life.

Characteristics of Life

How do we recognize life? We see the plants and animals that live about us. How do we know that they are alive? The seeds of a flower give little evidence of life. At the microscopic level it is especially difficult to distinguish living from nonliving forms.

The biologist has identified four characteristics basic to all living things: *metabolism, growth, reproduction,* and *sensitivity.* Associated with these basic characteristics are many functions that are performed by living things.

METABOLISM. All organisms, from the smallest single-celled forms to the largest living things, are maintained by chemical reactions, which provide the energy required for sustaining life.

The biologist uses the term *metabolism* (meh-TAB-uh-liz-um) to describe the chemical reactions in a living system. These reactions mark the difference between an organism and a lifeless mass of inert chemicals. To study the thousands of reactions that determine the metabolism of any organism is to study life itself. *Nutrition* is the sum of the processes by which an organism takes in and utilizes food. It includes the metabolic processes that provide the raw materials of life.

There are marked differences between nutrition in green plants and in animals. The first step in plant nutrition is the intake of such simple substances as water, minerals, and carbon dioxide. The second step is the conversion of these substances into such foods as sugars, starches, proteins, and fats.

Animals, unlike green plants, cannot make food. They obtain food by eating plants or other animals. The first step in animal nutrition is *ingestion,* the eating of food. This is followed by the chemical process, *digestion,* in which foods are changed into simpler, useful compounds. *Circulation* is the transportation of food materials of life to all parts of the organism.

Another important phase of metabolism is *respiration,* by means of which energy is extracted from foods. The energy is used by the organism to cause motion, or to begin other chemical processes necessary for life.

Part of the energy of respiration is used to reorganize simpler materials into complex substances that are characteristic of a particular organism. This process is sometimes called *assimilation.* Thus, grazing sheep convert grass into mutton. Cattle, grazing in the same field, convert grass into beef.

GROWTH. As metabolism produces living material, each organism follows a definite pattern of growth in which the living material develops new parts and replaces old ones. Seeds sprout and produce roots, stems, and leaves. As the infant grows, the proportions of its body change. The texture of its hair becomes coarser. In early childhood the teeth are lost and replaced by a permanent set. The pattern of growth in all organisms is marked by change.

If you were to observe the growth of a crystal with a hand lens, you would see the gradual accumulation of new material on the outside of the "seed" crystal. Crystal growth is rather simple compared with the growth of living things. Crystal growth is precise and uniform. The arrangement of particles within the crystal is repeated exactly over and over again.

In a living thing there is considerable variation in the types of materials used for growth, and there may be different rates of

2–4 Dinosaurs, which once flourished on earth, are now extinct.

growth in various parts of the body. Furthermore, the entire process is regulated by complex chemicals called *enzymes*. Biologists, in fact, view the processes of metabolism and growth as the result of the action of extremely complicated enzyme systems upon the chemicals of life.

REPRODUCTION. Living things have the ability to produce new individuals having the same characteristics. This ability to reproduce new generations provides for the continuity of life. The rate at which reproduction occurs must be at least as great as the rate at which the older generations perish. If it is not, the species becomes extinct. The history of life on earth contains many illustrations of animals and plants that did not reproduce rapidly enough to maintain themselves.

The reproductive rate of most successful species is generally high, although there are some exceptions to this general rule. L. L. Woodruf of Yale University calculated that the offspring of the single-celled *Paramecium* (par-uh-MEE-see-um) reproducing itself once each day would have a volume as great as the earth in 112 generations. The fruitfly, *Drosophila*, (dro-SOF-uh-luh) produces about 200 new flies that are ready to reproduce in eleven days. Some bacteria reproduce as often as once every 20 minutes. An oak tree may produce as many as 10,000 acorns in one season. When the reproductive rate is low, as in man, the adults usually provide better care for their offspring, thus preventing extinction.

SENSITIVITY. Living things respond to *stimuli* from their environment. Common stimuli are light, sound, heat, chemicals, moisture, and contact. The response may be quick or slow, depending upon both the strength of the stimulus and the nature of the organism.

Plants generally respond much more slowly than animals. *Mimosa* is one of the few plants that responds quickly. When its leaves are touched they sag in a drooping manner. The Venus's-flytrap is another plant that responds to the contact of an insect's body by folding its hinged leaf together.

Many plants open or close their flowers in response to sunlight. This movement is generally too slow to be seen. However, time-lapse photography enables us to see the process speeded up. Similar photographs show us how the stem grows toward light and how the roots grow toward water.

Animal responses usually consist of movement toward or away from the stimuli that cause them. Even the simplest one-celled organisms respond to heat, light, and chemicals. The highest forms of animal life have organs especially sensitive to different kinds of stimuli. The eyes respond to light, the ears to sound, the tongue and nose to chemicals, the skin to pressure, pain, and heat.

The Prologue to Life

Before there was life on earth, there was the earth itself. And before the earth there were the billions of stars we call the *Galaxy*, or Milky Way. And before our Galaxy, there were millions of other galaxies in the universe. Astronomers believe that about ten billion years ago our Galaxy consisted of a tremendous cloud of whirling hydrogen. Such great cosmic clouds are seen in the depths of space. As the Galaxy spun, ripples and eddies acted as the centers for the for-

2–5　Land crab caught in Venus's-flytrap.

mation of the stars. Then tremendous nuclear reactions occurred, and the heavens were brightened by starlight. One of the stars produced at that time was our sun.

Many hypotheses have been proposed to account for the earth's origin. A theory that has support among many astronomers was

2–6　Spiral Galaxy in Andromeda

proposed in 1944. Carl von Weizsacker suggested the *Dust-Cloud Theory* to explain the origin of the earth and other planets. More recently, Gerard Kuiper and Fred Hoyle have made certain modifications to this basic theory. According to the modified theory, dust particles came together because of gravitational attraction and the pressure of starlight. Eventually, the cosmic dust clouds condensed to form the sun and the planets.

THE YOUNG EARTH AND ITS ATMOSPHERE. As the dust clouds merged to form the earth, they were squeezed closer and closer together. As eons of time passed, radioactive elements in the planet produced enough heat to cause the earth to become molten. Heavier materials, like iron and nickel, migrated to the center of the planet. Lighter substances moved to the surface. Huge clouds of gas and water vapor arose from the molten interior. Rains fell upon the earth only to rise again as clouds of steam.

Gradually, the earth cooled and continents appeared. Above the continents were great clouds of water vapor. As the rains fell, the clouds thinned and sunlight streamed through. The sea basins received the torrents of rain water, and the oceans were born.

The atmosphere of the young planet was not the same as it is today. Hydrogen was an important part of the atmosphere, as you would expect from its abundance in space. Today, hydrogen is almost completely lacking. Three compounds of hydrogen were also present. The first compound, methane gas, is formed by the chemical union of a carbon atom with four atoms of hydrogen. The second compound, ammonia gas, is formed by the union of three atoms of hydrogen with one atom of nitrogen. The third compound, water, composed of two atoms of hydrogen and one atom of oxygen, was also very abundant in the earth's early at-

2–7 Diffuse Nebula in Constellation of Sagittarius. According to the Dust-Cloud Theory, our solar system may have been formed from such a mass of gas and dust.

mosphere. Thus, of the four components of the atmosphere, all contained hydrogen. Helium, another very light gas, was also present, but it plays no part in our discussion of the origin of life.

PANSPERMIA. Did life begin on the planet Earth? Did life begin in some other part of the universe and travel to the Earth? These questions have intrigued scientists for many years. In 1907 the Swedish chemist Svante Arrhenius suggested that the simple forms of life may have drifted from one solar system to another in interstellar space. This theory, the *theory of panspermia*, does not explain the ultimate origin of life. It does, however, offer one possible explanation for the beginning of life on earth.

Several facts, however, tend to reduce the possibility that life on earth came from another part of the Galaxy. Interstellar space is very cold, so cold that organisms would probably be killed in transit. It is also a very high vacuum in which no known organisms could survive. Finally, ultraviolet radiation and cosmic rays would probably be lethal to organisms in outer space.

LIFE BEGINS. In 1924, the Russian bio-chemist Alexander I. Oparin suggested that life on earth began as a result of chemical changes that required millions of years. To understand this idea, we must remember that living things are complex chemical systems. The most important compounds in living systems are *proteins.* Proteins, in turn, are composed of chemical units known as amino (uh-MEE-noh) acids. *Amino acids* are organic substances containing the four elements: oxygen, hydrogen, carbon, and nitrogen. Oparin believed that before life could begin, these elements must combine to form amino acids.

We have already seen that the earth's early atmosphere may have consisted of a mixture of hydrogen, methane, ammonia, and water vapor. These gases contain the four elements necessary to form the amino acids. Chance flashes of lightning could have combined these elements into amino acids in the early history of the earth. Amino acid linkages could then have formed the proteins. Upon further linkage of the proteins, a "living compound" might have been produced.

In 1953, Stanley L. Miller of the University of Chicago devised an apparatus to test this idea. His apparatus included an upper and lower flask connected by tubing. In the lower flask he placed water. In the upper flask he placed a mixture of hydrogen, methane, and ammonia. He heated the water causing it to rise as vapor into the upper flask. Here the vapor cooled, condensed to water that dissolved gases from the mixture, and then trickled back to the lower flask. An electric spark, injected into the return passage, provided the energy for recombinations of the key elements. After running his apparatus for about a week, he found amino acids in the lower flask. Thus, the building blocks of life had been made from their basic elements. Miller's experiment does not provide a final answer to the

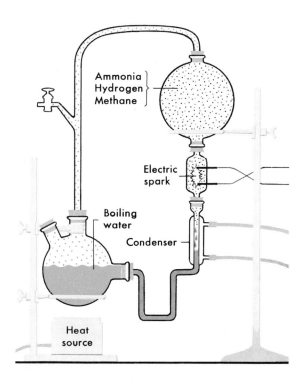

2–8 Diagram of the apparatus used by Miller to simulate conditions presumed to be present when the primitive earth had a continuous cloud cover of water vapor, methane, ammonia, and hydrogen. After the experiment had run one week, Miller found that amino acids had been formed in the circulation solution. Amino acids are basic components of proteins, which in turn are the basic substances of life.

origin of life, but it does suggest a way in which the first step could have occurred.

PROTEINOIDS AND MICROSPHERES. We have indicated that the next step along the path leading to the production of a living thing might be the combination of amino acids into proteins. Sidney W. Fox and some of his co-workers at Florida State University have done extensive research on this problem. Although Miller had produced only four amino acids in his experiments, Fox and his associates were able to produce twelve amino acids from methane, ammonia, and water. What would happen if a mixture of these amino acids was heated above the temperature of boiling water? When the Florida research team tried the experiment, they found that the amino acids combined to form protein-like molecules, which they called "proteinoid."

Later, experiments were performed in which a heated mixture of proteinoid was treated with water. Under the microscope the cooled mixture of proteinoid and water had formed tiny spheres. Fox called these cell-like units *microspheres.* They were about the same size and shape as spherical bacteria. Although microspheres show none of the complex structures of cells, they do have boundary layers, which separates them from their environment. Microspheres have also been observed with bud-like appendages that are structurally similar to the buds produced in the reproduction of yeast.

ATP. Proteins are not the only "life-sustaining" compounds. As we shall see later, there are other compounds that play a very important part in the chemistry of life. Biologists believe that the formation of these additional compounds under conditions similar to the conditions that existed on the early earth might further clarify the manner in which life began.

ATP is the abbreviation for *adenosine triphosphate,* a compound found in all living cells. Its importance derives from the fact that ATP supplies the energy that operates the cell, much as a battery supplies the energy to start an automobile. The complicated machinery of the cell requires energy to keep it operating. Could ATP have been formed from the chemicals existing on earth when life may have begun?

The American scientists Cyril Ponnamperuma and Carl Sagan conducted an experiment to see if they could make ATP. They prepared a dilute solution of a substance called *adenine* (AD-un-een), a complex compound of carbon, nitrogen, and hydrogen. To this they added the sugar *ribose* and some *phosphoric acid.* They believed that each of these substances might have been present in the primeval ocean. Since the scientists also believed that the early earth was bathed in ultraviolet light, they irradiated the mixture with this kind of light. When the resulting compounds were examined, it was found that much ATP had been produced.

2–9 Food energy is transferred to ATP, which releases energy for work of cell and becomes energy-poor ADP. ADP obtains energy from food, thus the cycle is completed.

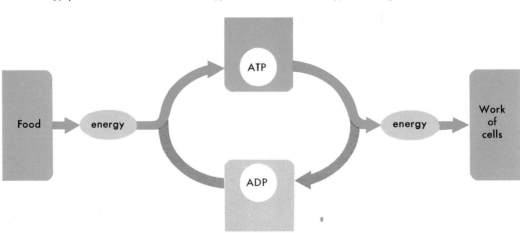

Nucleic Acids. Other compounds identified with life are the *nucleic acids.* These are so named because they were found in the nucleus of the cell by the Swiss biochemist Friedrich Miescher in 1869.

A nucleic acid of primary importance in the development of life is DNA. DNA is the abbreviation for *deoxyribonucleic acid.* Biologists believe that DNA is the most important compound needed in the reproductive processes of all organisms. Since the forerunners of living things could hardly have become "alive" without reproducing, the formation of DNA was crucial to the development of a living system. *Ribonucleic acid* (RNA) is also an important compound in the story of life's beginnings. In 1955 Severo Ochoa produced a compound remarkably like RNA in his New York University lab. A year later Arthur Kornberg (a former pupil of Ochoa) and his collaborators reported the making of synthetic DNA in their Stanford University laboratory. A compound very similar to ATP had been used in the formation of both RNA and DNA.

The important fact emerging from these laboratory experiments is that the chemical compounds necessary for the beginning of life could have been made spontaneously from materials existing on the young planet Earth.

Coacervates. Let us assume that the first steps in the development of a living thing have occurred. Amino acids have been formed from the primeval atmosphere. Proteins have been made by the union of the amino acids. Energy-rich ATP has been synthesized. DNA and RNA have been formed to enable the organism to reproduce. How is it possible for these chemicals to develop into the coordinated complex system we call a living thing?

The Russian biochemist A. I. Oparin believed that the original compounds of life formed large clumps, which he called *coa-*

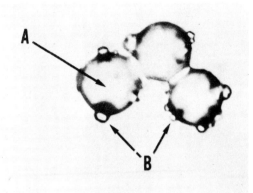

2–10 Microspheres with bud-like appendages. Derived from simple gases, they were called "proteinoids" by Sidney Fox and his associates.

cervates (co-as-er-vaits). A coacervate is an aggregation of organic molecules, such as proteins, which adhere to each other in a liquid. The Dutch chemist H. G. B. de Jong had experimented with coacervates in the 1930's. He found that they were about the same size as small bacteria. Coacervates also have a clearly marked boundary layer, a structure somewhat like a cell membrane. Oparin found that coacervate droplets absorb other materials into themselves, thus increasing their size, and react with the chemicals contained within those materials. This interchange of materials with a surrounding medium is similar to the reaction of a single cell with its surroundings.

Were the coacervates the first "living things"? It is extremely difficult to say because we lack a precise definition for life. The simplest organisms we observe today are highly evolved forms of life in comparison with the earliest forms. Modern living cells use DNA and RNA in the process of reproduction. Although coacervate droplets have been observed "budding," there is no indication that the chemicals of reproduction, DNA and RNA, are involved. For this reason, most biologists believe that co-

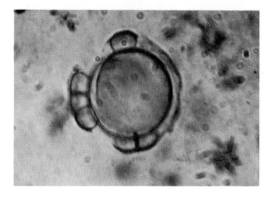

2–11 Photomicrograph of Barghoorn Fossil

acervates do not mark the point at which life came into being.

MICROFOSSILS. How old are the oldest forms of life man has discovered? The record seems to be held by bacteria-like fossils believed to be 3.1 billion years old. Harvard botanist Elso Barghoorn found the fossils of bacteria and primitive algae in rocks in Canada. *Fossils* are the impressions or the remains of ancient life embedded in rock. Dr. Barghoorn believes that many of the fossil algae, very simple protists, are about 2.7 billion years old. These ancient fossils are like no organisms currently living on earth. Since these examples are already somewhat advanced forms of life; the original living things must have begun many millions of years before.

Life in Space

Scientists did not expect to find life on the moon, which has no atmosphere and no water. Also, the temperature extremes are too great. Yet some scientists have not dismissed the idea that there may be very primitive forms of life living in the lower parts of the moon's crust.

The surface of Venus is hidden by dense clouds. Although some water vapor is believed to exist in the atmosphere of Venus,

the surface is probably hot and dry. Huge dust storms may sweep across the land under the force of violent winds.

Although space probes have not yet detected any indications of life on other planets, Mars seems the most likely planet to support life. It has a thin atmosphere consisting largely of nitrogen and carbon dioxide. Although the temperature extremes on Mars are greater than on earth, they are moderate in comparison with the temperature extremes on other planets. Daytime readings on Mars probably range from 70° F to a low of minus 200° F at night. There seems to be very little oxygen. Water may exist in polar regions as a thin layer of frost.

None of the remaining planets seems to have the conditions necessary to support life. Mercury, very close to the sun, is a hot, dry desert. Jupiter, Saturn, Uranus, Neptune, and Pluto appear to be extremely cold and have dense atmospheres containing gases unfavorable to the development of life.

BEYOND THE SOLAR SYSTEM. Biology and astronomy do not appear to be closely related sciences, yet the intriguing possibility of life in other planetary systems has drawn biologists and astronomers together. The Galaxy contains 100 billion stars. How many of them may be circled by planets where life has developed?

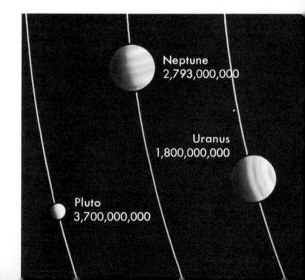

Neptune
2,793,000,000

Uranus
1,800,000,000

Pluto
3,700,000,000

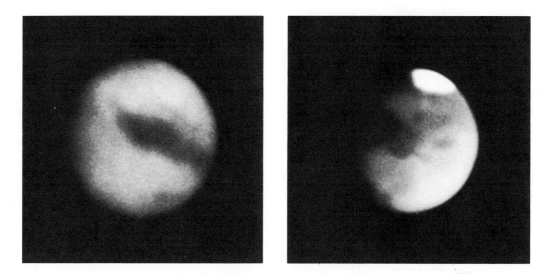

2–12 Seasonal Changes on the Planet Mars. The polar caps of Mars consist of frost that accumulates during the Martian winter and melts during the Martian summer.

Dr. Su-Shu Huang of the National Aeronautics and Space Administration has analyzed the conditions that must prevail to support life. Taking into account the size, temperature, and age of a star, Dr. Huang believes the flow of energy from the star must be moderate and must continue for about three billion years or more. As stars evolve from large, hot stars to small, cool stars, they pass through a period of moderation. The sun is a star in such a period. It is neither too hot nor too cold, too big nor too small. Its age is greater than three billion years.

How many stars at a similar stage in evolution are there in the Galaxy? Harlow Shapley of Harvard University thinks that ten per cent of all stars are like the sun. Therefore, ten billion stars just in our Galaxy may have planets that support life!

2–13 The Solar System. Of all the planets in the solar system, the earth is the only one that has conditions favorable to the development of life as we know it.

Sun

Jupiter
483,000,000

Earth
93,000,000

Asteroid
belt

Venus
67,000,000

Mercury
36,000,000

Mars
140,000,000

Saturn
886,000,000

IMPORTANT POINTS

• The conditions that sustain life on our planet seem to exist only on earth, where there is an abundance of water and gases suitable for life. Over most of the surface of the earth the temperature is maintained between 32° F and 212° F by the protective atmosphere. The elements necessary for life are abundant.

• Life is characterized by the ability to take in food, use energy, and grow. Metabolism is the term used to describe the chemical reactions that are fundamental to living things. All organisms have the ability to reproduce other living things like themselves. In addition, they are also sensitive and respond to stimuli.

• Life probably began on the earth after the compounds of life were formed from the primitive atmosphere. Amino acids, proteins, ATP, DNA, and RNA may then have formed aggregates of compounds which interacted and eventually led to the first cells. This process may have taken half a billion years.

• Mars is the only planet within the solar system where primitive life could possibly exist. Conditions on the moon and the other planets are unsuitable for the development of life. This does not rule out the possibility of the existence of life beyond the solar system.

REVIEW QUESTIONS

1. Make a list of places on earth where you think life may not exist.
2. Why is water important to sustain life?
3. Explain the importance of the atmosphere as a shield against radiations from the sun.
4. How do biologists distinguish living from non-living things?
5. What are some of the functions associated with metabolism?
6. Distinguish between the growth of a living thing and the growth of a crystal.
7. How is a high reproductive rate related to an organism's success?
8. What are some stimuli to which plants respond?
9. How are plant responses different from animal responses?
10. How do astronomers think the planets might have originated?
11. What gases might have been found in the early atmosphere of the earth?
12. List three steps you think may have been the preface to the beginning of life.

CHECK YOUR UNDERSTANDING

13. Why would you expect hydrogen to be an important building block of living matter?
14. What is the principal difference between plant and animal nutrition?
15. Why do some astronomers believe that as many as ten billion stars may have planets that are capable of supporting life?
16. Does Stanley L. Miller's experiment justify the belief that he showed us how life began?
17. Do Sidney W. Fox's microspheres mark the beginning of life?
18. Astronomers refer to the habitable zone about a star. What does this mean?

RESEARCH PROJECTS AND REPORTS

1. Obtain information from your school or public library and prepare a report on one of the following topics:

   Life in the Sea   Life in a Tropical Jungle   Exploring the Planets

2. *The Diversity of Life:* Prepare five columns on a sheet of paper with the following headings:

   Deserts   Oceans   Plains   Tropics   Polar Regions

   In each column list as many organisms as you can.

3. *Miniature Greenhouse:* Plan and construct a miniature greenhouse using plastic film instead of glass. What is the relation between this model and the atmospheric cover of the earth?

FURTHER READING

The World We Live In. Lincoln Barnett. Time, Inc., New York, N.Y. Articles that have appeared in *Life* about the origin of the Milky Way, the sun, and the planets. The diversity of living things is shown in hundreds of pictures and illustrations.

The Nature of the Universe. Fred Hoyle. Harper & Brothers, New York, N.Y. Discusses the origin and future of the sun and planets.

First Book on Mars. David C. Knight. Grolier Press, New York, N.Y. An introductory book with up-to-date information.

"Life Outside the Solar System." Su-Shu Huang. *Scientific American,* April, 1960, page 55. The characteristics and life history of stars provide information with which to speculate on the number of earthlike planets in the Galaxy.

"Could Life Originate Now?" S. W. Fox and R. J. McCauley. *Natural History,* August, 1968, page 26. Speculation on the creation of life spontaneously from non-living compounds.

CHAPTER

3

The Tools of Research

Iɴ ᴊᴜɴᴇ 1961, medical scientists and physicians from all over the world had gathered in Montreal, Canada, to discuss advances in their special fields of research. Three distinguished Nobel prizewinners discussed what each thought helps a scientist create new ideas.

Linus Pauling and Albert Szent-Györgyi believed there was something special about the personality and attitudes of the creative man of science. Lord Adrian, world-famous physiologist from Trinity College, England, had a different idea. He thought that new instruments and equipment, more than anything else, helped create new concepts. New tools of research, he said, produce more refined insights about everything the scientist investigates.

These three eminent scientists identified two important conditions upon which scientific progress depends. The first is the quality of the scientist himself; the second is the equipment with which he works.

Progress in biology is largely a history of the development of new instruments and techniques of research. The invention of the optical microscope altered the ideas of biologists about the structure of organisms.

It exposed the world of microscopic life for the first time. The electron microscope has revealed an even finer, more detailed view of microscopic life.

Chemists and physicists have further quickened the pace of research by offering new devices and techniques that were first developed for their own investigations. Some of these techniques and devices are the subject of this chapter.

Biological Techniques

The ancient Greeks and Romans seem to have known that a piece of glass, properly ground, could magnify objects. It was not until the 16th century, however, that hand lenses were widely used. Even with a single lens it was possible to enlarge objects about ten times. Such enlargement revealed very startling things. A popular pastime of the period was to examine fleas with hand lenses. As a result, the earliest microscopes were called "flea-glasses."

About 1590, Zacharias Janssen, a Dutch spectacle maker, combined several lenses within a single instrument. This increased the magnification of the simple hand lens several times.

The Dutchman Anton Van Leeuwenhoek (1632–1723) was a master of the art of grinding lenses. He was a self-educated man who developed a passion for examining everything under the microscope. Early in the course of his work he became dissatisfied with the instruments available and decided to make his own. During his lifetime he built over 400 simple microscopes. Many of these early microscopes were small enough to fit into the palm of your hand. So carefully were his lenses ground that some of them magnified objects 270 times.

Leeuwenhoek saw things no man had ever seen before: tiny single-celled organisms and the red blood cells of the frog and of man. Yet, all of his observations were made with instruments far poorer than the microscope you will use in your high school laboratory.

In a sense, Leeuwenhoek was as great an explorer as Columbus. Whereas Columbus discovered new continents, Leeuwenhoek discovered the amazing world of tiny organisms, so important to human health. He called these newly found organisms "animalcules," or little animals.

Although Leeuwenhoek made only simple microscopes consisting of single lenses, other men living at the same time began to use combinations of lenses to increase the magnification of their microscopes. Among these men was Robert Hooke (1635–1703), an Englishman, who created the basic type of instrument that is still used today.

THE COMPOUND MICROSCOPE. The modern *compound microscope* is a precision optical instrument consisting of two lens systems, the *eyepiece* and the *objective*. The eyepiece is at the top of the *body tube*. The objective is at the bottom.

The specimen to be observed is placed over a hole in the *stage* immediately beneath the objective lens. A *mirror* mounted

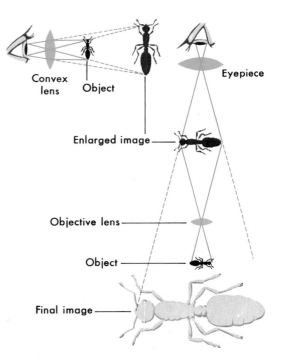

3–1 A single lens forms a magnified image of the object. A compound-lens system in a microscope magnifies further by enlarging the image formed by the objective lens.

below the stage may be adjusted to send light through the hole, thus illuminating the specimen for observation. The objective produces a magnified image of the specimen. This image is further enlarged by the eyepiece. The combined magnification results in a total magnification far in excess of that produced by a single lens. Most student microscopes have two objective lenses: a shorter, *low-power objective* and a longer, *high-power objective*. These are mounted on a rotating *nosepiece* and may be easily interchanged. Two magnifications are, therefore, possible.

Before beginning any laboratory work you should study the parts of the microscope. This will permit you to follow the directions given in class much more easily.

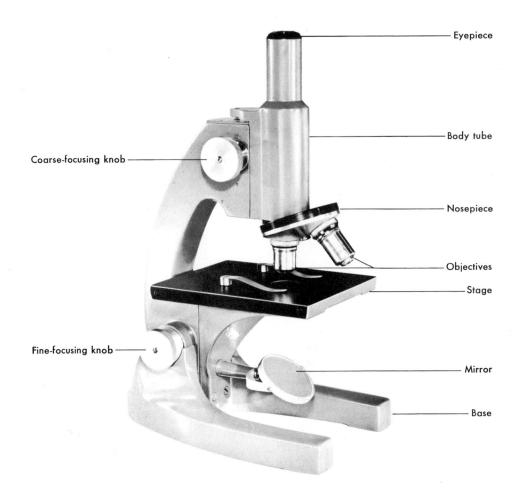

Eyepiece

Body tube

Nosepiece

Objectives

Stage

Mirror

Base

Coarse-focusing knob

Fine-focusing knob

3–2 A Typical Compound Microscope

USING THE MICROSCOPE. Learning to use any tool requires patience and a great deal of practice. Following the steps listed below will help you to acquire skill quickly.

1. Place the specimen over the center of the hole in the stage. Turn objective to low power.
2. Adjust the mirror so that it reflects light upward through the specimen. Blue light from the sky is best. Do not use direct sunlight.
3. Before looking through the eyepiece, lower the body tube as far as you can. The coarse focusing knob is used for

this purpose. *Do not touch the specimen with the objective.*

4. Look through the eyepiece and carefully *focus upward,* again using the coarse focusing knob.
5. Adjust the fine focusing knob to bring out details of the image.

PRACTICING WITH THE MICROSCOPE. A good way to learn to use the microscope is to practice with something simple. Single letters, such as an "e" cut from a magazine, are excellent. Place an "e" on a glass slide and add a cover slip, then focus it under low power. Examine the image carefully. Is it right side up? Move it to the right. How does it appear to move?

The total magnification is obtained by multiplying the magnification of the objective by the magnification of the eyepiece. The X number stamped on each of these parts is the magnification. Thus, a 10X eyepiece used with a 43X objective produces a total magnification of 430X.

STAINING OBJECTS TO BE STUDIED. If a small piece of the inner membrane of an onion is examined with the microscope, it will appear as a wall of irregular, colorless bricks. Adding a drop of dilute iodine solution to the onion skin produces a remarkable change. The outline of the bricks is now a distinct golden brown, and each brick contains a brownish spot.

Biologists make use of many stains and dyes. Sometimes two or more stains of contrasting colors are used. This helps us to see the parts of plants and animals more clearly. There are some stains that give different colors to various parts of the same tissue.

THE MICROTOME. Very thin sections of tissues are required for microscopic examination. The *microtome* is a device capable of cutting tissues thinner than a human hair. A hard specimen, such as a twig, may be cut in its natural condition. Softer tissues must first be embedded in paraffin. The paraffin is later dissolved, and the tissue is then stained and examined.

For rapid sectioning, a soft tissue may be quick-frozen by using carbon dioxide gas. This method is used during surgery when cancer is suspected. The suspected tissue is removed, quick-frozen, sectioned, stained, and examined in a matter of minutes. In this way the surgeon knows whether the patient has cancer while the operation is still in progress.

So fine are the tools of research that operations can now be performed upon single cells. Parts of the smallest cells can be removed, and chemicals can be injected. For

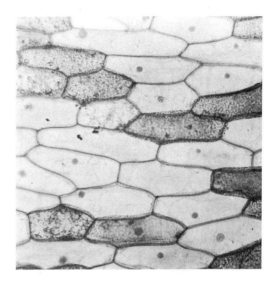

3–3 Stained Onion Cells

example, a small part of a microscopic organism, such as an ameba, can be removed by *microsurgery.* The needles used are mounted on the stage of the microscope. Control knobs attached to the needles produce the slightest movement, so that surgery can be performed.

PHOTOGRAPHY. The camera produces a lasting record of the observations the biologist makes. All that is necessary to take a picture through a microscope is to focus the camera carefully above the eyepiece. Enlargements of the original photograph bring out details not seen at first. Motion pictures can be made with the microscope in the same way.

One of the advantages of the movie camera is that it can make what are known as *time-lapse photographs.* In the case of movements too slow to be seen, time-lapse exposures can be made at intervals of an hour. When this type of film is shown, a seed appears to grow as if by magic, quickly sending out roots and shooting up the stem. Flowers seem to unfold their petals in seconds, a process that normally requires

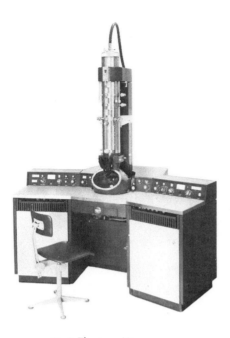

3–4 Electron Microscope

Instead of using light, the electron microscope uses a beam of electrons. The instrument does not resemble the ordinary optical microscope. It functions like a giant radio tube whose filament emits a stream of electrons under very high voltages. The electrons pass through the specimen and are then focussed by a series of magnetic coils. The coils, which bend electronic beams much as a glass lens bends light, are called *magnetic lenses.* The electrons finally strike a fluorescent screen similar to the front of your television set, producing the image to be observed.

Most electron microscopes include built-in cameras that can photograph images on the fluorescent screen. The photographic images can be enlarged even fur-

3–5 Lens components of electron microscope, which uses beams of electrons, compared with lens system of an inverted optical microscope.

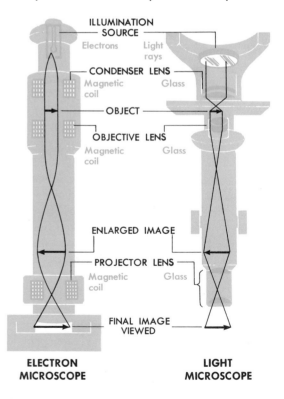

ILLUMINATION SOURCE

Electrons   Light rays

CONDENSER LENS
Magnetic coil   Glass

OBJECT

OBJECTIVE LENS
Magnetic coil   Glass

ENLARGED IMAGE

PROJECTOR LENS
Magnetic coil   Glass

FINAL IMAGE VIEWED

ELECTRON MICROSCOPE   **LIGHT MICROSCOPE**

hours, or even days. When motion is too rapid to be seen, the movie camera can also slow it down.

THE ELECTRON MICROSCOPE. The compound microscope is a fine tool for the biologist, but it is limited in what it can do. Since it depends on light rays, its magnifying power is limited to the shortest wavelengths of light visible to the eye. Theoretically, its upper limit of magnification is 3000X. In practice, however, the best compound microscopes do not exceed approximately 2000X. When magnifications beyond 2000X are needed, a compound microscope can no longer be of any help. Certain organisms, such as viruses, are so tiny that even the best compound microscope cannot "see" them.

Magnifications of 300,000X are possible with an entirely different kind of instrument called an *electron microscope.* Invented in Germany in 1932, it has been further perfected in this country by Dr. Vladimir K. Zworykin.

Milestones In Biology

Anton van Leeuwenhoek
(1632–1723)

ANTON VAN LEEUWENHOEK (LAY-vun-hook) is an example of a man whose hobby gave the science of biology new directions. His hobby was making microscopes and observing just about everything that interested him. Although his microscopes were small and fitted with simple lenses, they were far superior to any instruments that existed in his day. Man's knowledge of living things could not have progressed very far as long as his observations were limited by what he could see with his unaided eye.

Leeuwenhoek was born in Delft, Holland, where he lived for most of his 90 years. Although self-taught, he has been called "one of the most extraordinary scholars of all time." His only formal education consisted of a brief apprenticeship to the cloth trade in Amsterdam. In spite of his lack of scientific training, he gained a reputation as an expert naturalist and a careful research worker.

Continually dissatisfied with any microscope he was using, Leeuwenhoek set about with limitless patience to build new ones. He even tried grinding diamond lenses in an effort to obtain greater magnifications. His best instrument, using a spherical glass lens, had a magnification of 270 diameters.

During his lifetime, Leeuwenhoek made more than 400 microscopes. Being a suspicious man, he never shared his instruments with anyone. Visiting scientists were permitted to peer into his microscopes, but no one was allowed to borrow one.

During years of observation, Leeuwenhoek accurately described bacteria, protozoa, yeasts, the sperm cells of higher animals, the red blood cells, plant and animal structures, and many other subjects.

Leeuwenhoek described his observations in letters and articles, which he sent to scientific societies. Learned members of these societies at first suspected him of being a crank. In later years, however, he was elected to membership in the Royal Society and the Paris Academy of Science. To Leeuwenhoek goes the credit of revealing to all mankind the subvisible world of life.

ther. Under favorable conditions, this combination of techniques has led to total magnifications of 1,000,000X. The electron microscope is an important weapon in the fight against the virus diseases. It has revealed facts about these living things the biologist did not know before.

The electron microscope has undergone great improvement since it was first invented. Some idea of the unseen world it has enabled scientists to enter may be gathered from this fact: a human hair enlarged by a combination of electronic magnification and photography would appear to be more than 150 feet in diameter! However, similar to the optical microscope, the electron microscope has a definite upper limit of magnification.

Chemical and Physical Techniques

Many of the techniques of the chemist and physicist are also used by the biologist. The techniques discussed below will give you a better idea of the close relationship between chemistry, physics, and biology.

INDICATORS. The chemist uses substances called *indicators* to tell him whether a solution is an acid or a base. A common indicator is litmus, a water-soluble powder prepared from a plant. *Litmus paper,* which has been soaked in litmus solution, turns red in the presence of an acid and blue in the presence of a base. Since saliva is normally basic, a piece of red litmus paper turns blue when placed on the tongue. Using indicators, a medical technician can test blood or urine for acidity.

Indicators can also measure the relative acidity of a substance. The chemist rates acidity by a *pH value.* On this scale a neutral substance, such as water, has a pH value of 7.0. Values higher than this are basic; lower values are acidic.

Many tests are used to analyze the materials found in the body fluids. Glucose is a

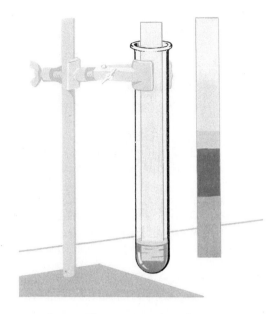

3–6 Paper Chromatography. The pigments in the solvent rise in proportion to their relative absorption. Dried filter paper is later examined for location of various pigments.

sugar found in the urine of patients suffering from diabetes. In testing for glucose, a sample of urine and an equal amount of a test solution (Benedict's or Fehling's) are placed in a test tube. The sample is then heated over a flame. If a series of color changes occurs, ending with an orange red, glucose is known to be present.

CHROMATOGRAPHY. *Chromatography* (kroh-muh-TOG-ruh-fee) is a method used to separate complex mixtures into their component parts.

For example, the green color of spinach is actually a mixture of four pigments, which can be separated by paper chromatography. To do this, sufficient spinach leaves are placed in acetone to produce a solution with an intense green color. A small amount of the green extract is then placed in a clean test tube. A narrow strip of filter paper is inserted, wicklike, in the tube. The paper should be slightly longer than the tube and extend to the bottom.

Each of the pigments in the extract has a different affinity, or attraction, for the filter paper wick. The pigment with the strongest affinity will rise the highest; the pigment with the weakest affinity will rise the least. Within ten to fifteen minutes, the separation of the four pigments will be seen as four distinct color zones.

Mixtures of amino acids can be separated by chromatography. Since the amino acids are colorless, they must be stained to be visible. A chemical is sprayed on the dried filter paper after the separation is complete. The amino acids appear as lightly-colored, purple spots. The analysis of the amino acids in a protein is sometimes done in this manner.

ELECTROPHORESIS. Because many molecules are electrically charged, it is possible to separate complex mixtures by placing them in an electric field. A positively charged molecule will be attracted to the negative pole of the electric field. Likewise, a negatively charged molecule will move toward the positive pole of the electric field. Biochemists call this electrical separation process *electrophoresis* (e-lek-tro-fah-REE-sis). The numerous proteins in human blood plasma have been separated by using this technique.

One method of electrophoresis is very similar to paper chromatography. A small amount of the mixture to be separated is spotted on paper midway between the poles of an electric field. The ends of the paper dip into troughs of a conducting liquid, wetting the paper throughout its entire length. A difference of several hundred volts is maintained between the two electrical poles. This difference causes the charged particles of the mixture to move toward the respective poles. The particles will move at different rates, depending on their size, shape, and charge.

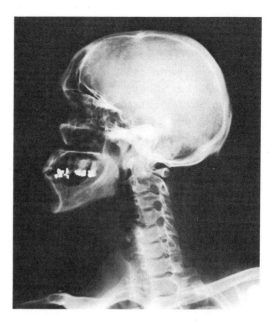

3–7 X-ray Photograph of Human Head

X RAYS. X rays were discovered in 1895 by the German physicist Wilhelm Roentgen. They were first called *roentgen rays* in honor of their discoverer. X rays affect photographic film. Unlike light rays, however, they are able to penetrate many solid substances. This characteristic makes them very useful.

Bones are much more dense than muscles. When X rays are passed through tissues, the denser tissue casts a heavier shadow on X-ray film. Bones appear very distinct. Physicians find X-ray pictures of injured bones very valuable in diagnosis. Dentists use X-ray photographs to locate hidden cavities in the teeth.

The softer parts of the body cannot ordinarily be x-rayed, since the rays penetrate them too easily. It is therefore necessary to outline the softer parts by some chemical means. For example, X-ray photographs of the digestive tract can be made if the patient drinks barium sulfate beforehand. Chemists use the name *radiopaques* for substances that X rays cannot pass through. Such substances make possible X-ray photography of specific organs. By this means diagnosis can sometimes be made without surgery.

When it is desirable to observe the working of the body by an X-ray technique, a *fluoroscope* (FLUR-uh-skope) is used. The X rays are made visible by placing a fluorescent screen where the photographic plate would normally be. With this technique the physician can observe body functions immediately without waiting for pictures to be developed.

RADIOACTIVE ELEMENTS. A most useful tool of the biologist is the radioactive element or *radioisotope*. The French physicist Henri Becquerel discovered natural radioactivity in 1896 while experimenting with crystals of a uranium salt. Rays given off by the salt penetrated the black paper around an unexposed photographic plate. When the plate was developed, Becquerel found that the rays had darkened the film. Many other natural radioactive materials have since been discovered.

In 1934, Irene Joliot-Curie and Frederic Joliot, her husband, learned how to make aluminum radioactive. Since this discovery, many other radioactive elements have been produced artificially. The production of radioisotopes has been increased by the development of nuclear reactors, such as that at Oak Ridge, Tennessee. The common form of phosphorus, for example, can be changed to radioactive phosphorus in a reactor. Chemists call the common form of phosphorus P-31 to distinguish it from its radioactive form, P-32.

RADIATION DETECTION DEVICES. Radioisotopes are sometimes called "tracer elements" because with proper detection devices they can be traced wherever they may be. Many radioisotopes continually give off a type of radiation called gamma rays. Gamma rays are very similar to X rays and

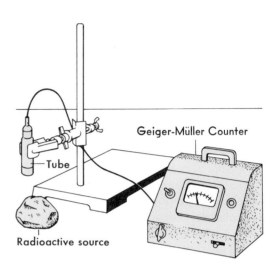

3–8 The Geiger-Müller counter detects the presence of radioactive sources.

can affect photographic film. Pictures exposed by radioisotopes are called *radioautographs*.

The *Geiger-Müller (G-M) counter* is probably the best known radiation detection instrument. The counter converts radiation into a clicking sound or a flash of light. The G-M counter may also be designed to operate a mechanical counting device so that the number of radiations may be recorded. The heart of the G-M counter is its G-M tube. The tube consists of a metal cylinder through which runs a central insulated wire. The wire is maintained at a positive voltage of about 800 to 1000 volts. Within the tube is a mixture of gases maintained under low pressure.

When radiation enters the G-M tube, it releases electrons from the gas molecules. The electrons, which are negatively charged particles of the atoms, are strongly attracted to the positively charged central wire. Speeding toward the wire, they strike other gas atoms and release more electrons. An avalanche of electrons is thus built up and speeds towards the wire. The flow of electrons to the center wire is an electric current and creates a pulse in the G-M tube. The pulse of electricity is changed by the G-M counter into a clicking sound or a flash of light.

Using radioisotopes and detection devices, the biologist can study the way plants take in minerals from the soil. He can also study the use of certain chemicals in the body. For example, iodine concentrates mainly in the thyroid gland. Physicians may use radioactive iodine to determine whether a patient's thyroid gland is underactive or overactive. A measured dose of radioactive iodine is swallowed by the patient. Twenty-four hours later, a detection device is used to measure the percentage of the dose that has been absorbed by the thyroid.

IMPORTANT POINTS

- Scientists have developed many tools to study living things. One of the most useful tools is the microscope. The compound microscope magnifies objects by using light rays that pass through a combination of lenses. The highest magnification of the compound microscope is about 2000X.

- The electron microscope uses a beam of electrons instead of light rays. Magnifications of 300,000X are possible with this instrument.

- Still pictures and motion pictures can be taken through the microscope to provide a permanent record for the biologist's observation. Time-lapse photography can be used to speed up motion when it is too slow to observe; slow-motion photography is used to do the reverse.

- The physicist and chemist have provided many techniques useful to the biologist. Chemical indicators identify the nature of different substances. Chromatography has made possible the analysis of complex mixtures.

- X rays may be used to photograph the body's interior. Denser tissue, such as bone, appears as a shadow on the photographic film. To observe body parts directly, a technique in which the X rays strike a fluorescent screen is used.

- Radioisotopes or radioactive tracer elements have a wide application in biology and medicine. With them, biologists have been able to learn much about the growth and functioning of living organisms.

REVIEW QUESTIONS

1. Distinguish between a simple and a compound microscope.
2. What are the main steps in focusing a microscope?
3. How does staining assist the biologist?
4. Why is the microtome important to anyone who wishes to examine plant or animal tissue under the miscroscope?
5. How can the techniques of microsurgery be employed in the study of cells?

6. What are the advantages of time-lapse and slow-motion photography?
7. What is an indicator?
8. What is chromatography?
9. How does a doctor or dentist make use of X rays?
10. List several ways in which the chemist and the physicist aid the biologist.

CHECK YOUR UNDERSTANDING

11. It has been said that Leeuwenhoek's work marked the beginning of modern biology. Explain this statement.
12. How can you determine the total magnification of a compound microscope?
13. Compare the operation of an electron microscope with that of an optical microscope.
14. A physician suspects that his patient is suffering from a stomach ulcer. What techniques can he use to confirm his diagnosis?
15. Which do you consider more important in the advance of biological research, the qualities of the scientist or the development of new research instruments and techniques?
16. List several additional research instruments or techniques you think might have been included in this chapter.
17. Why do you think that biological research is proceeding more rapidly today than it did 30 or 40 years ago?
18. A century ago, many men of science worked alone. Today, they have become more and more dependent on each other in advancing their research. Why is this so?

RESEARCH PROJECTS AND REPORTS

1. Obtain information from your school or public library and prepare a report on one of the following topics:

The Electron Microscope	**Paper Chromatography**
Leeuwenhoek	**Making Microphotographs**

2. *Making Charts with a Microscope:* In a dark room, tilt your microscope backwards until the body tube is horizontal. Direct the light from a 35 mm projector through the opening in the stage. Place a sheet of paper behind the eyepiece like a screen. With careful adjustment the image of the specimen will appear on the paper and can be traced to make a chart.

3. *Make a Simple Microtome:* A simple microtome can be made from a fine-threaded nut and bolt. Select a specimen that is no larger than the hole in the nut. Dip specimen in paraffin and allow to solidify. Warm the nut and push the paraffin-encased specimen into the hole. Thread the nut on the bolt and make small turns pushing the paraffin plug out of the hole a little at a time. With each turn make a thin slice of the paraffin plug with a razor. Examine several slices under the microscope. Which slices give the clearest viewing?

FURTHER READING

Microbe Hunters. Paul De Kruif. Harcourt Brace, New York, N.Y. The first chapter, "Leeuwenhoek: The First of the Microbe Hunters," is an account of a remarkable man who opened the world of the unknown for future explorers.

Guide to the Microscope. Arthur Beiser. E. P. Dutton & Co., New York, N.Y. A step-by-step guide for the beginner who wishes to enjoy his microscope as a hobby.

"Atoms Visualized." Erwin W. Muller. *Scientific American,* June, 1957, page 113. The author is the inventor of the field-ion microscope. In this article he describes how his instrument can be used to "see" and photograph atoms.

Experiments with a Microscope. Nelson F. Beeler and Franklyn M. Branley. Thomas Y. Crowell Company, New York, N.Y. The suggested specimens are easily obtainable materials from the home or yard.

Tools of Biology. Edward S. Lenhoff. The Macmillan Co., New York, N.Y. An explanation of how the instruments used by biologists work.

4

The Threshold of Life: Viruses

THE BIOLOGIST'S QUEST for meaning in the world of life has led him to examine living things with the utmost care. Where shall man search to understand the beginning of life? Will he find the answer among the single cells of the monerans and protists? Perhaps the biologist will approach the solution, if he confines his attention to the simplest life forms. But even single cells are unbelievably complex! The metabolism of bacteria, for example, is a complicated series of chemical systems. The chemical nature of the simplest organisms is marked by profound differences. Even the bacteria and the blue-green algae, simple monerans, differ considerably in the way they obtain their food.

For the past twenty years, the virus has been used by the biologist to help provide a simple model for understanding life. How are viruses classified? If you were to search through the phyla of the four kingdoms, you would not even find viruses listed. Many biologists do not even consider the viruses living! How, then, can a "nonliving" organism help us to understand the nature of life? The reason is that the viruses occupy a unique position between the living and the nonliving worlds. Viruses have some of the qualities of a living thing. They reproduce, for example. Viruses also have some of the qualities of the nonliving world. For example, viruses can be crystallized. One distinguished biologist said that viruses give him the feeling of being shown how the nonliving world of atoms gradually changes into the living world of organisms.

THE NATURE OF VIRUSES. The Latin word *virus* is usually translated as "a slimy liquid, a poison." The term virus was used by medical researchers at the end of the 19th century. At that time many biologists thought that all disease was caused by bacteria. Bacteria were trapped in filters and identified. In some cases, a filtered liquid, free of bacteria, could transmit disease. This liquid was called a *filterable virus*. The organisms had passed through the pores of the finest porcelain filter designed to trap the smallest bacteria.

It has been discovered that viruses will function only in living cells. They are almost unbelievably small. To measure such small objects, the biologist uses a unit length called a *micron*. A micron is one-millionth of a meter, the metric unit of length. Imagine a page of this book sliced into one hundred very thin slices. Each ultra-thin page would be about one micron thick. Now consider the size of a virus on this micron scale. Most viruses are about 0.02 microns thick. Bacteria, on the other hand, range in size from about one to five microns, roughly one hundred times larger.

The electron microscope permits the biologist to identify the shapes of the viruses, despite their very small size. Viruses have three basic shapes: spherical or oval, helical (like a coiled spring), and complex. Magnified 50,000 to 100,000 times, the smallest viruses show a precise kind of architecture that allows biologists to identify them rather easily.

The History of Viruses

Viruses were discovered long before anyone ever saw them. Optical microscopes do not have the ability to magnify objects enough to bring the world of viruses into view. Viruses are so small that new instruments had to be invented before they could be seen. Meanwhile, viruses were known to exist because of the diseases they produced.

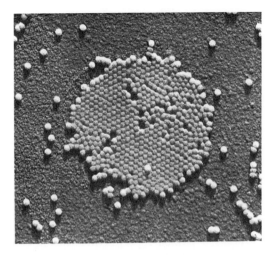

4–1 Polio Virus Particles (83,000 X). They appear to be spherical, but may be tiny icosahedrons, twenty-sided figures.

TOBACCO MOSAIC VIRUS (TMV). Between 1884 and 1894, tobacco growers in Holland asked biologists to help them find the cause of a disease of tobacco plants. Infected leaves developed a spotted appearance, or

4–2 Size and Shape of Viruses. The viruses, drawn to scale, show the variety of size and shape of some common forms.

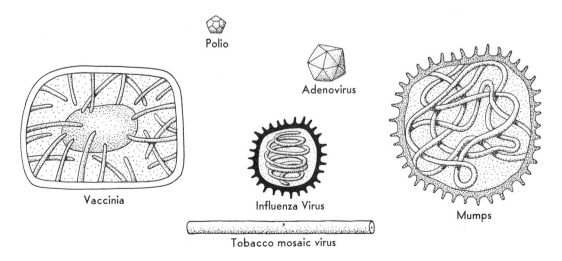

Polio

Adenovirus

Vaccinia

Influenza Virus

Mumps

Tobacco mosaic virus

mosaic, then withered and died. A small amount of sap from an infected plant rapidly produced the disease in a healthy one. Biologists could not find the bacteria they thought were the cause of the disease. In 1892 the Russian scientist Dmitri Ivanovsky filtered the sap of an infected plant through a bacterial filter. The filtered sap was capable of infecting tobacco. Ivanovsky still believed, however, that bacteria caused the mosaic disease.

In 1898, the Dutch botanist Martinus Beijerinck performed an experiment similar to Ivanovsky's. He came to a different conclusion. Beijerinck reported that the infectious agent was contained in the filtered fluid. He called the infectious agent a *virus* to distinguish it from bacteria. Beijerinck is often called the founder of *virology,* the science of viruses, because of these early experiments.

VIRUS CRYSTALS. Interest in the viruses continued to excite the imagination of both biologists and chemists. By 1931, many important diseases had been identified as viral diseases. Among them were included mumps, measles, and smallpox. One fact continued to impress the researchers: viruses were exceptionally small! No matter how fine a filter the scientists made, the

4–3 Leaf Infected with Tobacco Mosaic Virus

viruses passed through. Some chemists began to suspect that the viruses might just be huge molecules.

Wendell M. Stanley, an American chemist, reported in 1935 that he had crystallized a protein from the extract of Turkish tobacco plants infected with tobacco mosaic virus (TMV). The crystals were highly infective when injected into other tobacco plants. Stanley estimated that the crystals were about 1000 times more infective than

4–4 Virus Crystals. Are viruses really "alive"?

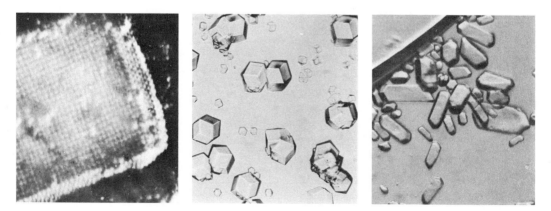

the sap of the infected plant. There seemed little doubt that the chemist had crystallized a "living thing." Normally, we would not expect crystals to reproduce in plant cells. The crystals of TMV did reproduce, however! Stored for a long period of time, the crystals were still able to infect tobacco plants.

Was TMV a "living molecule" that crystallized during a resting period? When is a crystal alive? How does a crystal become a living thing? These questions strike at the very basis of defining life. Perhaps the borderline between the living and the nonliving world could not be defined very clearly.

SEEING VIRUSES. The usual optical microscope cannot distinguish objects that are less than 0.2 micron wide. We now know that the width of a virus is about 0.02 micron. To observe viruses, an instrument had to be invented that would "see" about ten times better. Such an instrument would extend man's vision into the world of virus particles.

In the early 1930's teams of scientists in Germany, Belgium, and England were experimenting with microscopes that used electron beams in place of light rays. The early instruments, however, could achieve no better magnification than the optical

4–5 The nucleic acid core of the TMV can be seen in this electron micrograph (800,000 X).

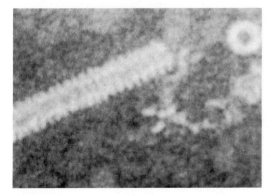

microscopes. In 1938 two German scientists, Ernst Ruska and his associate von Borries, made an electron microscope that enabled them to see objects 0.01 micron wide. In 1939, the Canadians Albert Prebus and James Hillier designed a similar instrument. Advances continued on both sides of the Atlantic. In 1940, the Radio Corporation of America marketed the first commercial electron microscope. It could produce images of objects as small as 0.0024 mciron, placing viruses well within its view. Further improvements have since brought the range of the electron microscope into particle sizes of the order of 0.001 micron.

You know that it is often very desirable to stain a specimen before examining it with the microscope. Staining of objects for examination under the electron microscope required the development of entirely new techniques. First, the specimens had to be thoroughly dried, for water scatters the electron beam. Furthermore, the drying had to be accomplished without changing the shape of the specimens, or wrinkling or collapsing them. Next, the dehydrated virus had to be coated with a metal, such as platinum. Otherwise, the virus could not be seen under the electron beam. Imagine how difficult it must be to find a way to coat viruses with a delicate film of platinum! Nevertheless, after years of painstaking effort, techniques for coating the platinum on the viruses were perfected. The perfection of techniques for photographing them followed. Today we can see viruses with remarkable clarity. Photographs with magnifications of 100,000X are no longer remarkable. Such photographs show the structure of viruses in fine detail.

ANALYZING THE VIRUSES. Virology has probably benefitted more from the cooperation of chemists, physicists, and biologists than any other branch of science. Physicists were mainly responsible for the development of the electron microscope. Now the

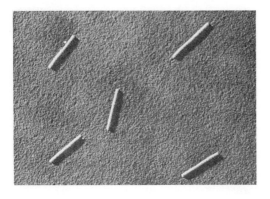

4-6 Electron Micrograph of TMV (50,000 X)

searchers had worked out the order and the kind of amino acids that formed the protein tube of TMV. Virus investigation had now reached the molecular stage. They found that each protein molecule consisted of 158 amino acid units. The analysis of such a complex array of amino acids was a truly remarkable accomplishment. Viruses, then, are really protein packages enclosing nucleic acid cores (RNA or DNA). Perhaps there was no real dividing line between living and nonliving chemical systems.

In a speech before the American Philosophical Society in 1957, Wendell M. Stanley said:

> "The discovery of viruses has permitted us to contemplate the nature of life with new understanding. It has enabled us to appreciate in a new light the inherent potentialities of chemical structure."

biologists could see viruses. TMV looked like a tiny piece of macaroni, about 0.015 micron thick and 0.30 micron long! The mumps virus was a sphere roughly 0.25 micron in diameter. The smallpox virus was a crude cylinder about 0.28 micron long, huge as viruses go! Now the chemists wanted to take the viruses apart. They wanted to analyze the viruses to find out what they were made of.

Since 1935, when Wendell M. Stanley had crystallized TMV, this virus has occupied center stage in the drama of virus research. There were several reasons for this. First, TMV can easily be cultured in large amounts. The researcher need only grow numbers of tobacco plants and inoculate them. Second, the infection is produced within a relatively short time. By 1955, chemists at the University of California under the direction of Heinz Fraenkel-Conrat could report the following about TMV:

- Tube-like, it is 0.3 micron long.
- It consists of a protein tube enclosing a rod-like center.
- The rod-like center is ribonucleic acid (RNA).

The work of many investigators has gradually made the chemical composition of viruses clear. By 1960, the California re-

Classifying the Viruses

So little has been known about the viruses until very recently that there is little agreement about how to name and classify them. Many viruses are named after the disease they cause, such as mumps, polio, and smallpox. Plant viruses are similarly named, such as tobacco mosaic virus, sugar beet curly top virus, and turnip yellow mosaic virus.

VIRUS HOSTS. One way to classify viruses is by means of their *hosts*. The host is the organism on which the virus lives. Four types of viral hosts exist.

1. *Plant viruses.* TMV is an example of a virus that lives only in the cells of a plant.
2. *Animal viruses.* These viruses live in the cells of animals and man. Common examples are the viruses that cause warts in man, and the foot and mouth virus of cattle.

3. *Insect viruses.* Viruses that live in the cells of insects include encephalitis (en-sef-uh-LI-tis) and yellow fever.
4. *Bacterial viruses.* These viruses are called *bacteriophages* (back-TEER-ee-uh-fay-jez), which means bacteria eaters. Some bacteriophages attack the bacteria that live in the lower portion of the human intestine.

SIZE AND SHAPE. Some virologists have suggested that shape and size might be used to classify viruses. The smallest viruses are about 0.010 micron in width. The largest viruses are about 0.3 micron in width. Size has not been a good method of classification, for few other important characteristics appear to be correlated with it.

Viruses have a remarkably ordered structure, which creates their precise shapes. Some biologists, therefore, classify them on the basis of their symmetry. *Symmetry* is the correspondence of parts of an object on opposite sides of a dividing line, or axis. Your body, for example, has symmetry because of the correspondence of its parts on either side of its midline.

Tobacco mosaic virus has *helical symmetry.* A *helix* is a coil formed by wrapping a wire around a cylinder. Imagine a cylinder passing through the length of the virus. The RNA forms a helix around this cylinder. The protein subunits are attached in such a way that they form a protective coat. The parts of the RNA chain and all the protein subunits are arranged as though strung on helical wires coiled about the central axis. Other viruses, such as mumps virus and influenza virus, have helical symmetry as well.

A common architectural plan for many viruses is one based on *cubic symmetry.* One special type of cubic symmetry is shown in a twenty-sided figure called an *icosahedron* (eye-koh-suh-HEE-drun). The viruses of hepatitis, warts, and turnip yellow mosaic have cubic symmetry.

Some viruses have a *complex symmetry* and cannot be as easily defined as the two previous types. Some biologists have described the bacteriophages as being shaped like tadpoles. Both cowpox and smallpox viruses have complex symmetry, as do the bacteriophages.

RNA AND DNA. Early in the history of virus research it appeared that only plant viruses contained RNA. Later investigations showed that this was not so. Both mumps and influenza virus contain RNA. Bacteriophages contain DNA. While it is well known that viruses contain either DNA or RNA, there has been little correlation found between the type of nucleic acid and other characteristics, such as shape, size, or host. Most RNA viruses have helical symmetry, but there are some exceptions.

The Genetics of Tobacco Mosaic Virus

Viruses are classified as living things because they can reproduce inside living cells. For the last decade, research in virus reproduction has been the most important method for understanding the chemistry of reproduction in all living things. Viruses

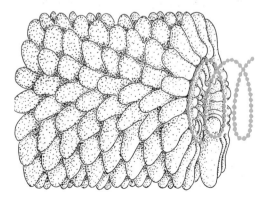

4–7 Helical Symmetry in Tobacco Mosaic Virus. The coil (helix) in the center is RNA. The individual units are protein capsomeres.

are simplified models of living systems. In the simplest viruses, therefore, we should be able to observe the process of reproduction in fundamental terms. This is why the study of viruses is so important to every student of biology. *Genetics* is the branch of biology concerned with the mechanism of reproduction and the inheritance of traits by organisms. Genetics is therefore concerned with a question such as: How does a "living molecule" reproduce itself? By studying the tobacco mosaic virus, we can probably find as good an answer as the modern biologist can give us.

CHEMISTRY OF TMV. In order to understand how TMV reproduces, we will have to know the chemical composition of this virus. You have already learned that TMV consists of a protein tube which encloses a coil of RNA. The coil is in the shape of a helix. It is difficult to imagine any organism with a simpler structure than this.

Extensive research by University of California biologists has shown that there are 2200 protein units that make up the protein tube. Each protein unit is identical with its neighbors and is called a ***capsomere.*** The capsomeres are strung along the RNA coil somewhat like beads on a coiled chain.

Proteins, as you have learned, are composed of smaller chemical units called amino acids. How many amino acids make up a capsomere of the tobacco virus? Exactly 158, according to Fraenkel-Conrat. Nineteen different kinds of amino acids are strung together in a precise sequence to form each protein molecule.

Let's summarize what we know about the protein tube of TMV:
- The tube consists of 2200 capsomeres.
- Each capsomere is a protein unit constructed from 158 amino acid subunits.
- Nineteen different kinds of amino acids are used in the structure.

RNA. The central helix of TMV is a single molecule, consisting of a long spiral strand of RNA. Although they are among the largest molecules in living organisms, nucleic acids are composed of only a few kinds of smaller units. The units of nucleic acids are called *nucleotides* (NOO-

4–8 RNA (ribonucleic acid) is composed of four fundamental units called nucleotides. Each nucleotide is shown as a distinct geometric figure. These figures will be used in other diagrams of RNA to distinguish the nucleotides from each other.

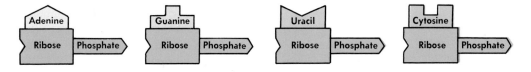

Four Nucleotides Combine to form the RNA chain

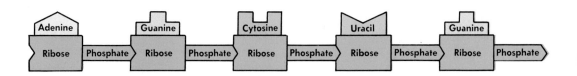

klee-uh-tides). Each nucleotide in turn consists of three parts: a sugar (ribose), a phosphate, and a base. In the nucleotides of RNA, the first two parts, the sugar and phosphate, are always the same. Only the bases vary. Four different bases combine with the sugar and phosphate to produce four different types of nucleotides. The composition of these four nucleotides is given below:

A contains Adenine + ribose and phosphate
G contains Guanine + ribose and phosphate
C contains Cytosine + ribose and phosphate
U contains Uracil + ribose and phosphate

How are the nucleotides of TMV assembled? Think of the molecule as a long chain with crosspieces attached at right angles to the chain. The chain units are links of ribose, phosphate, ribose, and phosphate. The four distinctive bases, adenine, guanine, cytosine, and uracil, are suspended at right angles from the ribose links. The arrangement is somewhat like a charm bracelet with the four bases attached to the ribose-phosphate links.

In 1955, using a delicate chemical procedure, Fraenkel-Conrat separated TMV into its two chemical components: the protein capsomeres and RNA core. He found that the protein units could reassemble themselves into a tube, much like the protective sheath of the original virus. Would the protein tube alone infect tobacco plants? When he tested it, he found it was *not* infectious. Next, he tried mixing RNA from a living virus with the separated protein particles. Now the RNA and the protein combined to form what appeared to be rod-like virus particles. These recombined particles, which contained RNA, proved to be infectious. The experiments proved that the nucleic acid RNA is the part of the virus that enables it to reproduce.

REPRODUCTION OF **TMV.** What happens when TMV invades the cells of a tobacco plant? We can identify three things that must happen if more viruses are to be formed:

1. Additional RNA molecules must be made, and they must be duplicates of the original.
2. Duplicate protein units like the original capsomeres must be made.
3. The RNA and protein units must be assembled.

The RNA duplicates itself within tobacco cells in several stages. In the first stage the single stranded RNA makes a double stranded molecule. The first strand serves as the "mold" into which the second strand is "cast." To go back to our idea of a charm bracelet, a parallel chain of ribose-phosphate links is formed. The bases of the second strand are not the same as the original bases, but are always *complements* of the first strand. The cross-links that unite the two strands are always paired bases, which are arranged at right angles to the strands. One base is the complement to another according to the following rules:

Adenine is the complement of uracil, and uracil the complement of adenine.
Guanine is the complement of cytosine, and cytosine the complement of guanine.

As a result, when cross-links are made between the two chains:

A always joins with U (or U with A)
G always joins with C (or C with G).

After the second strand of RNA has been formed, the two strands separate. The second stage in the process then begins. Now the second strand of RNA makes a complementary strand of itself. Because of the formation of complements, the third strand will be identical with the first. The entire process is like a sculptor making a cast of a statue, then pouring a mold to duplicate the original.

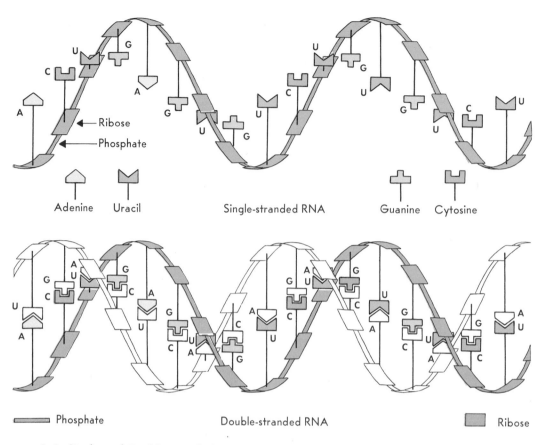

A   Adenine   Uracil   Single-stranded RNA   Guanine   Cytosine

Ribose
Phosphate

Phosphate   Double-stranded RNA   Ribose

4–9 Single and Double-stranded RNA. When a single strand of RNA forms a double strand, the two strands are connected by paired bases. The bases are complementary: they are not the same.

Consider the changes that would occur in the sequence of nucleotides according to the following scheme:

Original Strand	Second Strand	Third Strand
Adenine	Uracil	Adenine
Uracil	Adenine	Uracil
Guanine	Cytosine	Guanine
Cytosine	Guanine	Cytosine

Note that the sequence in the third strand is exactly like the first strand. Thus, the original RNA molecule has produced an exact replica of itself.

The original RNA also makes the protein for the virus coat or tube. Biologists have learned that the sequence of nucleotides along the RNA molecule is really a code to assemble amino acids into proteins. Each amino acid is specified by a three letter code. The three letter group that specifies a particular amino acid is called a *codon*. For example, the codon for the amino acid phenylalanine (fee-nil-AL-uh-neen) is UUU. The codon for the amino acid proline is CCC. The codon for serine is UCC. If the three codon sequence of nucleotides on an RNA molecule were CCC, UUU, UCC, then the amino acids specified would be proline, phenylalanine, and serine in that order. Thus, the sequence of nucleotides on the RNA molecule prescribes the 158 amino acids by means of 158 codons. These 158 amino acids form each protein capsomere of the outer tube.

One final step remains to make TMV: the protein units must be assembled in an orderly array around the core. Biologists believe that the assembly process, as well as other processes, is controlled by certain proteins called enzymes. *Enzymes* are proteins that regulate chemical processes in living things. Simple calculations have been made showing that the number of nucleotides is more than enough to form the protein coat. It is believed that the remaining nucleotides form about five or six other proteins, which act as enzymes that regulate the replication of RNA and the assembly of the finished virus. In this manner, the production of tobacco mosaic virus can be seen as a chemical production plus an assembly process.

Genetics of a Bacteriophage

Tobacco mosaic virus is one of the simplest viruses known. Nevertheless, we have seen that its reproduction is not easy to describe in chemical terms. Other viruses have been studied to clarify our ideas concerning how viruses reproduce. Among the most thoroughly studied viruses are the bacteriophages (bacteria-eaters). Like TMV, the bacteriophages offer certain advantages to the researcher. The principal advantage is the fact that they grow on bacteria that live in the human intestine and can be cultured in large numbers for experimentation. Bacteriophages are more complicated organisms than TMV. These viruses enable the virologist to examine the reproduction of organisms at a higher level of organization.

CHEMISTRY OF THE BACTERIOPHAGE. We have already noted that viruses may be

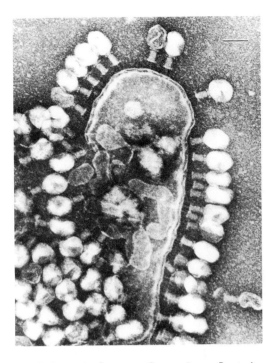

4–10 Bacteriophages Consuming Bacteria. Note the bacterium with viruses attached to it.

described in terms of their symmetry. TMV, for example, has helical symmetry. Other viruses, particularly the very small ones, have cubic symmetry and they are often constructed like an icosahedron. The T-4 bacteriophage has a complex symmetry. Its body consists of a large *head*, a narrow *tail*, topped by a *collar*, a lower *end plate*, and six *tail fibers*. The head is built on a plan similar to an icosahedron except that it consists of thirty faces. There are ten additional triangular faces around the middle of the head.

The outer coat of the T-4 virus is also composed of protein units. The head is composed of more than 300 identical protein units arranged in a precise pattern. The protein units making the tail and tail fibers do not seem to have the same chemical composition as those that make the head.

Like TMV, the protein coat of the T-4

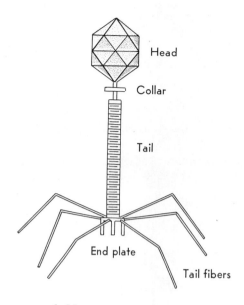

4–11 T-4 Bacteriophage

G contains Guanine + deoxyribose and phosphate

C contains Cytosine + deoxyribose and phosphate

T contains Thymine + deoxyribose and phosphate

Like RNA, the single strand of DNA is capable of forming a second, *complementary* strand. Double stranded DNA resembles a twisted ladder in which the rungs consist of paired bases. Somewhat like RNA, the bases join in the following complementary combinations:

• Adenine joins with thymine (or thymine with adenine).
• Guanine joins with cytosine (or cytosine with guanine).

Thus, if the nucleotide sequence on the first strand of DNA were G,T,C,G,A, the complementary sequence on the second strand would be C,A,G,C,T.

Biochemists believe there are about 200,000 nucleotides in the DNA molecule of the T-4 bacteriophage. Compare this with the 6400 nucleotides in the tobacco mosaic virus. Now you can begin to understand why the bacteriophage is a much more complex organism than TMV.

REPRODUCTION OF THE BACTERIOPHAGE. How does the T-4 virus reproduce itself inside the bacterial cell? Numerous studies have shown that the steps in the process are the following:

• The virus attaches itself to the bacterial wall by means of its end plate and tail fibers.
• The core of the tail is driven through the wall by the contraction of the tail sheath.
• DNA from the head section enters the bacterium through the punctured wall.
• Viral DNA takes over the machinery of the bacterial cell and directs the formation of viral proteins.

virus encloses nucleic acid. The nucleic acid in the T-4 virus is DNA, however. Although similar in many ways, there are basic differences between RNA and DNA. The DNA in the head of the T-4 virus is a coiled *double stranded helix.*

DNA. Let us compare a single strand of DNA with the RNA described on page 62. Both nucleic acids are made of similar nucleotide sub-units. The nucleotides of DNA consist of three parts: deoxyribose, phosphate, and a base. *Deoxyribose* is a sugar almost identical with ribose except that it contains one less atom of oxygen. So far, you will note, the only difference between DNA and RNA is one atom of oxygen. However, there is one other difference: *the bases are not the same.* In DNA the base *thymine* replaces the base uracil. We shall name the four nucleotides in DNA by the letters A,G,C, and T to correspond with the following composition:

A contains Adenine + deoxyribose and phosphate

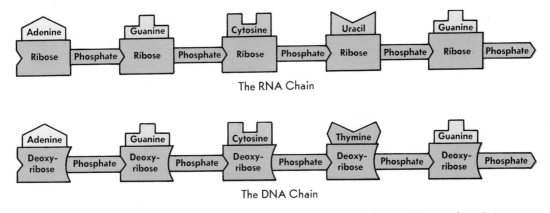

| Adenine | | Guanine | | Cytosine | | Uracil | | Guanine | |
| Ribose | Phosphate | Ribose | Phosphate | Ribose | Phosphate | Ribose | Phosphate | Ribose | Phosphate |

The RNA Chain

| Adenine | | Guanine | | Cytosine | | Thymine | | Guanine | |
| Deoxy-ribose | Phosphate | Deoxy-ribose | Phosphate | Deoxy-ribose | Phosphate | Deoxy-ribose | Phosphate | Deoxy-ribose | Phosphate |

The DNA Chain

4–12 Comparing DNA with RNA. The two fundamental nucleic acids found in living things consist of similar nucleotides with only slight differences. Ribose replaces deoxyribose and thymine replaces uracil.

- Within 25 minutes, 200 new viruses are formed.
- An enzyme formed by the virus destroys the bacterial wall, releasing the viruses.

One important fact must be emphasized: DNA *directs the entire production of new viruses.* The only part of the T-4 virus that enters the bacterial cell is DNA. As a result of the entry of the DNA, 200 completely new viruses emerge. DNA carries the code for the formation of every part of the new T-4 viruses. The function of DNA appears to be strikingly similar to RNA's role in the tobacco mosaic virus.

GENES. Now that we have begun to understand the chemistry of reproduction in viruses, let's make a calculation. Suppose that the average protein in the T-4 virus were composed of 333 amino acid units. Remembering that each amino acid needs 3 nucleotides to code it, we can calculate the approximate number of proteins encoded by the DNA molecule. Three times 333 is 999, or approximately 1000. Dividing the 200,000 nucleotides in DNA of the bacteriophage by 1000 gives us the answer 200. This means that approximately 200 proteins are formed by the coded instructions on the DNA molecule.

The entire DNA molecule can now be thought of in terms of several hundred segments. Each segment contains about 1000 nucleotides. Each segment specifies the formation of one protein. Biologists call each such segment a *gene.* A gene is a portion of the DNA molecule that specifies the code for the formation of one protein.

Biochemists believe that the RNA of tobacco mosaic virus encodes about six or seven genes with its 6400 nucleotides. The DNA of the T-4 virus encodes several hundred genes with its 200,000 nucleotides.

BUILDING THE T-4 VIRUS. Because of its complex symmetry, building a T-4 virus is much more difficult than building the tobacco mosaic virus. Nevertheless, biochemists believe that the process of building a T-4 virus is essentially the same as that of TMV. It consists of the following steps:

- Replication of DNA
- Formation of protein for each sub-unit, such as head, tail, and tail fibers.
- Assembly of each sub-unit.
- Assembly of the sub-units into the virus.

The replication of DNA is similar to the process already discussed for replicating RNA. Since the DNA is already double

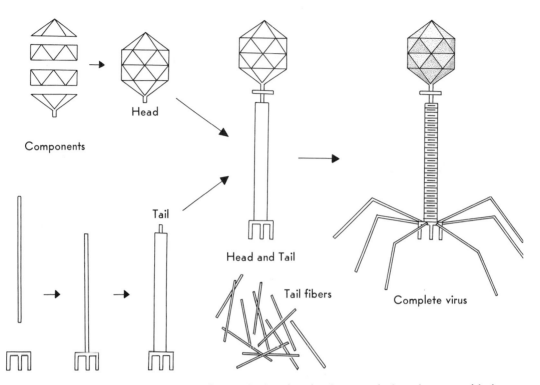

Components

Head

Tail

Head and Tail

Tail fibers

Complete virus

4–13 Assembly of a T-4 Bacteriophage. The head and tail are made first, then assembled. The tail fibers are made separately, then assembled to make the complete virus.

stranded, it first splits into two separate strands. Each strand is the complement of the other. Now each of the original strands forms a complementary strand of its own and joins with it. The result is the formation of two double strands of DNA identical with the first.

The process of forming proteins for each section is regulated by separate genes. For example, one of the 75 genes that have already been identified, number 23, specifies the protein units for the head. About six other proteins act as enzymes to construct the complicated thirty-sided head.

The manner in which each gene regulates the formation of a T-4 protein is not as simple as in the tobacco mosaic virus. We will have to wait until you know more about cell structure before more of the details can be given. However, the most important fact to note is that the sequence of nucleotide bases provides the biological code. Each group of three bases, the *codon*, prescribes an amino acid. The amino acids are joined into a three dimensional protein molecule. Each protein molecule has a specific function, either in the formation or in the assembly of parts.

IMPORTANT POINTS

• Viruses span the gulf between the living and non-living world. Most biologists consider them alive because they are able to reproduce in living cells. Viruses are very small and can be seen only with the electron microscope.

• Early virus research parallels the development of the electron microscope. Later, chemists crystallized viruses, then analyzed them. Most viruses consist of a protein coat which encloses DNA or RNA.

• Viruses are classified in a number of ways: by their host, by their size and shape, or by the kind of nucleic acid (DNA or RNA) they contain.

• Tobacco mosaic virus (TMV) consists of 2200 protein units surrounding an RNA chain of 158 nucleotides. The RNA is able to reproduce itself by forming a complementary strand. RNA encodes instructions for making the protein units of the virus coat. RNA also encodes instructions for forming enzymes.

• The T-4 bacteriophage is a more complicated virus that contains DNA. The principal difference between DNA and RNA is that in DNA, the base thymine replaces the base uracil. The DNA encodes instructions for making new T-4 viruses by means of its 200,000 nucleotides. Approximately 1000 nucleotides encode instructions for forming one protein. The segment of the DNA chain that encodes one protein is called a gene. About 200 genes form proteins that make the protein coat of the T-4 virus and assemble the parts into the completed virus.

REVIEW QUESTIONS

1. What quality of a virus enables the biologist to consider it alive?
2. Why was the study of viruses closely linked with the development of the electron microscope?
3. Why has TMV been the most-studied virus for many years?
4. What chemicals make up the typical virus?
5. List three possible schemes for classifying viruses.
6. Describe the composition of TMV.
7. What four bases are found in RNA?
8. How does RNA form a complementary strand?
9. What is the significance of a codon?
10. Compare the architecture of the T-4 bacteriophage with TMV.
11. How does the chemical composition of DNA differ from that of RNA?
12. In round numbers, approximately how many nucleotides encode one gene?
13. What two kinds of functions does a protein have in building a T-4 virus?
14. List the stages in the assembly of the T-4 virus.

CHECK YOUR UNDERSTANDING

15. Why do viruses occupy such an important position in biological research today?
16. What is the reason for using a special unit of length like the micron for measuring viruses?

17. From the biologist's viewpoint, what problem was created when viruses were crystallized?
18. Explain why you think that viruses are simplified models of living systems.
19. Virologists believe that TMV contains about six genes and know the function of one gene with certainty. What guesses can you make about the function of the other five?
20. Why is the function of enzymes more easily understood in the T-4 bacteriophage than in TMV?

RESEARCH PROJECTS AND REPORTS

1. Obtain information from your school or public library and prepare a report on one of the following topics:

The Discovery of Viruses	**Wendell M. Stanley**
Virus Diseases	**Geometry of Viruses**

2. Prepare a model of TMV and of the T-4 bacteriophage. As suggestions to get you started, you might use two colors of modeling clay for TMV, and the tail fibers of T-4 might be represented by pipe cleaners.

3. If chemistry is your interest, do research on the structural formulas of RNA, DNA, adenine, guanine, cytosine, thymine, and uracil. Prepare charts of their structure to present to your classmates.

FURTHER READING

Viruses and Molecular Biology. Dean Fraser. Macmillan Company, New York, N.Y.
"**The Structure of Viruses.**" R. W. Horne. *Scientific American,* January, 1963, page 48. A discussion of the molecular basis of virology for the advanced student.
"**The Genetic Code of a Virus.**" Heinz Fraenkel-Conrat. *Scientific American,* October, 1964, page 46. Discusses the structure of tobacco mosaic virus in great detail.
"**The Genetics of a Bacterial Virus.**" R. S. Edgar and R. H. Epstein. *Scientific American,* February, 1965, page 70. The T-4 bacteriophage is examined to determine how it is constructed.
"**The Genetic Control of the Shape of a Virus.**" Edouard Kellenberger. *Scientific American,* December, 1966, page 32. The sub-units and the assembly of viruses is controlled by genetic material.
"**Building a Bacterial Virus.**" W. B. Wood and R. S. Edgar. *Scientific American,* July, 1967, page 60. DNA in the T-4 virus directs the production of proteins that make the shell of the virus. Enzymes direct the assembly process that produces the final form.

5

The Cell: Unit of Life

As NEW TOOLS OF RESEARCH were developed and used by the biologist, he altered his ideas about the nature of living things. Before the microscope, only the obvious characteristics of life could be identified. Thousands of plants and animals were identified long before man could examine their structure in detail. With the invention of the microscope, however, man observed that all living things were made of small units called *cells*.

The Structure of Cells

Within a hen's egg is the secret of life, for the egg will hatch into a living chick. The chick develops from a tiny speck of jellylike material about the size of a pinhead. This material, named "protoplasm" by the Bohemian biologist Johannes Purkinje, was considered for many years to be the fundamental material of life. Purkinje must have recognized its importance because the word protoplasm means "first form."

Protoplasm was believed to be a mixture of many compounds, the most common being water. Biochemists referred to protoplasm as a *colloid*, a material that resembles gelatin or the white of an egg. Among the other common substances found that were in protoplasm are sodium chloride, oxygen, and carbon dioxide. In addition, there were other more complex compounds, such as starches, sugars, fats, and proteins. The complicated reactions of these substances with each other were thought to be the very basis of living systems.

Today, many biologists believe that the term protoplasm has become too vague to describe the fundamental living material. Research has shown that there is a delicate and complicated architecture in living things. What Purkinje called protoplasm is in fact a highly organized system of interrelated microscopic structures.

THE CELL THEORY. Even with his crude microscope Leeuwenhoek was able to see cells. He reported his discoveries to the Royal Society of London in 1674. Later microscopists, working with improved instruments, were able to find additional evidence that all living things are composed of cells.

The term *cell* was introduced by Robert Hooke in 1665 in his *Micrographia*. Having examined thin slices of cork, he observed:

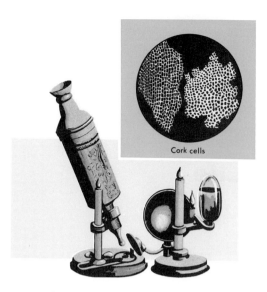

Cork cells

5–1 Robert Hooke used a compound microscope. His microscope and the cork cells that he sketched are shown above.

". . . I could exceedingly plainly perceive it to be all perforated and porous, much like a Honey-comb, but that the pores of it were not regular . . . these pores, or cells, were not very deep, but consisted of a great many little Boxes, separated out of one continued long pore by certain Diaphragms . . ."

In the 1800's more attention was given to *cytology* (cy-TAHL-o-gee), the study of cells. Scientists gradually discovered that cells were not the nonliving, empty boxes that Hooke supposed, but active, living structures. Staining techniques were developed. Various parts of the cell were identified and named. It was not until 1838, however, that the significance of cells was understood. In that year, the German botanist Matthias Schleiden wrote a treatise in which he described plant growth as arising from cells by cell duplication. In 1839, the German zoologist Theodor Schwann applied Schleiden's cell theory to animals. He stated that animal growth is also caused by the production of cells and that the cell is the structural unit of life. In 1858, another German biologist, Rudolf Virchow, carried the cell theory one step further by demonstrating that cells could arise only from other cells.

The Schleiden-Schwann cell theory was an important generalization in biology. The theory unifies our understanding of living things. Today's biologist still considers the cell the fundamental unit of life. Recently the electron microscope has provided more detail about the fine structure of the cell. This instrument has revealed the delicate architecture of the parts of the cell that were previously almost invisible.

THE MODEL OF THE CELL. Our understanding of the cell is derived from the study of many cell types, differing in shape, size, and organization. Under the microscope the cells of onion skin look like plastic bricks. Human red blood cells appear circular. Nerve cells generally have a very irregular appearance with numerous branching filaments. Plant and animal cells differ in fundamental ways.

A pattern of likeness derived from the observation of many cells led to the construction of a cell model in the minds of biologists. While there is no such thing as a typical cell, certain structures are quite common and basic types of organization have been observed. Because of this pattern of likeness, we can say that the cell consists of three main parts: the *cell membrane,* the *cytoplasm,* and the *nucleus.*

THE CELL MEMBRANE. The cell membrane surrounds the cell and forms its outer limits. Electron microscope studies indicate that it consists of two layers of protein enclosing a lipid, or fatlike, center. The membrane is a barrier that regulates the flow of all materials entering and leaving the cell.

Biologists have identified several ways in which materials pass through the cell mem-

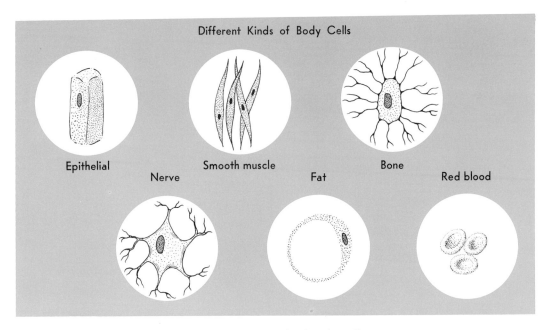

Different Kinds of Body Cells

Epithelial

Nerve

Smooth muscle

Fat

Bone

Red blood

5—2 Different Kinds of Body Cells

brane. Small molecules, such as those of water, are able to pass directly through the small pores in the membrane. Large protein molecules and food particles are sometimes taken into indentations in the cell membrane. These indentations are then pinched off as tiny bubbles that migrate to the cell's interior. This process is called *pinocytosis* (pin-o-cy-TOE-sis).

CYTOPLASM. The cytoplasm (CY-tuh-plaz-um) forms the bulk of the cell body. Within the cytoplasm are a number of structures, or *organelles,* which play important roles in the metabolism of the cell. Running through the cytoplasm is an elaborate network of fine membranes called the *endoplasmic reticulum* (en-doh-PLAZ-mik reh-TIC-yuh-lum). The membranes of the network are internal extensions of the cell membrane. The network provides a channel for materials to pass to and from the nucleus.

Lining the outer surfaces of the reticular membrane are dense rows of tiny spherical bodies called *ribosomes.* The ribosomes contain RNA and synthesize proteins. As you learned when you studied viruses, the codons of RNA specify the kind and sequence of amino acids. As we shall see later, the codons in RNA are specified by the DNA in the nucleus.

Continuous with the endoplasmic reticulum, but lacking ribosomes, are clusters of shorter membranes arranged in rows. These are the *Golgi* (GAHL-jee) *bodies.* They were discovered at the end of the nineteenth century by the Italian cytologist Camillo Golgi. It is now known that these tiny organelles make secretions and synthesize large carbohydrate molecules.

Two other structures in the cytoplasm are the *mitochondria* (my-tuh-KON-dree-uh) and the *lysosomes* (LYE-suh-sohmz). Mitochondria are oval bodies that release most of the energy required by the cell. For this reason they are often called the "powerhouses" of the cell. The lysosomes are pack-

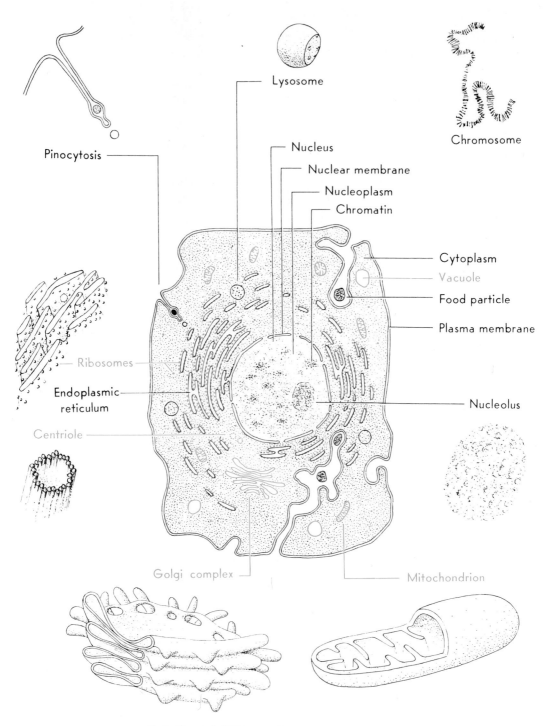

Pinocytosis

Lysosome

Chromosome

Nucleus

Nuclear membrane

Nucleoplasm

Chromatin

Cytoplasm

Vacuole

Food particle

Plasma membrane

Ribosomes

Endoplasmic reticulum

Nucleolus

Centriole

Golgi complex

Mitochondrion

5–3 The Cell, With Details of Smaller Structures

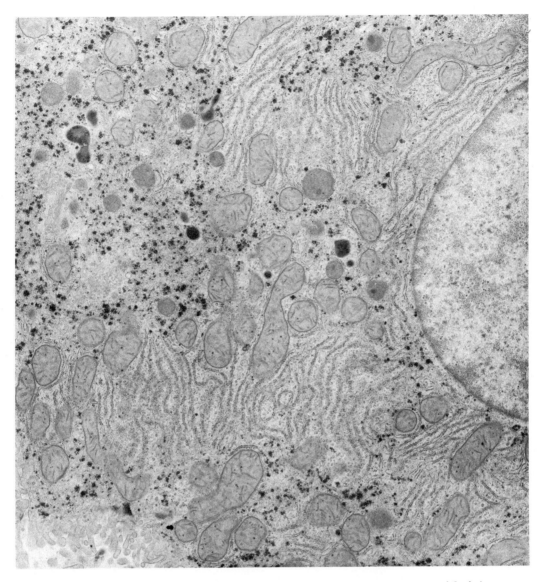

5—4 Electron Micrograph of a Cell. The figure on the opposite page is a simplified drawing of the actual cell cross section shown here.

ets of enzymes enclosed in a bubble-like membrane. When released, the enzymes act chemically upon proteins, fats, nucleic acids, or invading bacteria.

THE NUCLEUS. Most cells contain only one nucleus, but there are many exceptions to this rule. The nucleus is generally a spherical structure. It was first named by the British botanist Robert Brown in 1831. Experiments with the green alga *Acetabularia* indicate that the nucleus controls the life functions of the cell. When a single-celled organism is cut in two, the segment containing the nucleus usually continues to function. However, the part without the nucleus usually dies.

The nucleus of the cell is surrounded by a *nuclear membrane.* The membrane appears to consist of two layers with numerous pores. Pictures taken through the electron microscope seem to indicate that chemicals can be transported through the nuclear membrane and into the cytoplasm. This supports the idea that there is chemical interplay between the nucleus and cytoplasm.

When the cell divides, *chromosomes,* important structures found in the nucleus, transfer the characteristics of the parent cell to the daughter cells. When the cell is not dividing, the chromosomes are difficult to see. However, careful staining techniques have shown that they exist in the resting cell as fine, twisted threads of dark material sometimes called *chromatin.*

The number of chromosomes is characteristic of each plant or animal. Man, for example, has 46 chromosomes in each body cell. When the cell is dividing, the chromosomes become thicker, and it is then that special processes are used to stain, separate, and count them.

A rounded *nucleolus* (noo-KLEE-uh-lus) is often found within the nucleus. In some cells, there may be two or more nucleoli, each being attached to a certain chromosome. The nucleolus is especially rich in *RNA.* Surrounding the nucleolus and the chromosomes is a fluid called *nucleoplasm,* which gives the nucleus its shape and form.

THE PLANT CELL. Although plant and animal cells are fundamentally alike, there are some important differences. In the plant cell, the cell membrane is surrounded by a rigid, but porous *cell wall.* Usually, the cell wall is composed of *cellulose.* Animal cells do not have such cell walls. In the cytoplasm of the plant cell, there are many areas that appear empty or clear. These are *vacuoles* (VAK-you-ohlz), which contain water or oily substances.

Chloroplasts are the green, oval bodies that are found in many plant cells. They contain *chlorophyll,* a green pigment that is essential for food making. If we examine a leaf of Elodea, we can see hundreds of chloroplasts slowly circulating in the cells. Chloroplasts enable a plant to make the sugars and starches that support life on the earth.

THE ANIMAL CELL. Cell walls and chloroplasts are not found in animal cells. Usually, the vacuoles in animal cells are much smaller than those in plant cells. Most animal cells differ in still another respect. At the time of division a pair of small structures called *centrioles* (SEN-tree-ohlz) become more easily visible. They are seen close to the nucleus. During division they form a *spindle* consisting of tiny threads that pull the chromosomes to opposite ends of the cell.

5–5 Structure of Cell Membrane. A double layer of protein molecules encloses a double layer of fatlike lipid molecules.

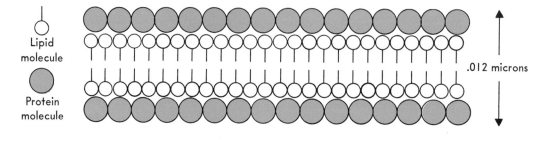

Lipid molecule

Protein molecule

.012 microns

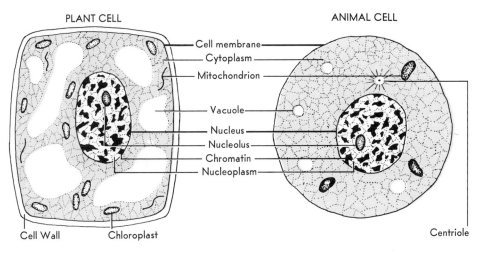

PLANT CELL   ANIMAL CELL

Cell membrane
Cytoplasm
Mitochondrion

Vacuole

Nucleus
Nucleolus
Chromatin
Nucleoplasm

Cell Wall   Chloroplast   Centriole

5–6 **Typical Plant and Animal Cells**

From Cell to Organism

Without the division of cells, growth would be impossible. An organism increases in size not only because its cells enlarge, but also because the number of cells increases.

MITOSIS. Cells do not increase indefinitely in size. They reach a certain size, then divide. The exact cause of cell division is not understood. The process of cell division is called *mitosis* (my-TOH-sis). Al-though mitosis is a continuous process, it can be described in a series of five phases.

1. *Interphase.* When the cell is not dividing, it is said to be in the resting condition. The chromosomes are not clearly seen during this phase. They appear as a mass of tangled threads.
2. *Prophase.* Changes in the nucleus are the first evidence to indicate that the cell is beginning to divide. The chrom-

5–7 **Stages of Mitosis in an Animal Cell**

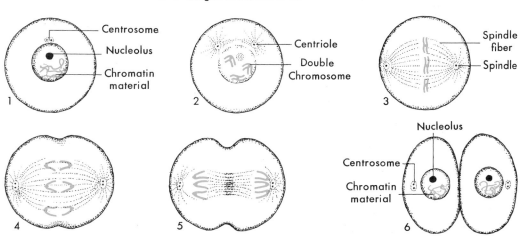

1. Centrosome
   Nucleolus
   Chromatin material

2. Centriole
   Double Chromosome

3. Spindle fiber
   Spindle

6. Nucleolus
   Centrosome
   Chromatin material

osomes coil and become shorter and thicker. The nucleolus fades and disappears. The nuclear membrane begins to dissolve. Close examination of the chromosomes reveals that they are really double, consisting of two *chromatids.* In the animal cell one of the first evidences of mitosis is the separation of the centrioles. These begin to move toward opposite ends of the cell, forming the spindle.

3. *Metaphase.* The chromosomes are now arranged in the middle of the cell. There is no nuclear membrane present. In its place a spindle has formed, a tapering structure made of fibers that are attached to the chromosomes. The animal cell now has one centriole at each end of the spindle.

4. *Anaphase.* The spindle fibers now begin to draw each chromatid member of a chromosome to opposite ends of the cell. In this manner a precise division of the chromatin material is brought about. The cell begins to pinch in two.

5. *Telophase.* Once the chromatids have reached opposite ends of the cell, the reverse of prophase occurs. The nuclear membrane reforms and the nucleolus reappears. The chromosomes (chromatids) become less distinct. In-

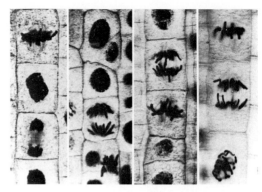

Carolina Biological Supply Company

5–8 Stages of Mitosis in an Onion Root Tip

terphase is resumed. In place of the original cell there are now two. The original chromosomes have been divided exactly between the two daughter cells. During the resting period, each chromosome will split to form a chromatid pair in preparation for the next division.

IMPORTANCE OF THE CHROMOSOMES. The exact division of chromatin material during mitosis was observed long before biologists realized its significance.

In the late 19th century, German biologist August Weismann pointed out the importance of the nucleus in transmitting the traits of one generation to the next when reproduction occurs. At the turn of the 20th

5–9 Chromosomes Contain DNA. At time of cell division, DNA molecule first doubles, then divides. Thus, daughter cells receive an amount of DNA equal to the parent cell.

REPLICATION OF DNA MOLECULE

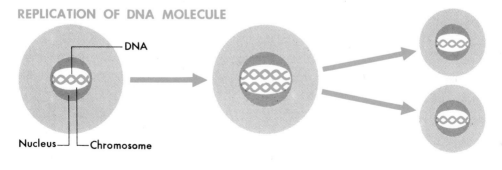

DNA

Nucleus — └─Chromosome

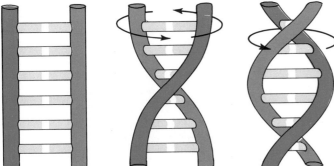

century, the chromosomes had become the center of interest in explaining the continuity of life. Later, Dr. Thomas Hunt Morgan and his students at Columbia University established the fact that certain parts of the chromosomes, the genes, are the principal determiners of the characteristics of plants and animals. When reproduction occurs, chromosomes in the reproductive cells transmit the characteristics of the parents to the next generation.

DNA. For many years chromosomes have been the subject of intensive study. In 1924, Robert Feulgen, a German chemist, used a special stain to show that the chromosomes contain DNA.

The Feulgen stain produced a deep crimson color when it acted upon the DNA. Furthermore, DNA seemed to be confined to the nucleus. Measurements of the amount of DNA in cells showed that it is constant for every cell in the body. The amount of DNA per nucleus for many different animals has been determined. It is constant for each animal type, but differs from one species to another. Evidence has accumulated that DNA is the primary substance that transmits characteristics from one cell to another during mitosis. Since mitosis is the fundamental method of growth, it follows that DNA provides the "master plan" that an organism follows as it develops.

5–10 The DNA molecule has the shape of a double helix. A helix winds around a cylinder; a spiral winds around a cone.

DNA plays the same role in cell duplication as it does in the T-4 virus that you

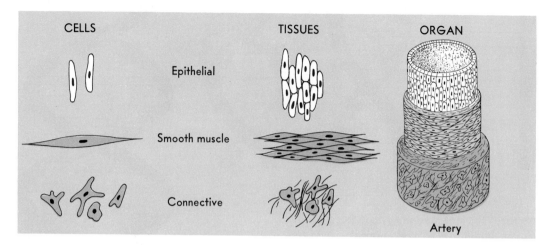

CELLS　　　　　　TISSUES　　　　ORGAN

Epithelial

Smooth muscle

Connective

Artery

5–11 Cells combine to form tissues, and tissues combine to form organs.

learned about in the previous chapter. Just as the T-4's DNA provides chemical instructions for making new viruses in an invaded bacterium, so cellular DNA provides instructions for making new cells during mitosis.

In 1953, biochemists Francis H. C. Crick and James D. Watson suggested what the chemical structure of DNA might be. According to their *double helix model,* the huge DNA molecule is constructed somewhat like a ladder that has been twisted into the shape of a loose spring.

The DNA molecule consists of two interlocking parts. When the halves are separated, each half has the ability to act as a mold to produce the other. It is this ability of DNA that permits the chromosomes to duplicate themselves. Arranged along the edge of the interlocking parts is a series of chemical groups that provides a code for producing a certain kind of organism. DNA thus encodes the information that enables a living cell to make a virus, a seaweed, or a mouse.

RNA. Biologists have recognized the dominating role of the nucleus in the life of the cell for many years. The discovery of

the role of DNA was, therefore, not much of a surprise. A new problem arose almost immediately: How was the information carried by DNA transferred from the nucleus to the cytoplasm where most of the chemical activity of the cell occurs? This transfer is effected by a second nucleic acid, RNA.

RNA is found in both the nucleus and the cytoplasm. It is one of the principal materials of the nucleolus. In the cytoplasm, RNA is found in the **ribosomes** that are widely distributed on the endoplasmic reticulum.

The ribosomes are the protein-making structures in the cell. Although most cells can make a thousand or more kinds of proteins, they do so only as they receive instructions from the nucleus. The elaborate chemical code which DNA carries is transferred to RNA in the nucleus. RNA then migrates into the cytoplasm, carrying instructions to the ribosomes. The ribosomes then form the proteins according to the information brought to them.

PLANT AND ANIMAL TISSUES. Not all cells of plants and animals are alike. As the cells of living things divide and redivide some begin to *differentiate* and perform certain special functions. Groups of similar cells that are specialized for some common function are called *tissues.* In many animals the highly specialized tissue called blood is formed. Muscle tissue enables animals to move from place to place. Nerve tissue of higher animals permits them to respond quickly to their environment.

ORGANS AND THE ORGANISM. Just as tissues are made of cells, so *organs* are made of tissues. Thus, organs are groups of tissues that perform a common function. Several kinds of tissue may be found in one organ. One of the principal organs of the plant, the leaf, contains different tissues that function together to make the plant's food. The heart is made of muscle tissue, connective tissue, and nerve tissue.

Just as organs are made of tissues, so the *systems* of the body are made of organs. Systems are groups of organs that function cooperatively. Some systems in the human body are the digestive system, the circulatory system, and the nervous system. Together, the systems form the entire plant or animal. An *organism* may be made of many millions of cells, all arranged to form tissues, organs, and systems.

IMPORTANT POINTS

• The cell is the fundamental unit of structure and function of all living things. The German biologists Matthias Schleiden and Theodor Schwann announced this cell theory in 1838–39.

• The cell model contains three main parts: the cell membrane, the cytoplasm, and the nucleus. The electron microscope has clarified many structures associated with each of these main parts. The cell membrane regulates the entry and exit of all materials in the cell. The cytoplasm contains several structures, or organelles, that regulate the cell's metabolism. The nucleus is the controlling structure of the cell and contains the chromosomes that transfer the characteristics of an organism when the cell divides.

• Mitosis is cell division in which the resulting daughter cells receive a complete set of chromosomes from the parent cell. DNA in the chromosomes contains the information required for the development of the organism. RNA is found in the nucleolus and the cytoplasm. Instructed by the DNA in the nucleus, RNA travels to the cytoplasm and directs the formation of proteins in the ribosomes.

• Tissues are groups of similar cells that perform a special function. Organs are groups of tissues that have a common function. Organs form systems, and systems form the complete organism.

REVIEW QUESTIONS

1. What tools and techniques have been responsible for the rapid advances in cytology?
2. How did the name *cell* originate?
3. What is the cell theory?
4. Do you know of any exceptions to the cell theory?

5. Why is it so difficult to describe a typical cell?
6. Why is the cell membrane such an important part of the cell?
7. What difference is there between the chromosome in a resting cell and a dividing cell?
8. Name two cell structures found in plant cells that are not found in animal cells.

CHECK YOUR UNDERSTANDING

9. Name the phase in mitosis associated with each of the following:
   a. Arrangement of the chromosomes in the middle of the cell.
   b. Reappearance of the nucleolus.
   c. Drawing of the chromosomes toward the ends of the cell.
   d. The chromosomes shorten and thicken.
10. In what part of the cell is DNA nearly always found?
11. What significance does the precise apportionment of chromosomes during mitosis have?
12. How have viruses aided DNA research?
13. What unusual quality of the DNA molecule enables it to duplicate itself?
14. How are DNA and RNA related to each other in cell function?
15. What does RNA do in a cell?
16. Millions of blood cells are destroyed in the human body each day. Why doesn't death result?
17. How would you explain this statement attributed to a famous biologist, "If I could understand the cell, I would know what life is."
18. DNA has been called the information transmitting substance in the cell. What does this mean?
19. What importance is attached to mitosis other than cell division and growth?

RESEARCH PROJECTS AND REPORTS

1. Obtain information from your school or public library and prepare a report on one of the following topics:

   Robert Hooke   **The Cell Theory**

   DNA, Chromosomes, and Genes   **Viruses and DNA**

2. *Epithelial Cells:* Rub the blunt end of a toothpick gently against the *inside* of your cheek. This will remove many of the epithelial cells. Smear the end of the toothpick against a clean glass slide. Add a drop of dilute iodine solution. Cover with a cover slip and examine under the microscope.

3. *Artificial Cell Division:* Place a small drop of mercury in the bottom of a watch glass and cover it with a small amount of nitric acid. Carefully place a small crystal of potassium dichromate on each side of the mercury about a quarter of an inch from it. Observe the results.

FURTHER READING

The Cell. Carl P. Swanson. Prentice-Hall, Inc., Englewood Cliffs, N.J. For the advanced student. The reproduction, development, and death of cells is treated in detail.

"**The Living Cell.**" Jean Brachet. *Scientific American,* September, 1961, page 50. This issue of the magazine is devoted exclusively to the cell.

"**Intercellular Communication.**" Werner R. Loewenstein. *Scientific American,* May, 1970, page 79. Recent research indicates that ions and some larger molecules move freely from one cell to another through junction points in their membranes.

The Microstructure of Cells. Stephen W. Hurry. Houghton Mifflin Co., Boston, Mass. Well illustrated with electron micrographs, this is an excellent survey of the cell.

"**The Synthesis of DNA.**" Arthur Kornberg. *Scientific American,* October, 1968, page 64. A Nobel prize winner discusses his research with the master molecules.

CHAPTER

6

The Chemistry of Life

THE CELL is the unit of life of which every living thing is composed. But what fundamental materials are cells made of? To answer this question the biologist seeks the help of the chemist.

The chemist believes that all matter is made of fundamental substances called *elements.* An element is a substance that cannot be decomposed into a simpler substance by ordinary chemical means. There are only a few more than a hundred elements presently known, yet the almost infinite variety of things we know about are made of these basic substances.

The ancient Greeks believed that all matter was made of four substances: earth, air, fire, and water. Later, Democritus (duh-MOCK-ruh-tus), a Greek philosopher, proposed that each substance was made of tiny, indivisible particles, which he named atoms. He had no proof of the existence of these atoms, however.

DALTON'S ATOMIC THEORY. In 1808, John Dalton, an English schoolmaster, offered his atomic theory to explain how elements combine to form new substances. The three main points of Dalton's theory may be summarized as follows:

1. All elements are composed of minute particles called atoms.
2. The atoms of a given element are all alike, but atoms of different elements are unlike.
3. Atoms are indivisible.

Additional knowledge that was not available to Dalton has since convinced scientists that atoms are not the simple, indivisible particles that Dalton believed them to be. We now know that atoms do indeed subdivide when they enter into certain types of reactions.

ELEMENTS IN LIVING THINGS. Although there are more than 100 elements, only about 24 have been found in living things. Many of the others are believed to occur in very minute amounts. Actually, four elements make up over 93 per cent of the weight of the human body. These are oxygen, carbon, hydrogen, and nitrogen.

1. *Oxygen.* The most common element in living things is oxygen, which makes up 60 to 65 per cent of the weight of the human body. Almost half of the weight of the earth's crust is due to oxygen. One fifth of the air is oxygen.

It makes up almost 90 per cent of the weight of our oceans.

2. *Carbon.* Of the four most common elements in the body, the only one that is a solid in its natural state is carbon. Wood-charcoal and coke are almost pure forms of carbon. Although carbon is found only in very slight amounts in the earth's crust, it makes up about 20 per cent of the human body.

3. *Hydrogen.* Hydrogen, the simplest of all the elements, is the most abundant element in the universe. The stars are largely made of hydrogen. Most chemists think it is the fundamental element that was somehow fashioned into all the others. Hydrogen, however, makes up less than 1 per cent of the earth's crust. As a component of water, it makes up about 10 per cent of the human body. Hydrogen is rarely found as an element on earth because it combines very readily with other elements.

4. *Nitrogen.* Nitrogen is almost 80 per cent of the air by volume. Although it is found in small amounts in the human body, it is one of the most important of all the elements, since it is a constituent of the proteins. Like oxygen and hydrogen, nitrogen is a colorless gas. Unlike both of these gases, it is rather inactive and combines slowly with oxygen. As a free element in the air, nitrogen is not very useful to living things. However, when combined with other elements in the form of nitrates, it becomes an important compound for living things.

5. *Calcium, sulfur, and phosphorus.* Each of these elements is a solid. Together, they make up about four per cent of the weight of the human body. Both calcium and phosphorus are necessary for proper bone formation. Calcium is an important agent in the clotting of blood. Sulfur and phosphorus are found in the proteins of the body.

ELEMENTS IN HUMAN BODY			ELEMENTS IN EARTH'S CRUST		
Element	Symbol	Approximate Percentage by Weight	Element	Symbol	Approximate Percentage by Weight
Oxygen	O	62	Oxygen	O	47
Carbon	C	20	Silicon	Si	28
Hydrogen	H	10	Aluminum	Al	8
Nitrogen	N	3	Iron	Fe	5
Calcium	Ca	2	Calcium	Ca	3
Phosphorus	P	1	Hydrogen	H	1
All Others		2	All Others		8

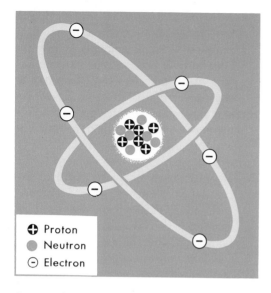

6–1 Carbon Atom. Six negative electrons surround a nucleus of six positive protons and six uncharged neutrons.

INSIDE THE ATOM. In 1910, Pierre and Marie Curie isolated radium from its ore. Radium gives off rays similar to the ones Henri Becquerel (Chapter 3) had discovered in his experiments with uranium compounds. Materials that emit rays or particles spontaneously are said to be *radioactive.*

The investigation of radioactive elements by other chemists and physicists has contributed much to our understanding of matter. The source of radioactivity was shown to be the atom itself. An atom, therefore, is made of still smaller particles. Dalton was not quite right. The atom is not an indivisible particle. Numerous smaller particles have been identified as part of the atom. We need only concern ourselves with three: the **proton,** the **neutron,** and the **electron.**

The proton is positively charged. The electron is negatively charged. The neutron has no charge.

MOLECULES AND COMPOUNDS. There are many more substances in the world than there are elements. The reason for this is that the elements combine to produce entirely new substances called *compounds.* A compound is a substance formed by the chemical combination of two or more elements. Just as the smallest part of an element is an atom, so the smallest part of a compound is a *molecule.*

When a piece of wood is burned, certain atoms that form the wood combine with oxygen to form new compounds. Among them are carbon dioxide (CO_2) and water (H_2O). These two substances do not resemble wood, nor does the ash that remains after the burning is completed. A change such as this is called a **chemical change.** In a chemical change the atoms are rearranged to form at least one new substance.

Some changes are much simpler. When ice melts or water boils, no new substances

6–2 Molecules of water and carbon dioxide show how atoms combine to form compounds.

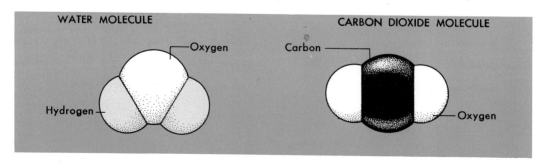

WATER MOLECULE

Oxygen

Hydrogen

CARBON DIOXIDE MOLECULE

Carbon

Oxygen

are formed. Ice, water, and steam are all composed of hydrogen and oxygen in the same proportions. The molecules of ice, water, and steam are identical in chemical composition. They are all H_2O. Such changes, in which no alteration in chemical composition takes place, are called *physical changes.*

Chemical and physical changes are very important in living things. The grinding of food by the teeth is an example of a physical change. When the saliva is mixed with the food, chemical changes break up the foods into simpler food molecules.

ORGANIC AND INORGANIC COMPOUNDS. About eight-tenths of most living things is water. In the water are dissolved a few salts, such as common table salt. The remainder of the body consists of carbon compounds containing hydrogen, oxygen, and frequently nitrogen. Chemists call these compounds *organic compounds* because they were once thought to be produced only by living organisms. This view is no longer held because chemists can now produce many organic compounds in the laboratory. The molecules of organic compounds are usually very large. A molecule of table sugar, a common organic compound, contains 45 atoms. Yet, even this molecule is small when compared with certain other organic molecules containing several thousand atoms.

With a few exceptions, *inorganic compounds* do not contain carbon. Their molecules are generally quite small, containing few atoms. Water and carbon dioxide, for example, have only three atoms per molecule. Most inorganic molecules have fewer than ten atoms. The chemistry of life is the story of how organisms make and use organic molecules.

THE ELECTROLYSIS OF WATER. *Electrolysis* (e-lek-TROL-uh-sis) is the separation of a compound into elements by means of electricity. A large amount of energy is

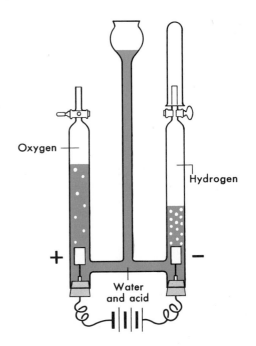

6–3 In Hoffman apparatus electrical energy splits the compound water into its constituent elements: oxygen and hydrogen.

often required to separate a compound into its elements.

In the Hoffman apparatus, electricity splits water into the elements hydrogen and oxygen. When the electricity begins to pass through the water, gas bubbles collect on the electrodes. The apparatus is arranged so that the gas from each electrode is collected separately. The gases accumulate at different rates. Hydrogen accumulates at twice the rate of oxygen. Thus, we see that electricity decomposes water into its two elements, hydrogen and oxygen. There is just twice the volume of hydrogen as oxygen in water.

CARBON DIOXIDE. Another inorganic compound of basic importance to all living things is carbon dioxide. Its formula is CO_2. Ordinarily, carbon dioxide is a gas found in minute amounts in the air. The carbon dioxide of the air is the main source of the carbon found in living things. How this compound becomes a part of a living thing is one of the most intriguing stories in the study of biology.

MINERAL SALTS. Most people know that sea water contains salt. Fresh water also contains a small amount of salt. A simple experiment will reveal that this is so. If we place some pond water in an evaporating dish and heat it gently over a burner for several minutes, the water boils away, and a small deposit of salt is left. Where did the salt come from? The salt was in the soil. It was washed from the soil by rain water that flowed into the pond.

Chemists call these salts found in soil *mineral salts.* There are many different kinds, not just the common one called sodium chloride, which you use on your dinner table. Among them are the nitrates, sulfates, and phosphates. All of these are essential for the health and growth of plants and animals.

The Large Organic Molecules

In 1828, a German chemist, Friedrich Woehler, made a significant discovery. Prior to that year, organic compounds found in living things were considered so special that no man could make them. Organic compounds had not been found anywhere outside the body of a living plant or animal. But after many attempts, Woehler produced *urea,* an organic substance found in the urine of animals. For the first time, urea was not produced by the kidney of an animal, nor by any other organ. It had been made in the laboratory.

CARBOHYDRATES. Sugars and starches are compounds of carbon, hydrogen, and oxygen. In these compounds, hydrogen and oxygen atoms are found in the ratio of two to one, the same ratio as in water. This is shown in the formula for *glucose,* a simple sugar: $C_6H_{12}O_6$. Compounds containing carbon, hydrogen, and oxygen in which the ratio of hydrogen to oxygen is two to one are called *carbohydrates.*

Note that the formula for glucose shows that the molecule contains 24 atoms. It is, therefore, a large molecule in comparison with water or carbon dioxide. This is an important fact to bear in mind when we consider that all of the materials that enter or leave cells must pass through the cell membrane. The size of the molecule is one of the factors that influence the ease with which the molecule can enter or leave the cell. Because of their greater size, organic molecules have more difficulty passing throuch cell membranes than the smaller inorganic molecules.

6–4 The story of how life began is the story of how carbon compounds became more complex. The chain and the structural formulas for a glucose molecule show how carbon atoms join with oxygen and hydrogen atoms to form a large molecule.

GLUCOSE

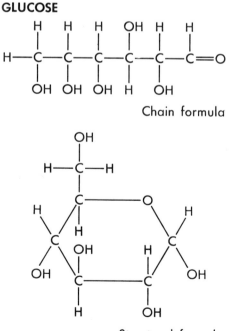

Chain formula

Structural formula

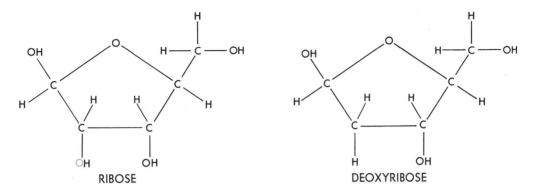

RIBOSE   DEOXYRIBOSE

6–5 Two Important Sugars. Ribose is part of RNA. Deoxyribose is part of DNA. Note that both are essentially the same except that ribose has one more atom of oxygen.

Just as fuel supplies energy to run a car, so carbohydrates provide the energy required by living things. Glucose is the chief energy carbohydrate used in the body. Glucose always is found in the blood. The concentration of this blood sugar is carefully regulated in the body.

Sucrose, or cane sugar, has a much larger molecule than that of glucose. Its formula is $C_{12}H_{22}O_{11}$. Its total number of atoms is 45, which is almost twice the number of atoms in the glucose molecule. Before it can be used in the body, however, sucrose first must be split chemically into two molecules of glucose.

Living things can store excess fuel in a form that does not readily dissolve in water. Both plants and animals can change glucose into insoluble *starches.* You can think of a starch molecule as a chain in which the individual links are glucose molecules. Thus, a huge starch molecule has a formula $(C_6H_{10}O_5)_n$. The letter *n* represents a variable number depending on the number of glucose molecules.

Starch stored in animal cells is called *glycogen* (GLY-ko-jen). Glycogen is especially abundant in liver and muscle cells. There is no one name for all the starches

found in plants. In both plants and animals, starch must be reconverted to glucose before it can be used. In your study of viruses, you have already learned about two important sugars, ribose and deoxyribose. Ribose is an important part of the RNA molecule.

6–6 Large organic molecules are synthesized from smaller inorganic molecules.

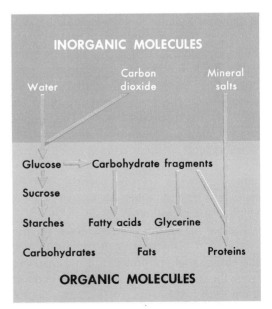

INORGANIC MOLECULES

Water   Carbon dioxide   Mineral salts

Glucose → Carbohydrate fragments

Sucrose

Starches   Fatty acids   Glycerine

Carbohydrates   Fats   Proteins

ORGANIC MOLECULES

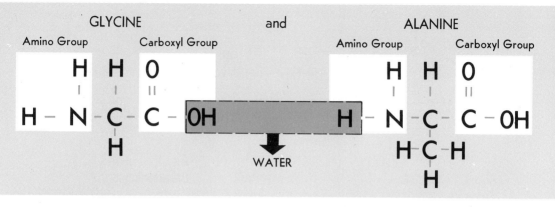

GLYCINE and ALANINE

6–7a Structural Formula of Glycine and Alanine. Glycine is the simplest amino acid. Notice the amino (NH₂) and carboxyl (COOH) groups. Alanine, the next simplest, has an additional carbon and two hydrogen atoms.

Deoxyribose is the corresponding sugar in DNA. RNA and DNA are master molecules in the metabolism of all organisms.

FATS. Fats also are compounds of carbon, hydrogen, and oxygen, but they are more concentrated fuels than carbohydrates. Fats yield more than twice as much energy as sugar, and they are a good means of storing much energy in a limited space. Fats, however, have one disadvantage: starches are changed quickly into glucose, but more time is required to convert fats into a useful form.

PROTEINS. Proteins are the largest of the organic molecules. The smallest protein molecule is about six thousand times as large as the hydrogen atom. The largest protein molecule is more than ten million times as large as the hydrogen atom. In addition to carbon, hydrogen, and oxygen, proteins always contain nitrogen. Often, they also contain other elements, such as sulphur and phosphorus.

Except for water, proteins make up the largest part of cytoplasm. All living things, therefore, contain proteins. No organism, from the simplest virus to man, is without them.

The number of different types of proteins is practically limitless. The difference in proteins distinguishes one form of life from another. The hemoglobin of horse's blood, for example, is different from that of human blood. Rabbit hair differs from dog hair, and so on. The proteins found in the nucleus of the cell, *nucleoproteins,* are of fundamental importance because they are the chief agents that cause organisms to differ.

AMINO ACIDS. More than a century ago, the French chemist Henri Braconnet broke down cellular protein and produced the simpler substance *glycine.* Glycine proved to be an *amino acid.* In the years that followed, some twenty amino acids were derived from proteins. All amino acids contained nitrogen as well as carbon, hydrogen, and oxygen.

In time, it became clear that amino acids are the subunits or "building blocks" of the giant protein molecules. By using advanced methods of chromatography, the biochemist can separate the amino acids that make up a particular protein.

Amino acids have certain chemical characteristics. Look at the structural formula

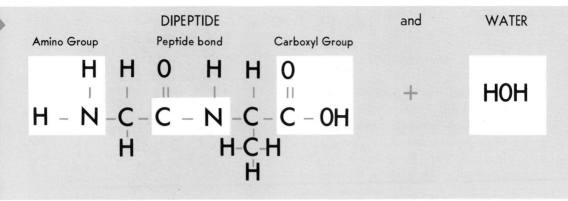

DIPEPTIDE   and   WATER

Amino Group   Peptide bond   Carboxyl Group

6–7b Peptide Bonding in Amino Acids. When glycine combines with alanine, water is formed. The amino acids join where the OH and H atoms are indicated in Figure 6–7a. The resulting compound is called a dipeptide.

for glycine shown in Figure 6–7a. Although glycine is the simplest amino acid, it has the basic structure of all amino acids. At one end of the molecule there is an *amino group* (NH_2), and at the opposite end there is a *carboxyl group* (COOH). The presence of the carboxyl group indicates to the organic chemist that glycine is an acid. Thus, amino acids are compounds containing an amino and a carboxyl group.

When two amino acids combine chemically, they join in the following manner. The oxygen and hydrogen from the carboxyl group of the first amino acid join with a hydrogen atom from the amino group of the second acid to form a water molecule. The resulting linkage of the carboxyl and amino groups of two amino acids is called a *peptide bond*. When two amino acids are thus joined by a peptide bond, the resulting compound is called a *dipeptide*. When many amino acids are linked by peptide bonds, the resulting compound is called a *polypeptide*. Proteins consist of hundreds of amino acids joined by peptide bonds. In some proteins several chains of amino acids are cross-linked by other kinds of chemical bonds.

The number of different proteins can run into the billions (the average human cell

6–8 Formation of a Protein. For simplicity, the chain includes only four symbols for amino acids. Twenty amino acids are commonly found in living things.

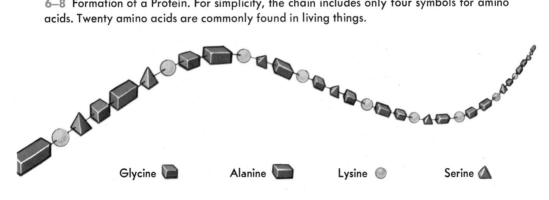

Glycine   Alanine   Lysine   Serine

contains some 2000) because the amino acids that make them up are different. *It is the number, kind, and sequence of amino-acid units that characterize each protein that is produced.*

To understand why the number of proteins is practically limitless, let us again compare a starch molecule, such as glycogen, with a protein molecule. The glucose molecules, which are the subunits of glycogen, are all alike. They can be represented by the letter **A.** A starch molecule made up of ten subunits then would be **AAAAAAAAAA.** Since there are 20 amino acids, however, we can represent them with 20 different letters, such as **B, C, D, E, F.** A very small protein consisting of only four amino acids could be **BCDE.** Because a change in sequence yields a different protein, the same four amino acids could build as many as twenty-four different proteins. Thus, we could have **CDEB, EBDC, CBDE,** and so on.

An average protein molecule contains several hundred amino acid subunits linked in a precise sequence. One chain of the hemoglobin molecule, for example, contains 146 amino acids. A change in one amino acid can produce a fatal anemia.

6–9 Model of Myoglobin Molecule. Myoglobin accepts oxygen from the hemoglobin in blood and temporarily stores it in the cell.

THE PRINCIPAL AMINO ACIDS

Alanine	Leucine
Arginine	Lysine
Asparagine	Methionine
Aspartic acid	Phenylalanine
Cysteine	Proline
Glutamic acid	Serine
Glutamine	Threonine
Glycine	Tryptophan
Histidine	Tyrosine
Isoleucine	Valine

The Kinetic Theory of Matter

You probably know that snowflakes are water in crystalline form. The water molecules in this case are closely packed together in precise geometric patterns. We say that these ice crystals are in the *solid state.* When ice is heated, the molecules are agitated. They do not keep the exact positions they had in the ice crystal. The water thus formed still consists of the same H_2O molecules, but they are free to move about. In the *liquid state,* most of the molecules are farther apart than in the solid state.

If we continue to apply heat to water, the molecules begin to move farther and farther apart. They also move faster. We no longer recognize the water as such. We now call it water vapor. In this *gaseous state,* the molecules are very far apart. Consequently, the gases are the lightest substances known. The air we breathe is so light it does not seem to exist, yet it is always about us. Its particles constantly bump into us, moving at a speed of a quarter of a mile per second. Molecules of water vapor move with even greater velocity.

It is this picture of a dynamic, moving mass of molecules that the chemist has in mind when he thinks of the states of matter. The *Kinetic Theory of Matter* states: *the molecules of every substance are in a constant state of motion.* Even in the solid state, the molecules are believed to move about fixed positions.

An understanding of the Kinetic Theory is important for biology students. It furnishes a picture of the dynamic condition that exists in all living things. Water molecules are in constant motion. They continually bombard the cell membranes, both from inside and outside the cell.

DIFFUSION. Let us try a simple experiment to demonstrate the Kinetic Theory. A small beaker is filled with water, then allowed to stand quietly until the surface appears completely calm. A pellet of potassium permanganate, a purple dye, is now dropped into the water. It settles immediately to the bottom of the beaker. Even as the pellet falls through the water, the purple color begins to spread. At first, the color rises in the beaker. The spreading of the dye is of special interest because we have done nothing to cause movement. In fact, we purposely waited for the water in the beaker to be still before introducing the pellet. How shall we explain the spreading of the dye?

According to the Kinetic Theory, the molecules of water began bombarding the dye as soon as it was placed in the beaker. As a result of this bombardment, some of the molecules of the dye were chipped away from the pellet. The evidence of this fact is the spreading of the color. Under constant bombardment, more and more of the dye molecules separate and the color spreads still more. Eventually, all of the dye is dis-

6–10 The individual molecules of solids, liquids, and gases are in constant motion. The more rapid their motion, the greater their kinetic energy, which is manifested as heat energy.

CHANGE IN STATE OF WATER

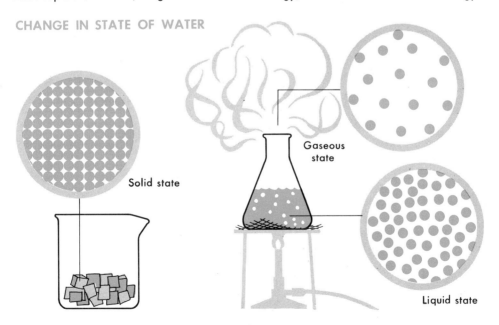

Gaseous state

Solid state

Liquid state

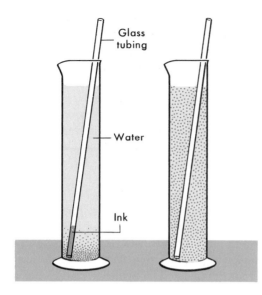

Glass
tubing

Water

Ink

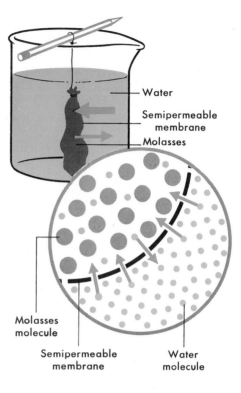

Water

Semipermeable
membrane

Molasses

Molasses
molecule

Semipermeable
membrane

Water
molecule

6–11 Whenever a substance is in solution, its molecules scatter from regions of high concentration to regions of low concentration. This can be demonstrated by introducing an ink solution to the bottom of a tall jar. To introduce the ink solution, place a glass tube in a bottle of ink and trap about an inch of ink by placing your forefinger over the open end of the tube. Then place the tube in jar as shown. When diffusion is complete, ink particles will be evenly distributed. Can you explain this in terms of the kinetic theory of matter?

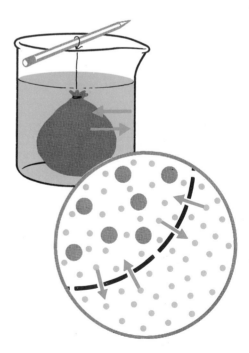

6–12 Diffusion occurs in nature in both living and non-living systems. In the demonstration illustrated, water molecules diffuse through a cellophane sac from a region of high concentration to a region of low concentration. In living systems, the molecules of water are constantly passing through cell membranes in a similar fashion. This diffusion of water across cell membranes is called osmosis. Does osmosis require any sort of energy? If so, what is the source of the energy?

solved; none remains in the solid state. Its color is spread evenly throughout the beaker.

The spreading out of the molecules of a substance as a result of molecular motion is called *diffusion.* The odor of alcohol or of ether is easily noticed when their containers are opened because their molecules diffuse quickly in the air.

Cells are surrounded by a *semipermeable membrane* that restricts the entrance and exit of materials. As you have learned, the membrane consists of a double layer of protein with a fatty layer between. Any substance that can dissolve these fats, or is soluble in them, can pass through the membrane. Pores are also believed to exist in the membrane, but they are so small that they have never been seen. Dr. Arthur K. Solomon, of the Harvard Medical School, measured the diameter of these pores indirectly and found it to be seven hundred millionths of a centimeter in width.

Cell membranes are said to be *selective.* The size of their pores generally limits the substances that can pass through them to those materials of small molecular size. The water molecule, which is one of the smallest in nature, being only three hundred millionths of a centimeter wide, enters cells with ease. Other factors, such as fat solubility and the presence of electric charges, affect the entrance of materials. These further indicate the selective nature of the cell membrane.

In order to demonstrate the selective, or *semipermeable,* nature of a membrane, let us try an experiment.

A sac made of cellophane is partly filled with molasses, which has large molecules. The sac is then immersed in water. The molecules of water pass through the small pores of the sac. The molasses molecules, which are much larger than the water molecules, cannot go through. Water accumulates inside the sac. The water molecules

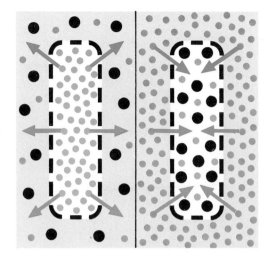

6–13 Diffusion of Water Through Cell Membrane. At left, there are fewer water molecules per unit area outside of the cell. At right, the concentration of water molecules is greater outside the cell; therefore, water molecules move into the cell. As the molecules move into the cell, the osmotic pressure against the inside of the cell membrane is increased. Note that water moves toward a region of higher osmotic pressure—not away from it.

cannot get out easily once they have entered, since they are hindered by the larger molasses molecules.

The passage of water through a semipermeable membrane is called *osmosis.* In a sense, osmosis is a special kind of diffusion—namely, the diffusion of water through a selective membrane. The accumulation of the water on the inside of the sac causes a pressure increase that is called *osmotic pressure.*

THE ABSORPTION OF MINERAL SALTS. Osmosis is concerned with the absorption of water, but minerals are also absorbed by the cells. How is the absorption of these minerals accomplished?

In the dissolved state each mineral compound forms a positive and negative *ion.*

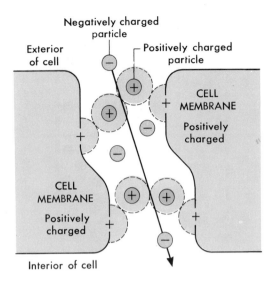

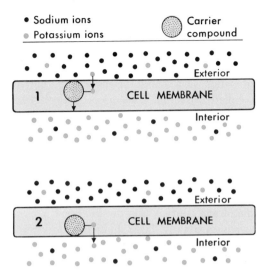

6–14 Diagram of a charged cell membrane, showing passage of charged particles through a pore. Charged particles, or ions, do not enter cells as easily as uncharged particles. However, negatively-charged particles enter more rapidly than do positively-charged particles. It is known that particles with like charges repel each other and that particles with unlike charges attract each other. Because the positively-charged particles seem to be repelled the most, the predominant charge of the cell membrane is assumed to be positive.

6–15 Active Transport. The diagrams show a possible method of transport against a high concentration gradient. On the exterior side of the cell membrane is a high concentration of sodium ions. On the interior side is a high concentration of potassium ions. A potassium carrier compound is shown combining with a potassium ion (1). The carrier and its ion move through the membrane to the interior side, where the ion is released into the cell (2). This is active transport because the cell supplies the energy to operate the system.

An ion is an electrically charged atom or group of atoms. For example, when potassium nitrate (KNO_3) is dissolved in water, it forms a positive potassium ion (K^+) and a negative nitrate ion (NO_3^-). These electrical charges complicate the passage of mineral salts into the cell.

The concentration of ions within cells is often higher than it is in the fluids surrounding the cells. In certain plant cells the concentration of particular ions may be 100 times higher than in the water surrounding them. This difference in concentration from one area to another is known as the *concentration gradient*. It is certain,

therefore, that some ions move into and out of cells against a concentration gradient. This is somewhat like a ball rolling up hill. In order for an ion to move against a concentration gradient, it must be given energy. The energy may be derived from several sources.

One source of such energy is the attraction that unlike electrical charges have for each other. If there are many positively charged ions on the inside of the membrane, they attract negatively charged ions. On the other hand, positive ions on the inside of a cell membrane would tend to prevent positive ions from entering.

Dr. Arthur K. Solomon found that negative chlorine ions (Cl^-) entered red blood cells at a rate that was a million times faster than positive potassium ions (K^+). From these facts he concluded that the pores of the red blood cell membrane were lined with a positive charge. In this situation, the chlorine ions are attracted as the result of an *electrical gradient.* However, potassium ions often move against both concentration and electrical gradients.

When a substance passes through a cell membrane in the direction of either a concentration or electrical gradient, biologists say that it undergoes **passive transport.** As a boat is moved by a current, the substance is transported in the direction of those forces that exist in the system. On the other hand, when a substance moves in a direction opposite to the gradient, or upstream, we say that it undergoes **active transport.**

Several theories have been proposed to explain active transport. One useful theory is based upon the idea of **carriers.** A carrier is a compound, probably a protein, that has the ability to transport a specific substance across the cell membrane. We might speak, therefore, of a potassium carrier, a magnesium carrier, or a sodium carrier. Thus, when a potassium ion reaches the surface of the cell membrane, it can combine with the potassium carrier and be transported into the cell by it. At the inner surface of the membrane, the carrier releases the potassium ion.

Many biologists have reported that the movement of ions into the cell is always accompanied by the movement of sodium ions (Na^+) outward. This has led them to the conclusion that the sodium in some way provides the energy for active transport. Because of sodium's role in this process, it is sometimes referred to as the "sodium pump."

IMPORTANT POINTS

• All living things are made of fundamental chemical substances called elements. The most abundant elements in organisms are oxygen, carbon, hydrogen, and nitrogen.

• Atoms are the smallest parts of elements. An atom is made of smaller particles. A molecule is the smallest particle of an element or compound that retains all the chemical properties of the element or compound. The chemical union of two or more elements produces a compound.

• Organic compounds are compounds of carbon and other elements. They were once thought to be found only in living things. Inorganic compounds generally do not contain carbon.

• Carbohydrates are organic compounds such as sugar and starch. Glucose, a simple sugar, is a chemical building block that is part of double sugars and starches.

• Fats are high-energy organic compounds. A fat stores more than twice as much energy as the same amount of sugar.

• Proteins are the largest molecules in nature. The building unit of the protein molecule is called an amino acid.

• Proteins are made from some twenty different amino acids. It is the number, kind, and sequence of amino acids that cause proteins to differ from each other.

• According to the Kinetic Theory of Matter, the molecules of every substance are in a continual state of motion. This property of matter provides a basis for explaining diffusion and osmosis.

• Diffusion is the spreading out of molecules as a result of molecular motion. Osmosis is the diffusion of water through a selective membrane.

• Active transport is the movement of ions and other substances into the cell against concentration or electrical gradients.

REVIEW QUESTIONS

1. What is the difference between an atom and a molecule?
2. List three important points of Dalton's atomic theory.
3. What are the four most abundant elements in living things?
4. Distinguish between a chemical and a physical change. Give an example of each.
5. What are the characteristics of organic compounds?
6. What are the main inorganic compounds that plants use to form foods?
7. What happens as a result of the electrolysis of water?
8. Why might proteins be considered the most important organic compounds?
9. How would you describe the differences between a solid, liquid, and gas in terms of the molecules that compose them?
10. What is the Kinetic Theory of Matter?
11. What is the fundamental difference between diffusion and osmosis?

CHECK YOUR UNDERSTANDING

12. Which of the four most abundant elements found in the human body are always found in sugar? in water? in proteins?
13. How did the discovery of radioactivity conflict with Dalton's atomic theory?
14. Why is the number of different starches small, and the number of different proteins practically limitless?
15. Arrange the following in order of increasing molecular size: starch, glucose, water, protein.
16. Why is the description of osmosis inadequate as an explanation of how materials pass in and out of the cell membrane?
17. How is the size of the water molecule related to its degree of importance in living systems?
18. How did the discovery that the compounds and the reactions that occur in living things are not unique accelerate biological research?
19. What is the significance of the fact that stored foods, such as the starches, are insoluble in water?
20. How does the idea of carriers support the explanation of active transport?

RESEARCH PROJECTS AND REPORTS

1. Obtain information from your school or public library and prepare a report on one of the following topics:

    Democritus   **Madame Curie**

    John Dalton   **Henri Becquerel**

2. *Atomic Charts:* Make diagrams of various elements. Look up the numbers of protons, neutrons, and electrons characteristic of each element in a chemistry book.

3. *Spinthariscope:* If the physics teacher at your school will lend you a spinthariscope, you can see sparks of light caused by particles striking a fluorescent material. You will need to wait for darkness before you can use this instrument. If a spinthariscope is not available, examine the luminous dial of a watch with a hand lens.

4. *Alcohol and Water Mixture:* Borrow two graduated cylinders from the chemistry teacher. In the first carefully measure 50 cc of water. In the second measure 50 cc of alcohol and add it to the water. Make certain your measurements are very accurate and that *all* of the liquid is added. Don't lose any drops. Can you explain why the mixture does not measure 100 cc?

FURTHER READING

The Chemicals of Life. Isaac Asimov. Abelard-Schuman, New York, N.Y. An introduction to the chemistry of living things.

Building Blocks of the Universe. Isaac Asimov. Abelard-Schuman, New York, N.Y. A popular introduction to the world of chemistry.

"How Things Get Into Cells." Heinz Holter. *Scientific American,* September, 1961, page 167. An advanced discussion of the many factors that influence the passage of materials through the cell membrane.

"Pores in the Cell Membrane." Arthur K. Solomon. *Scientific American,* December, 1960, page 146. Explains the techniques for measuring the size of the pores in the cell membrane.

"The Discovery of DNA." Alfred Mirsky. *Scientific American,* June, 1968, page 78. The history of the discovery of this master molecule by Friedrich Miescher is traced in great detail.

7

Energy and Living Things

LIVING THINGS grow, reproduce, and respond to stimuli. Within the cell, the ceaseless reactions of metabolism occur, and each requires energy. Without a continual supply of energy, life cannot exist. Much of life's story concerns the way in which cells trap, store, release, and use energy.

Where and how do living things obtain energy? All organisms need and use the energy from food. Organisms that can manufacture foods are called *autotrophs,* or "self-feeders." These organisms capture the energy of sunlight and convert it to the chemical energy of food. The energy is captured by autotrophs with the aid of the green pigment *chlorophyll.* Thus, autotrophs begin the energy flow upon which all life depends. Organisms that cannot make food are called *heterotrophs,* or "other feeders." Thus, heterotrophs are dependent on the autotrophs for their existence.

How do the autotrophs capture the sun's radiant energy and store it in foods? How do organisms release this stored energy to power their life functions? Before we can discuss these questions, we need to know something about energy and how it is converted from one form to another.

Energy

What is energy? The physicist defines *en-ergy* as the capacity to do work. When used by the scientist, the word "work" has a specific meaning. Work is accomplished when an object is moved.

A bowling ball may have energy. When it is raised to a throwing position, its energy is said to be *potential energy,* or stored energy. When the ball hurtles down the alley, it has *kinetic energy,* or the energy of motion. When the ball knocks over the pins, it causes them to move and therefore accomplishes work.

ENERGY CONVERSIONS. Energy exists in many forms. Under ordinary conditions energy can be converted from one form to another. For example, gasoline contains stored *chemical energy.* When this fuel is exploded in the engine of a car, its chemical energy is converted to *mechanical energy,* which causes the vehicle to move. A horse eating hay illustrates another energy converting process. The metabolic processes of the horse convert the stored chemical energy of the hay to mechanical energy, thus enabling him to do work.

The production and use of electricity are also examples of energy conversions. Most of our electricity is produced in hydroelectric power plants. When falling water is channeled into the power plant, mechanical energy of the falling water turns the generators and is thus converted to *electri-*

cal energy. Electrical energy is then converted in our homes to *light energy* and *heat energy.*

SOLAR ENERGY. For many years scientists have wondered how the sun (and the other stars) produced such huge quantities of energy. The sun's surface temperature is 6000° C. Its interior is much hotter— 20 million degrees! If the sun's surface were as hot as its interior, the earth would be vaporized in minutes.

The sun derives its energy from *nuclear fusion.* Its high internal temperature brings about the conversion of hydrogen to helium. In this *thermonuclear reaction,* the fusion of hydrogen nuclei into helium nuclei is accompanied by the release of enormous energy. Man has learned to duplicate this reaction in the hydrogen bomb.

Thermonuclear reactions result in a loss of mass. When hydrogen nuclei fuse to form helium nuclei, seven-tenths of one per cent of the total mass is converted into energy. By continually converting its mass into energy, our sun is, in a sense, destroying itself. However, there is no cause for alarm. At its present rate of mass-energy conversions, the sun will last 10 billion years.

Physicists have long known that in ordinary (non-nuclear) chemical reactions, energy is converted from one form to another without loss or gain. With their more recent knowledge of nuclear energy, which results in the partial destruction of matter, they have formulated the *Law of Conservation of Energy and Matter.* This law states that energy or matter can be converted into other forms of energy or matter, or both, but the sum total of energy and matter in the universe remains constant.

SOLAR RADIATION. The sun's energy reaches the earth as radiant energy. *Radiant energy* may be thought of as energy waves that travel through space at the speed of 186,000 miles per second. Solar

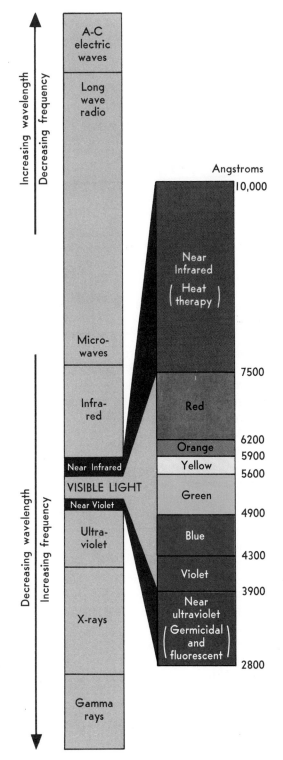

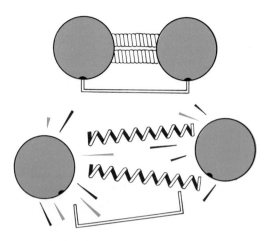

7–2 Chemical bond energy is like the energy of imaginary compressed springs holding atoms together. By unhooking the atoms, the energy of the springs is released.

radiations include energy waves of different wavelengths. Only certain of these wavelengths are visible as light. Wavelengths that are longer or shorter than the wavelengths of light are invisible.

The physicist measures wavelengths of radiation in units called *angstroms* (Å). Named after Anders J. Angstrom, a Swedish astronomer, an angstrom is equal to one hundred millionths of a centimeter (10^{-8} cm). The wavelengths of visible light measure between 3900 and 7500 angstroms. Violet light, for example, has the shortest visible wavelength, 3900 Å's. Red light has the longest visible wavelength, 7500 Å's. Wavelengths that are shorter than those of violet light include the invisible ultraviolet, X rays, and gamma rays. Wavelengths that are longer than those of red light include the invisible infrared and radio waves. It is mainly the energy of visible light that autotrophs use in food making.

LIFE's ENERGY. The energy of living things is largely chemical energy. Within the cell, chemical reactions are in progress at all times. While some chemical compounds are building up, others are breaking down. The endless movement of atoms and molecules as they rearrange themselves into new substances is a form of work requiring energy.

Where does this chemical energy come from? Chemical energy is contained in the bonds that unite atoms into molecules. Considerable energy is required to construct the larger organic molecules that contain many atoms. This energy is stored in the chemical bonds that hold the molecules together. When the larger molecules are broken into smaller ones, bond energy is usually released.

The chemist distinguishes between "low energy" and "high energy" bonds. When a low energy bond is broken, very little energy is released. When a high energy bond is broken, a large burst of chemical energy is freed.

In 1929, Karl Lohman, a German biochemist at the University of Heidelberg, discovered ATP (see Chapter 2) in muscle cells. Biochemists soon realized that ATP is the energy distributor in cells. ATP consists of familiar subunits bonded together: the nitrogen base *adenine*, the sugar *ribose*, plus three phosphate units. The third phosphate unit is attached by a high-energy bond. When broken, the third bond releases energy, which then becomes available for cell use.

The release of the third phosphate unit converts ATP to the two-phosphate compound ADP. ADP is "energy poor" and cannot provide energy for the cell's work. However, when a new phosphate unit is bonded to it, it is converted back to "energy rich" ATP.

ATP and ADP may be thought of as charged and discharged batteries. ATP is the charged battery. It releases its energy to power the cell's work. As ATP yields its stored energy it is discharged and con-

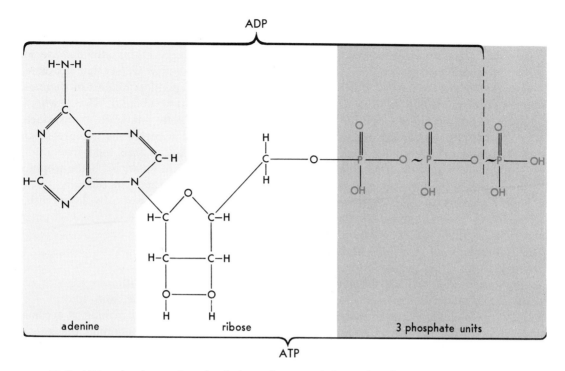

7–3 ATP molecule consists of adenine, ribose, and three phosphate units. The last two phosphates are attached by high energy bonds (~). When the third bond is broken, energy is released for the cell's work and ATP is converted to ADP.

7–4 ATP–ADP conversion can be compared to charging and discharging a battery. A third phosphate group changes ADP to ATP, which then releases the energy for cell work.

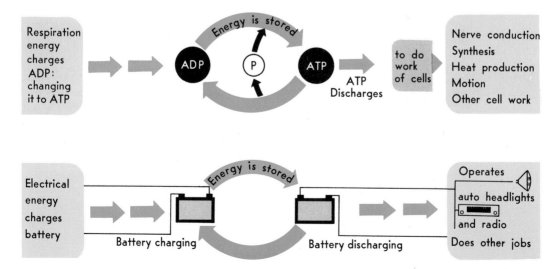

verted to ADP. ADP, the discharged battery, receives new energy (a new phosphate bond) and is converted back to ATP, the charged battery.

FOOD AND ENERGY CHAINS. Heterotrophs depend upon autotrophs for their existence because autotrophs alone capture the energy of sunlight. Once captured, this energy is transferred to vast numbers of heterotroph species by means of *food chains.*

To illustrate a food chain, let us consider a typical plant, such as grass. During the food-making process, grass captures the energy of sunlight and converts it to the chemical energy of food. A *herbivorous* (erb-BIV-uh-rus), or plant-eating, animal obtains the "stored sunlight" by eating the grass. A *carnivorous* (kar-NIV-uh-rus) or flesh-eating, animal obtains the energy of sunlight by eating the plant-eating animal. Thus, the flesh-eating mountain lion cannot live without plant life. Man is an *omniv-*

orous (ahm-NIV-uh-rus) animal; that is, he eats both plant and animal products.

Food and energy chains also operate in the sea. In the shallow waters that surround the continents, countless billions of diatoms and other protists abound. Here, where sunlight is able to penetrate the surface waters, these tiny organisms capture solar energy and store it in their food. The autotrophic protists are eaten by heterotrophic protists. They are eaten, in turn, by small fish. Smaller fish are eaten by larger fish, and so the chain continues.

Photosynthesis

Food making begins with the capture of radiant energy from the sun. Except for certain bacteria, all food making is accomplished by organisms containing the green pigment chlorophyll. Many of these organisms are familiar green plants. We will,

7–5 A food chain is a series of organisms, each of which is dependent on the one preceding it in the series. In the food chain illustrated, there are both "consumers" and "producers" of energy. Which are the consumers and which are the producers?

SIMPLE FOOD CHAIN

Microscopic organisms

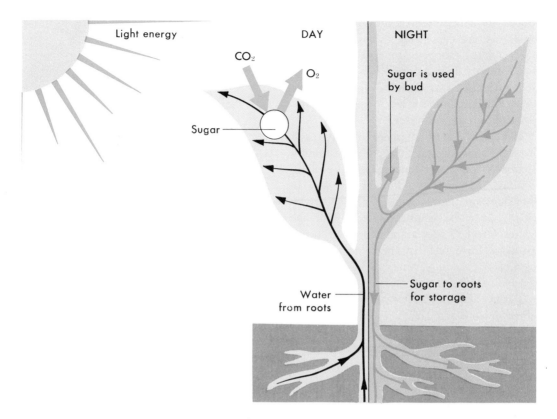

Light energy   DAY   NIGHT

CO_2

O_2

Sugar is used by bud

Sugar

Sugar to roots for storage

Water from roots

7–6 PHOTOSYNTHESIS. Carbon dioxide and water are used by green plants to make sugar, which is stored during the day as starch. At night, starch in leaf changes back into sugar and moves to other parts of plant. Some sugar goes to the roots for storage. Solar energy, stored by plants as chemical energy, powers all life's processes.

therefore, use the green plant as an example of this fundamental pattern of energy transformation. Using the energy of sunlight, chlorophyll in a green plant makes possible the combining of water and carbon dioxide into carbohydrate foods. The manufacture of carbohydrates from inorganic compounds by using the energy of light is called *photosynthesis* (foh-toe-sin-theh-sis), a term derived from the Greek, meaning "combining by means of light."

Photosynthesis creates the simplest carbohydrate, the sugar glucose. Just as wood is burned in a fireplace to release the energy required to heat a room, so glucose molecules can be "burned" in the cells to release the energy required for life func-

7–7 Word Formula for Photosynthesis

$$water + carbon\ dioxide \xrightarrow[\text{chlorophyll}]{\text{light energy}} carbohydrate + water + oxygen$$

tions. Notice then the significance of photosynthesis: by converting radiant energy to the chemical energy of food, it changes the sun's energy into a form that is useful to living things. The chemical reactions that occur during photosynthesis result in the release of oxygen and water.

We have described photosynthesis as if it were a simple reaction. Actually, photosynthesis consists of a complex series of reactions. Our understanding of the way in which green plants make food has grown slowly over the centuries. Only with the aid of tracer elements and the electron microscope have scientists been able to give us a clear picture of what has long been regarded a mystery.

EARLY INVESTIGATIONS. Aristotle and other ancient scholars believed that plants made their food from soil. More than 300 years ago, Jean Baptiste van Helmont, a Belgian physician, designed an experiment that disproved this. He planted a young willow tree weighing five pounds in a tub containing 200 pounds of soil. Within five years, the tree grew to a weight of 164 pounds. During this time, the loss in the weight of the soil amounted to only two ounces. Van Helmont concluded that the increased weight of the tree came not from the soil but from the water he had given it. His conclusion was not entirely correct. But he had made a basic discovery. He discovered that water was a raw material from which plants make food.

In 1772, Joseph Priestley, an English minister, made another basic discovery. He discovered that green plants absorb carbon dioxide and release oxygen—the reverse of what animals do. When he placed a mouse under a bell jar, the animal died of suffocation in a few hours. But when a second mouse was placed under a bell jar containing a green plant, it remained alive much longer. At the time of his investigations, Priestley could not identify the gases ex-

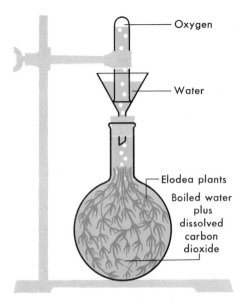

7–8 With the setup shown above, you can demonstrate that green plants give off oxygen. Boil some water to remove dissolved oxygen. After the water has cooled, bubble carbon dioxide through it. Then place water in the flask with a live Elodea plant as shown. When the test tube is inverted in the funnel, be sure that it is full of water and that no air bubbles enter. Place the setup in the sun. Bubbles of gas will rise in the test tube and displace the water. When sufficient gas has collected in the tube, test gas with a glowing splint. In presence of oxygen, the glowing splint will burst into flame.

changed by the plant and the mouse. He could write only that green plants, "reverse the effect of breathing."

Several years later, Jan Ingen-Housz, a Dutch physician, identified the gas that Priestley's plant absorbed as carbon dioxide. Ingen-Housz further suggested that plants never absorb carbon dioxide in the dark. "All plants," he wrote, "possess a power of correcting . . . air unfit for respiration; but only in clear daylight, or in the sunshine." Thus, the importance of light was established in the slowly unfolding picture of photosynthesis.

In 1837, R. J. Dutrochet, a French biologist, identified the plant's reliance on chlorophyll in the food-making process. For more than a century, then, the key factors of photosynthesis have been known. But the way in which photosynthesis takes place is, as we shall see, another story.

Raw Materials of Food Making. The two materials needed by green plants for the manufacture of carbohydrates are *water* and *carbon dioxide.*

Water is the most abundant compound on earth. Plants that live on land obtain water from the soil. It is absorbed by the roots, then transported through the stem to the leaf, where photosynthesis mainly occurs. Plants that live in the water readily absorb the water they require since it can easily pass through cell membranes.

Carbon dioxide, a gas found in small amounts in the air, is absorbed into the leaves of plants. Carbon dioxide also dissolves in water. It is estimated that ten times the atmospheric quantity of carbon dioxide is in solution in the sea and is available to marine protists.

Chemical Equation. Each year green plants combine 150 billion tons of carbon and 200 billion tons of oxygen with 25 billion tons of hydrogen to produce 375 billion tons of sugar. The energy supply created in a year by photosynthesis is at least 100 times greater than would be obtained by burning all the coal mined throughout the world in a similar period. A simple way of stating what happens is the following: *Carbon Dioxide* and *Water* combine to form *Glucose* and *Oxygen.* The chemist uses symbols to describe the reaction. Written in chemical shorthand, the above word equation appears as follows:

$$H_2O + CO_2 \xrightarrow[\text{Chlorophyll}]{\text{Light Energy}} C_6H_{12}O_6 + O_2 \uparrow$$

Elements and compounds combine to form new compounds in very exact ways. In a chemical reaction, every atom is accounted for. The equation we wrote is improper because we cannot have more carbon atoms at the end of the reaction than we started with. In order to *balance* the equation, we must write it as follows:

$$6H_2O + 6CO_2 \xrightarrow[\text{Chlorophyll}]{\text{Light Energy}} C_6H_{12}O_6 + 6O_2 \uparrow$$

The equation now tells us that six molecules of carbon dioxide are combined with six molecules of water to form one molecule of glucose and six molecules of oxygen. The equation is a convenient summary equation for the process. More exact knowledge of how photosynthesis takes place, however, has led to a refinement of the equation.

Experiments performed in 1941 by Samuel Ruben and Martin D. Kamen, of the University of California, showed that during photosynthesis the water molecule is split into its elements, hydrogen and oxygen. Furthermore, the oxygen released by the green plant comes only from the water and not from the carbon dioxide as had previously been supposed. This fact means that twice as much water is needed to balance the photosynthesis equation. To account for the extra water, the equation can be written:

$$12\,H_2O + 6\,CO_2 \xrightarrow[\text{Chlorophyll}]{\text{Light Energy}}$$
$$C_6H_{12}O_6 + 6\,H_2O + 6O_2 \uparrow$$

In this equation the water on the right side does not appear as an end product as does the oxygen. This water returns to the food-making reactions as soon as it is formed. For this reason, the shorter summary equation is usually more convenient to use.

Chlorophyll. The familiar green pigment found in most plants is *chlorophyll.*

7–9 Electron Micrograph Showing Chloroplast in Tobacco Leaf. Chlorophyll is concentrated in the darker areas called grana.

If we examine the water plant *Elodea,* the pigment is seen in tiny oval structures called *chloroplasts.* The role of chloroplasts in photosynthesis is of prime importance.

Before 1954, scientists found the function of chlorophyll difficult to investigate. It seemed to do its work only in the living cell. Experiments in which chlorophyll had been removed from the cell and provided with light, water, and carbon dioxide all failed to produce carbohydrates. Even a puncture of the cell halted photosynthesis.

In 1954, however, Dr. Daniel L. Arnon of the University of California succeeded in producing photosynthesis outside the cell for the first time. Arnon developed a special technique for extracting chloroplasts from spinach leaves. When he supplied the extracted chloroplasts with light energy, they converted water and carbon dioxide into carbohydrates.

Biochemists are constantly learning more about chlorophyll. The electron microscope has shown that the chloroplasts contain small, layered structures where the chlorophyll is concentrated. These structures are called **grana.** Grana have been compared to solar batteries that absorb the energy of sunlight. Each granum contains several million molecules of chlorophyll. Chemical analysis of the chloroplast shows that it consists of proteins, fatty substances, chlorophyll, and two yellow pigments.

CATALYSTS AND ENZYMES. How does chlorophyll enable photosynthesis to occur? Although chlorophyll is necessary in the production of glucose, it is not consumed in the process. It belongs to a group of substances called catalysts. A *catalyst* (CAT-uh-list) is a substance that changes the speed of a chemical reaction while remaining unchanged itself. We can see a catalyst at work in a simple experiment.

Suppose some hydrogen and oxygen gas are mixed in a test tube. When a burning splint is placed near the mouth of the tube, an explosion occurs. The gases combine to form water. Without the heat of the burning splint the gases do not combine. However, a pinch of powdered platinum enables the gases to combine at room temperature without heating. Just as much platinum remains after the union of the gases as before. In this reaction, therefore, the platinum acted as a catalyst.

Proteins that act as catalysts in living cells are called *enzymes.* Hundreds of different enzymes make possible the great variety of chemical reactions that occur in cells. Some enzymes control the synthesis of larger molecules from smaller ones. Other enzymes control the breakdown of large molecules into smaller ones. Enzymes are specific in their action. When a chemical change involves a series of intermediate reactions, each reaction in the series is controlled by a different enzyme. For example, the saliva in your mouth has an enzyme that breaks down foods. Chew a piece of bread for a few minutes, and you will notice a sweet taste. An enzyme in your saliva has begun the digestion of starch to sugar.

In photosynthesis, chlorophyll begins the series of chemical reactions that eventually produces glucose. Many enzymes aid chlorophyll in fashioning the glucose molecule. Each completes one stage of the job. Together, they make the final product.

LIGHT AND DARK REACTIONS IN PHOTO-SYNTHESIS. You might expect that if the light given a plant were increased, the rate of photosynthesis would also increase. However, experimenters have found this to be true only up to a certain point. When light energy is increased beyond this point, there is no further increase in the rate of photosynthesis. This observation is ex-plained by the fact that photosynthesis occurs in two phases: a *light phase* and a *dark phase*.

1. *The light phase.* During this phase, light energy is converted to stored chemical energy. The light causes energy poor ADP to change to energy rich ATP. The entire phase occurs within a fraction of a second. The water molecule is split, releasing oxygen. The hydrogen is freed for later reactions.

2. *The dark phase.* The dark phase follows the light phase and consists of a number of chemical reactions. These reactions do not require light energy because energy has already been stored in ATP. Since dark phase reactions are slower than light phase reac-

7–10 Photosynthesis may happen this way. During the light phase (left), the water molecule is broken down, liberating oxygen. The hydrogen atoms are transferred to the carbon dioxide (right) and united with it during the dark phase. The resulting combination is an "intermediate." The intermediates eventually lead to the formation of glucose molecules. Several enzymes are required to carry the process to completion.

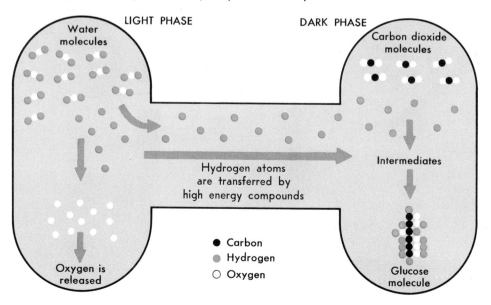

SUMMARY DIAGRAM OF LIGHT AND DARK REACTIONS OF PHOTOSYNTHESIS

$$12\,H_2O \;+\; 6\,CO_2 \;\longrightarrow\; C_6H_{12}O_6 \;+\; 6\,H_2O \;+\; 6\,O_2$$

Water   Carbon dioxide   Glucose   Water   Oxygen

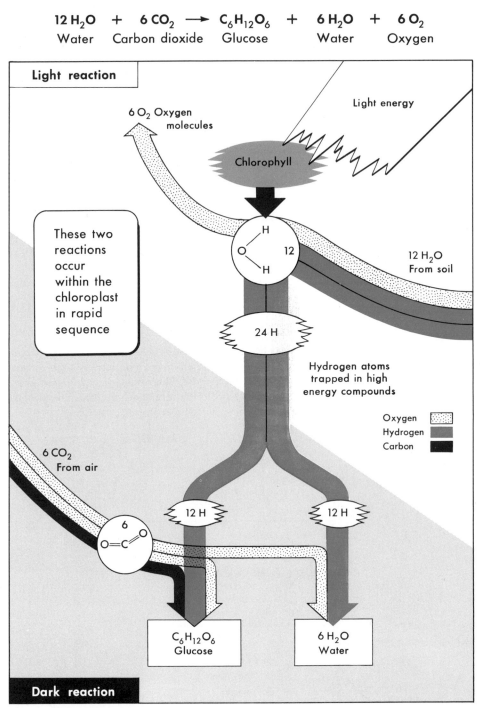

Light reaction

Light energy

$6\,O_2$ Oxygen molecules

Chlorophyll

These two reactions occur within the chloroplast in rapid sequence

$12\,H_2O$ From soil

O H H 12

24 H

Hydrogen atoms trapped in high energy compounds

Oxygen
Hydrogen
Carbon

$6\,CO_2$ From air

O=C=O 6

12 H

12 H

$C_6H_{12}O_6$ Glucose

$6\,H_2O$ Water

Dark reaction

tions, they act as a bottleneck that slows the rate of photosynthesis. The hydrogen released from water is linked with carbon dioxide to begin the formation of intermediate products, which eventually make glucose. During the dark phase, numerous enzymes act to produce many intermediate products. Experiments with radioactive carbon indicate that as many as a dozen different reactions may be in progress at once. The materials that will eventually become proteins and fats are produced along with glucose.

FORMATION OF FOODS. The manufacture of glucose through photosynthesis is only a first step in food making. Once fashioned, glucose molecules become the building blocks of carbohydrates, fats, proteins, and vitamins. Since cytoplasm is largely made of proteins, the accumulation of proteins is essential to plant growth.

As yet, scientists do not know how all the plant's additional foods are synthesized.

7–12 Food is manufactured in the form of glucose. Glucose molecules then link to form a long-chain, high-energy starch molecule. After temporary storage in the leaf, the starch molecules are then transported to other storage areas of the cell.

Generally, they are made in intermediate stages by enzyme action. Starting with glucose, smaller molecules combine to form larger molecules until the final product is made. As in any metabolic reaction, however, energy is required for additional food making. Much of the required energy is derived from the breakdown of newly made glucose.

FORMATION OF CARBOHYDRATES. The most common carbohydrates stored by plants are starches. Starches are made by linking glucose molecules into chains. Starches are often made during the daytime, when the rate of glucose production is high. They are stored temporarily in the leaf. At night they are transported to other parts of the plant. Since starch molecules are insoluble in water, they can easily be stored in cells. The roots and seeds of plants are likely to contain stored starch.

Cellulose, another carbohydrate, is also formed by linking together glucose molecules. In this case, many more glucose molecules are required than for starch. Cellulose is not a plant food. It forms the cell wall of most plant cells.

FORMATION OF FATS AND PROTEINS. Fats, like glucose, contain carbon, hydrogen, and oxygen. However, the arrangement of the atoms in fats is considerably different from the arrangement of these elements in glucose. Through a series of chemical changes, glucose is changed into two intermediate compounds: *fatty acids* and *glycerin*. A fat molecule is then constructed from three fatty acids linked to a glycerin molecule. The fat molecule, which contains much energy, is a reservoir of stored energy in both plants and animals.

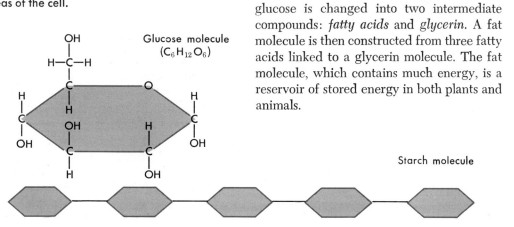

Glucose molecule
$(C_6H_{12}O_6)$

Starch molecule

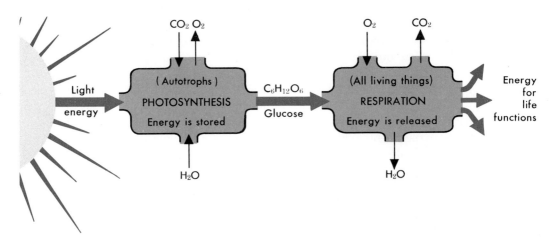

7–13 Solar energy is converted by autotrophs into the chemical energy of glucose. Oxidation of glucose in living cells releases the energy needed for life.

In addition to the elements found in glucose, proteins contain nitrogen and often sulfur and phosphorus. These additional elements are derived from dissolved minerals in the plant's water supply. They are linked to elements in the glucose molecule and rearranged to form the amino acids.

Much research has been directed toward understanding the details of photosynthesis. Still, there are gaps in our knowledge. For one thing, we do not yet know exactly how light energy splits the water molecule. Nevertheless, we are approaching a fuller understanding of the plant's food-making ability. A practical way of manufacturing food from abundant raw materials would be an enormous achievement.

Respiration: Releasing the Energy of Foods

Respiration is the process of releasing energy from foods. Whereas photosynthesis stores energy in foods, respiration releases energy from foods. Respiration, then, is the second stage of a cycle that begins with the radiant energy of the sun and ends with the chemical energy of organisms.

OXIDATION. Living things are sometimes compared to engines. Engines run on the energy they extract from such fuels as coal, oil, or gasoline. Living things "run" on the energy they extract from carbohydrates, fats, and proteins. In both cases, the fuel or food is oxidized to obtain its stored energy. The process of combining a substance, such as a fuel or food, with oxygen is called *oxidation.* In engines the oxidation of fuels is quite rapid and results in the quick release of heat energy. In cells, however, the oxidation of foods occurs in a series of controlled stages at low temperatures.

Chemists recognize two other kinds of oxidation besides the direct combination of a material with oxygen. In the early stages of oxidation of glucose, for example, some of the hydrogen atoms are removed from the 6-carbon glucose molecule. The removal of hydrogen atoms is a second form of oxidation. In this case, the hydrogen atoms later combine with oxygen to form water. A third kind of oxidation results from the release of electrons. In the cells, the energy of the electrons is then transferred to ATP by a special respiratory enzyme called a *cytochrome* (SITE-uh-krom). Oxidation, then, may be one of three kinds:

1. Chemical union with oxygen.
2. Loss of hydrogen atoms.
3. Loss of electrons.

CHEMISTRY OF RESPIRATION. In 1780, Antoine Lavoisier, the French chemist, became the first to recognize that respiration was a form of oxidation. By using an ingenious apparatus, he measured the amount of heat released by a piece of burning coal in a given period of time. He then compared this amount with the heat given off by a guinea pig in another known period of time. After making the necessary calculations he concluded, "Respiration is . . . a combustion, very slow to be sure, but perfectly similar to that of carbon."

Much has been learned about respiration since Lavoisier's time. Although respiration may be thought of as the oxidation of food in the cells of plants and animals, it is far more complex than "a slow combustion." Respiration consists of a number of chemical reactions. Each reaction is controlled by a different enzyme.

If we omit the individual reactions, we can summarize the respiration of glucose by an over-all chemical equation:

$$C_6H_{12}O_6 + 6\,O_2 \rightarrow 6\,CO_2 + 6\,H_2O + \text{Energy}$$

glucose   oxygen   carbon   water
                      dioxide

Notice that this equation is the reverse of the summary equation for photosynthesis. Notice also that when glucose combines with oxygen to yield energy, two waste

COMPARISON OF PHOTOSYNTHESIS AND RESPIRATION

Photosynthesis	Respiration
Energy storing process.	Energy releasing process.
Solar energy is converted to stored chemical energy in food.	Stored chemical energy in food is converted to heat and useful high energy compounds (ATP).
Food is made from water and carbon dioxide.	Food is oxidized to form water and carbon dioxide.
Oxygen is a released by-product.	Oxygen is required to combine with food.
Performed by autotrophs that contain chlorophyll.	Performed by cells of heterotrophs and autotrophs.
Takes place in chloroplasts.	Takes place in mitochondria.
Takes place when light is available.	Takes place in the light or dark.

products form: *carbon dioxide* and *water*. The waste products of respiration are the raw materials of photosynthesis. It is the reversal of the energy flow during photosynthesis that builds carbon dioxide and water back into glucose. The "slow" oxidation of glucose in the cell is far from slow. A single enzyme controlling one step in respiration can "process" 100,000 molecules per second.

The complete oxidation of glucose into carbon dioxide and water involves more than twenty chemical reactions. These reactions are divided into three phases: *glycolysis* (glye-KOL-uh-sis), the production of *active acetate,* and the *Krebs cycle.*

GLYCOLYSIS. The glucose molecule ($C_6H_{12}O_6$) consists of a chain of six carbon atoms linked with atoms of hydrogen and oxygen. *Glycolysis* is the process in which glucose is split into two three-carbon fragments accompanied by the release of energy. No oxygen is used in the process.

Prior to being split, glucose undergoes several **activation reactions.** These activation reactions supply energy to the glucose so it can divide. As you know, a matchstick burns only after it has been heated by the burning phosphorus compounds at its tip. The heat of the burning tip raises the wood to its kindling point, an activation reaction. In much the same way, the glucose molecule adds a phosphate unit at each end of the molecule before breaking in two. Enzymes control the addition of phosphates.

The three-carbon fragments are then converted to pyruvic (pie-ROO-vic) acid ($C_3H_4O_3$). In this series of reactions, several hydrogen atoms are removed. The energy released in this oxidation is stored in four molecules of ATP. Since two ATP molecules are required to supply the energy for the activation reactions, glycolysis ends with a net gain of two ATP molecules.

Up to this point, the oxidation of glucose

has occurred without oxygen. *Anaerobic* (an-air-OH-bik) *respiration* is the oxidation of foods without the use of oxygen. Very little of the energy stored in glucose is released by this method of respiration. A few types of bacteria rely exclusively upon anaerobic respiration for their energy. Other organisms, like yeast, carry anaerobic respiration one step farther. Yeasts change pyruvic acid into alcohol by a process called **fermentation.** Under certain circumstances, anaerobic respiration may occur in body cells also. When there is a poor supply of oxygen in muscle cells because of extra exertion, pyruvic acid is changed to lactic acid. The accumulation of lactic acid causes fatigue.

ACTIVE ACETATE. The remaining phases of respiration require oxygen. *Aerobic* (air-OH-bic) *respiration* is oxidation in which oxygen is used. Several chemical reactions convert the three-carbon compound pyruvic acid into the two-carbon compound *active acetate.* Active acetate is linked with the compound *co-enzyme A.* A co-enzyme is a compound that helps another enzyme control a chemical reaction.

Active acetate is the critical compound in the oxidation of every type of organic molecule. Glucose is converted to active acetate before it enters the final phase of oxidation. Fats and certain amino acids are also changed to active acetate before they are completely oxidized. The preparation of active acetate is, therefore, one of the key reactions in the oxidation of organic molecules.

THE KREBS CYCLE. The third and final phase of respiration consists of a complex series of reactions called the **Krebs citric acid cycle.** The sequence of these reactions was traced by the English biochemist Sir Hans Krebs in 1937. For his important contribution to our understanding of respiration, Krebs was awarded a Nobel prize in 1953.

SUMMARY DIAGRAM OF RESPIRATION

$$C_6H_{12}O_6 + 6O_2 \longrightarrow 6CO_2 + 6H_2O + ENERGY (ATP)$$

Glucose   Oxygen   Carbon Dioxide   Water

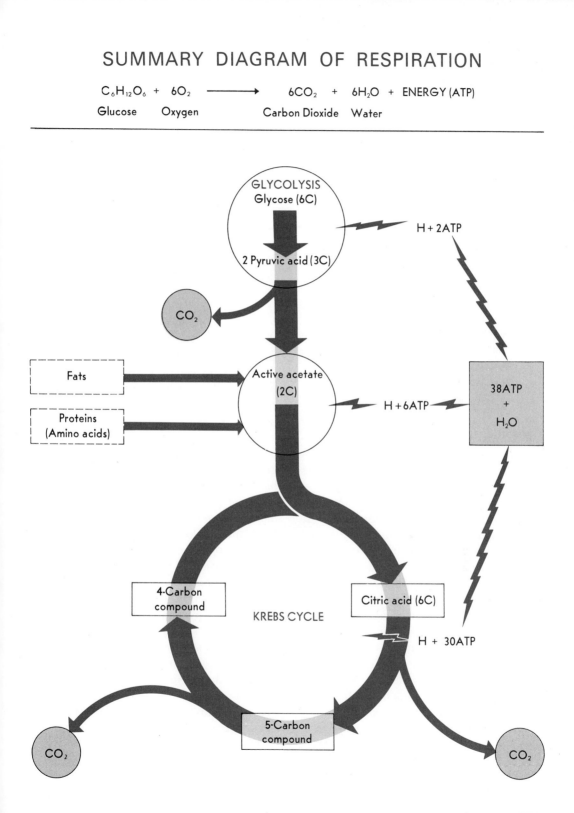

In the Krebs cycle the major part of the energy bound in glucose is released. Whereas glycolysis yields two ATP molecules, and the formation of active acetate yields six more, the reactions in the Krebs cycle yield 30. Thus, the complete oxidation of a glucose molecule yields a total of 38 ATP molecules for cellular energy.

Beginning with active acetate entering the Krebs citric acid cycle, the stages that follow may be summarized:

1. A 4-carbon compound unites with 2-carbon active acetate to form citric acid, a 6-carbon compound.
2. 6-carbon citric acid is converted to a 5-carbon compound, which is in turn converted to a 4-carbon compound.
3. The 4-carbon compound unites with 2-carbon active acetate to re-form 6-carbon citric acid, thus beginning the cycle again.

You will notice from the above steps that the Krebs cycle is a turning biochemical mill in which citric acid is endlessly decomposed and built up again. Coming out of the mill are energy rich ATP molecules plus carbon dioxide and water.

ROLE OF THE MITOCHONDRIA. As you already know from our discussion of the cell (Chapter 5), the structures in the cell where respiration occurs are the mitochondria. Biochemists have shown that it is within these "powerhouses" that the enzymes of respiration are located. The number of these tiny oval bodies scattered throughout the cytoplasm varies. A typical liver cell may have as many as 1000 mitochondria. One protist species, a large Ameba, contains half a million.

Enlarged several hundred thousand times by an electron microscope, a mitochondrion resembles a capsule made of a smooth outer membrane enclosing a wrinkled inner membrane. Thousands of buckshotlike particles lining both membranes are the enzyme particles that control the chemical reactions of respiration.

Mitochondria have been compared with chloroplasts. They resemble each other in structure, and both contain enzymes. Both deal with energy in the cell. While chloroplasts absorb light energy during photosynthesis, mitochondria release chemical energy during respiration.

BREATHING AND RESPIRATION. In common usage, the word "breathing" is frequently substituted for the word "respiration." To the physiologist, all respiration is cellular. It is in the cell that food is oxidized to yield energy.

The Ameba absorbs oxygen directly from the water in which it lives. The oxidation wastes of food are eliminated directly into the water. In complex animals, where millions of cells must be supplied with oxygen, special systems work together to bring oxygen to the cells.

Your blood contains one-fifth of an ounce of glucose. Each cell in your body takes the glucose and the oxygen it requires from the blood. Respiration occurs inside the cell, and energy is released. Water and carbon dioxide leave the cell and are carried to the lungs and exhaled into the air.

AUTOTROPHS AND OXYGEN. Oxygen is constantly used up in the process of respiration. Autotrophs, however, continually replenish the supply of this gas. Thus, autotrophs not only supply living things with food, but also supply the means for extracting the energy from that food. Oxygen makes up about one-fifth of the atmosphere. Yet, all the oxygen in the atmosphere would probably be used up by the respiration of organisms in about 2000 years if it were not continually being replaced by autotrophs.

IMPORTANT POINTS

• Energy exists in many forms, including heat energy, radiant energy, and chemical energy. Energy can be converted from one form to another. It can also be stored or released. Chemical energy is stored in the bonds that unite atoms into molecules.

• Living things "run" on chemical energy which they obtain from foods. The transfer of energy in cells is performed by the important compounds ADP and ATP. Energy poor ADP receives bond energy as it unites with a third phosphate unit and is converted to energy rich ATP. ATP yields energy for the work of the cell and is converted back to ADP.

• Foods are manufactured by autotrophic organisms during the process of photosynthesis. Photosynthesis captures the radiant energy of the sun and converts it to the chemical energy of foods. Acting as a catalyst, the green pigment chlorophyll causes carbon dioxide to unite with water to form the primary food glucose.

• Photosynthesis is a complex process consisting of many individual reactions. Active scientific research has identified many of the reactions in photosynthesis although the process cannot yet be duplicated.

• Respiration is the process whereby the chemical energy of foods is released in living things. Principally, it is the oxidation of glucose in three phases: glycolysis, the production of active acetate, and the Krebs cycle. The phases of respiration occur in the mitochondria of the cell and proceed step by step under enzyme control.

• Chloroplasts and mitochondria resemble each other. Both contain enzymes that control the chemical reactions in which these structures play a part. Chloroplasts absorb radiant energy during photosynthesis. Mitochondria release energy during respiration.

REVIEW QUESTIONS

1. Give two examples of the conversion of energy from one form to another.
2. In what part of the green plant does most of the photosynthesis take place?
3. What is the role of chlorophyll in photosynthesis?
4. Why are mitochondria called the "powerhouses" of the cell?
5. What is the difference between respiration and breathing?
6. Show by chemical equations that photosynthesis and respiration are the opposite of each other.
7. What additional foods do plants make besides glucose?
8. Enzymes may be compared to assembly line workers. Expain why.
9. Compare chloroplasts with mitochondria.

CHECK YOUR UNDERSTANDING

10. Lavoisier called respiration "a slow combustion." What is the basis for this idea?

11. In one experiment, a plant released as much oxygen on a dull day as it did on a brighter day. Can you explain this result?
12. Explain why a food chain is also an energy chain.
13. What are grana?
14. What are the functions of ADP and ATP in the cell?
15. Photosynthesis and respiration have been called the two stages in "the energy cycle of life." Interpret this statement.
16. What is meant by aerobic and anaerobic respiration?
17. Dr. Eugene I. Rabinowitch, a biochemist, has stated that, "All the animals on land and in the sea, including man, are but a small brood of parasites living off the great body of the plant kingdom." Can you explain this statement?
18. The giant squid lives deep in the sea and spends much of its time in total darkness. Explain how it gets its energy from the sun.
19. During athletic activity we breathe rapidly. During sleep we breathe slowly. Explain why.
20. Can you trace the energy of electricity in your home to the radiant energy of the sun?
21. A mouse will soon die of suffocation in a sealed jar, but will remain alive much longer if the jar also contains a green plant. Since plants as well as animals require oxygen for respiration, how does the addition of the plant help keep the mouse alive?

RESEARCH PROJECTS AND REPORTS

1. Obtain information from your school or public library and prepare a report on one of the following topics:

Joseph Priestley and Oxidation	**Enzymes and Their Action**
Photosynthesis Research	**Mitochondria**

2. *Products of Oxidation:* Hold a clean glass plate directly above a burning candle. After a few seconds examine the surface of the plate. Can you explain the black deposit on the glass? Repeat the experiment by placing the candle in a bottle of pure oxygen. When the flame dies out examine the plate again. Can you explain the difference in the appearances of the plate?

3. *Modified van Helmont Experiment:* Dry a quantity of soil sufficient to fill a tumbler by heating it in an oven. Weigh the soil accurately and replace it in the tumbler. Carefully weigh a lima bean and plant it in the tumbler of soil. Place the tumbler in a sunny spot and water daily. With good care the lima bean should germinate and grow into a fair sized seedling in a period of three weeks to a month.

  When the young plant is about 10 inches high, remove it from the soil, being careful not to break its roots. Weigh the plant and compare its weight with the seed from which it grew. How much did it gain?

  Remove all the soil from the tumbler, dry again in the oven, and reweigh it. Compare its loss in weight with the seedling's gain.

  Can you account for the increase in the weight of the plant?

FURTHER READING

"**The Mechanism of Photosynthesis.**" R. P. Levine. *Scientific American,* December, 1969, page 58. For the advanced student, a very thorough explanation of the complicated series of chemical reactions that result in the production of carbohydrates in cells.

"**How Cells Transform Energy.**" Albert L. Lehninger. *Scientific American,* September, 1961, page 63. For the advanced student. A clear and complete explanation of the process of respiration.

"**How Light Interacts With Living Matter.**" Sterling B. Hendricks. *Scientific American,* September, 1968, page 175. Among other life processes, the author discusses how light activates photosynthesis.

Cells and Energy. Richard A. Goldsby. The Macmillan Company, New York, N.Y. An advanced account of the complex chemical reactions of the cell and their dependence upon energy.

"**The Membrane of the Mitochondrion.**" Efraim Racker. *Scientific American,* February, 1968, page 32. Explains the role of the mitochondrion in the metabolism of the cell.

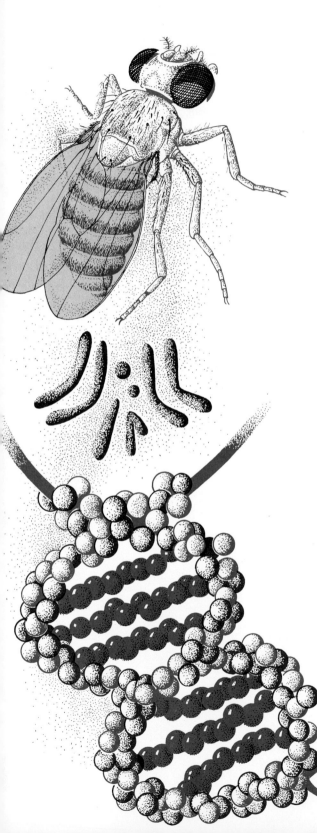

The Stream of Life

THE DEVELOPMENT OF LIFE is a paradox blended from two dissimilar facts: Living things exhibit a remarkable diversity, yet they have a fundamental similarity. More than a million and a half species of organisms now inhabit the earth. Add to this number the thousands of species that have become extinct, and this picture of diversity is considerably enlarged. Organisms vary in complexity from the simplest bacteria to man. But for all its diversity, there is a basic sameness to the stream of life—a sameness found in the biochemistry of living systems.

The numerous branches of the stream of life have appeared upon an earth that at one time could support no life at all. The primitive earth had no oceans, no atmospheric oxygen, no soil. Several billions of years elapsed before the earth could support even the simplest forms of life. Like a mountain stream whose origin is lost among freshets of melting snow, the origin of the stream of life is hidden by the vast span of time and by man's uncertainty about the conditions that produced the first living things. However obscurely life began, during several additional billion years a huge panorama of living things emerged.

What factors operating over a vast time span produced this diversity of life? Were the various forms of life created as they exist today? Or did they gradually change as they descended from the earliest living forms? What mechanisms have provided for the continuance of life's similarity while also providing for its change and diversity?

These questions have occupied man's thoughts for centuries. The early Greek philosophers, knowing little of the earth's great age, believed that living things arose spontaneously. Almost two thousand years later the experiments of Francesco Redi and Louis Pasteur discredited this theory of spontaneous generation. In 1859 Charles Darwin proposed the theory of evolution by natural selection to explain how the different forms of life arose. However, Darwin made no attempt to describe how the differences among living things began originally.

In the twentieth century, great advances have been made by biologists who have studied the process of reproduction. These scientists have been able to explain how the similarity of living things is preserved from generation to generation. These same biologists have also discovered the means by which slight changes occur in the hereditary material. Through millions of years, these slight changes have accumulated to produce radical differences in today's living forms. Likeness and diversity have woven the web of life we now witness on this planet.

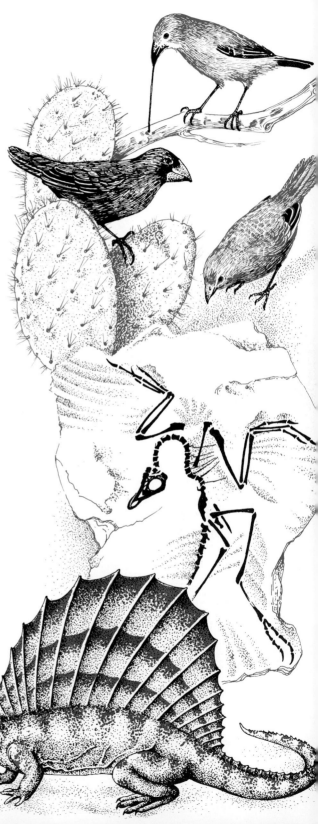

CHAPTER

8

Chromosomes and Genes

THE RESEMBLANCE between parents and their offspring is a common observation. The stream of life flows with a pattern of likeness from one generation to the next. However, there is also a pattern of difference. The offspring of the same parents are not all the same. Brothers are not identical, nor are sisters.

Heredity is the transmission of traits from one generation to another. *Genetics* is the branch of biology dealing with the mechanism of heredity. Genetics seeks to explain heredity in terms of biological processes. Modern genetics dates from the beginning of the 20th century, when the work of Gregor Mendel, an Augustinian monk, was rediscovered and amplified.

Reproductive Cells

What is the bridge that spans the gap between one generation and the next? In all organisms where sexual reproduction occurs, this bridge is the fertilized egg cell. The sperm cell contains determiners that transmit the characteristics of the male parent. The egg cell contains determiners that transmit the characteristics of the female

parent. The fertilized egg, formed by the union of sperm cell and egg cell, contains determiners from both parents and is thus a combination of both.

Reproductive cells contain half the number of chromosomes found in normal body cells. The human sperm cell, for example, contains 23 chromosomes. The human egg cell also contains 23 chromosomes. When the fertilized egg, or zygote, is formed, the number of chromosomes is increased to 46. Mitotic divisions of the zygote begin the formation of the embryo. Each of the cells formed by these divisions contains 46 chromosomes. When these 46 chromosomes are examined closely, it is observed that they are not all different. They can be arranged into 23 *homologous* (hoh-MOL-uh-gus) *pairs.* Each member of a homologous pair of chromosomes may be described as either paternal (originating in the sperm cell) or maternal (originating in the egg cell). In general, members of a pair of homologous chromosomes are the same shape and size, and control the same developmental processes.

The processes of genetics are intimately concerned with the formation and growth of

1 2 3 4 5 6   x   1 2 3 4 5 6   x

7 8 9 10 11 12   7 8 9 10 11 12

13 14 15 16 17 18 19 20 21 22 y   13 14 15 16 17 18 19 20 21 22

8–1 The 46 chromosomes in the body cells of a human male (left) and female (right). The chromosomes, which have been stained and separated, are arranged in homologous pairs according to size. Note that each chromosome is double-stranded and that, with the exception of the male sex chromosomes, the members of each pair resemble each other. Mature sex cells have only 23 single-stranded chromosomes, one from each pair.

reproductive cells, or *gametes.* The production of mature gametes follows a somewhat similar pattern in all living things. In the life cycle of every sexually reproducing organism, mature gametes are produced only after a sequence of cell divisions known as *meiosis* (my-OH-sis). The first meiotic division, sometimes called *reduction division,* reduces the chromosome number to half. The second division in meiosis does not change the chromosome number. The result of the two divisions is four reproductive cells, each of which contains one member of each homologous pair.

SPERMATOGENESIS. In the common fruit fly, *Drosophila melanogaster,* the primary sex cells contain eight chromosomes, or four pairs of homologous chromosomes.

Since this is a small number in contrast with that found in other animals, we shall use this insect to illustrate *spermatogenesis* (sper-mat-uh-JEN-uh-sis), which is the process by which mature sperm cells are formed. The primary sex cells of Drosophila contain the 2N or *diploid number* of chromosomes. The mature male sperm cells, the gametes, contain the N or *haploid number* of chromosomes.

The male sex cells in which meiosis occurs are called *spermatocytes.* As a spermatocyte prepares to undergo meiosis, the nuclear material becomes granular in appearance and forms thin threads, the chromosomes. The homologous chromosomes then come together and wind around each other. This process is called synapsis.

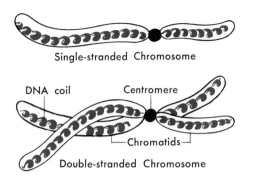

Single-stranded Chromosome

DNA coil   Centromere

Chromatids

Double-stranded Chromosome

8–2 The chromosomes of body cells have two strands (chromatids). The chromosomes of mature sex cells are single-stranded.

In *synapsis,* each member of a homologous chromosome pair joins with its partner so tightly it is difficult to identify the partners separately. During synapsis each chromosome pair *replicates.* Later, when the chromosomes are not so closely paired, each chromosome can be seen to consist of two *chromatids.*

The nuclear membrane has meanwhile disappeared, and a spindle has formed. The spindle threads are attached to the homologous chromosome pairs which arrange themselves in the middle of the spermatocyte. Each member of a homologous chromosome pair faces opposite ends of the cell, and is drawn to opposite ends of the spermatocyte by the spindle fibers. The nucleus re-forms and the cell is divided into two parts by a membrane formed midway between the opposite ends of the cell. This marks the end of the *first meiotic division.* Upon its completion the number of chromosomes has been reduced to half. Each of the two haploid cells resulting from the division contains only four chromosomes, one being from each of the four homologous pairs.

After a short interval, the nuclear membrane disappears and a spindle is again

formed. The chromosomes arrange themselves in the middle of the cell. Again the spindle fibers are attached. Now each chromatid part of the chromosome is drawn to an opposite pole of the cell. The nuclei are re-formed at each end of the cell. Each nucleus contains four chromatids, which are now called chromosomes. At the completion of this *second division of meiosis,* four cells have been formed from the original spermatocyte. Each of these cells is called a *spermatid.* A spermatid is an immature sperm cell containing the haploid (N) number of chromosomes. It contains one chromosome of each kind found in the primary sex cell.

Each of the spermatids undergoes further change in shape and appearance as it matures into a sperm cell. Often there is considerable reduction in the amount of cytoplasm. In many species of vertebrate animals the sperm cell has a characteristic tadpole shape consisting of sperm head and a long sperm tail. Generally, sperm cells are very small.

OOGENESIS. The corresponding process by which mature egg cells are formed is called *oogenesis* (oh-uh-JEN-uh-sis). The primary sex cells that form the egg cells are located in the ovary of the female, and each contains the diploid (2N) number of chromosomes.

The *oocytes* (OH-uh-sites) are the cells in which the first meiotic division occurs. Just as in spermatogenesis, the first meiotic division produces two cells, each cell containing half the original number of chromosomes. However, the two cells formed from the oocyte are unequal in size. Practically all of the cytoplasm remains in one cell. The small cell resulting from this unequal division is called the *first polar body.*

The second phase of meiosis results in the division of the first polar body into two very small haploid cells. Meanwhile, the large cell divides unequally to form a large

MEIOSIS. The process of meiosis consists of two successive cell divisions, during which the chromosome number is reduced to half. The special importance of meiosis is that it provides for the maintenance of inheritable variations among offspring of sexually reproducing species. As we shall see in chapter 45, their variations in turn provide the principal basis for evolutionary change. The sequence below shows chromosome reduction without crossing over. The sequence at the right illustrates crossing over.

1. For simplicity, only one pair of homologous chromosomes is shown. The white member of the pair is maternal. The red member is paternal.

2. The members of the pair come together in preparation for synapsis. During synapsis, each member of the pair replicates, forming four chromatids. Occasionally, crossing over occurs between a paternal and maternal chromatid (below).

SYNAPSIS
No crossing over

SYNAPSIS
Crossing over

3. First Meiotic Division. The synapsed pairs separate. The cell divides, and each member of the original pair is now a double chromosome consisting of two attached chromatids.

4. Second Meiotic Division. The chromatids in each daughter cell separate. The cells divide, and each chromatid passes to a different daughter cell. Note that there is no replication in this second division. At the end of the second division there are four cells, each of which contains one chromosome.

8–3 During meiosis, which occurs during the life cycle of all sexually reproducing organisms, two nuclear divisions occur. The first division results in the reduction of chromosomes from the diploid number (2N) to the haploid number (1N). The second division results in the segregation of chromosomes into different gametes or spores.

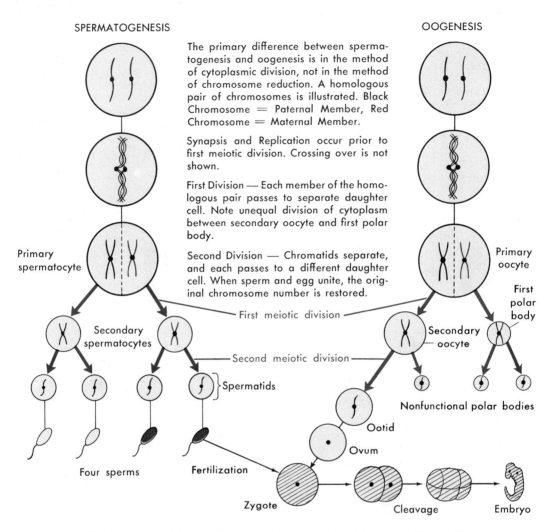

SPERMATOGENESIS

OOGENESIS

The primary difference between spermatogenesis and oogenesis is in the method of cytoplasmic division, not in the method of chromosome reduction. A homologous pair of chromosomes is illustrated. Black Chromosome = Paternal Member, Red Chromosome = Maternal Member.

Synapsis and Replication occur prior to first meiotic division. Crossing over is not shown.

First Division — Each member of the homologous pair passes to separate daughter cell. Note unequal division of cytoplasm between secondary oocyte and first polar body.

Second Division — Chromatids separate, and each passes to a different daughter cell. When sperm and egg unite, the original chromosome number is restored.

Primary spermatocyte

Primary oocyte

First polar body

First meiotic division

Secondary spermatocytes

Secondary oocyte

Second meiotic division

Spermatids

Nonfunctional polar bodies

Ootid

Ovum

Four sperms

Fertilization

Zygote

Cleavage

Embryo

8–4 Diagram of Certain Stages in the Maturation of Sperm and Egg Cells

ootid and a *second polar body.* Only the ootid develops into an ovum, or mature egg cell. Thus, each oocyte produces three nonfunctional polar bodies and one functional female gamete. By comparison, the spermatocyte produces four male gametes. In both spermatogenesis and oogenesis the result is the production of mature gametes containing the haploid number of chromosomes.

Chromosomes, Genes, and Alleles

Early in the twentieth century, geneticist Thomas Hunt Morgan and his students at Columbia University used Drosophila flies to investigate the laws of genetics. Since *Drosophila* has only four pairs of homologous chromosomes in its body cells, the chromosomes are easy to identify. More-

8–5 At the right are three homologous pairs of chromosomes illustrating three possible allelic gene combinations for eye color in fruit flies. Alleles are genes that control the development of a particular trait and occupy the same relative position on each chromosome of a homologous pair. When each gene of the allelic pair produces the same effect, they are said to be homozygous (1) and (2). When each gene of the allelic pair produces a different effect, they are said to be heterozygous (3).

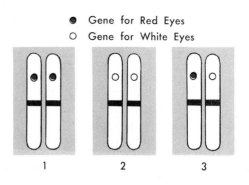

● Gene for Red Eyes
○ Gene for White Eyes

over, the flies reproduce rapidly, completing their development from egg to adult in about eleven days.

Millions of fruit flies were reared and examined. Their body traits were compared and grouped. Morgan and his students found that about four hundred traits could be grouped into four separate categories. The traits in each category always seemed to be inherited together, not separately. These observations confirmed the belief that chromosomes are composed of genes. A *gene* is a part of a chromosome that controls the development of a trait. At that time it was difficult to confirm the fact that chromosomes are made of smaller units. The optical microscope cannot reveal the detail necessary to see them. The electron microscope, however, has shown that chromosomes have a banded structure. These bands were believed to be the sites of the genes.

The traits that identify an organism are not always of simple genetic origin. The trait of tallness in people, for example, is due to a number of factors. Among these factors are the lengths of the lower leg, the thigh, and the torso. Thus, tallness in man is controlled by a number of genes, not just one. For the sake of simplicity in our explanations, however, we shall assume that each gene controls a single trait. Furthermore, since the chromosomes in normal body cells exist as homologous pairs, we shall assume

that one gene from each member of a homologous pair interacts with a corresponding gene to determine a trait.

Careful studies have shown that a gene that controls the development of a particular trait is located at a fixed distance from the end of the chromosome. In a corresponding position on the homologous chromosome is a second gene exercising control over the same trait. An *allele* (uh-LEEL) is one of a gene pair occupying the same site on homologous chromosomes and controlling the same hereditary trait.

Early studies showed that there were two eye colors in fruit flies. Wild flies generally had brick-red eyes, but some had white eyes. The two genes for eye color, red and white, are believed to be alleles. Three gene combinations for eye color are possible: (1) two red alleles, (2) two white alleles, or (3) one red and one white allele. Where both alleles are identical, the organism is said to be pure, or *homozygous* (hoh-moh-ZYE-gus), for that trait. If the alleles are different, the organism is said to be hybrid, or *heterozygous* (het-ur-oh-ZYE-gus), for that trait.

Mendel's Principles

The basic principles of genetics were already known in 1866. In that year Gregor Mendel published the results of crossing many generations of garden peas. For

TRAITS IN GARDEN PEAS STUDIED BY MENDEL

Dominant trait	Recessive trait
Round seed coat (R)	Wrinkled seed coat (r)
Yellow endosperm (Y)	Green endosperm (y)
Brown seed coat (B)	White seed coat (b)
Smooth seed pod (S)	Constricted seed pod (s)
Green pod (G)	Yellow pod (g)
Axial flowers (A)	Terminal flowers (a)
Tallness (T)	Shortness (t)

thirty-five years, however, Mendel's work received hardly any notice. Then in 1900 Hugo De Vries in Holland, Karl Correns in Germany, and Erich Tschermak in Austria found his almost forgotten work.

Mendel established certain rules for conducting his experiments that are models of scientific logic. He used a plant, the garden pea, that exhibited simple contrasting traits. By careful breeding, he isolated pure strains for particular traits. For example, many generations of tall plants were interbred to produce a pure tall strain. When pure tall plants were bred with pure tall plants, they always produced tall plants. A pure line of short plants was similarly established. At first Mendel limited his research to the study of one pair of contrasting traits at a time. Later, he studied two pairs of traits. Finally, he made a complete statistical analysis of the occurrence of traits in many generations of peas.

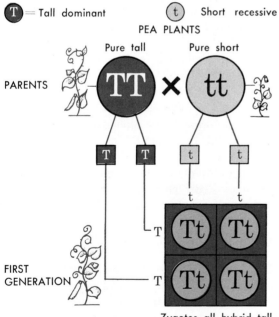

PEA PLANTS

Zygotes all hybrid tall

8–6 PRINCIPLE OF DOMINANCE. If two organisms with pure (homozygous), contrasting traits are crossed, all the offspring will generally exhibit only one of the traits. The trait that appears in the offspring is said to be dominant. The inherited—but concealed—trait is said to be recessive. In the example diagrammed at the left, each of the offspring received a gene for tallness (T) from one parent, and a gene for shortness (t) from the other parent. Since all the offspring are tall, tallness is dominant; shortness is recessive. All the offspring are hybrids for stem length; that is, each gene of the allelic pair controlling length acts in a different way.

DOMINANT AND RECESSIVE TRAITS. Mendel was able to identify seven pairs of contrasting traits in garden peas. In his first experiments he cross-pollinated two pure strains showing a contrasting trait. For example, he cross-pollinated flowers of short plants with pollen from tall plants, being careful not to permit any stray pollination. After the seeds developed, they were planted. The plants from these seeds were all tall.

All of the other pairs of contrasting traits yielded similar results. In each case one of the traits dominated or concealed the other. Mendel called this trait the *dominant trait.* The trait that was concealed he called the *recessive trait.* In the experiment with tall and short plants, tallness was dominant and shortness was recessive.

GENOTYPE AND PHENOTYPE. More recent information about meiosis enables us to diagram the results of Mendel's experiments. Tallness and shortness are alleles for plant size. We shall indicate the gene for tallness as capital *T,* since it is dominant. We shall indicate the gene for shortness as small *t,* since it is recessive.

In Figure 8–6 the normal cells of the pure tall plant are shown to contain two *T* genes,

one on each homologous chromosome. For simplicity, only one pair of chromosomes is shown. Similarly, the pure short plant is shown to contain two *t* genes. Note that the genes are identical in each parent, since each parent is pure (homozygous).

When gametes are formed by these parent plants, the number of chromosomes is halved. The gametes, therefore, contain only half the number of genes. The tall parent produces gametes containing one gene for tallness (*T*). The short parent produces gametes with one gene for shortness (*t*).

After the pollination of a short plant by a tall plant, the sperm nucleus (gamete) unites with the egg nucleus (gamete) in the ovule. The resulting zygote is a *Tt* combination. Since its alleles are dissimilar, it is called a *hybrid.* When such a hybrid seed is grown, the resulting plant is indistinguishable from a pure tall plant. Geneticists call this physical appearance of tallness the plant's *phenotype.* The phenotype

8–7 INCOMPLETE DOMINANCE. Mendel's Principle of Dominance does not apply to all hereditary traits. In some cases, neither of a pair of contrasting traits is dominant. The crossing of organisms homozygous for contrasting traits may result in offspring whose appearance is intermediate between the traits of the parents. A good example of incomplete dominance is found in Japanese four-o'clock flowers, which occur in red and white varieties. When a pure red (RR) is crossed with a pure white (WW), the offspring are all pink-flowered (RW). The pink flowered plants are all hybrids for color; that is, the allelic gene pair controlling the trait is heterozygous. Neither gene, however, is dominant over the other.

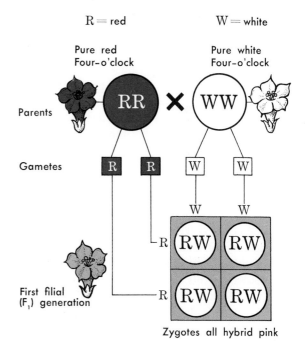

R = red   W = white

Pure red
Four-o'clock   Pure white
Four-o'clock

Parents   RR × WW

Gametes   R R   W W

First filial
(F₁) generation   R   W   W
    R   RW RW
    R   RW RW

Zygotes all hybrid pink

is the trait the observer can see. The genetic makeup, on the other hand, usually cannot be determined by observation. Genetic experiments are necessary to determine the genes present in the cells. The kinds of genes determine an organism's *genotype.* Thus, tallness is the phenotype of a hybrid tall plant, but its genotype is *Tt.*

INCOMPLETE DOMINANCE. Genetic experiments with other organisms have shown that alleles for contrasting traits are not always either dominant or recessive. When pure four-o'clock plants with red flowers are crossed with pure four-o'clock plants with white flowers, the resulting hybrids have pink flowers. Neither red nor white is dominant. The resulting pink color is due to the incomplete dominance of the red gene over the white gene. (See Figure 8–7.) Each plant and animal must be studied separately to establish the dominance of one allele over its partner.

THE PRINCIPLE OF SEGREGATION. Mendel established the facts that led him to formulate the *Principle of Segregation* by crossing hybrid plants and studying the results. Suppose pure *yellow-seeded* peas (*YY*) are crossed with pure *green-seeded* peas (*yy*). The offspring of this cross are called the first filial (F_1) generation. All are hybrids whose genotype is *Yy.* If these hybrids are crossed to produce the second filial (F_2) generation, the probability is that three-quarters of the offspring will be yellow-seeded and one quarter will be green-seeded.

When Mendel performed this experiment, he obtained 6,022 yellow-seeded plants and 2,001 green-seeded plants. Mendel found that the green-seeded plants bred true, but only one-third of the yellow-seeded plants bred true. The remaining two-thirds were hybrid.

If a gene diagram is used to explain this case, the observed results can be verified.

The gametes of the hybrid yellow-seeded plants contain either a *Y* gene or a *y* gene. When two hybrid plants are crossed, the resulting combinations in the zygotes are: *YY, Yy, Yy,* and *yy.* One-fourth of the plants are pure yellow, one-fourth are pure green, and one-half are hybrid yellow. Three-fourths of the phenotypes are yellow-seeded, exactly as Mendel observed.

Mendel's Principle of Segregation may be summarized as follows: *When hybrid plants are crossed, the recessive trait is segregated and appears in the next generation.* The ratio of the number of offspring with the dominant trait to the number of offspring with the recessive trait tends to be three to one.

Another illustration may serve to explain the principle even more clearly. When hybrid pink four-o'clocks are crossed, the probability is that one-quarter of the plants bear red flowers, one-quarter bear white, and the remaining half bear pink flowers. In this case, the ratio is 1:1:2. The genotype of hybrid pink four-o'clocks is *RW.* The gametes formed by a hybrid pink plant are of two types, either *R* or *W.* The zygotes formed are of the following genotypes: *RR, RW, RW,* and *WW.* The *RR* plant is red, the *WW* plant is white, and the two *RW* plants are hybrid pink. Another way of stating the Principle of Segregation in the light of modern genetics is: *The two members of a gene pair (alleles) separate when gametes are formed and act as independent units.*

THE PRINCIPLE OF INDEPENDENT ASSORTMENT. Mendel also investigated the results of crossing plants having two contrasting pairs of traits. In one case he crossed plants having *pure-yellow* and *pure-round* seeds with plants having *pure-green* and *pure-wrinkled* seeds.

In the first filial generation, the seeds of all the plants were yellow and round. These plants proved to be hybrid for both yellow-

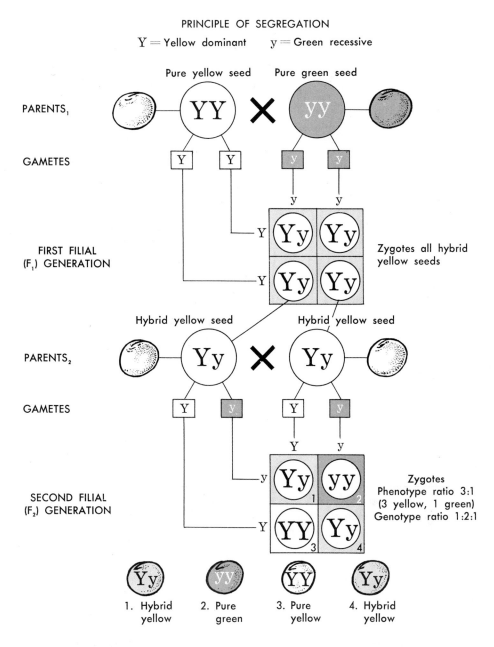

PRINCIPLE OF SEGREGATION

Y = Yellow dominant y = Green recessive

PARENTS₁

Pure yellow seed   Pure green seed

YY × yy

GAMETES

Y Y y y

FIRST FILIAL
(F₁) GENERATION

Yy Yy
Yy Yy

Zygotes all hybrid
yellow seeds

Hybrid yellow seed   Hybrid yellow seed

PARENTS₂

Yy × Yy

GAMETES

Y y Y y

SECOND FILIAL
(F₂) GENERATION

Yy yy
 1   2
YY Yy
 3   4

Zygotes
Phenotype ratio 3:1
(3 yellow, 1 green)
Genotype ratio 1:2:1

Yy yy YY Yy

1. Hybrid   2. Pure   3. Pure   4. Hybrid
   yellow   green   yellow   yellow

8–8 When two organisms homozygous for contrasting traits are crossed, the offspring of the F₁ generation are heterozygous and exhibit the dominant trait. In the gametes of the F₁ generation, however, the recessive genes are randomly segregated. When two of the F₁ offspring are crossed, the zygote may receive a pair of recessive genes. As a result, the recessive trait, which was hidden in the F₁ generation, may reappear in the F₂ generation. If a great number of F₁ hybrids were crossed, the offspring would show an average of three with the dominant trait for every one with the recessive trait.

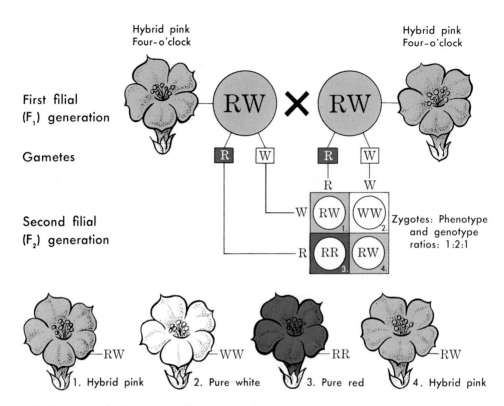

First filial (F₁) generation — Hybrid pink Four-o'clock **RW** × **RW** — Hybrid pink Four-o'clock

Gametes: R W   R W

Second filial (F₂) generation

	R	W
W	RW (1.)	WW (2.)
R	RR (3.)	RW (4.)

Zygotes: Phenotype and genotype ratios: 1:2:1

RW — 1. Hybrid pink   WW — 2. Pure white   RR — 3. Pure red   RW — 4. Hybrid pink

8–9 Crossing hybrid four-o'clocks results in the reappearance of contrasting traits in the F₂ generation. Compare genotype ratio with F₂ generation in Figure 8–8.

ness and roundness. Plants such as these that are hybrid for two traits are called **dihybrids.** When the dihybrids were crossed, the resulting second filial (F₂) generation consisted of nine *yellow-round,* three *green-round,* three *yellow-wrinkled,* and one *green-wrinkled.* Note that the ratio of yellow phenotypes to green is three to one. Note also that the ratio of round to wrinkled seeds is three to one. The three to one ratio is exactly what would have been expected if hybrid *yellow-seeded* plants had been crossed separately, or if hybrid *round-seeded* plants had been crossed separately. In other words, the traits acted in accordance with the Principle of Segregation even though they were originally combined in different parents.

Mendel's **Principle of Independent Assortment** may be stated as follows: *When dihybrid plants are crossed, there is an independent assortment of traits; the distribution of one pair of traits does not affect the other.* New combinations as well as old combinations occur, and every trait is inherited independently of every other trait.

The observed results can be verified by a gene diagram. The genotype of a dihybrid *yellow* and *round-seeded* plant is **Yy Rr.** The gametes produced by this hybrid are: **YR, Yr, yR** and **yr.** A systematic investigation of the results of the dihybrid cross may be made by preparing a sixteen-block square. The four gamete types are placed at the top of each column and to the left of each row. The sixteen possible combina-

PRINCIPLE OF INDEPENDENT ASSORTMENT

Key: Y = Yellow, dominant   y = Green, recessive
      R = Round, dominant   r = Wrinkled, recessive

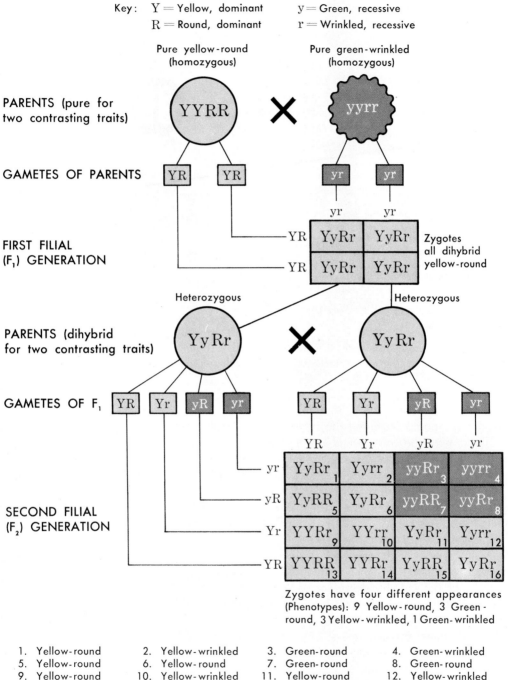

Zygotes have four different appearances
(Phenotypes): 9 Yellow-round, 3 Green-
round, 3 Yellow-wrinkled, 1 Green-wrinkled

1. Yellow-round	2. Yellow-wrinkled	3. Green-round	4. Green-wrinkled
5. Yellow-round	6. Yellow-round	7. Green-round	8. Green-round
9. Yellow-round	10. Yellow-wrinkled	11. Yellow-round	12. Yellow-wrinkled
13. Yellow-round	14. Yellow-round	15. Yellow-round	16. Yellow-round

8-10 The Principle of Independent Assortment for two or more pairs of genes is limited to cases where the pairs of genes lie on different pairs of chromosomes.

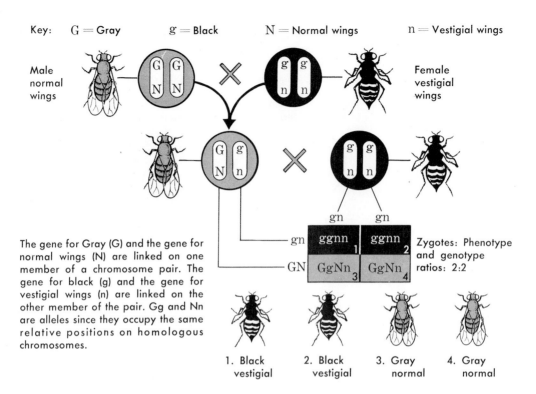

Key: G = Gray   g = Black   N = Normal wings   n = Vestigial wings

Male normal wings

Female vestigial wings

The gene for Gray (G) and the gene for normal wings (N) are linked on one member of a chromosome pair. The gene for black (g) and the gene for vestigial wings (n) are linked on the other member of the pair. Gg and Nn are alleles since they occupy the same relative positions on homologous chromosomes.

	gn	gn
gn	ggnn 1	ggnn 2
GN	GgNn 3	GgNn 4

Zygotes: Phenotype and genotype ratios: 2:2

1. Black vestigial   2. Black vestigial   3. Gray normal   4. Gray normal

8–11 When a dihybrid cross is made involving linked genes, the ratios depart from what might be expected from the combination of two independently assorting pairs.

tions are composed by filling the intersecting blocks with the column and row headings. The results of this genetic analysis confirm the 9:3:3:1 ratio Mendel discovered to be true of a dihybrid cross.

Another way of stating the Principle of Independent Assortment is: *The members of each gene pair separate freely from each other and from other gene pairs when gametes are formed.* It is as though all of the traits of the individual are sorted into separate units to be reassembled later when fertilization occurs. This sorting out of traits and their random reassembly accounts for the wide differences observed in children of the same parents.

Mendel's Principle of Independent Assortment has undergone considerable mod-

ification since his day. Later investigations have shown that independent assortment of traits is only possible when the genes for these traits are on different chromosomes. The garden pea is now known to have seven pairs of homologous chromosomes. The seven traits studied by Mendel were located on different homologous pairs.

Modern Genetics

The gene diagrams we have used to explain Mendel's laws would have delighted that quiet, studious monk. He had no such explanations in mind, for chromosomes and genes were not part of his vocabulary. Our current knowledge of cell mechanics was not available to support his ideas during

Key: G = Gray   g = Black
       N = Normal-winged   n = Vestigial-winged

HOMOLOGOUS PAIR. The genes for body color and wing-length are linked.

SYNAPSIS. The chromosomes double and exchange parts on homologous chromatids.

FIRST DIVISION. One of the chromatids of each chromosome contains a portion of its homologous partner.

SECOND DIVISION. Note that gametes 2 and 3 offer new combinations of linked genes.

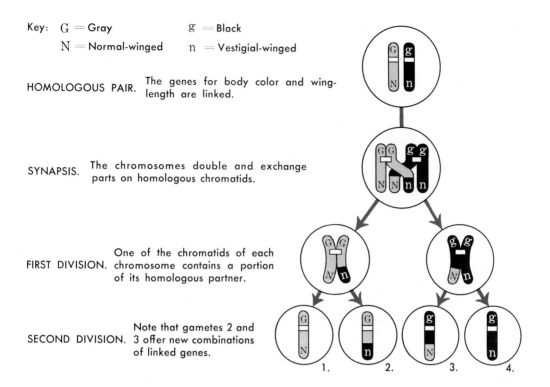

8–12 Linkage and Crossover. During meiosis, homologous chromosomes may exchange parts and produce new combinations of linked genes. The diagram above shows how a recombination of linked genes may occur during maturation of gametes in Drosophila.

his lifetime. The details of fertilization and the significance of meiosis were discovered later. The idea of gene localization in a specific position on the chromosome came much later.

GENE LINKAGE. Much of the credit for the gene-chromosome theory of genetics belongs to American biologists, such as Thomas Hunt Morgan. The fruit fly *Drosophila* has four pairs of homologous chromosomes. Three of them are quite large. The fourth is quite small. If one assumes that genes are located on chromosomes, we would expect that there are four separate groups of alleles corresponding to the four pairs of homologous chromosomes. Morgan found that many of the traits of *Drosophila* were inherited together. For ex-

ample, wing length and body color seemed to be transmitted as though the genes for these traits were located on the same chromosomes. Careful investigation of the more than four hundred fruit fly traits showed that there were four groups in exact agreement with the four pairs of homologous chromosomes. Genes may thus be thought to be *linked* to each other because they are on the same chromosome. A further confirmation of *gene linkage* came from the fact that three of the linkage groups in *Drosophila* were large and one was small, corresponding to the three large and one small pair of chromosomes.

CROSSING OVER. Certain unexpected genetic results led to the discovery of the phenomenon of **crossing over.** An example will serve to illustrate the results and the explanation for them.

In fruit flies gray body color (**G**) is dominant over black (**g**). Normal wings (**N**) are dominant over vestigial, or very short wings (**n**). Furthermore, body color and wing length are linked traits, their genes being on the same chromosome. When a pure gray, pure normal-winged fly (**GG NN**) is mated with a pure black, pure vestigial-winged fly (**gg nn**), all of the offspring are gray and have normal wings (**Gg Nn**).

Now suppose this dihybrid (**Gg Nn**) is mated with a pure black, pure vestigial-winged fly (**gg nn**). If the genes for the body color and for wing length are located on the same chromosome, we would expect to obtain two types of offspring: (1) gray, normal-winged and (2) black, vestigial-winged. When Morgan performed this experiment, the results were rarely in the expected ratio of one to one. Usually, about 83 per cent of the offspring exhibited this ratio. The remaining 17 per cent were evenly divided between gray, vestigial-winged flies and black, normal-winged flies. The last two combinations were entirely unexpected.

To account for these results one must assume that there is an exchange of part of one homologous chromosome with a corresponding part of its partner. It is well known that homologous chromosomes coil closely about each other (synapsis) during the early stages of meiosis. The chromosomes appear as double strands (chromatids). The two homologous strands, or chromatids, break at the same place. The end pieces become attached to the other chromatid. The genes on these remade chromatids now have new gene neighbors. The process by which new gene linkages are thus formed is called crossing over. As a result of crossing over, genes inherited by an individual from the female parent and the male parent can recombine in that individual and be transmitted to the third generation on the same chromosome. Crossing over, therefore, increases the variety of offspring. (See Figure 8–12.)

The percentage of unexpected offspring resulting from crossing over cannot be predicted exactly. Two factors control the process. First, the genes must be on homologous chromosomes. Second, the distance between two genes determines the frequency with which crossing over will occur. The farther two genes are apart, the greater the likelihood that crossing over will occur between them.

SEX DETERMINATION AND SEX-LINKED TRAITS. One pair of chromosomes in humans and many animals has been identified with sex determination. In the female fruit fly these chromosomes are identically rod-shaped and are designated as **XX**. In the male fly the sex chromosomes are not iden-

8–13 Chromosomes of Male and Female Drosophila

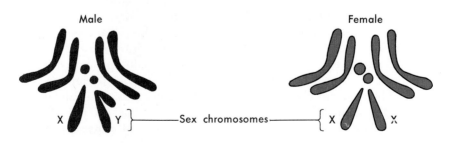

Male   Female

X Y } ——Sex chromosomes——{ X X

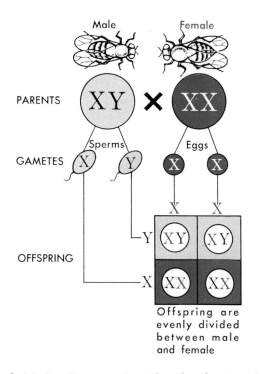

PARENTS

GAMETES

Sperms Eggs

OFFSPRING

Offspring are
evenly divided
between male
and female

8–14 Sex Determination. The identification of sex chromosomes in Drosophila provided the answer to the problem of sex inheritance. The diagram above illustrates that the sex of an offspring is determined at the time of fertilization and depends on whether the egg is fertilized by a sperm carrying an X chromosome or by a sperm carrying a Y chromosome. The zygote can receive only an X chromosome from the female parent.

tical; one is rod-shaped and designated as **X,** the other is shaped like a bent rod and is designated as **Y.**

What ratio will be obtained when fertilization occurs? All of the female gametes contain the **X** type. The male gametes contain either the **X** or **Y** type. Half of the male gametes contain a single **Y** chromosome; the other half carry a single **X** chromosome. When an **X**-type male gamete fertilizes the **X**-type female gamete, the result is **XX** or female. When a **Y**-type male gamete fer-

tilizes the **X**-type female gamete, the result is **XY** or male. From these facts, we can see that the sex of a person is a chance occurrence. A female gamete has a fifty-fifty chance of being fertilized by an **X**-bearing sperm or by a **Y**-bearing sperm. The number of offspring is evenly divided, therefore, between male and female.

Traits controlled by genes located on the sex chromosomes are said to be **sex-linked.** For example, in fruit flies the gene for red or white eyes is located on the **X** chromosome. In humans, the gene for color blindness is located on the **X** chromosome. Hemophilia, the disease in which excessive bleeding occurs, is also controlled by a gene on the **X** chromosome.

NONDISJUNCTION OF CHROMOSOMES. Early experiments with sex-linked traits helped establish that genes are located on particular chromosomes. One series of experiments was performed by Calvin Bridges, a graduate student of Thomas Hunt Morgan at Columbia University in 1916.

If you have worked out the problem indicated in Figure 8–16, you found that half the progeny are white-eyed males. The remaining half are red-eyed females. Working with a similar cross, Bridges found that his experimental results agreed almost exactly with this prediction. When the offspring were carefully counted, however, one or two per thousand were exceptional. *The exceptional offspring were either red-eyed males or white-eyed females.*

How could these exceptional results be explained? One possibility was that the genes themselves had undergone change. Bridges considered this possibility, but he rejected it since the rate of change was too high. Other changes in gene structure were known to occur at the rate of only about one in 100,000.

Bridges found the explanation in an unusual event during meiosis. In meiosis (see

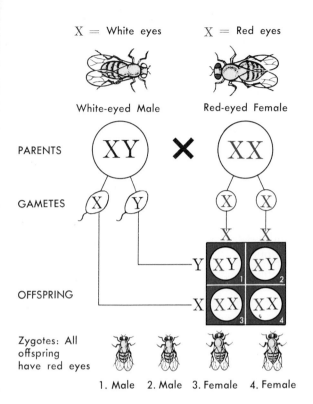

X = White eyes   X = Red eyes

White-eyed Male   Red-eyed Female

PARENTS   XY   ✕   XX

GAMETES   X   Y   X   X

OFFSPRING

	X	X
Y	XY 1	XY 2
X	XX 3	XX 4

Zygotes: All offspring have red eyes

1. Male   2. Male   3. Female   4. Female

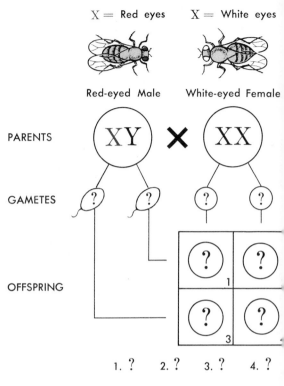

X = Red eyes   X = White eyes

Red-eyed Male   White-eyed Female

PARENTS   XY   ✕   XX

GAMETES   ?   ?   ?   ?

OFFSPRING

?	? 1
? 3	?

1. ?   2. ?   3. ?   4. ?

8–15 In Drosophila, the genes for red eye color or white eye color are located on the X chromosome and are, therefore, sex-linked. In sex-linked inheritance, the traits of the offspring depend on the sex of the parent that had the particular trait. This explains why certain traits appear more frequently in one sex than in the other.

8–16 If a red-eyed male is crossed with a white-eyed female, the resulting offspring will tend to be different than those obtained from the cross illustrated in 8–15 above. Can you predict the eye color and sex of the offspring resulting from the cross diagrammed at the right? Use a piece of scratch paper and fill in the diagram. Do not write on this page.

Figure 8–3), the members of a pair of homologous chromosomes divide to form four chromatids. Under normal conditions, each chromatid separates, or *disjoins*, from the others. Each chromatid then becomes one of the set of N chromosomes in a gamete. In rare cases, the chromatids do not disjoin. *Nondisjunction* is the lack of separation of chromatids during meiosis.

In the white-eyed female *Drosophila*, nondisjunction produces an egg cell that either lacks an X chromosome or has two

X chromosomes. (See Figure 8–17.) When fertilized by normal sperm cells, these egg cells produce the following combinations: $X_R\ X_r\ X_r$, X_R, $X_r\ X_r\ Y$, and Y. Thus, half the offspring have an extra chromosome, and half lack a chromosome.

Bridges was able to test this hypothesis by direct observation of the chromosomes. He discovered that the red-eyed females were $X_R\ X_r\ X_r$. The white-eyed female was $X_r\ X_r\ Y$. The red-eyed male was X_R. The offspring having only a Y chromosome

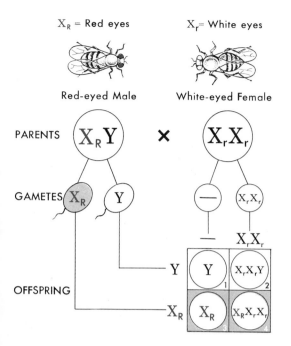

X_R = Red eyes X_r = White eyes

Red-eyed Male   White-eyed Female

PARENTS $X_R Y$ × $X_r X_r$

GAMETES X_R Y — $X_r X_r$

OFFSPRING

8–17 Nondisjunction in Drosophila. Note that the members of the $X_r X_r$ chromosome pair in the white-eyed female fly fail to disjoin when the gametes are formed. This nondisjunction allows for the appearance of a red-eyed male (X_R) and a white-eyed female ($X_r X_r Y$). If the $X_r X_r$ chromosomes had separated during meiosis, you could not have a red-eyed male or a white-eyed female.

died in an early stage of development. As a result of these observations, our theory of sex determination has been modified. Two or more **X** chromosomes produce a female. A single **X** chromosome produces a male. However, a male lacking the **Y** chromosome is sterile.

MULTIPLE FACTORS: CONTINUOUS TRAITS. Each of the seven pairs of traits studied by Mendel in garden peas was discontinuous. A *discontinuous trait* has two specific alternatives and lacks intermediate values. The seed, for example, is either yellow or green. The stem is either tall or short.

Many of the traits observed in living things display a range of intermediate values. Men are not just tall or short. Height in man is a continuously variable trait from extreme tallness to extreme shortness. A *continuous trait* exhibits a range from one extreme to another.

Gene theory easily explains discontinuous traits. How do we account for the continuous traits of living things in terms of genes?

Biologists use the following assumptions to explain continuous traits:

1. Continuous traits are believed to result from the interaction of more than one pair of alleles.
2. Each allele is incompletely dominant.

To illustrate how a continuous trait might be produced genetically, let us construct a theory about height determination in man. For simplicity, assume that one pair of alleles, F_L and F_S, determines the length of the femur. Another pair, T_L and T_S, can be assumed to determine the length of the tibia. The genotype of the very tall man might then be $F_L F_L, T_L T_L$. The corresponding genotype for the very short man would be $F_S F_S, T_S T_S$. An intermediate type of tallness would be $F_L F_S, T_L T_S$.

Five classes of height can be discovered in the previous illustration. If height depends upon three pairs of alleles, it can be demonstrated that seven gradations of height should be observed. When many alleles determine a trait, a continuous distribution will result.

The Heredity of Man

Although human genetics is of more concern to us than the genetics of plants or animals, we know less about it than we do about the genetics of the fruit fly. Since man cannot be controlled like a laboratory animal, it is difficult to obtain necessary information. Observation of human traits and deficiencies indicates that all living things are subject to the same genetic laws.

TWINS AND HEREDITY. Geneticists recognize two kinds of twins: *identical* and *fraternal*. **Identical twins** are formed from a single egg, which divides into two halves after its genotype is set at fertilization. Since they are identical genotypes, these twins are always of the same sex and are strikingly similar in appearance. **Fraternal twins** develop from two different eggs, each fertilized by a separate sperm cell. They are no more alike than children of the same parents born at different times. They may be of the same sex or different sexes. About five of every six sets of twins are fraternal. Triplets, quadruplets, and quintuplets may develop from a single zygote or from several zygotes. Twins occur about once in every 100 births. Triplets occur about once in every 11,000 births. Quadruplets occur about once in every 900,000 births. The Dionne sisters of Canada

were identical quintuplets—an extraordinary chance occurrence.

Studies of identical twins provide opportunities for observing the relative effects of genotype and environment in determining traits. When blood types are compared, for example, they are always found to be the same in identical twins, but often not the same in fraternal twins. This fact suggests that blood type is genetically determined. Studies of cases of tuberculosis and poliomyelitis indicate that there is some genetic basis that predisposes certain people to these diseases. When one twin gets tuberculosis, the identical twin gets the same disease in about 74 per cent of the cases.

Mental traits and abilities can also be compared by studying identical twins. Schizophrenia, a mental disease, is coincident in about 86 per cent of the cases identified in identical twins. Some twin studies indicate that intelligence has a genetic basis. However, other studies of twins indi-

8–18 Since identical twins develop from the same zygote, they have identical genotypes. Differences that develop in later life are reasonably attributed to environment.

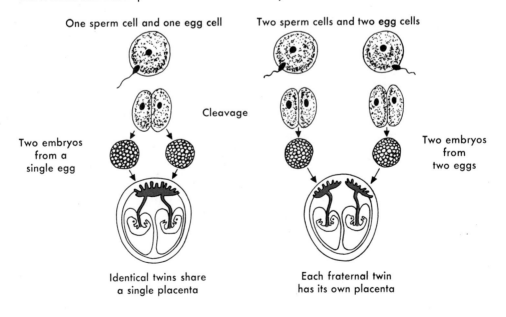

One sperm cell and one egg cell

Two sperm cells and two egg cells

Cleavage

Two embryos from a single egg

Two embryos from two eggs

Identical twins share a single placenta

Each fraternal twin has its own placenta

cate that environment is a stronger factor in the development of mental ability.

EYE COLOR. The color of the human eye is due to the pigments present on the front and back of the iris. If there is no pigment on either surface, the person has pink eyes and is called *albino. Albinos* carry genes that fail to produce skin, hair, and eye pigment.

8–19 Differences in eye color are due to differences in the development of brown pigment particles on the back and front of the iris. Newborn babies of every racial variety have blue eyes because the particles have not yet developed in the front of the iris.

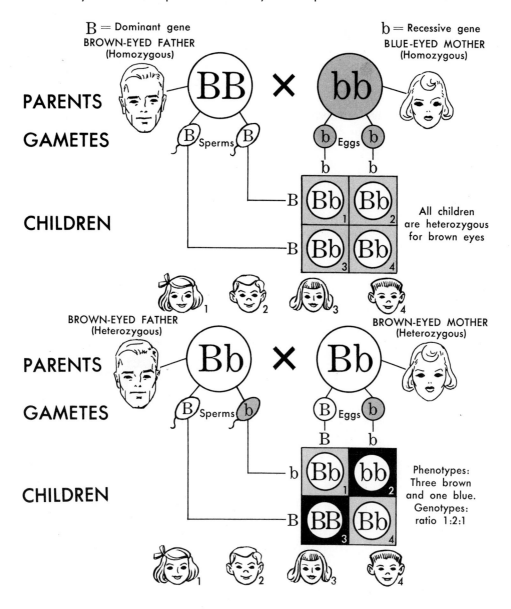

B = Dominant gene
BROWN-EYED FATHER
(Homozygous)

b = Recessive gene
BLUE-EYED MOTHER
(Homozygous)

PARENTS   BB × bb

GAMETES   B Sperms B   b Eggs b

CHILDREN

All children are heterozygous for brown eyes

BROWN-EYED FATHER
(Heterozygous)

BROWN-EYED MOTHER
(Heterozygous)

PARENTS   Bb × Bb

GAMETES   B Sperms b   B Eggs b

CHILDREN

Phenotypes:
Three brown and one blue.
Genotypes:
ratio 1:2:1

The pink color of an albino's eyes is due to small blood vessels showing through the iris. If there is pigment only on the back of the iris, the person's eyes exhibit various shades of blue. When the front of the iris is also pigmented, the eye shows a color range from hazel to almost black.

There seem to be at least five pairs of genes responsible for the color of the human eye. One determines whether there will be any pigment at all. Another determines the amount of pigment in the front and back of the iris. Several other genes determine the density and distribution of the pigment.

The easiest way to think of eye color is that it is controlled by dominant brown and recessive blue alleles. Blue-eyed people are always homozygous, **bb**. Brown-eyed people are either homozygous, **BB**, or heterozygous, **Bb**. The children of a homozygous brown-eyed father and a blue-eyed mother are all brown-eyed. If the parents are both brown-eyed heterozygotes, **Bb**, the chances are that one-fourth of their children will have blue eyes. This reappearance of the blue-eyed phenotype is due to the segregation of the recessive genes in accordance with Mendel's principle.

COLOR BLINDNESS. A common form of *color blindness* is the red-green type in which the individual cannot distinguish between these two colors. Color blindness is a *sex-linked*, recessive trait controlled by a gene located on the X chromosome. A homologous gene for normal color vision is

8–20 Red-green color blindness is a result of a defective gene on the X chromosome. In the example shown, can you explain why none of the daughters and half of the sons are color-blind?

X = Chromosome with gene for color blindness.

1. Color blind son   3. Carrier daughter
2. Normal son   4. Normal daughter

8–21 Since the gene for normal vision is dominant and the gene for color blindness is recessive, a woman will be color-blind only when she inherits a recessive gene from her mother and from her father.

X = Chromosome with gene for color blindness.

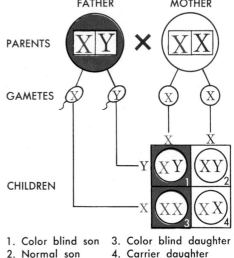

1. Color blind son   3. Color blind daughter
2. Normal son   4. Carrier daughter

also found on the X chromosome. The Y chromosome has no genes for color vision. If we designate the color blindness gene as **X**, and the normal color vision gene as **X**, we can identify the following genotypes:

XX = female with normal color vision

XX = female with normal color vision, but a carrier of the trait of color blindness

XY = male with normal color vision

XY = male, color blind

XX = female, color blind

Color blindness is much more common among men than among women, since the female must have both recessive genes for the defect in order to exhibit it. Among white males, about 8 out of every 100 lack the ability to distinguish red and green. Less than 1 out of every 200 women suffer from the same defect. It is possible for a carrier mother with normal color vision and a father with normal color vision to have color blind sons.

HEMOPHILIA. *Hemophilia* is a condition in which a deficiency of blood-clotting factors results in excessive bleeding. Like color blindness, the trait is believed to be caused by a defective recessive gene on the X chromosome. Few authentic cases of hemophilia in women have been reported. The defect is found almost exclusively in men.

Women with normal blood-clotting reactions may be carriers of hemophilia, a notable illustration being Queen Victoria of

8–22 Hemophilia is due to a mutation in the gene controlling blood clotting. Like color blindness, the trait is sex-linked, recessive on the X chromosome.

8–23 A female will be a "bleeder" only if both her father and her mother's father had the disease. Female carriers can now be identified by special blood tests.

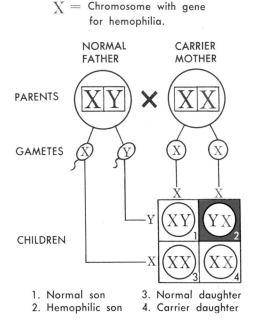

X = Chromosome with gene for hemophilia.

1. Normal son
2. Hemophilic son
3. Normal daughter
4. Carrier daughter

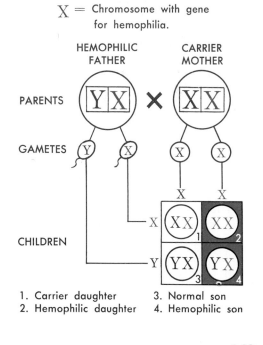

X = Chromosome with gene for hemophilia.

1. Carrier daughter
2. Hemophilic daughter
3. Normal son
4. Hemophilic son

England. Victoria is reported to have transmitted the condition through her daughters to the ruling families of Spain and Russia. Careful statistical studies indicate that one person in ten thousand is hemophilic. About 30 per cent of its victims have no traceable family history of the condition. In such cases, the defective gene is probably a new mutant.

For a female to suffer from hemophilia, it would be necessary for her to inherit a defective gene on her mother's X chromosome and a defective gene on her father's X chromosome. Since a father with a defective gene for blood clotting does not pass on his X chromosomes to his sons, the sons of a hemophilic father never suffer from the disorder—except in the rare event that the father married a carrier. The daughters of a hemophilic father transmit the defective X chromosome to about half their sons and half their daughters.

BLOOD-TYPE INHERITANCE. Three genes control the inheritance of blood-group types. These may be called *A*, *B*, and *a*. Both *A* and *B* are dominant to *a*, but are incompletely dominant to each other. The genotype of each blood group is then:

AA or *Aa* = blood type *A*

BB or *Ba* = blood type *B*

AB   = blood type *AB*

aa   = blood type *O*

The determination of the possible blood groups of children can be made if the parental blood types are known. Suppose the father is type *A* and the mother is type *O*. If the father is *AA*, the gametes would be A. If the father is *Aa*, the gametes would be either *A* or *a*. The gametes of the mother would be only *a*. The resulting combinations for the children could only be *Aa* or *aa*, that is, type *A* or type *O* blood.

INHERITANCE OF BLOOD TYPES

The table shows the blood types that occur in children when the parental blood types are known. Also shown are the blood types that are not possible.

Parents	Children	Impossible types
O × O	O	A, B, AB
O × A	O, A	B, AB
O × B	O, B	A, AB
A × A	A, O	B, AB
A × B	A, B, AB, O	None
B × B	B, O	A, AB
O × AB	A, B	AB, O
A × AB	A, B, AB	O
B × AB	A, B, AB	O
AB × AB	A, B, AB	O

RH FACTOR. The *Rh factor*, or Rhesus factor, is another genetically controlled trait of human blood. *Rh-positive* individuals have the same Rh antigen on their red corpuscles as the Rhesus monkey. In the United States about 85 per cent of the population is Rh-positive, and the remaining 15 per cent is *Rh-negative*. Rh-negative individuals lack the Rh antigen. Among Oriental people, especially the Chinese, individuals with Rh-negative blood are almost unknown.

The marriage of an Rh-positive man to an Rh-negative woman can cause serious problems if an Rh-positive child is conceived. The problem is usually not great with the first child. If the second child also has Rh-positive blood, the antibodies produced by the mother during the first pregnancy may be sufficient to cause the child's death; and in about one case in twenty, death does result.

The Rh-positive parent may be either homozygous for the trait (RR) or heterozygous (Rr). The Rh-negative parent is homozygous for this recessive trait (rr).

The children resulting from the marriage of an Rh-positive man and Rh-negative woman will be Rh-positive (Rr) if the father is homozygous. If the father is heterozygous, the children will be either Rh-positive or Rh-negative.

IMPORTANT POINTS

• Heredity is the transmission of traits from parents to offspring. Genetics is the science that deals with the mechanisms of heredity.

• The chromosomes are the carriers of the hereditary material. The zygote, formed by the union of an egg cell and sperm cell, contains pairs of homologous chromosomes. One member of each pair is maternal in origin, the other paternal.

• During the formation of gametes, the normal number of chromosomes is reduced by half during the nuclear process called meiosis. The union of the gametes at the time of fertilization restores the full number of chromosomes.

• The traits of an organism are controlled by localized parts of chromosomes called genes. At least two companion genes, called alleles, located on similar sites of homologous chromosomes control a given trait. Some traits are controlled by numerous genes. A pure trait is controlled by two identical genes. When the genes for a given trait are not the same, the organism is said to be hybrid for that trait.

• Gregor Mendel formulated the basic laws of genetics. He identified the dominance of certain traits over others. He also discovered that the recessive traits in hybrids remain separate and reappear in succeeding generations.

• Twentieth century geneticists have modified Mendel's work in certain ways. All genes do not act independently, but are linked in groups corresponding to their location on specific chromosomes. The genes located on the sex chromosomes are said to be sex-linked.

• Calvin Bridges related chromosomes, genes, and traits by directly observing nondisjunction in the sex chromosomes of *Drosophila*.

• Continuous traits result from the interaction of several pairs of incompletely dominant alleles.

• Human traits are of genetic origin in many cases. Eye color, color blindness, hemophilia, and blood types are all genetically determined.

REVIEW QUESTIONS

1. Distinguish between heredity and genetics.
2. Compare the chromosome numbers of gametes and the zygote.
3. What relation exists between genes and chromosomes?
4. Give one example of a simple cross in garden peas that illustrates dominance.
5. Compare the genotype of a hybrid, tall, garden pea plant with its phenotype.
6. How does the crossing of hybrid pink four-o'clocks illustrate Mendel's Law of Segregation?
7. What is the genotype of a dihybrid, yellow, round-seeded pea plant?
8. Give three examples of human traits that are controlled by multiple genes.
9. What is the shape of the sex chromosomes of the female Drosophila in comparison with those of the male?
10. How did Bridges link the development of traits with chromosomes?
11. If three pairs of alleles determined the trait of tallness in man, how many grades of tallness would result?
12. List three human traits that are genetically determined.

CHECK YOUR UNDERSTANDING

13. Why must gametes hold the solution to the problem of transmitting hereditary traits?
14. Explain why meiosis is such an essential process in the development of gametes.
15. Diagram the result of a cross between a hybrid yellow-seeded pea plant with a pure green-seeded plant.
16. Diagram the result of self-pollinating a dihybrid tall yellow-seeded pea plant.
17. Show by a simple diagram the phenomenon of crossing over.
18. Show by a genetic diagram that it is impossible for the children of parents having A and AB type blood to have O type blood.
19. Sexual reproduction has been called the great adaptive mechanism in nature. How do you interpret this statement?
20. Under what circumstances can the son of a hemophilic father inherit the disease?

RESEARCH PROJECTS AND REPORTS

1. Obtain information from your school or public library and prepare a report on one of the following topics:

    Gregor Mendel   **Heredity versus Environment**

    Thomas Hunt Morgan   **Genetics and Evolution**

2. *Colchicine and Plants:* Colchicine can be purchased as a solution or a salve from biological supply houses. If you want to study the effect colchicine has upon flowering plants, keep at least one untreated plant as control. Apply colchicine to the other. Compare the plants to see the effects of the chemical.

3. *Taste Papers:* Not all people can taste the chemical phenyl thiocarbamide. Ask your teacher if you can make a study of this hereditary characteristic in a group of students. Select about ten and work out a plan to test them. Have them in turn test members of their families. When testing individuals, be careful not to suggest that they should taste something. The taste papers can be purchased from a biological supply house.

4. *Model of Meiosis:* Make a feltboard model with which you can explain meiosis to your class. Paste felt on a piece of carboard or masonite about three feet square. Make chromosomes out of pieces of felt about 4 inches long and one-half inch wide. Use Drosophila as your model for them. The chromosomes are pasted on the smooth side of sandpaper strips. The rough surface of the sandpaper makes them stick to the felt for demonstration purposes. They can be placed on the felt and lifted off with ease.

FURTHER READING

Evolution, Genetics, and Man. Theodosius Dobzhansky. John Wiley and Sons, New York, N.Y. A very clear account of genetic principles and the role of heredity in the evolutionary process.

The New You and Heredity. Amram Scheinfeld. J. B. Lippincott Co., Philadelphia, Pa. An interesting account of heredity as it applies to man.

Genetics, Heredity, Personality, and Environment. Warja Honegger, Hans Burla, and Marco Schnitter. Dell Publishing Co., New York, N.Y. A well-illustrated account, in color, of modern genetic principles with special emphasis on human applications.

Human Heredity. Ashley Montagu. World Publishing Co., Cleveland, Ohio. A balanced explanation of heredity and environment that contains a census of inherited disorders.

"Chromosomes and Disease." A. G. Bearn and James L. German III. *Scientific American*, November, 1961, page 66. Describes the advances made in chromosome study, and the connection between chromosome abnormalities and disease.

"General Tom Thumb and Other Midgets." Victor McKusick and David Rimoin. *Scientific American*, July, 1967, page 103. The history of a famous Barnum midget is analyzed and the condition traced to recessive genes.

9

Chemical Genetics

During the first half of the twentieth century, the chromosome theory of inheritance was firmly established as the cornerstone of modern genetics. The genes were recognized as the parts of chromosomes that controlled the processes by which the characteristics of an organism developed. How were the genes able to transform the fertilized egg into the organism? How did the genes provide instructions for making the organism? What special characteristic did the molecules in genes possess that could direct the growth of a plant or animal? Questions such as these have been crucial for biochemists for the last two decades.

The second half of the twentieth century began the era of molecular biology. Prior to this time, the principal concern of biochemists was the analysis of living systems. Organisms were carefully taken apart to determine what they were made of. Now the direction of research shifted. Today, biochemists investigate the methods by which molecules direct the construction of an organism. The fact that an organism is alive is an expression of the molecules that compose it.

For many years, biologists have been searching for the chemical that controls the life process in the nucleus. In 1869, the German chemist Friedrich Miescher extracted a substance from white blood cells which he called *nuclein* (NOO-klee-in). Miescher thought that he had discovered the hereditary compound, but was unable to prove it. It has taken almost a century for chemists to identify what nuclein really was. Today we know that nuclein was mostly DNA. Miescher is generally given credit for having discovered the most important compound of life.

THE CHEMICAL NATURE OF CHROMOSOMES. How would you set about trying to find out what chromosomes are made of? You would first have to devise a method of separating the nucleus from cells. Then, you would have to devise still another method to separate the chromosomes from other nuclear material. After that, all the methods of analysis must be used to determine what chemicals the chromosomes contain. Proceeding in this manner, chemists learned that chromosomes consist of two main substances, protein and DNA.

What is the relation between the protein and DNA? Using an enzyme that removed the DNA, it was found that the main body of the chromosome remained. When chromosomes were treated with an enzyme that digested the protein, they broke into small pieces. The results of these two experiments seem to indicate that chromosomes consist of a protein core, with DNA embedded along its entire length.

DNA: The Genetic Material

The principal genetic material found in chromosomes is deoxyribonucleic acid, commonly called DNA. You have already learned that DNA directs the construction of the T-4 bacteriophage. (See Chapter 4.) Viruses, however, are generally not considered to be "typical" living things. In every other organism that has been studied extensively, it appears that double-stranded DNA is the hereditary material. DNA's function in heredity is to direct the construction of proteins from amino acids. A molecule of DNA contains the elements carbon, hydrogen, nitrogen, oxygen, and phosphorus. These five elements are organized into six different compounds: a sugar, a phosphate, and four kinds of nitrogen bases. *The sequence of the nitrogen bases provides the genetic code for the reproduction of all organisms.*

Is DNA the Hereditary Material? In 1944, bacteriologists Oswald Avery, Colin Macleod, and Maclyn McCarty reported the results of an interesting group of experiments. They had been investigating two strains of bacteria, one of which produced pneumonia. The second strain, closely related to the first, did *not* produce the disease. A substance extracted from the infectious bacteria was able to transform the second strain into an infectious form. When the researchers analyzed the transforming substance, they discovered that it was DNA. In 1927, the English bacteriologist F. Griffith was able to transform a non-infectious bacterium into an infectious form. However, Griffith had not proved what the chemical nature of the transform-

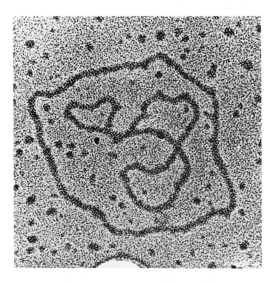

9–1 Electron micrograph of DNA loops synthesized by Kornberg, Goulian, and Sinsheimer.

ing material was. The great value of the Avery experiment was that it highlighted the role of DNA at a time when the function of DNA was still unknown.

Later investigations with bacteria and molds yielded similar results. When transformations of these microorganisms occurred, the researchers discovered that in each case the transforming agent was DNA. Viruses have been very helpful in establishing the role of DNA in the genetic process. You learned in Chapter 4 about the method of reproduction in the T-4 bacteriophage. This bacteriophage injects its DNA into the colon bacteria. The result of injecting the DNA is the production of new viruses. The assumption, therefore, is that DNA is the hereditary material.

The most conclusive evidence that DNA is the genetic material comes from the production of synthetic DNA. In 1968, Mehran Goulian, Arthur Kornberg, and Robert Sinsheimer reported that they had synthesized DNA in their laboratory. The synthetic DNA was tested by mixing it with colon bacteria. The synthesized DNA proved just as effective against the bacteria as the DNA from a virus. In 1970, Nobel Prize winner Dr. Har Gobind Khorana at the University of Wisconsin reported that he had synthesized a gene. The gene was a short (77 subunits) molecule of DNA. This gene codes the production of the transfer RNA (see page 151), which carries the amino acid alanine to sites of protein synthesis in cells.

THE DOUBLE HELIX. The DNA molecule consists of two long parallel strands of molecular subunits called *nucleotides,* joined at regular intervals by crosspieces. The crosspieces are composed of the nitrogen bases. This ladder-like structure is twisted, much as a flexible ladder might be twisted about a cylinder. The resulting structure is a *double helix.*

The exact way in which DNA is constructed has been explained in our discussion of the T-4 virus (Chapter 4). It will be well for you to review this material so that you understand how DNA codes the instructions that build a virus. Strung along the parallel strands of sugar and phosphate groups are 200,000 crosspieces in this virus. Joining the two bases that comprise the

rungs of this molecular ladder are weak hydrogen bonds. These bonds play a key role in the duplication of DNA molecules.

FOUR NUCLEOTIDES. Four different bases form the four nucleotides which are the DNA subunits. These are adenine (A), guanine (G), cytosine (C), and thymine (T). When these four bases form the DNA rungs, only two combinations are possible: A combines with T (or T with A), and G

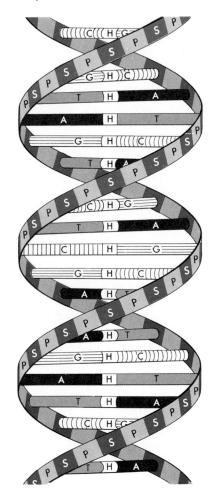

9–3 Diagram of a Portion of the DNA Molecule. The sequence of bases comprises the genetic code for the formation of proteins from the twenty different amino acids.

9–2 The sugar-phosphate strands of the DNA molecule are linked by four different nitrogen bases, which are joined by hydrogen bonds.

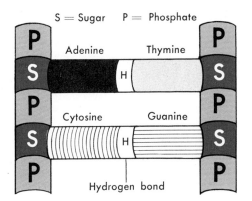

S = Sugar   P = Phosphate

Adenine   Thymine

Cytosine   Guanine

Hydrogen bond

combines with C (or C with G). The restriction in the combinations is caused by the kind of hydrogen bonding. Adenine and thymine are joined by *two* hydrogen bonds. Guanine and cytosine are joined by *three* hydrogen bonds. We describe A as the *complement* of T (or T of A). Similarly, G is the complement of C (or C of G).

If the sequence of bases on a single strand of DNA is known, therefore, its complementary sequence is also fixed. Consider the following sequence on the left strand, and notice how the right sequence follows:

Adenine–Thymine
Thymine–Adenine
Guanine–Cytosine
Cytosine–Guanine

Since the hydrogen bonds restrict the linkage of these bases, these combinations alone are possible. Neither **A-C** nor **G-T** combinations are known to occur.

We learned that the sequence of the nucleotides in the T-4 virus provides the "blueprint" for the construction of that bacteriophage. In the same way, the sequence of the nucleotides in every living thing is believed to specify its construction from a single fertilized egg cell. The simplest virus we have studied, the TMV, contains only 6,400 nucleotides. Other viruses contain as many as 200,000 nucleotide pairs. On this scale how many nucleotides would be required to "blueprint" a dog, or cat, or man? Biologists guess about 5.5 billion!

DNA Replication. During mitosis, DNA molecules in the chromosomes replicate. *Replication* is the process by which DNA molecules make exact copies or replicas of themselves. The process is believed to occur in the following manner. During cell division, each half of the double-stranded DNA molecule separates from its partner, a process resulting in two parallel strands. The points of separation are the midpoints of the rungs, where the bases are joined. The hydrogen bonds at these

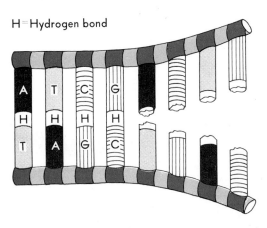

H=Hydrogen bond

9–4 The sequence of bases in one DNA strand determines the sequence in the second strand, since adenine forms hydrogen bonds only with thymine, and cytosine forms bonds only with guanine. These characteristic bonding properties give rise to a molecule in which the sequence of bases in one strand is complementary to that in the second strand.

points break. Each separated strand with its half-rungs now produces a new half.

If the base sequence on the left strand had been **G, C, T, A**, it would have formed a new half consisting of the sequence **C, G, A, T**. Meanwhile the right strand which had a sequence of **C, G, A, T** forms a complementary half in which the sequence is **G, C, T, A**. Thus, the two separate halves of the original DNA molecule form two identical DNA molecules.

RNA: The Assisting Molecule

RNA performs several functions. We have already seen that it is the genetic material in the tobacco mosaic virus. However, the role of RNA in most organisms is to assist DNA by carrying genetic information into the cytoplasm of cells. Two kinds of RNA assist DNA in the performance of its genetic function, messenger RNA (m-RNA) and transfer RNA (t-RNA).

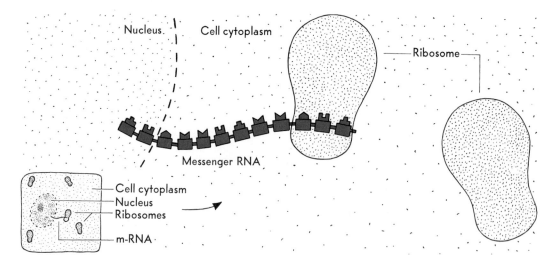

9–5 Migration of m-RNA. The migration of m-RNA is seen as it passes from the nucleus to a ribosome. The sequence of nucleotides is shown by the symbols. These nucleotides will be interpreted in groups of three (codons) to begin the assembly of proteins in the ribosome.

Messenger RNA. DNA, which encodes the genetic message, remains in the nucleus. In the nucleus, m-RNA is formed as the complement of one of the DNA strands. Only one of the two DNA strands is used for this purpose. The reason why one strand is used rather than the other is not understood by biologists at present. If the three letter base sequence on DNA is A,A,C, the complementary sequence on RNA becomes U,U,G, where the U represents uracil. The m-RNA migrates from the nucleus through pores in the nuclear membrane. Note that m-RNA is a *single stranded* molecule carrying a transcription of the genetic information. In the cytoplasm, m-RNA becomes attached to the ribosomes, which are the centers of protein formation.

Transfer RNA and Protein Formation. If you have ever played a tape recorder, you might know that the tape has recorded the information in the form of magnetic pulses. The tape recorder then changes this information back into sound.

In a similar way, you might think of m-RNA as a chemical tape that runs through the ribosome. The ribosome is assisted by transfer RNA (t-RNA), which "reads" the coded information of the m-RNA.

As we learned in our study of TMV, the sequence of bases along the m-RNA chain is a three-letter code. Each three-letter group, or *codon*, specifies one of the twenty amino acids which form proteins. For example, GCU is the codon for alanine; GGU is the codon for glycine. Corresponding to the twenty amino acids are twenty kinds of transfer RNA.

Transfer RNA consists of about 70 nucleotides. The molecule is much shorter than either m-RNA or DNA. The nucleotides are folded into a double stranded loop. At the open end, each kind of t-RNA carries its special kind of amino acid. At the looped end, each t-RNA carries the *anti-codon* for its special amino acid. The anti-codon is the complement of the three letter codon. For example, since the codon for alanine is

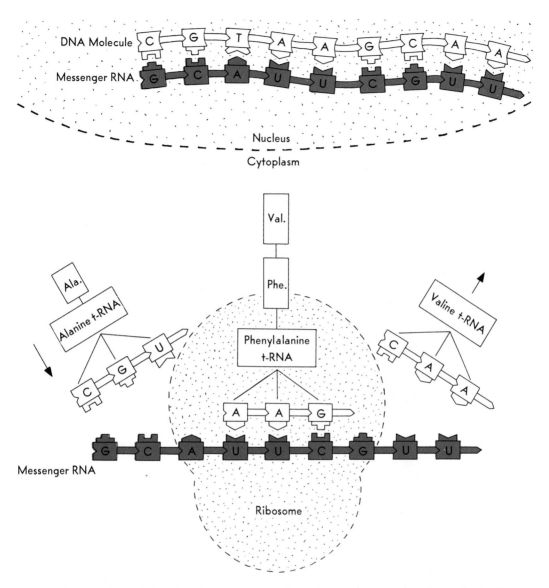

9–6 Formation of Protein. Messenger RNA from the nucleus carries the code to the ribosome. Valine t-RNA has read the code GUU and has transferred valine to the ribosome. Phenylalanine t-RNA is in the process of adding phenylalanine to the valine. Alanine will follow in the growing polypeptide chain.

GCU, the anti-codon is CGA. The t-RNA for alanine therefore carries the anti-codon CGA. The function of t-RNA is to bring the correct amino acid to the ribosome that has been encoded by messenger RNA. The ribosome then joins the amino acids into the correct sequence, forming polypeptides and proteins.

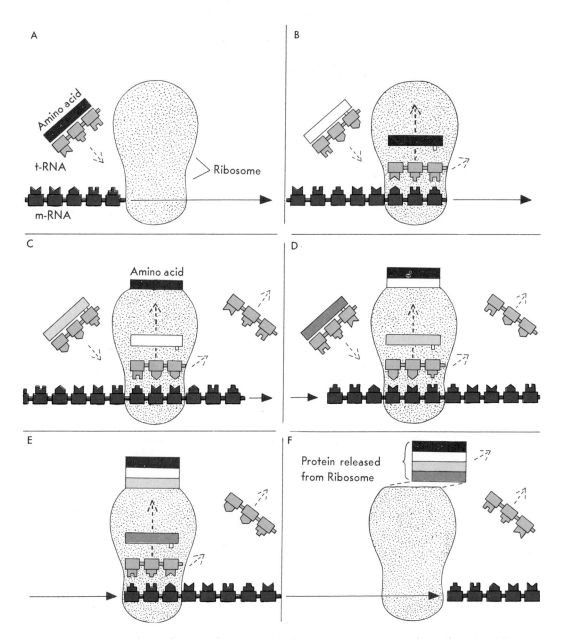

9–7 Protein synthesis does not begin until m-RNA makes contact with a ribosome (A). As the ribosome "reads" the m-RNA code, a molecule of transfer-RNA carrying a particular kind of amino acid is attracted to the ribosome (B). The amino acid disassociates from the transfer-RNA and becomes attached to the ribosome, after which the transfer-RNA leaves. As the m-RNA continues to pass through the ribosome, the process is repeated with other molecules of transfer-RNA, each adding its particular molecule to those already attached in sequence to the ribosome (C,D). In this way a series of linked amino acids is built up to form a protein (E), which is released from the ribosome after the m-RNA completes its passage. (F)

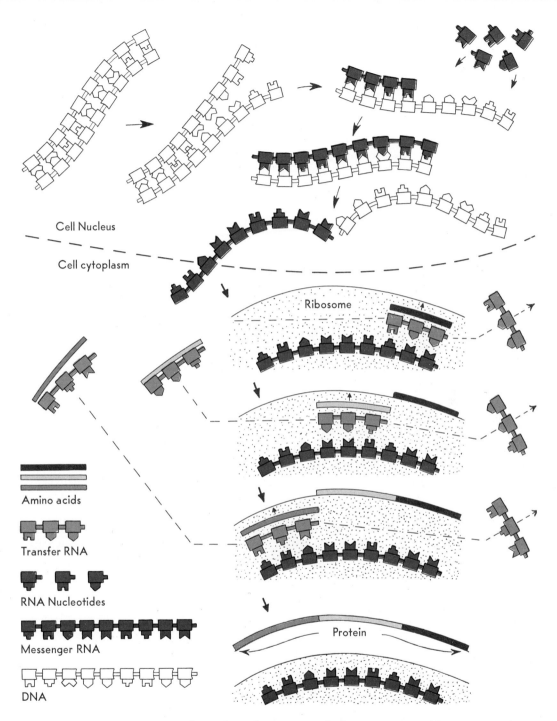

Cell Nucleus

Cell cytoplasm

Ribosome

Amino acids

Transfer RNA

RNA Nucleotides

Messenger RNA

DNA

Protein

9–8 Protein Formation. In the nucleus, the master code for protein assembly is contained in DNA. The code is transferred to m-RNA in the nucleus by assembling complementary RNA nucleotides. The m-RNA migrates to the cytoplasm. In the cytoplasm, t-RNA "reads" the code in a three-letter sequence called a codon. The t-RNA brings the correct amino acid for each and assembles a chain of amino acids into a protein molecule.

The end product of the genetic mill appears to be the manufacture of proteins. This result is somewhat surprising. Living things are made of many organic materials besides proteins. How can the growth of an organism be controlled by the manufacture of proteins alone? Proteins have two functions in living things. The first function is to provide the structure of certain body parts. Hair and skin, for example, are almost pure protein. The second function of proteins is to regulate organic chemical reactions. As enzymes, proteins control and regulate all the reactions of the organism. *All enzymes are proteins.* In green plants, enzymes control the stages of photosynthesis. In all living things, enzymes control every step of respiration. Through the manufacture of enzymes, DNA and RNA control the reproduction and growth of all living things.

Genes, Enzymes, and Mutations

Now that genetics can be understood at the molecular level, let us re-examine our definition of a gene. Prior to this point, we have thought of a gene as a part of a chromosome that controls the development of a trait. From a chemical point of view, however, a "trait" may be the expression of a long series of chemical reactions. The discussion of hemophilia in the previous chapter, for example, shows how traits and chemistry are related. A hemophilic is a person who has the trait of bleeding. The bleeding is due to a fault in the chemical reactions that produce normal clotting.

FAULTS IN METABOLISM. At the beginning of the twentieth century, the British physician Sir Archibald Garrod investigated a number of diseases due to what he called "metabolic errors." One of these was the disease *alcaptonuria* (al-kap-tuh-NEW-ree-uh), a condition in which the urine becomes black after exposure to air. The blackening of the urine is due to the presence of the chemical *alcapton.* In normal people, alcapton is converted into other chemicals before being excreted, hence the urine does not turn black. Thus, alcaptonuria represents a metabolic error. Furthermore, the condition is inherited and appears to be due to a single pair of genes.

Another disease due to an inherited metabolic error is phenylketonuria (**PKU**). In affected individuals, phenylpyruvic (fee-nil-pie-ROO-vic) acid is found in the urine. PKU victims are of low mental ability and have rather light pigmentation.

ONE GENE-ONE ENZYME. Nobel prize-winners George Beadle and Edward Tatum believed that each gene controls the production of one enzyme. Since an enzyme controls a specific reaction in a chain of chemical reactions, the failure of one enzyme would interfere with normal metabolism. To test their belief, Beadle and Tatum used the pink mold *Neurospora* (new-RAH-spoh-ruh). *Neurospora* was selected because it can synthesize all its requirements, including pyridoxine (vitamin B_6), from mineral salts, cane sugar, and the vitamin *biotin.* Spores of the mold were irradiated to produce genetic changes, or "metabolic errors." One of the spores, for example, could no longer produce vitamin B_6. Many other genetic changes confirmed the idea that one gene controls one enzyme.

In his Nobel Prize lecture on December 11, 1958, Edward Tatum summarized the basic concepts in chemical genetics.

1. All biochemical processes are under genetic control.
2. Biochemical processes may be resolved into a series of steps, or reactions.
3. Each reaction is controlled by a single gene.
4. Alteration of a single gene changes the ability of the cell to carry out a single reaction.

If we return now to an idea expressed under the discussion of protein manufacture, we can formulate a new concept of a gene. *A gene is that part of the DNA molecule that specifies the formation of one protein.* Most of the proteins specified by genes act as enzymes. In this manner the genes regulate all life processes.

MUTATIONS. Many of the defects and malformations of the human body are believed to be due to changes in the structure of genes. A *mutation* is a change in an inherited trait due to a change in the chromosomes or genes. The change is transmitted to offspring. Children born with extra fingers or fused fingers are examples of mutational effects. Certain kinds of dwarfism and idiocy are believed to have arisen as mutations. *Spontaneous mutations* may be caused by cosmic rays or by background radiation from radioactive materials in the earth. The exact nature of the process by which spontaneous mutations are produced is not understood. It is estimated, however, that every fifth child carries a mutation that originated in the gametes of one of the parents. Some of these mutations are dominant traits; others are recessive. In some cases the mutant gene causes death at an early age. In this case the gene is said to be a *lethal gene.*

Geneticists, as well as plant and animal breeders, have observed sudden changes in a pure hereditary line many times. Dr. Morgan, for example, bred wild, red-eyed fruit flies by the thousands for several generations. One day, he noticed that several of the flies had white eyes. White eyes appeared as a result of a change in the gene determining eye color.

Many experiments and observations have confirmed that mutations fall into three broad classes. First, there may be a change in the number of chromosomes. The diploid number (2N) that is characteristic of the body cells may be changed to a 3N or 4N

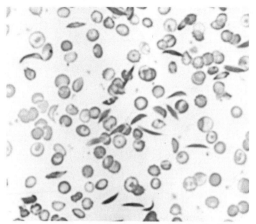

Carolina Biological Supply Company

9–9 Sickle-cell anemia results from the inheritance of a mutant or defective gene.

number by a fault in cell division. Second, there may be changes in the chromosomes themselves, such as part of one chromosome breaking off and uniting with part of a nonhomologous partner. Third, there may be changes in the chemical nature of the genes themselves. Hemophilia is an example of the latter type of mutation.

Mutations have been produced experimentally by exposure to radiation and by the use of chemicals. In 1926, Dr. Hermann Muller produced mutations in fruit flies by exposing the flies to X rays. The mutations included changes in the body structure, in the eye color, and in the length and shape of the wings.

The increasing use of radioactive materials, as well as the threat of nuclear warfare, has raised many questions about the effect of radiation upon human genetics. One thing is certain: the increased exposure of living things to radiation increases the number of mutations produced. Furthermore, most mutations are harmful. This leads to the conclusion that every safeguard should be established to protect people from radiation exposure.

9–10 The Hardy-Weinberg Law. When random mating occurs in a population, the gene frequency remains constant as shown.

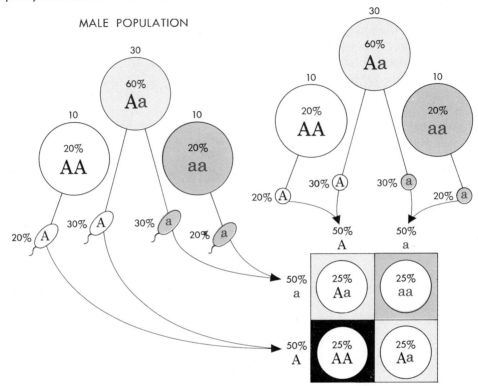

MALE POPULATION

FEMALE POPULATION

Population Genetics

Prior to this point, we have discussed the genetic process in individuals. Living things, however, usually are associated with each other in large numbers. *Population genetics* is the study of the mechanics of heredity in large groups, or populations. A *population* consists of all of the members of a group of living things inhabiting a certain geographical region. The inhabitants of a city could serve as a population for a genetic study of man. An insect population in a particular region also could be studied.

Population genetics has one very important outcome: *It enables the biologist to study the process of genetic change.* Populations residing in different parts of the world can be compared. Past and present

populations residing in the same area can be analyzed. The goal in each case is to discover the course of genetic change.

GENE FREQUENCIES. It is common observation that there is great variety in human racial characteristics. There are blue-eyed and brown-eyed people. Some are tall; others are short. Some have blond, straight hair; others have black, curly hair. Some have normal color vision; others are color blind. Each person has a specific blood type: A, B, AB, or O. Each is either Rh positive or negative. All of these traits have a genetic basis, so there are many genes in a population's gene pool. The *gene pool* consists of the total number of genes distributed within a population.

The distribution of genes within the gene pool of different populations is not the same. The **gene frequency** is the ratio between the alleles that control a trait. Blond hair and blue eyes are more common in Scandinavia than in countries bordering the Mediterranean Sea. The gene for O type blood is more common in London than in Kharkov, Russia. The gene for B type blood is more common in Kharkov than in London. The gene frequency of the type B gene gradually increases from 4 per cent in London to 15 per cent in Kharkov to 25 per cent in the Ural Mountain area of the Soviet Union.

Differences in gene frequencies are observed in related populations of many living things. These differences lead the biologist to raise the following questions:

1. Do the gene frequencies within a given population remain constant?
2. What causes gene frequencies in related populations to differ?

THE HARDY-WEINBERG LAW. The answer to the first question came in 1908. Working separately, English mathematician Godfrey Hardy and German physician Wilhelm Weinberg arrived at the same conclusion. *The Hardy-Weinberg Law states that within a random-mating population the gene frequency remains constant.*

An illustration will serve to show how the Hardy-Weinberg conclusion was reached. Fifty male and fifty female *Drosophila* are placed in a closed container to establish a small, isolated population. To simplify the illustration, consider only one pair of alleles, **Aa.** From previous experiments, the genotype of each fly used in the experiment is known. The distribution of genotypes for each sex is the same: 10**AA**, 30**Aa**, and 10**aa**. Note that the gene frequency distribution in each group, male and female, is 50 per cent **A** and 50 per cent **a**. Thus, the 10**AA** males contribute 20**A** genes, and the 30**Aa** males contribute 30**A**. In a similar manner, the 30**Aa** males contribute 30**a**, and the 10**aa** males contribute 20**a** genes. Out of the total of 100 genes among the males, 50 are **A**, and 50 are **a**.

The results in the F_1 generation for this population of *Drosophila* are shown in Figure 9–10. When the male gametes are formed, note that segregation of the genes results in a 50 per cent distribution of type **A** and type **a** sperm. The same reasoning applies to the egg cells produced. In the F_1 generation, the distribution of genotypes is 25 per cent **AA**, 50 per cent **Aa**, and 25 per cent **aa**. At first glance, it would appear that the Hardy-Weinberg distribution is *not* upheld. However, the Hardy-Weinberg Law applies to the *gene* distribution, not to the genotype distribution. Calculating the gene distribution, we arrive at the same result as in the original population, namely, 50 per cent **A** and 50 per cent **a**.

In his original analysis, Hardy used a simple mathematical expression to derive the results. He let p represent the frequency of the **A** gene in the general population and q the frequency of the **a** gene. The sum of $p + q$ equals 1, or 100 per cent. In our illustration, $p = 50$ per cent and $q = 50$ per cent, and the sum of $p + q$ is equal to 100 per cent. When random mating occurs in a population, p and q gametes combine with other p and q gametes. Mathematically, $p + q$ is multiplied by $p + q$. From your algebra, you know that:

$$(p + q)(p + q) = p^2 + 2pq + q^2$$

If we substitute 50 per cent for p and 50 per cent for q, the predicted results in the F_1 generation are:

25 per cent **AA** representing p^2,
50 per cent **Aa** representing $2pq$, and
25 per cent **aa** representing q^2.

Note that these results are in exact agreement with the results obtained by a completely different method.

POPULATION CHANGES. Despite the prediction of the Hardy-Weinberg Law, gene frequencies in populations do change. Four factors that produce changes in gene frequencies have been identified—mutation, selection, migration, and isolation.

Mutations are caused by changes in the chromosomes or genes. Gene mutations are caused by changes in the sequence of nitrogen bases that comprise the DNA molecule. The rate at which mutations occur can have a great effect upon the composition of the gene pool. Generally, the rate is low; but the effect accumulates with the passage of time. For a given gene on a chromosome, it has been estimated that a mutation occurs in man in one out of 50,000 to 100,000 gametes in each generation.

Gene frequencies are strongly influenced by any selective factors in a population. Selective factors in mating, for example, prevent the flow of genes of nonmating individuals into the next generation. Any gene that reduces the chances of the organism to survive tends to disappear from a population. The gene for hemophilia is selective because it reduces the chance of survival.

Under natural conditions, it is almost impossible for one population to be completely isolated from others. Consequently, there is migration both into and out of the original population. In either case, gene frequencies will shift unless the migrant population happens to have an identical gene distribution.

Occasionally, isolation of part of a parent population does occur in nature. Unless the isolated group is very large, it is unlikely that it will have the same gene distribution as the original population. The isolated group then begins the formation of a new population with a new gene frequency distribution.

SICKLE-CELL ANEMIA. An interesting example of how mutation and selection act to alter gene frequencies in a population is provided by sickle-cell anemia. Sickle-cell anemia is a fatal disease resulting from the inheritance of a mutant or defective gene. The disease is identified by the presence of sickle-shaped red blood cells in place of the usual round or disc-shaped cells.

The cause of sickling is a mutation that alters the sequence of amino acids in the hemoglobin molecule. The normal hemoglobin molecule contains four chains, each containing more than 140 amino acids. In sickle-cell hemoglobin, the position normally held by glutamic acid is occupied by valine.

The sickle-cell allele, which is recessive, is designated by s. The allele for normal hemoglobin is designated by S. Three combinations of alleles exist in a large population: SS, normal cells; Ss, heterozygotes who are healthy carriers of the sickle-cell condition; and ss, recessive homozygotes to whom the condition is usually fatal.

Sickle-cell anemia is particularly prevalent among inhabitants of malarial regions of Africa. In such regions, the gene frequency of the s allele may be 40 per cent. Although the homozygous (ss) condition is lethal, it has been found that the heterozygous (Ss) condition increases resistance to malaria, a disease often fatal to inhabitants of tropical regions.

The reason for the high incidence of what appears to be a harmful gene is now apparent: *the Ss gene combination offers an adaptive advantage to people living in malarial territories.* This example shows that shifts in gene frequency result from different adaptive values that gene mutations give to a population.

PLANT AND ANIMAL BREEDING. The scientific application of population genetics is well illustrated by breeding experiments. Improving plant and animal stock means changing gene frequencies in a population. The development of new plants or animals depends on applying the principles which alter gene frequencies.

An experimental group of plants or animals is an *isolated* part of a larger population. Members of the isolated group have been *selected* for desirable qualities. For dairy cattle, the selection of cows is based on milk production. Sweeter-tasting carrots have been developed by selection.

Plant and animal breeders watch for *mutations*. A short-legged mutant led to the development of the Ancon breed of sheep. Plant mutations also have been used to change the characteristics of flowers, fruits, and vegetables. All mutations are inheritable because the chromosomes are changed. When selected and isolated, mutations quickly alter gene frequencies.

IMPORTANT POINTS

• Many recent investigators have shown that DNA is the hereditary molecule. DNA consists of subunits called nucleotides. Each nucleotide consists of a sugar, a phosphate, and a nitrogen base. The sequence of four nitrogen bases provides the genetic code.

• DNA is a double-stranded molecule arranged in a long helix, like a twisted ladder. The crosspieces of the ladder are the nitrogen bases, arranged in pairs, and joined by hydrogen bonds.

• DNA replicates itself during the process of mitosis. Mitosis insures the continuous supply of DNA to each new cell.

• RNA assists DNA in the chemical reactions of genetics. Messenger RNA is formed in the nucleus as a complement of one DNA strand; m-RNA migrates into the cytoplasm to the ribosomes, carrying the genetic code it received from DNA.

• Proteins are formed in the ribosomes when transfer RNA molecules "read" the m-RNA message. The t-RNA molecules bring the correct amino acids specified by codons on the m-RNA.

• A gene is a part of the DNA that specifies the formation of one protein. Since enzymes are proteins, genes regulate all the chemical systems of the body.

• Mutations are changes in inherited traits due to a change in genetic material. Mutations can be caused by changes in chromosome number, chromosome breaking, or chemical changes in the genes.

• The study of population genetics deals with the process of genetic change in a large group of organisms. Although the Hardy-Weinberg Law predicts that gene frequencies will remain constant in a random-mating population, the factors of mutation, selection, migration, and isolation produce gene frequency shifts.

REVIEW QUESTIONS

1. Of what two parts are chromosomes constructed?
2. Give two reasons why biologists believe DNA is the hereditary molecule.
3. What three types of substances form a nucleotide?
4. Why are the nitrogen bases in DNA so important?
5. Compare the approximate number of nucleotides in TMV, the T-4 bacterio-phage, and a dog.
6. Describe the replication of the DNA molecule.
7. How is messenger RNA made?
8. Why are there twenty kinds of transfer RNA?
9. How has molecular biology modified the definition of the gene?
10. Describe the one gene-one enzyme theory.
11. Explain how a chemical mutation might occur.
12. What four factors produce gene frequency changes in a population?

CHECK YOUR UNDERSTANDING

13. Why should the synthesizing of DNA provide clear evidence of its role in heredity?
14. If you knew the approximate number of nucleotides in an organism's cells, how might that number indicate something about its size and complexity?
15. Explain how the idea of complementary base pairs provides the means of replicating molecules.
16. What is the significance of the fact that DNA provides only for the manufacture of proteins?
17. How is a disease resulting from a metabolic error related to the Beadle-Tatum theory of one gene-one enzyme?
18. Why should a "defect" like sickle-cell anemia be retained in a population?
19. Why do gene frequencies remain constant in a random-mating population?
20. Using your knowledge of chemical genetics, how would you explain the origin of a radiation-induced mutation?

RESEARCH PROJECTS AND REPORTS

1. Obtain information from your school or public library and prepare a report on one of the following topics:

DNA and RNA	George W. Beadle
Radiation and Mutations	Blood Types and Geography

2. *Color Blindness Study:* If your school population is large, you may be able to get reliable statistics on red-green color blindness among your classmates. Obtain your teacher's and your principal's permission before proceeding. Most color-blind individuals have discovered this trait before they reach high school and are not reluctant to cooperate. Set up a standard testing procedure with color testing charts, then follow it uniformly. Compare the number of color-blind

students with those who have normal vision. Which sex has the greater number of color-blind persons? Try to trace the defect in affected families as well. What is the ratio of color-blind people in the general population?

3. *Human Heredity Study:* Make a study of several genetic characteristics in your class or school. Eye color, hair color, and height might be three to consider. How are these traits distributed in this population?

FURTHER READING

The Genetic Code. Isaac Asimov. Clarkson N. Potter, New York, N.Y. A biochemist describes the chemistry of DNA, the basic hereditary material.

Life's Key—DNA. Carleen M. Hutchins. Coward McCann, Inc., New York, N.Y. A short, well-illustrated account of fundamental genetics.

The Coil of Life. Ruth Moore. Alfred A. Knopf, New York, N.Y. An extensive account of man's attempts to understand life's beginnings with emphasis upon the men who have clarified our concepts of the cell and its reproduction.

"**The Genetic Code-III.**" F. H. Crick. *Scientific American,* October, 1966, page 55. A Nobel Prize winner describes the manner in which DNA forms proteins.

The Language of Life. George and Muriel Beadle. Doubleday and Co., Inc., Garden City, New York. A Nobel prize winner in genetics and his wife have written an excellent introduction to the science of heredity.

Threads of Life. Aaron E. Klein. The Natural History Press, Garden City, New York. A fascinating account of the lines of inquiry that led to the molecular genetics revolution in biology.

10

The Changing Stream of Life

THE WORLD OF LIFE is a world of change. The stream of life has flowed upon this planet for two billion years or more. However simply it began, it has gradually changed to include the numerous forms of life now inhabiting the earth. A generation of living things is but a small fraction of a second in relation to the vast span of time, and its change is not readily noticed. But if we look at the record of life through millions of years, we observe an immense panorama of change.

Exploration of the earth's surface has uncovered many interesting facts. It is known that huge dinosaurs once roamed upon the earth. Today they are gone. Gone also are the ancient fern forests. Dried are the ancient seas that once covered mountains. Gone are the small, fox-like ancestors of the modern horse. Camp sites and a few scattered bones mark the remains of prehistoric man.

Searching through the layers of rock, man has found the beginning of modern forms of life. Wherever man has searched, there is the story of slow, steady change. The change is noticed only when the life of the present is contrasted with the life of the distant past.

Evidences of Change

Important evidence of change comes from geology. *Geology* is the study of the history of the earth—especially as it is recorded in rocks. Interpreting the record of rocks, the geologist uncovers the story of vast upheavals in the earth's past. He learns of great mountain ranges that once lay submerged beneath the sea, of the wintry lands that once had tropical climates, of continents that were once joined. He uncovers the story of an ever-changing earth.

A changing earth poses important questions to the biologist. Could life have remained unchanged while the physical environment was severely altered? When geologic changes were sudden, plants and animals probably perished. When changes were gradual, living forms may have become adapted and thus changed over long periods.

FOSSILS. This view of slowly changing life is borne out by *fossils,* the remains and traces of organisms found embedded in the rocks. Fossils are interpreted by the *paleontologist.* Examining fossils from the most ancient rocks, he finds that the organisms are rather simple in structure and bear little resemblance to present forms of life. However, fossils from more recent rocks tend to be more complex and frequently exhibit resemblance to modern plants and animals. Thus, fossils tell a story not only of changing forms of life, but of the increasing complexity of organisms from the remote past to the present. Fossils are still being formed today, but only in places where they are not likely to be seen.

TAXONOMY. Organisms are classified according to their structure into phyla, classes, orders, families, genera, and species. Linnaeus, who contributed so much to this system of classification, was convinced that each species of plant and animal was distinct. It descended unchanged and was, therefore, incapable of change. Today, over a million and a half species are known. With the examination of so many species, it has become clear that they are not as distinct as Linnaeus thought. In many cases, much debate surrounds the attempts to classify organisms.

Why do living things resemble each other in the first place? Are horses and donkeys related? They readily interbreed to produce mules. Are cattle and buffaloes related? They too can interbreed. Such similarities suggest relationship. Perhaps they resemble each other because they are descended from common ancestors. Not too long ago, they may have separated from some common trunk, then branched their separate ways.

ANIMAL DISTRIBUTION. Similarities are seen among animals living in different parts of the world. These similarities indicate changes resulting from geographic distribution. For example, the llama shows a striking resemblance to the camel. One lives in South America, the other in Africa. Both animals have long legs and a very long neck. They look like distant cousins.

According to paleontologists, camel-like animals roamed the North American conti-

10–1 Mule

nent many years ago. Some migrated into South America becoming the ancestors of today's llama. Others migrated northward across the land bridges that once joined the entire northern hemisphere. Their descendants, the present-day camels, are found in Asia and Africa. Through millions of years the basic ancestral traits have persisted, although many changes have occurred. The camel became adapted to the dry desert regions, the llama to mountainous areas. The alpaca, a close relative of the llama, became even more specialized. Living in the highest parts of the Andes, it has developed a thick, shaggy coat.

Although this type of change is seen in many parts of the world, it is especially noticed in island animals. After islands are separated from the mainland, their animal populations become isolated from their ancestral stock. In time, they may become strikingly different as they become adapted to a different environment.

This difference is dramatically illustrated by the animals of Australia and Tasmania. These islands are practically the only places

10–2 Dromedary Camel

10–3 Llama

in the world where the pouched mammals, the *marsupials,* are native. This results from the fact that Australia and Tasmania were separated from the Asiatic mainland before the more advanced *placental* mammals developed. On the islands, such marsupials as kangaroos and koalas continued to exist unhampered by competition from the more aggressive placentals that appeared on the mainland. On the mainland, the marsupials disappeared, probably killed off by the more aggressive mammals.

Changes that result from geographic isolation occur very slowly, often requiring millions of years. At least one case, however, has been documented in fairly recent times. During the 15th century, a few European rabbits were introduced into the Madeiras, islands off the west coast of Africa. Today, their descendants are smaller and darker than their recent ancestors. But far more important than their physical appearance is the fact that they can no longer be mated with the European species. So great has been the change that they are now considered a separate species.

COMPARATIVE ANATOMY. In studying the skeletons of widely different vertebrates, the comparative anatomist finds basic similarities of structure. For example, consider the forelimbs of man, whale, bat, and horse. In man, the forelimbs are hands adapted for manipulation. In the whale, the forelimbs are flippers adapted for swimming. In the bat the forelimbs are wings adapted for flying. In the horse the forelimbs are legs adapted for running. In each case five fingers, or *phalanges,* may be found. In the whale, the phalanges are imbedded in the flipper. In the bat, the phalanges are elongated into the wing supports. In the horse, they are gathered into bone splints above the hoof.

The limbs of men, whales, bats, and horses are used for different purposes, but have the same plan of construction. To the biologist, this similarity of structure indicates common descent. He refers to organs having the same structural plan as *homologous organs.* Homologous organs are believed to originate from some common ancestor in the remote past. As the descend-

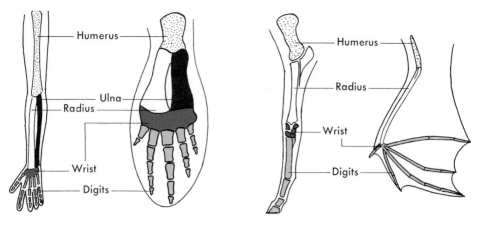

HUMAN ARM   PADDLE OF WHALE   FORELEG OF HORSE   WING OF BAT

10–4 Homologous Structures. The forelimbs of the mammals shown are different in function but are fundamentally similar in structure and arrangement of bones. Such similarities suggest that all the mammals developed from some common ancestral form.

ants develop along different lines, a change in usage gradually results.

The progressive development of animals also results in organs that become useless and reduced in size. Such structures are called *vestigial* (ves-TIJ-ee-al) *organs.* Snakes, for example, have tiny leg bones attached to the spinal column. In the python, these "hind legs" actually protrude about an inch from the body.

In man there are more than 200 vestigial structures. The best known is the appendix. This small intestinal projection appears to have no function in man. In the rabbit, however, the appendix is a large and functioning part of the digestive tract. Other vestiges in man include the *coccyx,* the tiny "tail bones" at the base of the spine, and a "third eyelid" in the corner of the eye. What is the significance of vestigial organs? In all likelihood, vestigial organs are "leftovers" along the path of change.

COMPARATIVE EMBRYOLOGY. During their early stage of embryonic development, different types of vertebrate animals appear practically alike. In this stage, even the expert cannot distinguish a cat from a turkey, or a monkey from a squirrel. (See Figure 10–5.)

The development of all vertebrate animals begins in the same way. The fertilized egg divides repeatedly until many cells are formed. Then the tissue layers begin to form. Shortly afterward, gill slits appear. All vertebrates also develop a tail during their early embryonic life. In most of them the tail persists and is used in adult life.

The early development of related plants also shows patterns of likeness. Plants like the cabbage, watercress, mustard, and radish develop seedlings that are so much alike that it is difficult to tell them apart. Only later do they develop the characteristics that enable us to distinguish them.

This similarity among embryos of different species was first observed by Karl von Baer. Based on similar observations, Ernst Haeckel, another German biologist, established his *Recapitulation Theory* in 1868. In it he stated that the embryonic development of the organism recapitulated, or summarized, the long development of its spe-

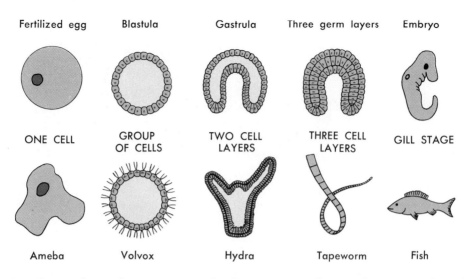

Fertilized egg	Blastula	Gastrula	Three germ layers	Embryo
ONE CELL	GROUP OF CELLS	TWO CELL LAYERS	THREE CELL LAYERS	GILL STAGE
Ameba	Volvox	Hydra	Tapeworm	Fish

10–5 Recapitulation Theory. During its development, a vertebrate embryo passes through certain stages that bear some resemblances to the embryos of its evolutionary predecessors. This characteristic of development is often stated as "ontogeny recapitulates phylogeny." An early embryo does not resemble any previous ancestral adult form.

cies. According to the theory, we can find clues in the embryo of the great changes that occurred in the ancestry of the species.

Modern biologists find Haeckel's theory much too general. True, the pattern of embryonic growth reveals a probable kinship among species. But the embryo itself is not to be considered a speeded up version of species change.

COMPARATIVE BIOCHEMISTRY. The biochemist finds that organisms having a structural similarity also have a chemical similarity. Furthermore, degrees of chemical similarity establish degrees of kinship. A simple procedure may be used to illustrate this point.

If a small amount of human blood plasma is injected into a rabbit, the animal reacts by producing antibodies. It becomes *sensitized* to human plasma. If a sample of rabbit plasma is now mixed with human plasma in a test tube, a cloudy precipitate forms. If another sample of rabbit plasma is mixed with plasma from an ape, the mix-

ture is less cloudy. If we try a third test with horse plasma, the result is still less cloudy. In the procedure we have described, a *chemical index* is established for man, ape, and horse. Since the horse is less closely related to man than to the ape, less precipitate is formed.

Protein analysis by chromatography further emphasizes physiological kinship among species. Linus Pauling, a 1954 Nobel Prize winner in chemistry, analyzed the amino acid chain sequence in the hemoglobin of human beings and rhesus monkeys. Both kinds of hemoglobin molecules contained a 146 amino acid chain. However, Pauling found only six amino acid differences between them. A comparison of human with gorilla hemoglobin indicated only one amino acid difference.

Cytochrome C, the enzyme used in cell respiration, is a more basic protein than hemoglobin. It is found in the cells of practically all organisms. Its molecule consists of a chain of 104 amino acids arranged in a precise sequence. Yet, a comparison of the cytochrome *C* of human beings and rhesus monkeys revealed a difference of only one amino acid. A comparison with horse cytochrome *C* indicated eight differences. In tuna fish, twenty-one differences were found.

An Ancient Planet

How old is the earth? How old are the ancient forms of life? Some geologists believe the earth may be five billion years old. But the beginnings of life occurred much later, perhaps between two and three billion years ago.

Physicists have discovered accurate ways of determining the age of the rocks. Radioactive elements in the rocks provide us with "atomic clocks" of considerable accuracy. Radioactive uranium, for example, disintegrates at a known rate. In 4.5 billion years, one half of a given amount of this element will have transformed itself into lead. By knowing the percentage of lead contained in a sample of uranium ore, the age of the ore can be calculated.

Radioactive dating can only be used to determine the age of rocks after the earth's crust was formed. Before this time, the earth was probably a hot mass of molten material. The earth, then, may be considerably older than the oldest rocks.

THE ORIGIN OF LIFE. We may never know how life originated. Perhaps small inorganic molecules combined by chance to produce amino acids, which in turn combined to form proteins. (See Chapter 1.) Certainly these "pre-organisms" left no trace of themselves. Perhaps, in some unknown way, these larger organic molecules began to use energy for growth and reproduction. When they did, life began.

Some biologists believe these pre-organisms derived energy from inorganic materials like sulphur, iron, and nitrogen. Sooner or later, however, some developed chlorophyll and began to use the energy of sunlight to make food. Thus, the autotrophs were born. The coming of "self feeders" meant that heterotrophic life could develop. The stream of life had begun.

HOW FOSSILS ARE FORMED. Fossils found in the rocks may be parts of an organism itself, imprints, molds, or casts. From them we can reconstruct the long history of life.

Rock deposits about 2.7 billion years old have been found that suggest the imprints of one-celled algae. Iron deposits about one billion years old seem to show traces of bacteria. These interpretations, however, may be subject to doubt. Usually it is the larger, more complex forms of life that leave unmistakable remains.

The earliest certain fossils are seldom more than half a billion years old. Beginning with this period, we find an increasing abundance and variety of fossils. If we assume that life began between two and

10–6 Fossil Fern

10–7 Petrified Lobster

three billion years ago, then the stream of life ran more than three quarters of its course before leaving its first traces.

Nearly all the organisms that ever lived died without leaving a trace. Only a few have been preserved because the formation of fossils is an accidental occurrence. An organism is suddenly buried in the mud of a swamp or ocean bottom. Its soft parts decay and only its hard parts (teeth, bones, shells) remain. In many cases the organ-

10–8 Dinosaur Track

ism leaves an imprint or mold in the mud that is later filled with some harder material. The harder material then becomes the cast of the organism. In this way, even softer organisms have left clues as to their form. Sometimes the cast is removed leaving only the imprint. In this way, dinosaur tracks have been preserved.

While this is happening, the original mud sinks under layers of new sediment that pile over it. Layer piles upon layer for millions of years until the mud, with its trapped organisms, is pressed into *sedimentary rock.* Future upheavals, however, push the sedimentary rock above the sea level, and thus it becomes possible for the fossil hunter to find his specimens.

In rare cases entire animals are preserved intact. In the Siberian wastes, mammoths living 25,000 years ago have been found in the deep freeze of the tundra. In the Baltic regions, prehistoric insects have been discovered in preserved amber. In the La Brea tar pits in Los Angeles, many complete skeletons of giant ground sloths, camels, elephants, mastodons, horses, and saber-toothed tigers have been found. During certain seasons, these tar pits were covered with pools of water. Animals that came to drink became trapped in the soft tar. These trapped animals attracted predators, which in turn became trapped. Eventually, the animals sank into the tar.

Fossils in sedimentary rock can frequently be dated with considerable accuracy. This is because sedimentary rock is formed layer by layer until it becomes *stratified* and resembles a layer cake. The lower strata contain the oldest fossils while the upper ones contain the most recent remains. Geologists estimate that in some parts of the earth the sedimentary rock is almost 70 miles thick. Since sedimentation averages one foot of new rock every 1,000 years, the age of a fossil can be calculated from its depth.

The History of Life

Without dates to establish a sequence of events, the study of history becomes meaningless. To understand the long history of life, we also need a dating system. In the case of life's development, the time scale is so vast that we reckon it on a different calendar. Instead of using years and months, the paleontologist records biological events in terms of *eras* which are subdivided into *periods.* Each of these time units is millions of years long. The last half billion years, when fossils became increasingly abundant and varied, is divided into three large eras:

> *Paleozoic Era:* the era of *old life* that began about 600 million years ago.
> *Mesozoic Era:* the era of *middle life* that began about 225 million years ago.
> *Cenozoic Era:* the era of *recent life* that began about 70 million years ago.

THE PALEOZOIC ERA. The Paleozoic Era is the longest of the three eras. It covers about 375 million years, more than half the entire period of varied fossilized life. It is divided into seven periods.

For half of the Paleozoic Era, the land masses of the earth were barren. The seas were larger and warmer than they are today. During the *Cambrian Period,* life was confined to the water. Representatives of each invertebrate phyla were present; there is no record of vertebrates. *Trilobites,* aquatic arthropods believed to be the ancestors of the present arthropods, became abundant. Algae filled the waters. But plants had not yet invaded the land.

During the *Ordovician Period,* giant sea scorpions flourished and became the dominant animal forms. It was during this period that *ostracoderms,* the armored fishes,

PALEOZOIC ERA

Periods	Duration (Millions of Years)
Cambrian	100
Ordovician	60
Silurian	40
Devonian	50
Mississippian	45
Pennsylvanian	35
Permian	45

appeared. Thus, the vertebrate line became established early in the Paleozoic.

Near the middle of the *Silurian Period,* life took a giant step forward. Plants and animals invaded the land. The tidal beaches were probably the first places where organisms were able to establish themselves out of the water. The earliest plants were related to the mosses and present-day ferns. The first land animals were probably scorpions.

The *Devonian Period* that followed is also known as the Age of Fishes. The jawless, armored fishes now gave way to more advanced types. Many fresh-water fishes appeared. Some of the older sea monsters grew to 30 feet in length. While these sharklike giants engaged in mortal combat for conquest of the seas, the amphibians began the vertebrate land conquest. The land now was a scene of strange forests of giant ferns, club mosses, and horsetails. Many arthropods, centipedes, spiders, and insects had already settled there. No flowering plant had yet appeared.

The *Mississippian* and *Pennsylvanian Periods* (sometimes together called the *Carboniferous Period*) were times of great bogs and swamps. Lush fern forests sank

10–9 Artist's representation of a scene during the Silurian Period—the period that first witnessed the invasion of the land by plants and animals.

beneath the muddy ooze and other forests grew above them. Each in turn added its weight to the layers beneath, beginning the formation of our giant coal beds. Over these ferny jungles, dragonflies with wingspans of two feet swooped down on smaller insects.

10–10 Although known as the Age of Fishes, the Devonian Period was also characterized by dense forests of giant ferns, club mosses, and horsetails.

The amphibians, so well adapted to their swampy world, began to decline as the first reptiles appeared and challenged their supremacy.

Toward the end of the Paleozoic Era, great geologic upheavals occurred. The *Permian Period* was marked by the rising of huge mountain ranges, sharp changes in climate, and the formation of deserts. Many plants and animals became extinct. Others adapted to the changing conditions. Insects became smaller and more numerous. Primitive *gymnosperms*, ancestors of our cone-bearing trees, appeared on the drier land.

Reptiles increased in size and variety. But they were still relatively small.

THE MESOZOIC ERA. The Mesozoic was a shorter era than the Paleozoic. It lasted about 155 million years and is divided into three periods.

The *Triassic Period* was one of quickening change in living things. Older species became extinct while new species appeared. The giant mollusks trailed off to extinction. The larger, more primitive fishes were replaced by smaller, more advanced types. The huge amphibians gave way to smaller, more modern ones. Giant ferns, the

10–11 An artist's representation of a waterhole in the Upper Jurassic Period shows a variety of dinosaurs among primitive vegetation of ferns and coniferous trees.

MESOZOIC ERA	
Periods	**Duration** (Millions of Years)
Triassic	45
Jurassic	45
Cretaceous	65

coal forest trees, were gradually replaced by the advancing gymnosperms.

At this time, the reptiles thrived, increasing in size and diversity. Mammal-like, "dog-jawed" reptiles appeared. Birdlike reptiles scurried about on strong hind legs. Fishlike reptiles reverted to the seas.

With the beginning of the *Jurassic Period*, the giants had arrived. The huge dinosaurs, the best known of all the earth's extinct creatures, now began their extraordinary rise. By the middle of the Jurassic, the 70-foot Brontosaurus reached the peak of its development. It was the world's largest vegetarian. The 14-foot-high Allosaurus dominated the carnivorous reptiles. The pterosaurs, the flying reptiles, appeared as if from nowhere. It was during this period

10–12 In 1925 a nest of dinosaur eggs was discovered in the Gobi Desert of Mongolia. In some cases the fossilized remains of young dinosaurs have been found inside the shells.

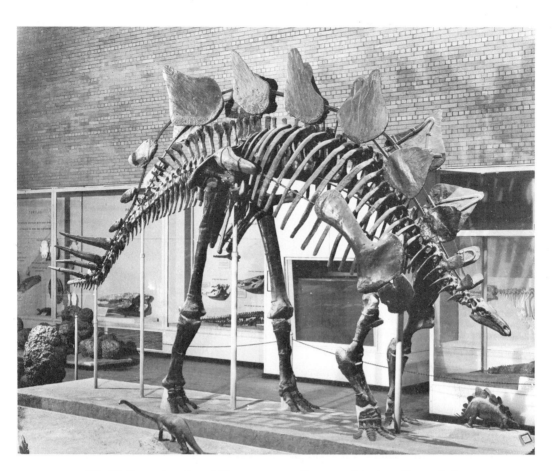

10—13 Reconstruction of Stegosaurus, a dinosaur of the late Mesozoic Era.

that the *Archeopteryx* (ar-key-op-teh-rix), the linking form between reptiles and birds, left its fragile fossils in the rocks. It was during this period that the first mammals appeared. Small, nocturnal animals, they probably escaped the notice of the huge flesh-eaters.

The *Cretaceous Period* marks the climax of dinosaur development. The 20-foot-high *Tyrannosaurus* became the largest flesh-eater the land had ever seen. Some of the hunted vegetarians, such as *Triceratops*, had leathery armor and stout horns, but were too heavy to run.

Like the earlier Permian Period, the Cre-

taceous Period closed with great geologic changes. Land masses shifted. New mountain ranges, among them the Rockies, rose from the ocean floor. Many regions became colder. More swamps disappeared. Toward the close of this period, mammals began their ascendancy. In many parts of the world the marsupials became plentiful. It was during this time that Australia and Tasmania separated from the mainland of Asia, and flowering plants appeared.

Perhaps the most outstanding event that marked the close of the Mesozoic, was the disappearance of the dinosaurs. No satisfactory explanation has yet accounted for

10–14 The Cretaceous Period saw great geologic changes and the climax of dinosaur development. Both of these aspects are indicated in this artist's portrayal of the period.

their sudden end. They had dominated the living scene for more than 100 million years. Now they declined with dramatic abruptness. With their decline, the Mesozoic Era, appropriately called the Age of Reptiles, came to an end. Henceforth, the mammals would dominate the world of life as it entered the Cenozoic Era.

THE CENOZOIC ERA. The Cenozoic Era is often called the Age of Mammals. This era saw the rise in number and variety of these highest forms of animal life. It is the era that led to man, the highest form of mammal. It is the era in which we are still living. The Cenozoic Era is divided on the Geologic Time Scale into two periods and seven epochs.

Beginning with the *Paleocene Epoch,* the world took on a more familiar look. Broad grasslands and forests of modern trees became more abundant. Brightly colored flowers increased in number. The mammals increased in size. And as mammals became specialized in their diets, the herbivorous and carnivorous lines became established.

During the *Eocene Epoch,* some forerunners of modern mammals appeared, such as *Eohippus,* the "dawn horse," and *Hyrachyus,* a small, quick rhinoceros. Rodentlike animals were unmistakably present, as were flying mammals, the ancestors of today's bats. Tree-dwelling insectivores began the long line of development that led to the primates.

A burst of strange mammalian forms brought the *Oliogocene Epoch.* The rhinoceroslike *Baluchitherium* grew to a height of 18 feet. Its very size probably doomed it. The horse, now the *Mesohippus,* was larger. The ancestor of the dog, the *Cynodictus,* appeared. The saber-toothed "tigers" appeared. By the end of the Oligocene, ancestral lines of pigs, camels, elephants, and great apes were firmly established.

The *Miocene Epoch* was marked by cooling climates. Many of the earlier mammals became extinct. Deerlike and giraffe-like mammals appeared. The four-tusked

CENOZOIC ERA

Periods and Epochs	Duration
Tertiary Period	(Millions of Years)
Paleocene Epoch	10
Eocene Epoch	20
Oligocene Epoch	15
Miocene Epoch	14
Pliocene Epoch	10
Quaternary Period	
Pleistocene Epoch	1,000,000 years
Recent Epoch	10,000 years

The beginning of the *Pleistocene Epoch*, a mere 1,000,000 years ago, coincides with the beginning of the Ice Age. The movement of masses of polar ice southward caused many animals to become extinct. Some species migrated to the south and survived. Others became adapted to the extreme cold of the northern hemisphere.

The most notable event of this period was the coming of man. Although recent fossil finds in Africa suggest man's appearance in the late Pliocene, as early as two million years ago, his undisputed remains in Asia and Europe date from the middle Pleistocene Epoch. Several types of man arose in the last million or more years. But our own species, Homo sapiens, appears to have arrived no earlier than the last glacial stage, 25,000 to 50,000 years ago.

THE RECENT EPOCH. This epoch dates from 10,000 years ago to the present. It is the time that marks the rapid rise of man. Using his superior intelligence, he fashioned tools and weapons of stone, then of bronze, and finally of iron. He developed the techniques of agriculture and built huge cities. The control that man exercises over his environment is greater than that achieved by any other animal.

mastodon thundered across the North American continent. Ancestral seals and walruses left their bones near the shore.

By the time the *Pliocene Epoch* began four-fifths of the world's present mammals had arrived. During this period they underwent further changes as they migrated from continent to continent across land bridges now submerged.

10–15 An artist's conception of a scene at La Brea Tar Pits in Los Angeles as it may have appeared during the Pleistocene Epoch.

GEOLOGIC TIME SCALE

ERA AND DURATION	EPOCH OR PERIOD AND YEARS AGO	CALENDAR DATE IF ENTIRE HISTORY REPRESENTS ONE YEAR	LIFE RECORD FOR CERTAIN PLANTS AND ANIMALS
CENOZOIC 70,000,000	QUATERNARY — Recent Epoch 10,000		
		Dec. 31, 11:59 PM	
	Pleistocene Epoch 1,000,000		
		Dec. 31, 8 PM	
	TERTIARY — Pliocene Epoch 11,000,000		
		Dec. 30, 10 PM	
	Miocene Epoch 25,000,000		
		Dec. 29, 11 PM	
	Oligocene Epoch 40,000,000		
		Dec. 28, 6 PM	
	Eocene Epoch 60,000,000		
		Dec. 27, 3 AM	
	Paleocene Epoch 70,000,000		
		Dec. 26, 8 AM	
MESOZOIC 155,000,000	Cretaceous 135,000,000		
		Dec. 21, 1 AM	
	Jurassic 180,000,000		
		Dec. 17, 10 AM	
	Triassic 225,000,000		
		Dec. 13, 6 PM	
PALEOZOIC 375,000,000	Permian 270,000,000		
		Dec. 9, 2 AM	
	CARBONIFEROUS — Pennsylvanian 305,000,000		
		Dec. 6, 6 AM	
	Mississipian 350,000,000		
		Dec. 2, 3 PM	
	Devonian 400,000,000		
		Nov. 28, 1 PM	
	Silurian 440,000,000		
		Nov. 25, 7 AM	
	Ordovician 500,000,000		
		Nov. 20, 11 AM	
	Cambrian 600,000,000		
		Nov. 13, 8 AM	
		Jan. 1–Nov. 13	

Life record labels: ALGAE, FUNGI, MOSSES, FERNS, CONIFERS, SPONGES, ANGIOSPERMS, TRILOBITES (EXTINCT), CRUSTACEANS, INSECTS, ARACHNIDS, OSTRACODERMS (EXTINCT), FISHES, AMPHIBIANS, REPTILES, DINOSAURS (EXTINCT), BIRDS, MAMMALS

IMPORTANT POINTS

• Life may be viewed as an ever-changing stream. It began on the earth between two and three billion years ago. The earliest forms of life were very simple. But with the passage of time, more than a million and a half species of organisms have appeared. Many of the earlier forms of life are now extinct.

• The evidences of change are numerous: fossils, the distribution of species, similarities of anatomy and embryonic development, vestigial organs, the sameness of chemical reactions among different organisms.

• Although life is estimated to have begun more than two billion years ago, only a fraction of that time, about 600,000,000 years, is clearly recorded by fossils.

• The last 600 million years is divided into three eras: Paleozoic, Mesozoic, and Cenozoic. Each era is divided into periods. The eras and periods are marked by geologic changes that influenced the kind of life that could survive.

• Life was abundant during the first part of the Paleozoic, but it was confined to the water. Later in the era certain plants and animals established themselves on the land. During the late Paleozoic, amphibians became the dominant forms of vertebrate life.

• The Mesozoic Era is often described as the Age of Reptiles. The Cenozoic Era is the Age of Mammals. Modern man appeared upon the earth only during the last 50,000 years.

REVIEW QUESTIONS

1. How do more recent fossils differ from older ones?
2. Why do island animals frequently differ from animals of the nearby mainland?
3. Can you offer an explanation for the "finger bones" in the whale's flipper?
4. What is the Recapitulation Theory?
5. How does the study of fossils establish the sequence of change in plants and animals?
6. Describe several ways in which fossils are formed.
7. Which era is called the Age of Reptiles?
8. What is the most outstanding occurrence of the Pleistocene Epoch?
9. Why are pouched mammals confined mainly to Australia and Tasmania?
10. Why are vestigial organs regarded as evidence of long-term changes in the organisms bearing them?

CHECK YOUR UNDERSTANDING

11. How may animal relationships be established from a study of their embryos?
12. How can "blood tests" establish a degree of relationship among different animals?
13. How can radioactive rocks be dated?
14. How is stratified rock formed?
15. How does the paleontologist estimate the age of a fossil?
16. What is the chief cause of extinction of species?
17. What are the distinguishing features of the Paleozoic, Mesozoic, and Cenozoic Eras?
18. Fossils suggest that the first land plants appeared before the first land animals. Can you suggest reasons why this is so?
19. Has the stream of life "arrived," or is it likely to change as much in the future as it has in the past?
20. Numerous fossils of early horses and numerous fossils of dinosaurs have been found in our western states. They are never found in the same rock strata. Why is this so?
21. Why are fossils of marine animals sometimes found in mountainous areas?
22. How could coal deposits at the bottom of the sea be explained?

RESEARCH PROJECTS AND REPORTS

1. Obtain information from your school or public library and prepare a report on one of the following topics:

   The Distribution of Animals   **The Dating of Rocks**

   The Recapitulation Theory   **The Pleistocene Epoch**

2. *Collecting and Identifying Fossils:* Is your region of the country rich in fossils? There may be more fossils in the rocks of your area than you imagine. Consult the curator of a nearby museum to learn how to collect them.

   Keep a systematic record of your fossils. Note the location, the types of rocks in which they were found, other fossils that have turned up nearby, and other information that you think may be important. Identify and label your fossils from illustrations in textbooks of geology and paleontology, and by comparing them with museum specimens. This project may be undertaken singly, or with several members of your class.

3. *The Geographic Distribution of Mammals:* Select five or six wild mammals and their close relatives (same family or genus) and determine the areas of the world where they are native. Mark the places where they are found on an outline map of the world by using a different color for each mammal (colored pins or crayons).

   Can you advance any reasons as to their overall distribution? Why are certain mammals confined to one or two continents? Why are certain others more widespread?

FURTHER READING

The Fossil Book: A Record of Prehistoric Life. C. L. Fenton. Doubleday and Co.,
New York, N.Y. An excellent account of life's long history as documented by
fossils.

Life of the Past. George G. Simpson. Yale University Press, New Haven, Conn.
A foremost paleontologist has written an excellent introduction to his subject
field.

"**The Ancient Life of the Antarctic.**" George A. Doumani and William E. Long.
Scientific American, September, 1962. The snow and ice of the Antarctic continent cover a land where temperate forests once grew.

"**Pre-Cambrian Animals.**" Martin F. Glaessner. *Scientific American,* March, 1961.
Discovery in South Australia of fossil animals that lived before the Cambrian
Period may extend our knowledge of life's early beginnings.

The Age of Reptiles. Edwin H. Colbert. W. W. Norton and Co., New York. A well-
illustrated account of one of the most remarkable ages in the history of life.

11

The Mechanism of Change

As THE EVIDENCES of change in living things accumulated, older ideas gave way to newer ones. For many years it was believed that each species of plant and animal came into being as a result of some special and separate creation. Today's biologist, however, no longer holds these views. He has evidence that species arise from pre-existing species, and that new species result from changes in older ones. The process by which species change is called *evolution.* Evolution is a gradual process. Operating over millions of years, however, it changes the stream of life.

The idea of evolution came to be more and more accepted over the last few centuries. But its mechanism was not always understood. By what means do living things change? What factors operate to cause these changes? And finally, how do new species arise?

Many theories of evolution have been advanced to answer these questions. Most have been discarded, however, because they have not stood the test of observation. But one theory proposed more than 100 years ago has become one of the foundations of modern biology. This is the *Theory of Natural Selection* of Charles Darwin. With certain modifications, natural selec-

tion is still regarded as the explanation of the change the biologist observes.

Theories of Change Before Darwin

For many years the significance of fossils was misunderstood. Although they had been found at different times and in different places for several thousand years, most naturalists considered them oddly formed pieces of rock. Only in the last few centuries did their true nature become clear. In 1770, Charles Bonnet, a Swiss naturalist, suggested that fossils were ancient forms of life that perished during the great upheavals of the earth's past.

The study of fossils was placed on a firmer foundation by William Smith, an English geologist. In 1791, while digging a canal, he noticed that different layers of rock contained different kinds of fossils. Smith argued that rock strata are laid down successively with the passage of time. Thus, the fossils in strata provide the paleontologist with a rough calendar of events. The deeper he goes into this natural "layer cake" of fossils, the less the organisms resemble modern forms. The most recently formed layers, however, contain fossils that are strikingly similar to modern plants and

11–1 Fossil in ripple-marked Cambrian sandstone. About 500 million years ago, a worm-like animal left tracks in the soft mud of the sea floor which later hardened into rock.

animals. Although the early fossil hunters observed both change and continuity, they had no ideas to explain the evolution that had occurred.

LAMARCK AND THE THEORY OF USE AND DISUSE. The first plausible theory of evolution was proposed by the French naturalist Jean Baptiste Lamarck in 1809. In his book, *Zoological Philosophy,* Lamarck suggested that animals would change over long periods of time because of:

1. The use and disuse of certain structures.
2. The development of these structures in response to need.
3. The inheritance of acquired characters.

Lamarck argued that organisms adapted themselves to their environments by using certain parts and neglecting others. The continual use of certain structures would lead to their increased development, while neglected or "disused" structures would tend to disappear.

There is some logic in these assumptions, as can be confirmed by common observation. Runners, for example, develop strong leg muscles; pitchers develop strong arm muscles. Similarly, the failure to exercise muscles causes them to become flabby.

To illustrate how this theory could explain change in an animal, Lamarck selected the giraffe as an example. How did the giraffe get its long neck? According to Lamarck, the giraffe probably descended from an antelopelike ancestor that continually stretched its neck in order to browse on the leaves of trees. In a lifetime of stretching, its neck became a little longer. This trait (the longer neck) was then passed on to its offspring who continued the habit of stretching. Each generation added to the length of the neck by stretching higher and higher as it browsed. Over thousands of generations, small changes added up to big changes. In this manner, the antelopelike ancestor finally produced the longnecked giraffe of modern times.

THE FALLACY OF LAMARCK'S THEORY. Lamarck's theory had the appeal of logic, but its basic fallacy lay in the assumption that acquired characteristics could be transmitted to offspring. The modern biologist might accept the idea that a giraffe's neck would be somewhat lengthened by a lifetime of stretching. But he would not accept the idea that the added neck length would appear in the next generation—*acquired characters are not inherited.*

Traits are transmitted from parent to offspring by way of the genes. Altered body structures based on use and disuse do not alter the genes. In fact, it is just the reverse. It is the altered gene that can alter body traits in the offspring.

We must remember that Lamarck knew nothing of genes. Even the basic laws of heredity, later discovered by Mendel, were unknown at the time. And the discovery of genes and their role in heredity was a full century away.

11–2 Giraffe

11–3 Jean Baptiste Lamarck

Nevertheless, even in Lamarck's day, some biologists were skeptical of his views. One reason for their skepticism was the fact that his theory was incomplete. Certain characteristics could not be "explained" at all. How, for example, did the giraffe get his mottled coat? "Use and disuse" had no answer.

WEISMANN AND THE CONTINUITY OF THE GERM PLASM. The German biologist August Weismann is generally credited with disproving Lamarck's theory of evolution in the laboratory. Weismann cut off the tails of new-born mice for twenty generations. Yet the tails of the twenty-first generation turned out to be just as long as those of the first generation. Removing a mouse's tail apparently had no effect on future generations. Most biologists today regard Weismann's experiment with mice as trivial. However, his observations led to an important advance in biological thinking. The alteration of body cells, Weismann argued, could not be transmitted to the next generation because the alterations did not affect the reproductive cells. Organisms, he explained, had two types of cells: body cells, or *somatoplasm* and reproductive cells, or *germ plasm.* Although the somatoplasm was the carrier of the germ plasm, it did not directly affect it. Instead, the reverse was true. It was the germ plasm that moved from generation to generation in a continuous stream and produced the somatoplasm in each generation.

Weismann's *Theory of the Continuity of the Germ Plasm* turned old ways of thinking upside down. One wit explained it by saying, "a hen is only an egg's way of making another egg." However, the later discovery of genes verified the basic correctness of his views.

Darwin's Theory of Natural Selection

In 1859, Charles Darwin published a book entitled *On the Origin of Species by Means of Natural Selection, or the Preservation of Favoured Races in the Struggle for Life. The Origin of Species,* as it is now known, had an immediate and profound impact upon biological thinking—more perhaps than any other scientific work. In his book, Darwin advanced the Theory of Natural Selection as the explanation of how species evolve. With some modification, his theory is still adhered to today.

How Natural Selection Works. Darwin's Theory of Natural Selection rested upon four key ideas:

1. All organisms tend to *overpopulation.*
2. Overpopulation leads to a *struggle for existence.*
3. The individuals of any species exhibit *variations.*
4. Variations may assist or hinder individuals in the struggle for existence, and the *best adapted individuals survive,* reproduce, and pass on favorable variations.

All species, Darwin noted, overproduce offspring. Plants produce thousands of seeds. Fish produce millions of eggs. If all the seeds of a single type of tree grew to maturity, the descendants would cover the earth in a few centuries. If all the eggs of a single pair of salmon developed to adulthood for a few dozen generations, the seas would be choked with salmon. These situations do not and cannot occur. In spite of their great reproductive potential, the populations of organisms tend to remain stable. The limitations of food and space, plus the destructive work of natural enemies mean that more offspring die than survive. Life is a "struggle for existence" in which the young of a species compete with each other for the necessities of life. The individuals that are favorably adapted compete successfully and live to reproduce and pass on favorable adaptations to offspring. Thus, in each generation the fittest individuals are naturally selected to be the parents of the next generation.

Why are some individuals successful in the struggle for life, while others are not? The members of any plant or animal population, Darwin pointed out, are never exactly alike. Individual animals, for example, vary in such traits as size, shape, color, speed, intelligence, and so forth. If certain variations make the animal better adapted to its environment, it survives and transmits its favorable traits to its offspring. If certain variations make the animal poorly adapted to its environment, it does not survive long enough to transmit its adverse traits to the next generation. Thus, in time, certain traits within a species become accentuated, while other traits disappear.

Natural selection can explain the giraffe's long neck more logically than Lamarck's "use and disuse." In any population of giraffes, the neck lengths vary. The longer-necked individuals compete more successfully for food since they are able to reach

11-4 Study in Charles Darwin's house at Down.

the leaves on the higher branches. Thus, they survive and transmit their favorable trait (a longer neck) to their offspring. The shorter-necked individuals, however, can reach only the lower branches where food is less plentiful. Competition for a limited food supply causes many of them to starve and die off. Thus, their unfavorable trait (a shorter neck) is less frequently transmitted to offspring and, in time, disappears.

Furthermore, natural selection can just as easily explain the giraffe's mottled coat, a trait which "use and disuse" could not account for. Giraffes with splotchy coats are not easily noticed in the dappled shade of trees and are therefore less likely to be killed off by predators. Giraffes with solid coats, however, can be more readily seen and are killed off in larger numbers. In time, more mottle-coated giraffes survive and transmit this trait to their offspring, while giraffes without mottling gradually disappear.

To support his theory of natural selection, Darwin pointed out that plants and animals change under domestication. The farmer produces high-milk-yielding cows; the horse breeder produces muscular horses for work and light horses for racing. The agriculturist produces superior grains for human consumption. In each case these different plants and animals are produced by selection of the parental stock having the desired traits.

THE FINCHES OF GALAPAGOS ISLANDS. Darwin's conclusions did not arise full-blown out of thin air. They represented years of thoughtful interpretation of his observations. At 22, young Darwin was appointed naturalist aboard the *H.M.S. Beagle* on her five-year voyage of exploration. The specimens he collected on this long voyage came from many regions of the earth. By voyage end, Darwin had numerous notebooks crammed with observations and discoveries. These became the basis of *The Origin of Species* 23 years later.

In September 1835, Darwin landed in the Galapagos (guh-LAH-puh-gus) Islands, a Pacific group 600 miles off the coast of Ecuador. There he found and described 13 closely related species of finches. These sparrowlike birds are known to this day as "Darwin's finches." All of them resembled and were probably descended from a single species that lived on the South American mainland. This discovery marked a turning point in the young naturalist's ideas about how species might have evolved.

What puzzled Darwin was the fact that the Galapagos Islands had never been connected to the mainland but had arisen by volcanic activity from the ocean floor. The original finch ancestor, therefore, had probably come from the mainland. Yet now there were 13 separate species, each with differently shaped bills and different diets. Some were insect feeders, some fed on cacti, and some were seed eaters like the mainland finch.

Here was a case of *adaptive radiation.* A single species, by adaptation to different

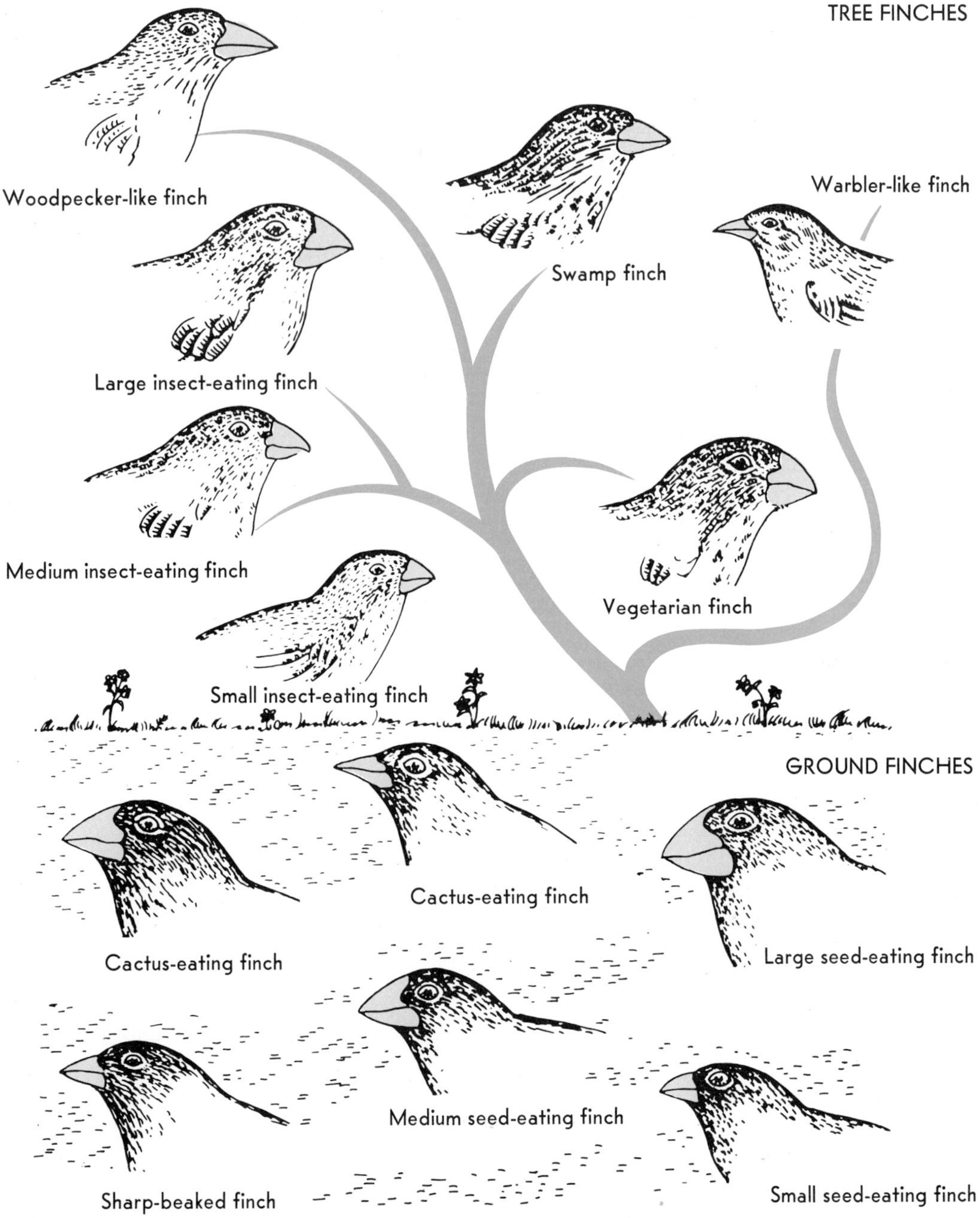

Woodpecker-like finch

Swamp finch

Warbler-like finch

Large insect-eating finch

Medium insect-eating finch

Small insect-eating finch

Vegetarian finch

GROUND FINCHES

Cactus-eating finch

Cactus-eating finch

Large seed-eating finch

Sharp-beaked finch

Medium seed-eating finch

Small seed-eating finch

11–5 "Darwin's finches" demonstrate adaptive radiation of species on the Galapagos Islands. The first finches that came to the islands from the mainland probably had bills adapted for eating small seeds. When such seeds became scarce, bill variations enabled some finches to survive on different kinds of seeds and on other available food.

diets, had radiated into a number of species. Yet on the mainland the finch had not followed this adaptation to different diets and had remained a single species.

What mechanism of life explained these facts? This question occupied Darwin's thoughts for a long time. Years later the pieces fell into place. He found the answer while reading an *Essay on the Principle of Population* published in 1798 by Thomas Malthus, an English clergyman. In his *Essay,* Malthus advanced the theory that since human population tends to double every twenty-five years, while food resources increase at a much slower rate, the pressure of population against limited food would, in time, mean starvation for a large portion of humanity.

Here was the answer to the problem of the finches—*population pressure.* The seed-eating finches that first arrived from the mainland soon multiplied to a point where seeds became scarce. In the struggle for existence the weaker, less well adapted, failed to survive and reproduce. **Variations** in the structure of the bill assisted some birds in the struggle. Finches with longer, broader, or stronger bills could obtain different kinds of food. They switched their diets to insects, cactus stems, or harder seeds that the original finches could not eat. With each generation these variations in bill structure became more pronounced. Through the years, development along different lines produced the many species of Galapagos finches Darwin had observed. The finch that remained on the more crowded mainland did not evolve into other species because com-

11–6 Wallace observed marked differences between the plants and animals of the eastern and western islands of the East Indies. "Wallace's line," which curves between Borneo and Celebes and between Bali and Lambok, extends from Asia to Australia.

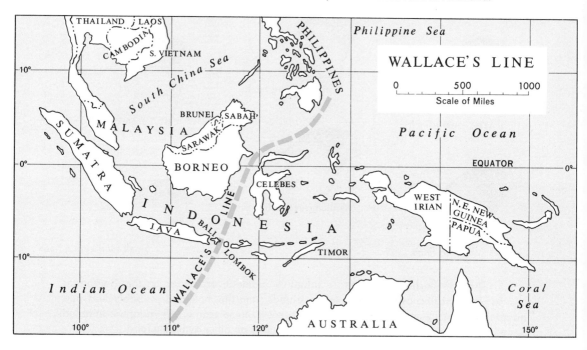

peting birds monopolized other types of food and restricted the finch to its original diet of seeds.

DARWIN AND WALLACE. The history of scientific discovery abounds with instances where persons arrive independently and simultaneously at the same conclusions. Such was the case with the theory of natural selection. In 1858, a year before *The Origin of Species* was published, Darwin received a manuscript from his friend Alfred Russell Wallace, a Welsh naturalist in the East Indies at the time. Wallace was unaware that Darwin had been working on his book for the past 14 years. Yet in his manuscript he advanced a theory of evolution that was exactly like Darwin's.

Like Darwin, Wallace also traveled around the world studying plants and animals. During his voyage he was struck by the sharp differences between the animals of the eastern and western islands of the East Indies. Because of his accurate descriptions, the boundary separating these different forms is still called the "Wallace line." Puzzling over his observations he, too, read Malthus and arrived at the same conclusions: the explanation for these differences lay in natural selection.

Darwin was so amazed by this coincidence that he offered to present his theory as a joint discovery. On July 1, 1858, at a meeting of the Linnean Society, papers submitted by both men were read and given equal credit. The next year *The Origin of Species* was published. The first edition was sold out on the day of publication.

THE SPEED OF EVOLUTION. Normally we think of evolution as a process requiring millions of years to effect change. When organisms reproduce rapidly, however, we can observe some changes within a comparatively short time.

About 25 years ago, when antibiotics were first introduced into medical practice, they were hailed as "miracle drugs." In a given population of bacteria, practically all were killed. But a few resistant bacteria survived. These were the variants that have since produced "antibiotic-resistant" strains that cause concern to physicians today.

A similar situation developed in connection with the use of the insecticide DDT. At first it was highly effective against houseflies and mosquitoes. The war against them seemed to have been won. But among these insects there were individuals whose resistance to DDT was very high. These survived and produced a DDT-resistant population. Today this chemical is not as effective as it was originally.

Evolution Since Darwin

Although Darwin's Theory of Natural Selection is the backbone, the major supporting framework, of modern evolutionary theory, it is still only part of it. One question remained unanswered even after the widespread acceptance of his theory. We know that plants and animals vary. But how do these variations arise? Darwin did not attempt to answer this.

It is not difficult to understand the problem this question raised in Darwin's time. Mendel's work was published in 1866, seven years after Darwin's. His study of heredity might have supplied some of the answers, but it was overlooked. The investigation of the nucleus of the cell was just beginning. Chromosomes and genes were undiscovered. The mechanism of reproduction was not clearly understood. And it is this mechanism that provides us with an understanding of how variations can occur.

Today, more than a century after the publication of Darwin's work, biologists understand that variations arise in two ways by:

1. Gene recombination.
2. Mutation, or change in the nature of the genetic material.

Milestones in Biology

Charles Darwin
1809–1882

DARWIN'S THEORY OF EVOLUTION provides a foundation for all current biological theory. One of the unusual facts in the history of biology is that the man responsible for the theory was not trained as a biologist. Some of his contemporaries considered Darwin a dilettante rather than a scientist. Yet Darwin's theory has been acclaimed as one of the truly great achievements of the human mind.

Charles Darwin was born in Shrewsbury, England, February 12, 1809. His family was a distinguished one. His grandfather was Erasmus Darwin, an eminent botanist and physician. Young Charles found school a dull place. It was much more fun to spend his days outdoors collecting plants, insects, and minerals. When it was time to attend the university, his father thought he should become a physician. Two years at the University of Edinburg convinced both father and son that a medical career would be a mistake. Charles then entered Cambridge University to study for the ministry, but he soon proved little suited for this career as well.

At Cambridge, Darwin met and became friends with Professor John Henslow. Henslow encouraged Darwin to continue with his work in natural history. Darwin kept his interest alive by collecting birds and insects and by reading the works of the famous naturalists of his time.

In 1831, shortly after his graduation from Cambridge, Darwin was invited to become the naturalist aboard H.M.S. Beagle, a ship that was embarking upon a round-the-world cruise.

Setting sail from Plymouth, December 27, 1831, the Beagle did not return until October, 1836. During these five years the Beagle stopped at many places along the coast of South America, at Tahiti, New Zealand, and Australia. In the Galapagos Islands Darwin first began to formulate the theory of natural selection. But it was not until November, 1859, that the first edition of The Origin of Species was published. In this book Darwin explained how he thought new species must have arisen by natural selection.

RECOMBINATION. In your study of genetics (Chapter 8), you learned that the genes are segregated when the *gametes* (GAM-eets), or reproductive cells, are formed. During fertilization, the segregated genes recombine, forming new combinations of the genetic material. The simplest kind of gene recombination was illustrated by the crossing of pink four-o'clocks. You will recall that when the hybrid pinks are crossed we get three kinds of flowers: white, pink, and red. In other words, identical parents produce three varieties of offspring as a result of segregation and recombination of genes. The value of gene recombination generally is that it can create new phenotypes that have survival advantage in a given environment. An example of this may be seen in sickle-cell anemia (page 160). In this condition, the combination of the allele for normal hemoglobin, S, with the allele for sickling, s, increases resistance to malaria. The ss combination of alleles results in early death. The SS combination produces normal hemoglobin with no resistance to malaria. In a malarial environment, therefore, the Ss combination has great survival value.

Now consider a more complicated case of recombination when Mendel crossed dihybrid, yellow-round garden peas. These identical parents produced nine different gene combinations (genotypes) resulting in four different phenotypes (Figure 8–10). From the illustrations of four-o'clocks and peas an important fact emerges: *identical parents can produce a variety of offspring through genetic recombination.*

We can calculate the number of different types of gametes that are possible from the number of chromosome pairs in the parent. A parent cell having only a single pair of chromosomes can produce at most two different gametes. A parent cell having two pairs of chromosomes can produce four gamete types. A parent cell containing three pairs can produce eight gamete types. And a human being with twenty-three pairs of chromosomes has the potential of producing 2^{23} gamete types which is 8,388,608! This calculation does not include the possibilities presented by other means of gene recombination, such as crossing over and nondisjunction (page 137). Crossing over increases the number of recombinations of linked genes. Nondisjunction alters the number of chromosomes in the zygote and produces changes in the phenotype.

The effects of recombination are clearly seen in the human family. The rich variety of human differences and varying human talents is the result of recombining the huge number of genes which are part of the forty-six chromosomes. In the small family unit we might expect a degree of likeness, and this is often the case. Families do have strong resemblances running through them. But brothers and sisters differ in many ways. These differences we attribute to the enormous number of gene recombinations that are possible, even though the parents are the same.

Several important points should be noted about recombination. In the first place, no change in the genetic material occurs. The same genes exist in the gene pool, although they occur in different combinations in the individuals. Secondly, sexual reproduction is necessary to produce the recombination of genes. Thus, we see the great advantage of sexual reproduction is that it provides the means for creating variety in organisms. Finally, recombination is a random process; it gives no direction to evolution but only provides a basis by which evolution can occur.

MUTATIONS. Mutations are sudden alterations in the genetic material of an organism. Many biologists consider mutations to be the raw material of evolution, since the changes occur in the chemical structure of the genes themselves. A gene may be

KAIBAB

NORTH RIM   GRAND CANYON   SOUTH RIM

ABERT

11–7   Separated by the Grand Canyon, the Kaibab and Abert squirrels demonstrate genetic isolation and are now unable to interbreed.

thought of as a sequence of nucleotides on the DNA molecule that specifies the formation of one protein. In some cases, a gene may specify the formation of a smaller polypeptide which is part of a large protein molecule. Hemoglobin, for example, is composed of four polypeptide chains, each of which is specified by a separate gene. *Any change in the nucleotide sequence of the gene alters the polypeptide or protein formed and produces a mutation.*

Let us consider sickle-cell anemia again. The cause of the mutant allele for sickling is an altered *codon*. Recall that a codon is a triplet of nucleotides that specifies one amino acid. The codon GAA specifies glutamic acid. The codon GUA specifies valine. The substitution of one nucleotide changes GAA to GUA. The change in the codon changes the amino acid specified from glutamic acid to valine. The substitution of valine in the polypeptide chain is

the cause of the mutation known as sickling. Experiments with bacteria and viruses have confirmed the fact that the alteration of the sequence and kind of nucleotides in DNA is the cause of mutations.

Sudden changes in the characteristics of organisms were known even in Darwin's day. The changed organism, or *mutant*, was called a 'sport.' However, the first scientific investigations of mutations were made at the turn of the century by Hugo DeVries, the Dutch botanist who rediscovered Mendel's earlier work. Examining a field of evening primroses, he noticed a few plants that were distinctly different from the rest. When he bred these plants, he found that they preserved their new traits.

DeVries coined the term "mutation" to explain his new strains, then went on to formulate his Mutation Theory of Evolution. Mutations, he argued, could give rise to new characteristics in a population very quickly. Hence, evolution probably proceeded by sudden jumps rather than by gradual advances.

Although they did not understand their origin, breeders have been quick to exploit mutations to establish new lines. For example, the Ancon sheep, a short-legged variety of sheep that cannot jump fences, was established from a mutant that appeared in a normal flock in Massachusetts in 1791. Short-horned breeds of cattle are also mutants. Some common plants, such as seedless oranges and Concord grapes, began as mutants.

Modern genetic studies indicate that most mutations are harmful. Very few confer survival advantages. For example, the mutation of hemophilia would probably cause the death of a person attempting to live in primitive surroundings. Further, mutations are found to occur at very low rates. The rate at which they occur varies from one gene to another. Hemophilia appears as a mutant once in every 50,000 reproductive cells. An average figure for the rate of mutations in higher organisms is one gene per 100,000 gametes.

The fact that mutations are rare and are generally harmful has led some people to question their role in evolution. But the facts about mutations can be misleading. To begin with, if we multiply the mutation rate of one per 100,000 by the enormous number of gametes produced by organisms, the number does not appear to be low at all. In the case of most mammals, about five million genes are required to provide instructions for the reproduction of the organism. A single change in any nucleotide sequence in the DNA of a gamete results in a mutation. Thus, the actual number of mutations produced can be quite high even though the mutant may not exhibit such marked changes as the short-legged sheep or hornless cattle. Furthermore, even mutations that appear to be harmful, as in sickle-cell anemia, may give the organism an advantage that is not obvious. Still another factor to keep in mind is that the living things of the present world have evolved over several billion years. In this vast period of time, the number of mutations having survival value that have accumulated in organisms represents a staggering figure.

HOW NEW SPECIES ARISE. How do today's biologists define a species? You may think this is an easy task, but it is not. We may begin by saying that *a species consists of a population of living things having a common gene pool.* Because they share the same gene pool, the members of the population generally have the same structural and functional characteristics. All horses resemble each other and have functions in common. The same is true of various breeds of domestic dogs. A second characteristic of a species is that, *under natural conditions, the members of the species do not interbreed with other species.* Note that the statement reads *"do not interbreed."* This does not mean that different species *cannot* interbreed. For example, the horse and donkey, which are separate species, can interbreed to produce the mule. The hybrid mule, however, is sterile and cannot reproduce. The inability of the mule to have offspring blocks any further mingling of the gene pools of the horse and donkey. Similarly, certain species of plants do not cross-pollinate in nature, yet can produce hybrids when they are artificially cross-pollinated by man. What conditions produce the populations of related organisms that do not interbreed? If we identify these conditions, we can explain how new species arise.

Darwin's finches offer a good example of how new species may have arisen through *geographic isolation.* The first finches to reach the Galapagos Islands carried a very small sampling of the gene pool of the parent finch population on the mainland. Six

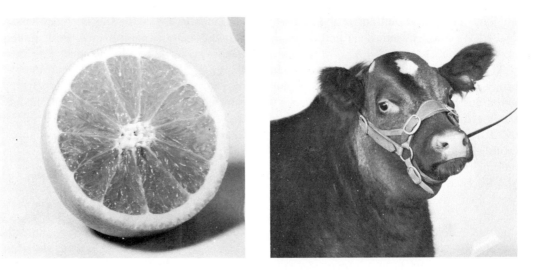

11–8 The seedless orange and the shorthorn steer are mutants of special value to man.

hundred miles of ocean now separated the island finches from the mainland birds. As the island birds reproduced, a new gene pool having different gene frequencies was established. Mutations altered the gene pool further. *Selection* within the gene pool also occurred because of food differences on the islands. Isolation from the mainland population sharpened whatever variations were produced. In time, thirteen distinct species evolved among the island finches.

Why do the gene frequencies of isolated populations differ from those of the parent group? Perhaps we can understand this as a chance factor if we use an analogy. Think of a gene pool as a large number of marbles in a container. For simplicity, imagine that there are equal numbers of red and white marbles totalling one thousand. Suppose we take a random sample of this gene pool by removing ten marbles with a scoop. By pure chance we might scoop up two white marbles and eight red ones. In another sample we might obtain six white and four red. The small sample (in all probability)

would not be representative of the gene frequency of the large group. In the same way, the gene distribution of the small group of finches that made their way from the mainland to the Galapagos Islands was not representative of the gene pool of the parent group.

Over long periods of time, geographic isolation may produce *genetic isolation.* Genetic isolation is the inability of closely related species to interbreed. This kind of isolation is the ultimate step in separating one species from another.

DARWINISM IN THE LAST CENTURY. Darwin's explanation of the processes of change in species immediately provoked a storm of opposition. His ideas ran counter to the science and religion of his day. The principal criticism came from those who felt that he reduced man's position from the center of all living things to that of a single species, subject to the same evolutionary processes as other species.

With the passage of time his work came to be more and more accepted. Today, natural selection stands as one of the great unifying theories of biology. Perhaps the most eloquent description of the changing stream of life was written by Charles Darwin himself in the final paragraph of his book, *The Origin of Species*.

"There is grandeur in this view of life, with its several powers, having been originally breathed by the Creator into a few forms or into one; and that, while this planet has gone circling on according to the fixed law of gravity, from so simple a beginning endless forms most beautiful and most wonderful have been, and are being evolved."

IMPORTANT POINTS

• New species arise as a result of changes in pre-existing species over long periods of time. This process of change is called evolution. Several explanations of evolution have been proposed.

• The first modern theory of evolution was Lamarck's theory of "use and disuse." Lamarck's theory rested on the assumption that traits acquired during an organism's lifetime could be transmitted to offspring. Weismann and other scientists demonstrated that acquired characters could not be inherited and Lamarck's theory failed.

• Darwin's theory of natural selection is accepted today as the explanation of the mechanism of evolution. Organisms overproduce, then struggle to survive. The success or failure in this struggle depends on inherited variations. Organisms with favorable variations survive and transmit these variations to the next generation. Organisms with unfavorable variations are eventually eliminated because they do not survive and reproduce. Natural selection results in better adaptation to ever changing environments, hence it results in new species.

• Variations arise through gene recombinations and through mutations. Since mutations result from changes in the genetic material of the organism, the changing stream of life is essentially a changing genetic stream.

• Modern biologists recognize isolation as one of the most important factors in the origin of new species. Small fractions of larger populations that become geographically isolated from the larger group generally carry gene pools that are not representative of the larger group. Mutations and selection within isolated groups eventually lead to genetic isolation and the creation of new species.

REVIEW QUESTIONS

1. What is the major fallacy of Lamarck's theory of use and disuse?
2. According to Weismann's theory, what is the difference between the germ plasm and the somatoplasm?
3. How does the struggle for existence lead to the development of new species?

4. What is the importance of variation in natural selection?
5. Why would domesticated animals be considered an example of man-controlled evolution?
6. What is meant by adaptive radiation? Give an example.
7. List two ways in which variations arise.
8. Suppose a certain animal depended for its survival on the speed by which it was able to escape its carnivorous enemies. How would its species develop according to the theory of use and disuse? According to the theory of natural selection?
9. Suppose the animal in question 8 also depended on protective coloration to survive in the midst of its enemies. Could the Lamarckian theory explain the development of coloration in the species? Could the Darwinian theory explain it?
10. Upon what four key ideas does the theory of natural selection rest?
11. Why is Darwin's visit to the Galapagos Islands considered a turning point in his formulation of the theory of natural selection?

CHECK YOUR UNDERSTANDING

12. Most mutations that arise in species soon disappear. Why?
13. Why did Darwin's ideas provoke opposition when they were first advanced?
14. Why do you think Darwin's ideas are generally accepted today?
15. Why are mutations said to be the raw material of evolution?
16. Why is the rate of evolution likely to be greater in micro-organisms than in mammals?
17. Suppose, as a result of atomic explosions, that world-wide radioactivity were raised to a much higher level than it is today. What effect would this have on species in the future? Discuss.
18. A powerful insecticide discovered today is likely to be less effective ten years from now. Why?
19. Many animals that live in caves are born blind. Can this fact be explained by natural selection?
20. How does geographic isolation lead to genetic isolation?

RESEARCH PROJECTS AND REPORTS

1. Obtain information from your school or public library and prepare a report on one of the following topics:

The Voyage of the Beagle	August Weismann
Alfred Russell Wallace	Flora and Fauna of the Galapagos

2. *Study of Variations:* You may select a number of characteristics in any species to study variations. For example, you can:
   (a) Secure 100 lima beans and measure their individual lengths in millimeters. Some will be shorter, some will be longer, but most of them will cluster around an "average" length. Make a graph of your results.

(b) Measure the following traits among members of your school population who are of the same age and sex: height, weight, shoe size, glove size, hat size, and so forth. Make a graph of your results.

(c) Select some other trait in a common organism and measure its variation. The height, date of blooming, or color of certain garden flowers are some possibilities.

3. ***Origin of Certain Domesticated Plants and Animals:*** Angus, Jersey, and Holstein cattle; hybrid corn; Leghorn chickens; French poodles; German shepherds; St. Bernard dogs; and Ancon sheep are but a few of the useful breeds that man has developed.

Select one or two domesticated breeds of plant or animal and find out how they have been developed and maintained. Your best sources for information are full-size encyclopedias. If you are researching the origin of a particular breed of dog, your local kennel society can suggest sources of information.

What are the chances that these breeds would come into being through natural selection? Could these breeds continue without man's intervention? Why is artificial selection sometimes called "man-controlled evolution"?

FURTHER READING

The Origin of Species. Charles Darwin. Frederick Ungar, New York, N.Y. This is an abridged edition of Darwin's great classic. Preserves the gist and flavor of the original.

The Voyage of the Beagle. Charles Darwin. Bantam Books, Inc., New York, N.Y. The journal of Darwin's trip around the world, which led to his famous theory of evolution.

Evolution. Ruth Moore. Life Nature Library, Time Inc., New York, N.Y. Beautifully illustrated story of man's understanding of evolution from the early thinkers to the present-day geneticists.

Evolution in Action. Julian Huxley. Harper and Brothers, New York, N.Y. One of today's foremost scientists discusses evolution and how it affects man's future.

Human Evolution: Physical Anthropology and the Origin of Man. Gabriel W. Lasker. Holt, Rinehart and Winston, Inc., New York, N.Y. A concise and nontechnical presentation for the student and general reader.

Evolution and Human Behavior. Alexander Alland, Jr. Natural History Press, Garden City, New York. The author combines a discussion of evolution with genetics and human behavior in a stimulating manner.

The Primitive Forms of Life

IN THE 2400 YEARS that mark the growth of biology as a science, over a million and a half different forms of living things have been discovered. Biologists, however, do not believe that all the forms of life have been identified. There are still large areas of the earth that have not been thoroughly explored: the polar regions, deserts, and dense jungles. The depths of the seas still conceal many mysterious forms of life.

The organization of the life sciences began with the ancient Greeks, with Aristotle and his student Theophrastus. Classification was given new direction by Linnaeus, the Swedish botanist, and by Darwin, the English naturalist. The similarities of living things have led to new ideas about their origin.

Most people have little acquaintance with the primitive forms of life. In their experience, living things consist of the higher forms of plant and animal life seen in gardens and on farms. These highly specialized organisms did not even exist on the earth 200 million years ago. Most ancient organisms were probably single-celled and resembled the Monerans and Protists of today.

When the seas were formed, the land was rocky and barren and without soil. There were no living things. Much later, the simplest organisms began to appear in the seas. Some of these early living forms used radiant energy from the sun to make their food and build protoplasm.

What these first organisms were like is something of a mystery. There is little evidence of these soft-bodied, primitive ancestors of modern life that have been preserved in the rocks. The only clues we have are given by their descendants, the monerans and protists that abound in the modern seas.

The outlines of the early seas were marked by constant change. In some places the entire sea floor slowly dried as the land masses pushed upward. In other places only the shore rose, leaving land where the edge of the sea had been. As the seas dried, some living things became established on land in the sun and air. Certain ones remained at the tidal edge of the shore. Others survived on land to which the sea would never return. Hundreds of millions of years were required for the slow change from a sea-dwelling to land-dwelling existence.

More complex forms of life resulted from this invasion of the land. Conditions on the land were harsher than in the sea. Tiny mosses and liverworts appeared. Simple animals established themselves on the tidal flats. Tall ferns appeared later. These ferns formed the huge forests that became coal. Meanwhile, other organisms obtained food without chlorophyll. These were the bacteria and fungi. Last to develop were the organisms that were more completely adapted to life on the land.

CHAPTER

12

The Monerans
Blue-Green Algae and Bacteria

THE MONERAN KINGDOM consists of only two phyla: the phylum Cyanophyta, the *blue-green algae,* and the phylum Schizophyta, the *bacteria.* One fundamental difference separates the two phyla: the blue-green algae contain the pigment chlorophyll; the bacteria do not. Since they contain chlorophyll, the algae are *autotrophs,* or self-feeders. They make their food by photosynthesis. The bacteria, however, cannot make their food and must depend on organic material from outside sources. They do not need sunlight. Often, they dwell in darkness.

The members of the Moneran Kingdom are generally believed to be the most primitive of all living things. Although some of them exist in filaments or colonies, most are typically single-celled. Their cells reveal their primitive nature. They have no organized nucleus; there are no chloroplasts or mitochondria. It is this absence of organized cell structures that has led biologists to believe that the blue-green algae and bacteria are closely related. In the distant past, these two phyla may have evolved from a common ancestral cell. The typical

method of reproduction is *fission,* the process whereby a single cell divides to become two "daughter cells." So primitive are the cells of monerans that many biologists are of the opinion that they furnish us with clues about the nature of the first living things that appeared on earth.

Cyanophyta: Blue-Green Algae

The blue-green algae are the simplest of all the self-feeding organisms, or autotrophs. Despite their name, their color also ranges from light green to red. Besides chlorophyll, the cells are known to contain four other pigments: yellow, orange, red, and blue. The blue pigment *phycocyanin* is characteristic of most species and gives the phylum its name. The chlorophyll is not contained in chloroplasts, but is found on layers of membranes near the edge of the cell. DNA is not organized into chromosomes within a nucleus. Protein bodies and DNA are found scattered near the center of the cell. A few species grow as single cells, but many form slender filaments. The indi-

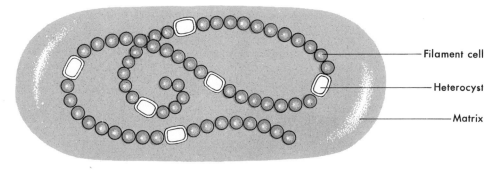

12–1 Filament of Nostoc, a blue-green alga, consists of loosely joined cells surrounded by a gelatinous matrix. Heterocysts, or empty cells, indicate fragmentation points.

- Filament cell
- Heterocyst
- Matrix

vidual cells are surrounded by a jelly-like sheath.

Blue-green algae are likely to be found almost anywhere—in ponds, ditches, lakes, streams, and even sewage disposal plants. They are often a problem in water reservoirs, since large accumulations of certain species may poison the water.

Nostoc. If you wish to find this common blue-green alga you will have to look for something that doesn't resemble a living thing at all! The *Nostoc* colony is like a tiny ball of yarn surrounded by a firm layer of gelatine. The colonies vary from the size of a bean to that of a hen's egg. Frequently, the colony is mistaken for a bird's egg lying at the edge of a pond.

When the dark green jelly is examined under the microscope the cells are seen to be arranged like beads on a string. Each cell is a separate organism and reproduces other cells by fission. The daughter cells remain attached, however, increasing the length of the colony. Many strings of cells are intertwined, and the entire colony is surrounded by a firm layer of gelatine. At intervals along the "string" you will notice hollow cells, slightly different in shape from the others. These are the *heterocysts*, cells where the string can conveniently break into shorter strands to spread the colony. This process is called *fragmentation.*

OSCILLATORIA: THE SWAYING ALGA. Most blue-green algae do not move. Here is one that not only moves, but practically dances. It gets its name from the fact that it sways, or oscillates, back and forth. When some of these algae are placed in a dish they sometimes rise up the side of it.

12–2 Oscillatoria, a blue-green filament, sways to and fro. Some researchers believe movement is connected with secretion. The fragmentation will usually occur at dead cells.

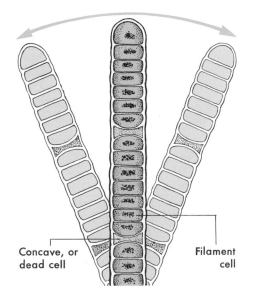

Concave, or dead cell

Filament cell

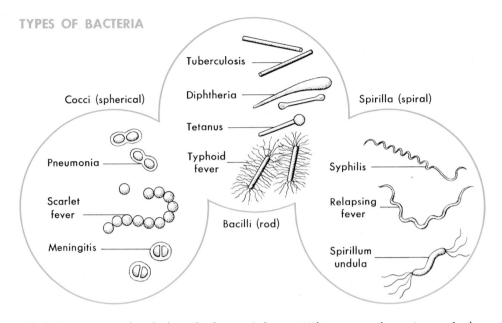

12–3 Bacteria are classified on the basis of shape. Within groups, bacteria are further differentiated according to appendages, colonization, and physiological reactions.

Most species of *Oscillatoria* are a brilliant blue-green, the filament consisting of many disk-shaped cells. Some concave, dead cells occur at intervals along the filament. At these intervals fragmentation produces new filaments. Strange as it may seem, the Red Sea gets its name from a species of Oscillatoria. This species contains a large amount of red pigment in addition to chlorophyll. At certain seasons large numbers of these organisms float close to the surface of the sea, giving it a red tinge.

Schizophyta: Bacteria

The bacteria are the smallest of the monerans. It would take between 10,000 to 50,000 bacteria of average size, placed end to end, to stretch out to a length of just one inch! And about 50 billion of them would fit comfortably in a single drop of water.

Bacteriologists usually talk in terms of *microns* when they discuss the size of these microscopic organisms. A micron is 1/1000 of a millimeter or about 1/25,000 of an inch. The average bacterium is between 1 and 5 microns long, but the tiniest are as small as 1/10 micron, about 1/250,000 inch.

The electron microscope, more than any other instrument, has helped us understand the structure of bacteria. It is capable of magnifying objects over 300,000 times. It therefore offers tremendous advantages in studying these tiny monerans.

Bacteria live mostly as single cells. Sometimes they clump together in colonies. Because of their size, it has been difficult to study the structure of the individual cell. Although no nucleus exists, nuclear material is present in the cytoplasm in the form of DNA. Vacuoles, stored food, and pigments have also been observed. A cell wall is present, and it is generally surrounded by a jelly-like *slime layer*. When the slime layer becomes thickened, it is called a **capsule.** This may be a protective layer since it retards drying.

Some of the bacteria have protoplasmic extensions that propel them through the water. In certain species there is a single flagellum, but in others the flagella are numerous. The flagella make locomotion possible.

KINDS OF BACTERIA. Bacteriologists have identified about 2000 different species of bacteria, which they group into three categories. Because they are so small, one of the few ways to classify them is on the basis of shape. Generally, the cells are either spherical or rod-shaped. The rod-shaped species are either straight or curled in the form of a spiral. The three groups are:

Spherical or **coccus** (pl. *cocci*)

Straight rod or **bacillus** (pl. *bacilli*)

Spiral rod or **spirillum** (pl. *spirilla*)

Although the spirilla exist only as single cells, the other types frequently form colonies. After cell division some of the species of cocci remain joined together in pairs (*diplococcus*), in chains (*streptococcus*), or in clusters (*staphylococcus*). Bacilli are also found in pairs (*diplobacillus*) or in chains (*streptobacillus*).

There are some exceptions to these basic types. One, called a *vibrio*, is a shortened spirillum–like form that causes the disease cholera. Another, called a **spirochete** (SPY-ruh-keat), is a spiral organism that has no cell wall. The venereal disease *syphilis* is caused by one of the spirochetes, and the tropical disease *yaws* is caused by another spirochete.

REPRODUCTION OF BACTERIA. The simplest type of reproduction is cell division, or **fission** (FISH-un). Bacteria reproduce by this method almost exclusively. When fission occurs, a single bacterial chromosome replicates the huge DNA molecule. This

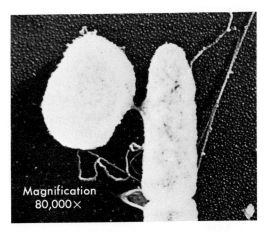

12–4 Bacterial Conjugation. Long bacterium passes its chromosome into short bacterium through the bridge that connects them.

genetic material is then divided between the two daughter cells formed. This process is very similar to mitosis in advanced plant and animal cells. There have been some investigations that reveal sexual differences in bacteria. Sexual reproduction occurs rarely, however. When fission does occur, the halves of the cell either separate completely or remain attached to form a colony.

The most startling feature of reproduction in bacteria is the speed with which it occurs. Under favorable conditions they may divide every 20 minutes. If you calculate the number of bacteria resulting from the continued division of just one bacterium over a twelve-hour period, you'll find it is about 70 billion! A single bacterium could produce descendants weighing 2000 tons in 24 hours.

Fortunately, there are factors that limit this amazing growth. Bacterial populations use up the available food and water very quickly. Their own waste products further slow down their activity. Nevertheless, their rapid growth rate causes extensive food spoilage in a very short time or makes the onset of disease swift and sudden.

BACTERIAL SPORE FORMATION. Many bacteria are able to survive even when the conditions for their growth are very unfavorable. This is especially true of the bacilli. The cytoplasm of the cell contracts and surrounds itself with a thick protective layer. In this form it is called a *spore.* The old cell wall remains, and the entire bacterium becomes rounded or oval in appearance. The spores are not motile, but they can be carried about by currents of air.

Spores may remain *dormant,* or inactive, for a period of several years. In this condition bacteria can resist great extremes of temperature, drought, sunlight, and poisonous chemicals. Some spores have been known to withstand prolonged boiling in water. When conditions become favorable again, they are able to throw off the thickened layer and resume their life as normal bacterial cells. Bacterial spores are not able to move about, nor do they increase the numbers of bacteria. Spore formation in bacteria is considered a survival device.

The ability of bacteria to produce spores makes the problem of controlling them much more difficult. The spores of the *anthrax* bacillus may live in the soil for years. The spores of the *tetanus* (lockjaw) bacillus, which live in the soil or dust of the air, are among the most resistant known. Since these spores can get into an open wound, an inoculation against tetanus should always be given when the skin is punctured by dirty objects such as nails.

Foods and Respiration

Bacteria use almost any organic material as food. When they invade the body of a living animal or plant they may cause disease. Most people are aware that some bacteria can do this. In this case, where they are living directly on living tissues, they are said to be parasites. The organism they attack is called the **host.**

The great majority of bacteria live upon nonliving organic substances and are classed as **saprophytes** (SAP-ro-fytes). Such substances as wood, leather, milk, and sugar (all derived from living plants or animals) are favorite foods for bacteria. The dead remains of plants and animals are quickly attacked by many different types of bacteria, causing decay.

Bacteria cannot use organic materials as foods directly. Most of these food materials are complex proteins or carbohydrates that must be simplified before they can be absorbed. When there is sufficient moisture and the temperature is high enough, the bacteria release *enzymes* that act upon the large molecules, splitting them into smaller ones. These smaller molecules can then enter the bacterial cell and serve as food. Enzymes, as we have seen, are very specific in their action, acting on a certain food and no other. Because of this, different species of bacteria have food preferences.

Most bacteria feed upon organic compounds to obtain their energy and are therefore *heterotrophic.* There are a few bacteria, however, that synthesize food from inorganic materials, even though the bacteria do not contain chlorophyll. These kinds of bacteria are *autotrophic,* or self-feeding, bacteria.

CHEMOSYNTHESIS AND PURPLE BACTERIA. To make their food, autotrophic bacteria obtain energy in one of two ways. In one group, inorganic substances, such as iron, sulphur, or ammonia, are oxidized to release the required energy which can then be used to make organic compounds from carbon dioxide. This process is called *chemosynthesis.* By means of it, certain bacteria in the soil make nitrogen compounds needed for the growth of green plants.

Other autotrophic bacteria are able to use the energy of sunlight to make their food. These unusual organisms contain a purple pigment that takes the place of chlorophyll. In this type of "bacterial photosynthesis" oxygen is not liberated.

AEROBES AND ANAEROBES. Like other organisms, bacteria obtain the energy for their life processes by respiration. For this process, many of them use the free oxygen of the air. These bacteria are called *aerobes.* However, some bacteria cannot use free oxygen and are, in fact, killed by it. These are called **anaerobes.** They get their energy from the chemical decomposition of their foods, the special kind of respiration called *fermentation.* Most bacteria are intermediate between these two types, obtaining energy in either way depending upon the available supply of oxygen.

Anaerobic bacteria are especially troublesome to man since they can cause food to spoil even in carefully sealed containers. One anaerobe, *Clostridium botulinum,* grows in improperly prepared canned foods and produces one of the most toxic poisons known. Estimates place the fatal dosage at three ten-millionths of an ounce. It produces an illness known as *botulism* characterized by difficulty in swallowing and speaking. About two-thirds of its victims die.

Not all anaerobes are poisonous. Some produce the flavor of such foods as sour cream, cheese, and sauerkraut. Others are responsible for the souring of milk and the rancid taste of spoiled butter.

Useful Bacteria

Man cannot escape from bacteria. They are in the air all around us. They live in our drinking water and they thrive in the soil. Some have been found in the air many miles above the earth. Others have been discovered in the cold ooze of the ocean deeps where no other form of life can exist.

Most bacteria are harmless to man. More than a hundred kinds have been found living in the human mouth. Many thrive in the human intestine. There is even some evidence to indicate that they supply us with vitamin K while they live in our digestive tract. This vitamin prevents excessive bleeding from injuries. Perhaps the most serious problem is caused by the disease-producing forms, the *pathogenic* (path-o-JEN-ik) bacteria. Fortunately, there are only about 150 species of this type.

BACTERIA CAUSE DECAY. The woodlands and meadows are covered by the dead twigs and leaves of plants. Along the seashore the decaying remains of animals cause the unpleasant odors we associate with the mud banks and tidal flats. The cycle of life is being completed as the bacteria convert the remains of the once-living to materials that can be used again by the living.

Decay is a chemical process in which bacteria and other organisms break down the complex organic molecules into simpler forms. A substantial part of the carbon dioxide in the air is being continually replenished by the decay of organic matter. Many nitrogen compounds, vital for plant growth, are returned to the soil in the same way. The bacteria of decay thus make possible the re-use of the materials of life by successive generations of plants and animals. Decay is beneficial not only in supplying food, but also in preventing the accumulation of these organic materials that would otherwise be very objectionable.

THE NITROGEN CYCLE. Soil bacteria play important roles in converting nitrogen and its compounds into chemical compounds useful to plants. Nitrogen is essential to the growth of all plants and animals since it is a fundamental element in proteins. The nitrogen cycle traces the chemical changes that occur as different organisms use this important element.

The air is the principal source of nitrogen. Nitrogen makes up 80 per cent of the volume of the atmosphere. Yet the nitrogen of the air is almost useless to most plants.

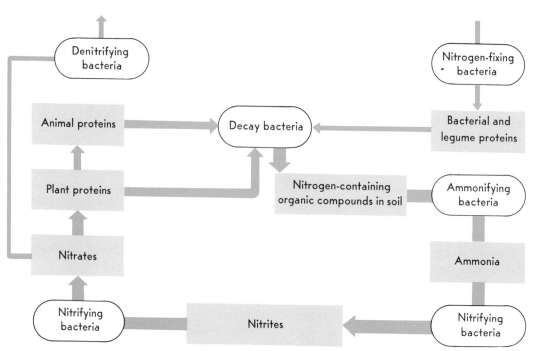

12–5 NITROGEN CYCLE. Although surrounded by free nitrogen in the atmosphere, all animals and most plants can obtain the nitrogen they need only in the form of nitrogen compounds. The diagram illustrates how a limited supply of nitrogen compounds is kept in constant circulation and made available to future generations of plants and animals.

Gaseous nitrogen must be chemically combined into a compound before it can be used. Lightning combines, or fixes, small amounts of nitrogen and oxygen in the air to form oxides. These oxides of nitrogen are washed out of the atmosphere by rain or snow and thus reach the soil. Some industrial firms combine nitrogen with hydrogen to form ammonia. Ammonia is now the main commercial source of nitrogen for agriculture. But the chief source of nitrogen compounds for the farmer is a natural one, resulting from the action of certain soil bacteria.

Some of the *nitrogen-fixing bacteria* live on the roots of *legumes*—plants like beans, peas, clover, peanuts, and alfalfa. Others live independently in the soil. The nitrogen-fixing bacteria are able to combine nitrogen with sugars to form proteins. With the exception of a few blue-green algae, no other organisms can do this. In the legumes these bacteria live on the roots in small swellings called *nodules.* So important are the nitrogen-fixing bacteria that commercial legume seed is often inoculated with these bacteria during planting.

Farmers have learned to rotate their crops to take advantage of the increased soil fertility produced by legumes. Clover, or some other legume, is plowed under before planting a crop of wheat or corn the following season. The decaying legumes, rich in fixed nitrogen, increase the nitrogen content of the soil without the use of commercial fertilizers. Rotation of crops has been used for many centuries.

Vast reserves of nitrogen exist in the soil in the form of organic compounds derived from decaying plants and animals. It is believed that these organic compounds are mainly proteins. In this form the nitrogen is useless to plants since the molecules are too large to penetrate cell membranes. Soil bacteria change these complex molecules into the simple, useful compounds of nitrogen.

Two kinds of bacteria change the large protein molecules into simpler forms. One kind, called *ammonifying bacteria,* converts nitrogen compounds into ammonia. Ammonia can be changed into ammonium compounds and absorbed into the roots of a plant.

The odor of ammonia, so common around a barn or stable, is due to the action of ammonifying bacteria upon plant and animal waste. The second kind of bacteria, called *nitrifying bacteria,* converts ammonia into *nitrates,* compounds of nitrogen and oxygen that are easily absorbed and used. Nitrifying bacteria effect the change from ammonia to nitrates in two stages. In the first stage the ammonia is changed into a *nitrite.* In the second stage the nitrite is changed into a *nitrate.*

One kind of bacteria is responsible for the loss of nitrogen from the soil. These *denitrifying bacteria* convert useful nitrogen compounds in the soil into free nitrogen that returns to the atmosphere. The steps in the nitrogen cycle can be traced in the growth and use of clover:

1. Atmospheric nitrogen is changed into proteins by the action of nitrogen-fixing bacteria growing in nodules on the clover roots.

2. After being plowed under, the pro-

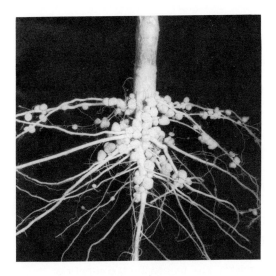

12–6 Nitrogen-fixing bacteria, which live in nodules on the roots of legumes, can change atmospheric nitrogen into nitrogen compounds useful to themselves and to other plants.

teins of the clover are changed into ammonia by ammonifying bacteria.

3. Ammonia is changed into nitrates by nitrifying bacteria.

4. Both ammonia and nitrates are used by other plants to form plant proteins.

5. The plant proteins are used by animals as food.

6. Some of the nitrates in the soil are converted to atmospheric nitrogen by denitrifying bacteria.

BACTERIA IN INDUSTRY. The dairy industry finds many uses for bacteria. Buttermilk is made by fermenting skim milk under carefully controlled conditions to produce its characteristic sour taste. Cheese is made by souring milk to separate the solid from the liquid. Lactic acid bacteria usually start the process. Bacteria also play an important part in the curing of cheese.

Tobacco flavoring depends upon bacteria. The raw leaves are dried, then packed tightly in wood containers. After several months of fermentation, or "curing," the desired aromas are produced.

The fibers used in the making of linen and rope come from plants. In each case the fibers are separated from the rest of the plant by a process called *retting* in which bacteria decompose the soft plant parts.

Chemical processes brought about by bacteria are responsible for quite a number of other products. Among these are lactic acid, acetic acid (vinegar), butyl alcohol, and ethyl alcohol.

Food Preservation

Bacteria are in constant competition with man for food. They can cause the rapid decomposition of practically every foodstuff, making it useless for human consumption. In some cases they produce extremely poisonous products, called *toxins,* that cause violent illness or death. Common forms of food poisoning are due to staphylococcus or salmonella infection of the food.

Bacteria need moisture, warmth, and the proper food. When these conditions are denied them, they cannot grow.

DRYING FOODS. When the water content of a food is very low, bacteria cannot live upon it. Even primitive people, who did not know anything about bacteria, learned that dried meats and fish do not spoil quickly. Today, by means of careful dehydration processes, we preserve many foods that could not be preserved in the past. Such foods as dried milk, powdered eggs, and dehydrated potatoes are common. By adding water we restore much of the original flavor and appearance.

REFRIGERATION. Most bacteria cannot thrive unless the temperature is between 72 and 82 degrees Fahrenheit. This varies considerably with the species, however. Most of the disease producers flourish at temperatures close to 98° F. Some bacteria can survive even at the freezing point of water.

Control slice

12–7 Bread exposed to radiation retains its freshness. Compare with control slice.

Your home refrigerator maintains a temperature between 35° F and 50° F. Most bacteria cannot grow under these conditions. It is important to realize, however, that they are usually not killed in this temperature range. Some bacterial growth still occurs, and food can spoil if it is kept too long at these temperatures. For long periods of storage it is best to use "deep freezers." These maintain a temperature of 0° F, which kills nearly all bacteria.

CHEMICAL PRESERVATIVES. Many kinds of chemicals can be used to prevent bacteria from growing on foodstuffs. You probably are familiar with the names of some of them. Sodium benzoate appears frequently on the label of food products. Such common substances as salt and sugar prevent bacterial growth by reducing the water content of cells through diffusion. The salting of meat and fish and the pickling of olives in brine are ancient ways of preserving these foods. Vinegar is another common preservative. It is very effective since bacteria cannot live in even weak acids.

CANNED FOODS. When foods are canned all the bacteria must be completely destroyed along with their spores. We call this *sterilization*. Boiling the food is usually a safe method of destroying most bacteria, especially if the food being preserved is acidic. Many spores, however, can survive boiling and cause food spoilage later. Meats, fish, and other foods that have a tendency to spoil easily are cooked in live steam under pressure for a period of 15 minutes to an hour to destroy bacterial spores.

Recent experiments with radioactive materials may result in entirely new methods of preserving foods. Foods that have been subjected to radiation, and thus sterilized, can be sealed in plastic bags and kept indefinitely at room temperature. No spoilage results in foods so treated. In the future, we may, therefore, be able to store meats, eggs, leafy vegetables, and fruits without refrigeration.

PASTEURIZATION. This process is used to kill pathogenic bacteria in milk. You probably know that it is named after the famous French biochemist Louis Pasteur who developed this technique to prevent the spoiling of wine.

Raw milk contains so many bacteria that many communities regulate its processing by law. In the past, many cases of tuberculosis, diphtheria, and typhoid fever were traced directly to contaminated milk. *Pasteurization* makes milk safe for human consumption by killing these pathogens.

Milk is most commonly pasteurized by subjecting a thin film of it to a temperature of 160° F for 15 seconds or more. Following heating, the milk is cooled rapidly and kept under refrigeration until used. The temperature is not high enough to alter the taste or other properties of the milk, nor does it destroy all bacteria. It is a common observation that pasteurized milk still sours if it is not refrigerated.

Bacteria in the Laboratory

Much progress in bacteriology has been due to the development of methods of *culturing*, or growing, bacteria in the laboratory. In the course of his work the bacteriologist isolates one particular species and grows it as a *pure culture*. Such cultures afford ideal conditions for studying just one kind of bacteria. Bacterial research has resulted in discoveries that have improved health and lengthened lives.

Bacteria may be cultured on a variety of organic materials. Meat broth, potato broth, blood serum, or a combination of nutrients may be used, depending upon the species to be grown. The nutrient is usually mixed with warm, liquid agar or gelatine, which solidifies upon cooling. The agar provides a solid surface on which the bacteria may

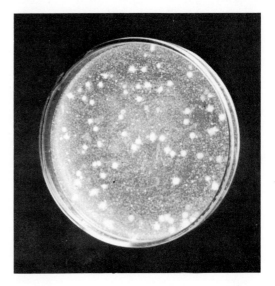

12–8 Bacteria cultures are grown on agar in covered Petri dishes, then later transferred to test tubes containing nutrients.

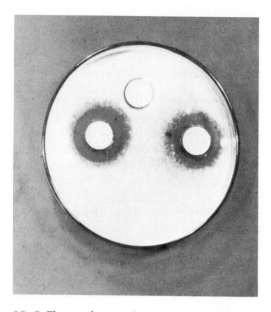

12–9 The antibacterial action of penicillin is demonstrated here. Two sensitivity disks soaked in penicillin solution were placed on the bacterial culture in the Petri dish. A third disk soaked in a different antibacterial solution was also placed on the culture. The antibacterial action is indicated by the clear (dark) rings around the disks.

place; the culture grows. In a few days large colonies appear on the surface of the agar. The experienced researcher can often identify the bacteria from the shape and color of the colony.

Careful procedures are followed in preparing slides for examination. A bent loop of sterile wire is used to transfer a droplet of the culture to a sterile slide. The droplet is then spread into a thin *smear*, dried, and drawn through a flame or dipped into alcohol to kill the bacteria. The bacteria are then stained with organic dyes so that they may be identified more easily.

Bacteria are sometimes observed in the living state in a *hanging drop* preparation. This is made by placing a droplet of the bacteria on a cover slip, adding sterile water, and inverting the cover slip over a special slide with a circular depression in the center.

One of the most important methods of identifying bacteria is the **Gram stain.** In this method a prepared bacterial smear is first stained with either crystal violet or gentian violet for about a minute. The smear is then washed briefly in water and covered with Gram's iodine solution for another minute. At this point, the smear is decolorized by immersing it in an alcohol solution. It is again washed in water and counterstained with safranin, a red dye.

Bacteria that retain the original violet color are called **Gram-positive.** Bacteria that lose the violet color during the decolorizing phase and take up the red color of the safranin are called **Gram-negative.** The staining procedure thus separates bacteria into two major groups and aids the bacteriologist in tracking down some of the dangerous bacterial forms. Penicillin is usually more effective against Gram-positive bacteria than against Gram-negative.

be easily seen. The liquid mixture of agar and nutrient, called the *culture medium,* is poured into glass containers. These may be test tubes or shallow, covered Petri dishes.

All of the materials used in preparing the culture medium must be sterile. The nutrients, the glassware, and the instruments used to handle them must be boiled in a water or steam bath. If these precautions are not followed, the culture becomes contaminated with unwanted bacteria.

INCUBATION AND STAINING. The inoculated culture is kept in a warm, dark place or in an oven where the temperature can be controlled. *Incubation* now takes

IMPORTANT POINTS

- The Moneran Kingdom consists of two phyla: the blue-green algae and the bacteria. Monerans are generally single-celled. Their cells lack an organized nucleus, chloroplasts, or mitochondria.

- The blue-green algae contain chlorophyll and the blue pigment phycocyanin. These algae are widely distributed autotrophs of great importance to man.

- Bacteria are tiny, one-celled organisms that occur almost everywhere—in water, in air, in soil, and in the bodies of plants and animals. There are three main kinds of bacteria—cocci, bacilli, and spirilli.

- Bacteria multiply very rapidly under proper conditions of food, moisture, and temperature. When conditions are unfavorable many bacteria form spores. Spores may remain dormant for long periods, resisting drying, extremes of temperature, and poisonous chemicals.

- Heterotrophic bacteria feed upon organic substances which they decompose by enzyme action. Autotrophic bacteria synthesize their food from inorganic materials. Bacteria that require oxygen to obtain energy are called aerobes. Anaerobes are those bacteria that obtain energy without using oxygen.

- Many bacteria are beneficial to man, but a few are very harmful. Disease-producing bacteria are called pathogens. Decay is produced by many bacteria that live in the soil, replenishing the supply of inorganic compounds for plant growth.

- The main phases of the nitrogen cycle are controlled by bacteria. Nitrogen-fixing bacteria convert the nitrogen of the atmosphere into proteins. Ammonifying bacteria change proteins into ammonia. Nitrifying bacteria change ammonia into nitrates. Denitrifying bacteria change nitrates into free nitrogen.

- Common methods of preserving foods are drying, refrigeration, the use of chemicals, canning, and pasteurization.

- Bacteria are cultured in the laboratory for identification and study. Staining methods help the biologist to identify them.

REVIEW QUESTIONS

1. List two reasons why the monerans are considered primitive organisms.
2. Why is Oscillatoria an appropriate name for this blue-green alga?
3. The Red Sea is named after a blue-green alga. Explain.
4. Give one example to show how small bacteria are.
5. What are the three main types of bacteria?
6. How do bacteria survive under unfavorable conditions?
7. What is the source of the energy for anaerobes?
8. List three ways in which bacteria are beneficial to man.
9. List four methods of preserving foods.
10. What are three materials used to culture bacteria?

CHECK YOUR UNDERSTANDING

11. Why would life be impossible without the bacteria of decay?
12. Why are autotrophic bacteria exceptional?
13. Why must pathogenic bacteria be parasites?
14. What are the main steps in the nitrogen cycle?
15. Would aerobic or anaerobic bacteria be more likely to cause spoilage of canned foods?
16. Describe the steps in the Gram stain method for identifying bacteria.
17. Since bacteria reproduce so rapidly, why do they not cover the earth in a short time?
18. If all bacteria suddenly acquired chlorophyll, what effect would this have upon other organisms?
19. Bacteria are being increasingly used in the research laboratory to study genetics. What advantages and disadvantages do they offer the researcher in this field?

RESEARCH PROJECTS AND REPORTS

1. Obtain information from your school or public library and prepare a report on one of the following topics:

    Making Cheeses   **The Atom and Food Preservation**

    Staphylococci   **Louis Pasteur**

2. *Collecting and Observing Bacteria:* Soak some beans or a piece of potato in a test tube partly filled with distilled water and leave it exposed to the air for several days. Stopper the tube lightly with absorbent cotton, and allow to stand in a warm place for a few more days. Remove some of the water with a pipette, place a drop on a clean slide, and examine under the high power of your classroom microscope. The bacteria you will find are rather large. Observe their size and shape. Make accurate drawings of what you observe and keep notes on your procedures. Can you explain the occurrence of these organisms in your test tube? *Note:* These bacteria are harmless.

3. *Effects of Temperature on Bacteria:* Place a small piece of potato in each of three test tubes. Add a small amount of distilled water to each tube. Label the tubes A, B, and C. Allow all three to remain uncovered at room temperature for 24 hours. At the end of this period:

    1. Stopper tube A with cotton and allow to stand.
    2. Boil water in tube B for 15 minutes, stopper with cotton, and allow to stand.
    3. Stopper tube C with cotton and place in a refrigerator.

    Examine the water in each tube for bacteria at the end of a week. Stopper each tube immediately after withdrawing water specimen. In which tube did you find the greatest number of bacteria? Explain. Allow tubes B and C to stand another 24 hours. Examine each for bacteria again. Do you notice a difference between B and C? Explain.

FURTHER READING

Pasteur and the Invisible Giants. E. F. Dolan. Dodd, Mead and Company, New York, N.Y. An interesting account of the famous Frenchman who contributed so much to the founding of modern bacteriology.

"**The Bacterial Chromosome.**" John Cairns. *Scientific American,* January, 1966, page 37. The bacterial chromosome is a gigantic molecule of DNA which has been successfully photographed by researchers.

"**The Blue-Green Algae.**" Patrick Echlin. *Scientific American,* June, 1966, page 75. The blue-green algae bear a close resemblance to the bacteria in many ways and are very important to man.

"**Death From Staphylococci.**" Ian Maclean Smith. *Scientific American,* February, 1968, page 84. What parts of the human body are most susceptible to attack from the staphylococci? How do these bacteria cause death?

13

Protists: Algae

ALL ABOUT US are thousands of tiny green organisms we seldom notice. They form the green scum on the surface of stagnant ponds. They make the green film on the sides of an aquarium. They turn the bark of trees "mossy" with their green growth. Some of the larger forms are washed up as brilliant green "sea lettuce" on the beach. They form dense brown mats of rockweed on the tidal ledges of the shore. Although most species abound in the water, especially the sea, a few have been able to establish themselves in moist places on the land. These simple organisms, most of them single-celled, are the *algae,* the living descendants of the earth's earliest autotrophs.

CHARACTERISTICS OF ALGAE. With the exception of the moneran phylum *Cyanophyta,* all of the algae belong to the Protist Kingdom. Biologists do not agree completely about classifying the algae. We have subdivided the algae in the Protist Kingdom into five phyla.

The body plan of the algae is very simple. Many of them are single cells. Sometimes the cells are joined together in colonies. These colonies may be flat, spherical, or have their cells joined end to end to form threadlike filaments. In other cases millions of cells form huge, ribbonlike seaweeds, called *kelps.* Even where there are large numbers of cells in the plant body, they are all very similar. Little specialization of cells occurs in the algae.

All algae contain chlorophyll. They are, therefore, autotrophs. They make their own food by photosynthesis from water and carbon dioxide. This is one of the reasons biologists believe they were among the earliest forms of life to exist on the earth. We can summarize the characteristics of algae as follows:

- They are simple organisms, lacking specialized organs.
- They consist of cells that are very similar to each other.
- They are autotrophs, containing chlorophyll.
- They live in the water, or in moist places on land.

DISTRIBUTION OF ALGAE. Countless billions of algae live in the sea, the ponds, the lakes, the streams, and rivers. It has been estimated that in terms of sheer bulk, algae outweigh all the land plants combined! Biologists have classified about 27,000 species of algae.

Algae are likely to be found in the most

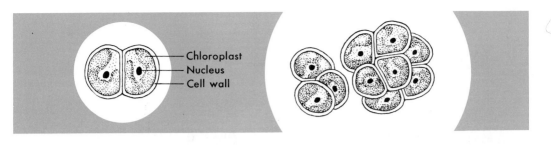

13–1 Protococcus (green alga) cells are independent and occur singly or in colonies.

unusual places. Have you ever seen an animal with green fur? The clumsy, three-toed sloth of tropical America has a green coat. It is due to thousands of algae growing on his gray fur! The giant blue whale is often called the "sulphur-bottomed" whale because diatoms, which are yellow algae, grow in abundance on its under surface. The alligator often harbors an algal garden on its back!

In Glacier National Park, high on the side of the mountains where the snow remains all through the summer's heat, blood-red streaks are sometimes found. These are due to algae that contain a red pigment. Even in the hot springs near Old Faithful in Yellowstone Park certain algae thrive at temperatures approaching that of boiling water. The melting point of ice and the boiling point of water are the limits of the temperature range in which life can exist. Algae thrive near both limits.

THE COLORS OF ALGAE. Although all algae contain the green pigment chlorophyll, some have a different color due to the presence of other pigments. Some pigments give a yellow color to the yellow-green or golden algae. Other pigments color the brown and red algae. Algae were once divided into classes on the basis of color. Although color is still considered, other features, such as cell structure and methods of reproduction, are also taken into account in present classification.

REPRODUCTION IN THE ALGAE. The algae reproduce both asexually and sexually. The simplest kind of asexual reproduction is fission, or the splitting of the parent cell into two daughter cells. Following fission each new daughter cell becomes like the parent.

Some algae produce *spores*, reproductive cells that are released singly or in groups. Certain spores resist unfavorable conditions, such as dryness. When favorable conditions return they grow into new plants. Some algae produce swimming spores equipped with *flagella*. Because these swimming spores resemble microscopic animals, they are called *zoospores*. Before growing into new algae, zoospores lose their flagella and await favorable growth conditions. Reproduction by spores is asexual because single spores grow into new plants.

Many algae reproduce sexually. Specialized sex cells or gametes are produced. In some algae the gametes look alike and resemble swimming zoospores. However, new algae do not result unless two gametes unite. In some algae the gametes are different in size. The larger gamete is called the *egg* cell and does not swim. The smaller gamete is the *sperm*, which can swim to the egg and unite with it. When sperm and egg unite, a *zygote* (ZY-goat), or fertilized egg, is formed, which becomes a new organism.

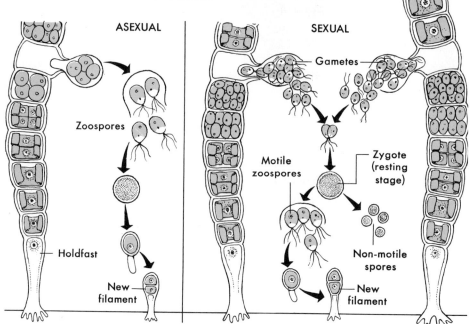

13—2 In asexual reproduction, filament cells divide many times to form zoospores with four flagella. The zoospores swim about, lose their flagella, and grow into new filaments. In sexual reproduction, filament cells liberate motile gametes with two flagella. Fusion of two gametes, each from different filaments, forms a zygote that may produce zoospores with four flagella or nonmotile spores. The zoospores grow into new filaments.

Chlorophyta: The Green Algae

The green algae have a well-defined nucleus in each cell, and the chlorophyll is contained in chloroplasts. Generally, the chloroplasts contain one or more *pyrenoids*. The pyrenoids store starch manufactured by the chloroplast.

Of the more than 6000 species of green algae, many live in the sea, but most of them live in fresh water. They are of particular evolutionary interest to botanists, since the modern, highly specialized land plants are probably the descendants of green algal ancestors.

Many of the green algae occur as single cells that are either *motile* or *nonmotile*.

Almost any sample of pond water will reveal both types when examined with the microscope. The motile forms can be seen darting about, propelled by one or more flagella. The nonmotile forms may float in the water, or be attached to floating objects or larger aquatic plants. Still others may grow on the trunks of trees or on moist rocks. Some colonies of green algae grow as simple, unbranched filaments. Others form branched filaments. Still others form motile colonies.

PROTOCOCCUS. Have you ever noticed the green growth on the bark of trees or on moist rocks? This is *Protococcus*, which is one of the most widely distributed algae in the world. When it is examined under the

13-3 VARIETIES OF ALGAE

GREEN ALGAE

BROWN ALGAE

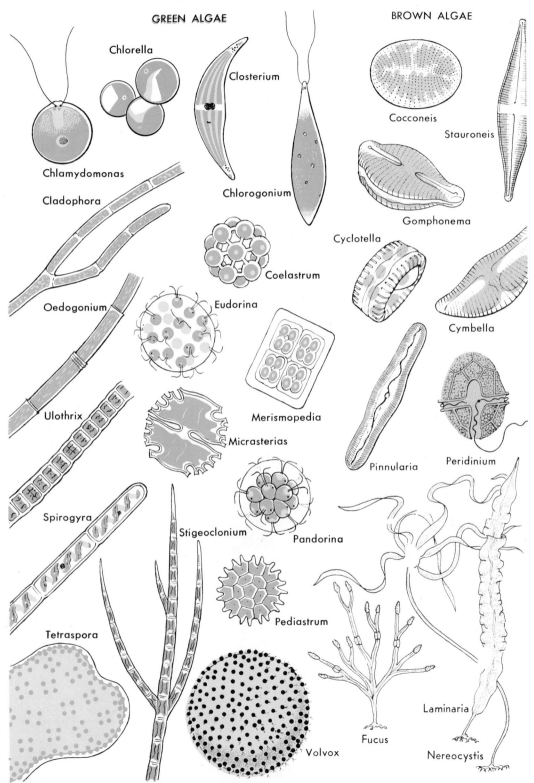

Chlorella

Closterium

Chlamydomonas

Chlorogonium

Cladophora

Cocconeis

Stauroneis

Gomphonema

Oedogonium

Coelastrum

Eudorina

Cyclotella

Cymbella

Ulothrix

Merismopedia

Micrasterias

Pinnularia

Peridinium

Spirogyra

Stigeoclonium

Pandorina

Tetraspora

Pediastrum

Volvox

Laminaria

Fucus

Nereocystis

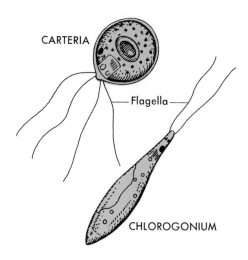

CARTERIA

Flagella

CHLOROGONIUM

13–4 Motile Algae with Flagella

microscope, the green growth is seen to consist of hundreds of single cells. Within each cell there is a large chloroplast and a nu-

cleus. This single cell is able to perform all the functions of life.

Protococcus takes in raw materials to make food. It also grows and reproduces. When it divides in two, the cells frequently cluster together. Groups of two or four cells are not uncommon. Such *aggregates* of cells are thought by some biologists to be the first step toward many-celled plants.

SPIROGYRA: A GREEN FILAMENT. You may have seen large masses of pond scum, or "water silk," floating on the surface of many ponds. These are common names for *Spirogyra*. The green, silky mats have a decidedly slippery feel. Spirogyra filaments may grow as long as 15 inches.

A single filament consists of numerous cylindrical cells attached end to end. The most striking feature of each cell is the spiral, ribbonlike chloroplast. In some species there is only one of these; but in others there may be several, giving the cell a

13–5 Spirogyra may be made to conjugate in the laboratory between mid-February and the beginning of May. Place Spirogyra strands in a small amount of water in a sunny place. Control filaments may be placed in a large tank of water in a cool place away from the direct rays of the sun. Another method of stimulating conjugation is to place Spirogyra in a 4 per cent solution of cane sugar.

REPRODUCTION IN SPIROGYRA

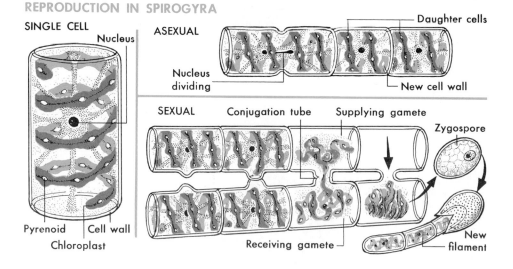

SINGLE CELL
Nucleus

ASEXUAL
Nucleus dividing
Daughter cells
New cell wall

Pyrenoid   Cell wall
Chloroplast

SEXUAL   Conjugation tube   Supplying gamete
Zygospore
Receiving gamete
New filament

coiled-spring appearance. At regular intervals along the chloroplast are the starch-storing pyrenoids. The nucleus is situated in the center of the cell, supported by strands of cytoplasm extending to the cell membrane.

Spirogyra reproduces asexually by fission and sexually by **conjugation.** The additional cells that are formed by fission increase the length of the filaments. There are no special cells where the filaments may break, but the nibbling of fish can break off smaller pieces producing new filaments.

During conjugation, two filaments lie side by side. From each pair of adjacent cells a small projection grows. These become larger until they meet and fuse, forming a hollow tube joining the two cells. This is the *conjugation tube.* The two paired cells act as gametes. The contents of one cell move through the tube and unite with the other. The fused mass, or zygospore, resulting from this union of gametes surrounds itself with a thick wall.

The numerous conjugation tubes give the two filaments a ladderlike appearance. Examination of this ladder formed by the two filaments shows that all the zygospores are formed in one filament. The cells of this filament are designated as *receiving gametes* because the movement of the cell material is toward them. The cells of the other filament are called *supplying gametes.* No difference between these filaments can be observed before conjugation, but some biologists refer to them as male and female because of the different roles they play in the reproductive process.

The zygospores fall to the bottom of the pond as the cell walls of the filament decay and release them. The thick covering of the zygospore protects it during the winter when the pond is likely to be frozen. In the spring, the zygospore develops into a new Spirogyra cell. After repeated cell divisions, a new filament of Spirogyra is formed.

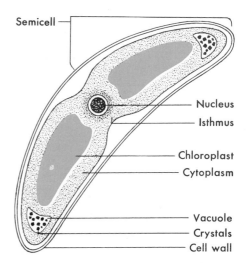

13–6 Closterium is a common desmid. Fission occurs along the isthmus that divides it into two semicells. Crystals in the vacuoles at each end are continually agitated.

DESMIDS. Perhaps the most strikingly beautiful of all the green algae are *desmids.* The water of almost any pond contains many different types. Some are round, others triangular. Still others are rods, or crescents, or star-shaped. They have a surprising variety of forms, but all have one feature in common—they are bright green. The two halves of the desmid, called *semicells,* are joined by a narrow bridge of cytoplasm, the *isthmus,* in which the nucleus is located.

Desmids reproduce by fission. Each semicell separates after the nucleus has divided. The daughter semicell then grows into a new desmid. A few desmids form colonial filaments by joining end to end.

If you examine a living specimen of the desmid called *Closterium* under the high power of a microscope, you can see a rather interesting thing. In each end of this crescent-shaped cell is a vacuole that contains crystals of calcium sulfate. These jiggle and vibrate due to bombardment by water mol-

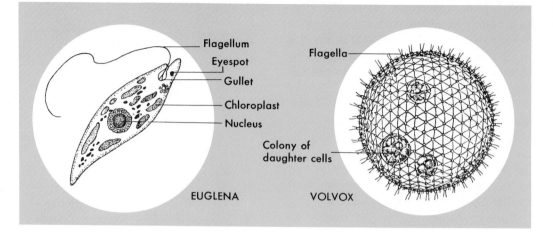

Flagellum
Eyespot
Gullet
Chloroplast
Nucleus

EUGLENA

Flagella
Colony of
daughter cells

VOLVOX

13–7 Euglena and Volvox move about with the aid of whiplike flagella.

ecules. Here is an excellent illustration of the kinetic theory of matter.

VOLVOX, CELL SPECIALIZATION. One of the most spectacular sights you may see in a drop of pond water is *Volvox*, a transparent hollow ball of cells about 1/25th of an inch in diameter—just visible to the naked eye. The cells on the outside of the ball beat their flagella causing the colony to swim with a slow, rotating movement.

Colonies such as these are more advanced than the cell aggregates of Protococcus. In an aggregate, the cells are all alike, but in a colony certain cells are modified to perform special functions. Cell specialization is characteristic of higher organisms. Each cell of the Volvox colony is connected to others by strands of cytoplasm that make coordination possible.

Specialization is most clearly seen when reproduction occurs. The process may either be asexual or sexual. In asexual reproduction, a new daughter colony is formed within the sphere. One cell withdraws inward, enlarges, then divides repeatedly. Several colonies may be produced in this manner within the parent colony.

Eventually, the parent colony breaks open and the daughter colonies swim free.

In sexual reproduction in Volvox, one cell becomes enlarged with stored food and forms the egg, or female cell. Another cell in the same colony divides many times to form tiny, flagellated sperms, or male cells. The sperm cells emerge and swim about. One of them finds and unites with the enlarged egg cell. The union of sperm and egg cell is called fertilization. The fertilized egg then undergoes repeated divisions and becomes a new colony.

Mastigophora: The Flagellates

Although many of the algae do not have a means of moving about, some are extremely motile. Among the latter are those single-celled forms that bear a long, whiplike thread called a *flagellum*. Like many of the protist phyla, there are a number of different types classified within the *Mastigophora*. Some closely resemble the green algae. Others differ so widely from the algae that they are classified by some biologists in different phyla entirely. All the forms we have included here move about by lashing their flagella back and forth.

EUGLENA. Euglena (you-GLEE-na) is somewhat of a biological puzzle. At times it behaves as an autotroph, making its own food. At other times it changes its mode of living and acts as a heterotroph. It has no cell wall, but it contains numerous chloroplasts. The chloroplasts enable it to perform photosynthesis. The green color at the surface of a pond is often due to millions of these organisms swimming close to the surface to absorb sunlight.

The flagellum is attached to one end of the tapered cell. At the base of the flagellum is the gullet. Next to the gullet is a bright red granule sensitive to light. This *eyespot* is a sort of navigational aid that directs the Euglena towards light. Without light the Euglena would not be able to make its food. The gullet is used by certain species to ingest food. Other species are completely autotrophic.

The different species of Euglena give us some insight into what the early forms of life may have been like. As autotrophs containing chlorophyll, and also possessing a gullet, they may represent an early unspecialized cell. Such cells may have existed early in the history of the development of life on earth. They could synthesize their food from inorganic compounds. They could also ingest other living things or food materials in the water. They also had the tremendous advantage of being able to move about to find more favorable conditions for living.

DINOFLAGELLATES. Perhaps you have seen or heard of the silvery glow on the surface of the sea at night. Even on the darkest nights a ship's wake can be seen.

Sea glow is produced by billions of tiny algae called *dinoflagellates* (dy-no-FLAJ-uh-lates). Each tiny cell emits a small amount of light. It is said to be *phosphorescent*. Billions of these cells give the water the appearance of sprinkled stardust, especially when the surface of the water is disturbed.

Dinoflagellates are single-celled, brown-red algae that live mainly in salt water, although there are a few fresh-water species. The cell wall is furrowed so that it looks as though it is made of armor. One species resembles a tiny, irregularly shaped, red golf ball. A deep furrow runs completely around the equator of the cell. Another crosses the equator at right angles, but extends up one side only. A flagellum in each furrow enables the cell to swim.

THE RED TIDE. Sometimes the number of dinoflagellates increases so rapidly that a part of the sea "blooms" with a red color. Newspapers report such an event as a "red tide." The numerous organisms produce a substance that kills fish. In the winter of 1946, millions of dead fish littered the Florida beaches, victims of the red tide. Biologists estimated there were 60 million dinoflagellates in a single quart of sea water. No one is sure what causes the tremendous increase in their numbers.

Chrysophyta: The Diatoms

The *diatoms* are among the most beautifully formed cells. The cell wall is composed of silica molded into patterns. Frequently, there are markings on the walls that, together with the golden-brown color of the cytoplasm, give these plants a jewel-like appearance. They can be gathered in the ooze of a lake bottom or on submerged reeds. An unusual feature of the cell is that the wall is made of two halves, or valves, that fit over each other like the top and bottom of a pillbox.

Because of their hardness, diatom cell walls do not decay when they die. Consequently, billions of their skeletons are deposited on the ocean bottom or on land once covered by water. These accumulations are called *diatomaceous earth*. In Lompoc Valley in California, deposits have been found that are a quarter mile deep. Diatomaceous earth is used as an ingredient in metal polishes, as an insulating material, and as a filtering substance.

Brown and Red Algae

Practically all of the brown and red algae live in the sea. If you have visited the seashore, you may have seen a feathery red seaweed in the surf. Perhaps you saw rockweed attached to the breakwater at the harbor entrance. *Brown algae* live in cooler northern waters, while the *red algae* live in warmer seas. Very few are found in fresh water. Some species of brown algae grow to a length of 150 feet. These are the giant kelps. The red algae rarely exceed three feet in length.

THE SARGASSO SEA. Early mariners told stories of ships trapped in a vast sea of vegetation. Between the Bahamas and the Azores in the western Atlantic Ocean, there is in fact a large area of floating seaweed known as the Sargasso Sea. Here the brown alga *Sargassum* may form dense mats 100 yards or more across. The captains of the early sailing vessels tried to avoid getting caught in this seaweed, for it meant great delay in their voyages.

FUCUS: THE COMMON ROCKWEED. *Fucus* is a common brown alga that grows upon large boulders exposed at low tide. The brown, rubbery, branches cling in great masses to tidal rocks by means of *holdfasts.*

The swollen tips of the alga are called *receptacles.* On the receptacles are small openings in which the eggs and sperms are produced. The gametes are set free in the water, and the sperms swim to the egg. After fertilization, the zygote attaches itself to a rock and grows into a new organism. Scattered along the branches are a number of small bladders, or air vesicles. These contain air that "floats" the seaweed upright in the water.

Importance of Algae

Those of us who enjoy oysters, clams, shrimps, and other seafoods seldom stop to

13–8 Food and oxygen requirements for space travel have led to experiments with various types of algae. Chlorella, a green alga, shows promise of being able to produce the food and the oxygen needed in the closed system of a manned spacecraft.

think that the algae make them possible. Just as the animals of the land are dependent upon plants for food, so the animals of the sea are dependent on the food-making algae. The diatoms and dinoflagellates, the most numerous algae in the sea, furnish food for microscopic crustaceans, the *copepods*. Billions of floating algae and copepods make up the "pastures of the sea." Smaller fish that "graze" in these pastures are eaten by larger fish who are, in turn, eaten by still larger fish, and so the food chain continues. Indirectly, therefore, we consume algae whenever we eat a seafood dinner.

FOOD RESOURCE. Although most Americans never use them as food, many algae provide tasty dishes throughout the world. In Japan, kelp is made into a variety of dishes. Kelps are rich in iodine, an element essential for the proper functioning of the thyroid gland. It is significant that the disease of the thyroid called *goiter* is practically unknown in Japan.

In Hawaii and Japan, the red alga *Porphyra* is eaten as a delicacy. In the British Isles, the same red alga is boiled and eaten with lemon juice. Another red alga is used as a relish in Scotland.

As the world's population increases, farming and fishing may not be able to supply the needs of man. In some parts of the earth people subsist on inadequate diets. To meet future needs scientists are experimenting with ways of growing algae for food. The single-celled green alga *Chlorella* has been grown in large experimental tanks and gives great promise. It can be made into flour, then into cakes. The estimated yield of fat and protein from this organism is greater than that from many regular farm crops.

OTHER USES OF ALGAE. We have discovered many other uses for algae besides food. Ice cream, for example, is likely to contain *algin,* an extract of brown algae,

Walter Dawn

13–9 Sea lettuce has expanded crinkly green fronds and is sometimes used in salads.

that keeps it smooth when frozen. Algin is also used in other products, such as ointments, toothpastes, shaving creams, and cosmetics. *Agar,* a jelly extracted from a red alga, is widely used in medical laboratories for culturing bacteria. The same jelly is used in Japan for thickening soups and sauces. Seaweeds make excellent fertilizers, since they contain all the minerals necessary for good plant growth.

HARMFUL ALGAE. Sometimes the algae are troublesome to man. They become a nuisance when they grow in large numbers in water reservoirs. They clog the filters and form scum on the walls. Their removal increases the cost of water for our homes. A small amount of copper sulfate added to the water at regular intervals usually keeps the algae under control. This chemical is harmless to man in dilute concentrations. Not only may algae be annoying, but some species in large numbers become poisonous. Watering places that became clogged with these algae have killed livestock.

IMPORTANT POINTS

● The algae (with the exception of the blue-green algae) belong to the Protist Kingdom. They are simple organisms that contain chlorophyll and lead independent lives. Because of their photosynthetic activity, they make possible the abundance of animal life in the water.

● Algae exist as solitary cells, colonies of cells, or as multicelled forms. They vary in color because they contain pigments in addition to chlorophyll. The green algae are thought to be related to the ancestors of plants.

● Algae reproduce by a variety of asexual and sexual methods ranging from fission to the production of motile spores and gametes. Many of their cells and reproductive spores have flagella.

● Algae are economically important because they begin the food chains that end in seafood. The larger algae are directly useful as foods, ingredients in pharmaceutical products, and as fertilizers. The tiny green alga Chlorella holds promise as a major source of food for the future. Some types of algae may pollute water and become a source of trouble.

REVIEW QUESTIONS

1. What characteristics separate the algae from other protists?
2. Describe conjugation in Spirogyra.
3. How do desmids differ from diatoms?
4. What is the cause of "sea glow"?
5. What is meant by a "red tide"?
6. Discuss the unusual features of red algae.
7. Give several uses for seaweeds.
8. Why is a weak solution of copper sulfate sometimes added to aquariums?

CHECK YOUR UNDERSTANDING

9. Without algae, fish could not exist in the sea. Explain.
10. Describe various types of algal spores and explain their function.
11. How is the ability to move an advantage to certain algae?
12. All algae contain chlorophyll, yet they have a variety of colors. Explain.
13. How does the zygospore of Spirogyra enable the alga to survive from season to season?
14. How does Fucus remain upright when submerged?
15. Algae make up only five per cent of the autotrophic species that inhabit the earth. Yet they account for about 90 per cent of the photosynthetic activity. Can you explain why?
16. Why is Chlorella likely to become more important to man in the future?
17. A diver finds fewer and fewer algae as he goes deeper into the sea. Why?
18. Why is Protococcus found mostly on the north side of tree trunks?
19. Algae can live in hot springs and in snow, but they are least likely to be found in the desert. Explain.

RESEARCH PROJECTS AND REPORTS

1. Obtain information from your school or public library and prepare a report on one of the following topics:

   Algae and Man's Food Supply   **Food Chains in the Sea**

   The Red Tide   **Life in a Stagnant Pond**

2. *Collecting Algae:* Collect some algae from the following places: the greenish scum on the edge of a pond or lake, the blackish material from the outside layer of a damp flower pot, and the green covering of damp bark or rocks. Examine this material under the microscope and identify as many algae as possible. Make drawings of algae observed and compare them with illustrations in various textbooks. How many can you find and identify?

3. *Observing Flagellates:* Observe specimens of stagnant pond water under high and low power. How many different green flagellates can you observe? Are any of them zoospores? Keep notes and make drawings of your observations.

4. *Rockweed (Fucus):* Obtain rockweed on submerged rocks at low tide at the seashore, or in the dried state at a local seafood market (it is used to pack crabs and lobsters shipped to inland cities). If you obtain the dried seaweed, it can be made limp and pliable by keeping it in salt water for a short time. Identify the holdfast, receptacles, and air vesicles. Squeeze the vesicles between the fingers. What is their function? Draw and label the parts.

FURTHER READING

The Wonders of Algae. Lucy Kalvaler. John Day Company, New York, N.Y. Very readable book on food value of algae and on making more use of the sea.

How to Know the Fresh Water Algae. Gerald W. Prescott. Wm. C. Brown Company, Dubuque, Iowa. Hundreds of drawings of the algae and an excellent key enable the interested student to study these organisms on his own.

The Sea. Editors of LIFE. Time, Inc., New York, N.Y. Chapter 6, entitled, "The Great Pyramid of Life," contains an interesting account of food chains in the sea.

CHAPTER

14

Protists: Fungi

THE LATIN NAME for mushroom is *fungus.* The term fungus has been used for many years to describe those organisms that resemble the mushrooms in many ways. Fungi are many-celled protists that lack chlorophyll. They form a large group of organisms inhabiting virtually all of the earth's varied environments. Often they are highly specialized plantlike forms with complex reproductive processes. The largest number of fungi are classified in the phylum *Mycophyta* (my-KAHF-uh-tuh), which contains some 60,000 species. The slime molds are placed in the phylum *Myxomycetes* (mix-so-my-SEE-tees). Although the slime molds are included with the fungi, certain characteristics of their life history cause them to be classified in separate phyla.

Many fungi are large enough to be visible to the naked eye. We see them growing on foods, on leather, on the decaying trunks of trees, and on cultivated plants. Some of the names by which you may have known them are: *molds,* which often grow on bread or jelly; *mildews* and *rusts,* which attack living plants causing plant diseases known as *blights;* and *mushrooms.* Certain microscopic species have been identified as the cause of ringworm and "athlete's foot."

Characteristics of Fungi

The fungi resemble the algae in many ways. There are differences, too. The fungi do not have chlorophyll. Their methods of reproduction are adapted to living on land rather than in the water.

THE FUNGUS BODY. The body of a fungus consists of colorless, branching filaments called *hyphae* (HY-fee). Each hypha is a long slender tube, about as thick as the strand of a spider's web. It contains cytoplasm and nuclei. Some of the tubes are continuous. Others are divided into shorter tubes by cross walls. The biologist usually refers to the tangled mass of hyphae as the *mycelium* (my-SEE-lee-um). Individual hyphae have special functions. Some take nourishment from organic material. Others form reproductive structures.

REPRODUCTION. Have you ever wondered where the mold you see growing on bread or fruit comes from? Samples of air have been found to contain the spores of molds, sometimes at heights of several thousand feet. If you examine the bread mold, you

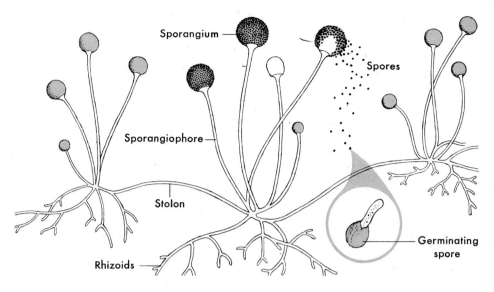

14–1 Asexual reproduction in bread mold, showing germination of spore.

will see the spores on special hyphae in immense numbers. After the spores have been scattered by the wind, they may find a suitable place to grow. They then germinate, much like a seed, and produce a new mold mycelium. Of course, the conditions for their growth must be just right.

The classification of fungi is based largely on their method of reproduction. The classes of fungi are established by the way in which spores are formed.

Some Representative Fungi

Bread mold is probably the most common household fungus. Its scientific name is *Rhizopus nigricans.* Although bread seems to be especially suitable for its growth, it can grow on many other things of a similar nature.

If a moistened piece of bread is exposed to the air for a day or so and then covered by a plate, the conditions for the growth of the spores are established. Usually in several days a thick, fluffy, cottony mycelium

develops. The use of mold inhibitors by bakeries will sometimes prevent rapid growth of the mold.

If a small area of the mycelium is examined with a hand lens, three kinds of hyphae can be identified. The first kind consists of the rootlike structures that penetrate the bread, the *rhizoids* (RYE-soidz). Extending sideways along the surface of the bread are runners, or *stolons,* a second kind of hyphae that establish new clumps of rhizoids. The third kind consists of upright hyphae that bear knoblike structures on their tips. These are the *sporangiophores,* and the knob is the *sporangium.* Inside the sporangium thousands of spores are produced. When part of the mycelium is examined under the microscope it looks like a forest of curious trees, each trunk supporting a large, dark ball, instead of leaves and branches.

The rhizoids of bread mold remind us of bacteria by the way they get their food. Before any of the organic material can be absorbed by the mold, the large molecules

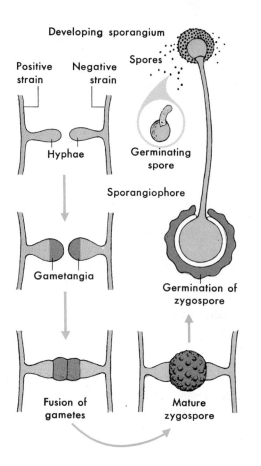

Positive strain   Negative strain

Hyphae

Gametangia

Fusion of gametes

Developing sporangium

Spores

Germinating spore

Sporangiophore

Germination of zygospore

Mature zygospore

14–2 Sexual reproduction in bread mold, showing how hyphae fuse to form zygospore.

must be split into smaller ones that can enter the cell membranes. Enzymes, secreted by the rhizoids, split the large molecules into substances the plant can use.

The growth of molds is extremely rapid under favorable conditions. The stolons grow across the surface of the bread and send down new rhizoids. In a few days an entire piece of bread may be covered. Under ideal conditions it has been estimated that the total growth of new hyphae may be as much as a half mile in a day.

REPRODUCTION OF BREAD MOLD. Bread mold reproduces asexually and sexually. In the asexual method, special hyphae pro-

duce knoblike sporangia in which the spores are produced. These are released and carried by the air to new places where the spores can germinate.

In sexual reproduction two hyphae send out short branches that meet and fuse. The process is similar to conjugation in Spirogyra. In fungi, however, cytoplasm flows from both hyphae into the point of fusion where a *zygospore* is formed. This is a thick, warty ball that is able to remain dormant for periods of three months or more. Eventually the zygospore germinates into a new mold plant, producing hyphae that bear spores.

Because of the behavior of molds during sexual reproduction, certain strains are called positive and others negative. Both strains look alike, but when the hypha from a positive spore grows close to the hypha of a negative spore, conjugation readily occurs. Some species of molds produce hyphae that conjugate even though they have originated from the same spore.

MUSHROOMS. These umbrella-like fungi belong to a large group that also includes the puffballs and bracket fungi. Most of them are quite common in the woods, fields, and meadows. Occasionally, particularly after a rainy spell, you may have seen them growing on your front lawn. Most of the relatives of the mushroom are saprophytes, living on the organic remains of plants and animals. Generally they are white or gray.

The part of the mushroom we know is actually just a small portion of the entire fungus. Most of it is underground, a tangled, twisted jungle of threads that forms the mycelium. The mushroom itself is the reproductive part of the fungus, the *fruiting body.*

If we examine the umbrella structure carefully, we note that it consists of a stalk, or *stipe,* that supports the *cap.* In most species the lower surface of the cap contains

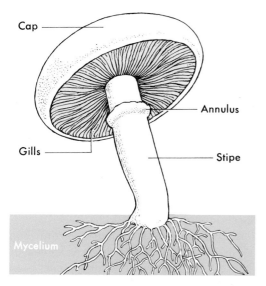

Cap

Annulus

Gills

Stipe

Mycelium

14–3 Fruiting Body of Mushroom. Underground mycelium is similar to the mycelium of mold and consists of many hyphae.

hundreds of sheetlike *gills* radiating outward from the center stalk. When the gills are examined under a microscope, they are found to be made of hyphae that have been closely pressed together. On the sides of the gill are special hyphae that produce the spores, thousands being made by each gill. The common field mushroom produces about two billion such spores.

Mushrooms grow so rapidly that the cap will often push its way through the soil overnight. While working its way through the soil, the cap is kept closed by a protective veil that attaches its edges to the upper portion of the stipe. Once above ground, the veil breaks and allows the cap to open. The part of the veil that remains attached to the stipe is called the *annulus.* The annulus often serves as an identifying feature in classifying mushrooms. The gills of the newly opened mushroom are pink, but gradually turn brown or purple as the spores mature.

POISONOUS MUSHROOMS. Although some mushrooms are used as a food, there are others that are very poisonous. Such is the deadly *Amanita,* sometimes called the "destroying angel." It can cause death in less than six hours.

Some poisonous species resemble edible

14–4 Morel   14–5 Puffball   14–6 Deadly Amanita

mushrooms so closely that it takes an expert to tell them apart. There are no simple ways of identifying the harmful forms. One false belief is that a silver spoon will tarnish if cooked in the presence of the harmful varieties. The best advice for an amateur is to buy mushrooms from a reputable dealer.

TRUFFLES AND MORELS. Both of these fungi, like the mushroom, are considered great delicacies. They are quite expensive, much more so than mushrooms. Canned truffles may sometimes cost as much as twenty dollars a pound.

Truffles grow several inches below the ground and cannot be seen. They are gathered by farmers using dogs or pigs specially trained to locate them by smell. The sight of a French farmer following a pig on a leash may seem odd, but it is simply the routine way of picking truffles! These fungi are not abundant in the United States; however, they are quite common in Spain, Italy, and France, where they grow under oak and chestnut trees.

Morels are fairly common in the United States. The fruiting body, as in the mushroom, grows above the ground and resembles a sponge. This makes them rather easy to identify, and it is safe for the collector to gather them for the table. Usually they are found in apple orchards just about the time the trees are blooming. Many people find the taste of morels to be superior to that of mushrooms.

PUFFBALLS. Perhaps you have seen one of these fungi in a woodland. They grow very commonly on decaying logs and appear as small, reduced mushroomlike "buttons" with practically no stalk. The young puffball is almost white. As it matures it turns dark brown and takes on a leathery appearance. All the puffballs are edible, but they must be taken before they turn dark. The older puffball will release thousands of spores in a fine powder when it is squeezed. Puffballs often attain enormous size. The giant puffball has been known to grow three feet in diameter.

Fungi and Plant Diseases

Mildews are extremely troublesome fungi that are very difficult to control. Although some species grow on cloth or leather, most *mildews* are parasites that cause great damage to farm plants. Among the plants they attack are: grapes, lettuce, tomatoes, roses, tobacco, and potatoes. Generally they form a gray or white powderlike coating on the surface of the leaves.

In 1845, a mildew caused a potato crop failure in Ireland. This disease, known as "late blight" of potatoes, had not been known before in Europe. It struck again in 1846. Widespread famine followed the crop destruction. Over a million people died of starvation. As a result of the crop destruction, many Irish people emigrated to the United States—about 200,000 in 1847 alone.

SMUTS. Occasionally a fresh ear of corn appears to have a large sac or tumor growing among the kernels. The sac contains a large mass of black spores. This fungus and other similar ones are called *smuts.* They attack such grains as wheat, barley, rye, corn, and oats. It has been estimated that over 120 million bushels of corn are lost each year in the United States alone because of corn smut.

Smuts act upon the host plant in a different way from most parasitic fungi. The mycelium that grows among the cells of the host stimulates them to produce a swelling, or *gall.* The spores develop as a black mass within the gall and are thrown into the air when the gall breaks. This is the swelling that can be seen on an ear of corn.

The spores of corn smut are very difficult to control. Unlike the spores of many other fungi that attach themselves to the seed, these spores lie dormant in the ground through the winter. In the spring they germi-

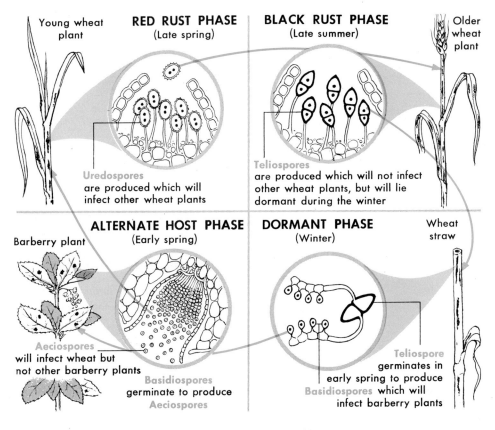

RED RUST PHASE
(Late spring)

BLACK RUST PHASE
(Late summer)

Young wheat plant

Older wheat plant

Uredospores
are produced which will
infect other wheat plants

Teliospores
are produced which will not infect
other wheat plants, but will lie
dormant during the winter

ALTERNATE HOST PHASE
(Early spring)

DORMANT PHASE
(Winter)

Barberry plant

Wheat straw

Aeciospores
will infect wheat but
not other barberry plants

Basidiospores
germinate to produce
Aeciospores

Teliospore
germinates in
early spring to produce
Basidiospores which will
infect barberry plants

14—7 LIFE CYCLE OF WHEAT RUST

nate new kinds of spores that reinfect corn plants. Treating the seed is not very effective as a prevention. Crop rotation and the development of smut-resistant strains seem to be the only methods of control.

Wheat Rust. This fungus is called a *rust* because it produces red spores that give the host a rusty color. Many kinds of rusts attack the cereal grains, trees, and ornamental plants, but the most destructive by far is wheat rust. In the past, great epidemics of this disease have ravaged the wheat fields. In 1935, wheat rust ruined one-quarter of the combined wheat crop of the United States and Canada. Wheat rust has a life history characterized by the formation of different kinds of spores.

1. *Uredospores.* These are the red spores that appear on an infected wheat plant in the late spring. Blown about by the wind, they readily infect new wheat plants. In ten days the newly infected plant is a source of more red spores. The cycle of infection is continued rapidly during the summer months by these red spores.

2. *Teliospores.* At the end of the summer black spores are produced. These are thick walled and enable the fungus to survive the winter. The teliospores may be seen as black patches on old wheat stalks. The black teliospores do not infect other wheat plants, but lie dormant over the winter.

3. *Basidiospores.* The black spores that remain on the wheat during the winter undergo a series of changes in the spring that results in the production of new spores. These, too, do not infect wheat. They are able to survive only if they fall upon a barberry plant. In the life history of wheat rust, the barberry plant is said to be an **alternate host.**

4. *Aeciospores.* An infected barberry plant produces spores that do not infect other barberry plants, but can infect wheat. When these spores infect wheat plants, the entire cycle is complete. The red spores that infect wheat plants are again produced, and the disease is spread.

Wheat rust is but one example of a parasite that requires two hosts for the completion of its life cycle. Some of the disease-producing parasites of man also require an additional host. Malaria is an example. In this case a specific mosquito is the alternate host, transmitting the parasite from man to man.

The control of diseases having alternate hosts may not be difficult. In the case of wheat rust, the destruction of the barberry plant is the obvious thing to do. Following the wheat rust epidemic of 1916 in the United States, the removal of barberry bushes was made compulsory in ten of our wheat-growing states. This control measure alone is believed to have reduced our loss from an annual average of $50,000,000 to $9,000,000.

But wheat rust has still not been completely controlled. Red spores are blown northward from Mexico and Texas. In these mild regions the red spores are able to survive the winter and infect the wheat again in the spring. No alternate host is required. Agricultural experts believe that under these conditions the only thing that can be

14–8 The fly has been lured by the secretion of this slime mold almost in the spore stage.

done is to develop strains of wheat that are rust resistant. The discouraging thing about this is that the fungi also develop new strains that attack the rust-resistant varieties of wheat.

Slime Molds

The *slime molds* are among the most unusual organisms in the Protist Kingdom. Growing as a shapeless mass of thin slime on a rotting log, a slime mold resembles an oversized ameba. The mass of cytoplasm, called the **plasmodium,** may be several inches across and contain many nuclei. There are no individual cells, and there is no cell wall. The slime molds are placed in the phylum *Myxomycetes* because of their method of reproduction.

REPRODUCTION. Slime molds develop sporangia, much like bread mold. Sometimes these are stalked. The spores are scattered by the wind, but do not develop directly into new slime molds. Coming to rest in a drop of water, the spores develop into

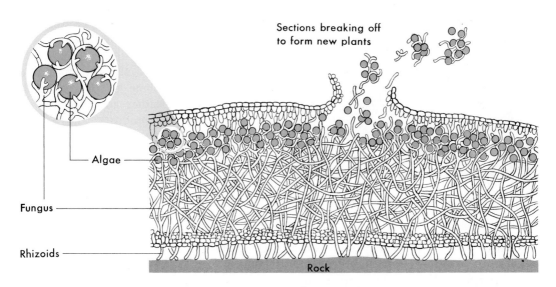

Sections breaking off
to form new plants

Algae

Fungus

Rhizoids

Rock

14–9 Cross section of lichen, showing mesh of fungal hyphae surrounding unicellular green alga. Alga supplies food for fungus, which protects alga and supplies it with water.

moving zoospores, or gametes. The gametes eventually join in pairs to form zygotes. New plasmodia develop from the growth of these zygotes.

The Lichens

Lichens are among the hardiest protists in the world. They are generally quite small, gray-green tufts or crusts that are found upon the trunks of trees or even upon bare rock. Some forms, however, are quite large and conspicuous. There are about 16,000 known species and they live in a wide range of habitats. Some lichens are found in polar regions. Others live on the sides of mountains near the snow line. Still others survive in the heat of arid deserts. They seem to be able to exist on small amounts of moisture. In periods of extreme dryness lichens often become almost papery in appearance. With the return of moisture they become soft and green again.

Lichens are really two organisms, a combination of a fungus and an alga living to-

gether in close association. When first identified, lichens were considered to be an intermediate form between the algae and the fungi. However, the Swiss botanist Simon Schwenderer showed that they are actually two organisms. Within the tangled mycelium of the fungus numerous algal cells are found.

An association in which two organisms live together for mutual benefit is not uncommon in the living world. Biologists call this association *mutualism,* which is a form of *symbiosis* (sim-by-oh-sis), meaning living together. Both the alga and the fungus derive benefit from each other. The fungus obtains food from the photosynthetic alga and in turn protects the alga from drought by its ability to absorb and retain water.

Some biologists argue that the fungus is really a parasite on the alga. However, since it does not harm the alga, its status as a parasite is uncertain. The alga, usually a green or blue-green type, can live independently, but the fungus cannot survive alone.

14–10 Lichen growing on the bark of a tree.

REPRODUCTION OF LICHENS. How would a double organism reproduce? The fungus produces spores that can be carried some distance by the wind. If they happen to fall on just the proper kind of alga, they germinate into hyphae, but this rarely occurs. The chances against it are too great.

The main way in which these organisms reproduce is by breaking into small pieces that contain both protist types. In some cases tiny, easily broken fragments are produced on the parent. These are really miniature lichens. When they are scattered and find a suitable place, they grow into larger lichens.

USES OF LICHENS. Through the centuries lichens have been useful in beginning the formation of soil from rocks. In this respect they are pioneers for other living things. While growing on rock, lichens secrete an acid that slowly dissolves it. Furthermore, as they swell and shrink during periods of moisture and drought, they rub away small particles of the rock to form soil.

One type of lichen, *Cladonia*, grows abundantly in the barren wastes of the far north. It is the principal food of reindeer and is called "reindeer moss." While lichens are not very digestible for human consumption, they are sometimes used for food. *Cetraria* (Iceland moss) is dried, powdered, then boiled to make a gelatin. The latter can be used to make soups, bread, and porridge. Litmus, the indicator dye used by chemists, is obtained from the lichen *Lecanora*. Some of the chemicals used in tanning leather and making perfumes are also lichen products.

Molds and Medicine

In 1928, Alexander Fleming, a Scottish bacteriologist at St. Mary's Hospital in London, prepared several cultures of *Staphylococcus aureus*, the dangerous bacterium that causes boils. Something spoiled the development of one of the cultures because a clear spot showed where the microbes had been killed. This type of culture spoilage had been observed before by other bacteriologists, but the problem had never been pursued. Apparently, Fleming was the first scientist to realize that if he could isolate whatever was killing his bacteria, he would have a new weapon in the fight against disease.

Dr. Fleming removed the killer from the culture. It was a common green mold that grows all over the world, a member of the genus *Penicillium*. The mold was then carefully cultured, and the brown chemical it manufactured was identified. Fleming named it **penicillin** after the mold from which it was extracted. This was a tremendously powerful germ killer, but the amount that could be obtained from the mold was very small. Fleming used most of his supply on just one infection to convince himself that it was effective. After that his interest waned, and he tried no further experiments with it at that time.

At the beginning of World War II a search was begun for a more effective germ killer. Fleming's work with penicillin was rediscovered by two British biochemists, Howard W. Florey and Ernst B. Chain. They tried new methods for the extraction

Milestones in Biology

Sir Alexander Fleming
(1881–1955)

MOMENTS OF DISCOVERY are sometimes lucky accidents. At other times they are the result of painstaking research. Most often, however, the great moments of discovery result from a combination of these two factors. Such is the story of the events that led to the discovery of penicillin.

The son of a Scottish farmer, Fleming was born in Lochfield, Scotland. At the age of thirteen he moved to London. At the age of twenty, he was admitted to St. Mary's Hospital Medical School, having passed the entrance examinations at the top of the list. After graduation, he joined the staff of St. Mary's as a bacteriologist. On the faculty at that time was Sir Almroth Wright, who was among the first to develop a vaccine against typhoid fever. Fleming was strongly influenced by Wright's experimental attitude.

During World War I, Fleming was assigned to a research center in Boulogne, France. He spent many hours considering the nature of infection and the body's defenses against it. In 1922, Fleming returned to St. Mary's. He was still interested in substances that could kill bacteria. While studying cultures of staphylococci in 1928, he stumbled upon an unusual fact. He recorded it in his notebook: "On a plate planted with staphylococci a colony of mould appeared. After about two weeks it was seen that the colonies of staphylococci near the mould colony were degenerate."

The trained mind had observed the lucky accident. Growing in the bacterial culture was the mold Penicillium notatum. For his work with Penicillium mold and for demonstrating its antibacterial activity, Alexander Fleming was knighted in July, 1944. In the following year he was awarded the Nobel Prize for Medicine by the Swedish government. Sharing it with him were Sir Howard Florey and Dr. Ernst Boris Chain. Florey and Chain developed methods of extracting large amounts of penicillin from the mold.

of larger amounts of this substance. Culture after culture was tried under various conditions. Each new method produced the same small amount of penicillin.

In 1941, Florey came to the United States to assist the Department of Agriculture in the production of penicillin. The following year, a more productive strain of the Penicillium mold was discovered growing on a moldy cantaloupe in a Peoria, Illinois, fruit market! Eventually this mold, *Penicillium chrysogenum*, produced 200 times as much penicillin as the original Fleming type. For their discovery, Fleming, Florey, and Chain shared a Nobel prize awarded to them in 1945.

Penicillin, once a laboratory curiosity, is today one of the most important germ killers used by the physician. But more important still is the fact that its discovery led to the search for other drugs effective against bacteria, many of them derived from the molds.

THE ANTIBIOTICS. Many of the microorganisms that live in the soil prey upon each other. The discovery of penicillin was one of the first cases where the natural antagonism of these microbes was put to a good use. If the Penicillium mold destroyed bacteria, was it not possible that other fungi in the soil would do the same thing?

The search for more of these germ killers, or *antibiotics*, became more intense. Dr. Selman Waksman at Rutgers University, who coined the term "antibiotic," prepared over 10,000 samples of soil cultures seeking a germ-killing agent that would help man fight disease. His search finally led to the discovery of *streptomycin*, for which he also was awarded a Nobel Prize. After much patient effort, other laboratories discovered *aureomycin* in 1948 and *terramycin* in 1950. Other antibiotics are being discovered as man enlists the aid of the natural enemies of disease in his fight against human suffering.

IMPORTANT POINTS

● The fungi are a large group of protists that lack chlorophyll. They include the molds, mushrooms, mildews, rusts, and smuts. Like bacteria, the fungi live as saprophytes or parasites.

● Most fungi have a body, or mycelium, made of numerous threadlike hyphae. Individual hyphae are modified for the absorption of food, for growth, and for the formation of spores.

● Fungi reproduce asexually or sexually. Their spores, which are produced in great quantities, are scattered by the air. Coming to rest on organic material or on a living host, the spores grow into new fungi.

● The most valuable fungi are the edible mushrooms and the molds that yield antibiotics. The most destructive fungi are the rusts, mildews, and smuts, which cause more than $2,000,000,000 in crop damage each year.

● A lichen is a dual organism in which an alga and a fungus live in a close association known as symbiosis. Lichens are valuable because they form soil by slowly wearing away the rocks on which they grow.

REVIEW QUESTIONS

1. Name three kinds of fungi.
2. List two ways in which fungi are beneficial and two ways in which they are harmful.
3. Explain how a piece of bread may become moldy.
4. Describe asexual reproduction in bread mold.
5. Where does most of a mushroom plant grow?
6. How can the farmer identify corn infected with smut?
7. How is the barberry plant related to the life cycle of wheat rust?
8. What two kinds of organisms are part of a lichen?
9. How do lichens begin the formation of soil from rock?
10. How did Alexander Fleming discover penicillin?

CHECK YOUR UNDERSTANDING

11. Compare conjugation in Spirogyra and bread mold.
12. Describe the life cycle of the wheat rust.
13. How do lichens illustrate the principle of symbiosis?
14. Why is corn smut very difficult to control?
15. In what ways can wheat rust be controlled?
16. Can you think of a reason why some molds prevent the growth of bacteria?
17. Why do parasitic fungi attack specific types of plants?
18. Why is it easier to control wheat rust in cold climates than in warmer ones?
19. Why do fungi grow faster than chlorophyll-bearing organisms?
20. Why is fungus growth so rapid in the tropics?

RESEARCH PROJECTS AND REPORTS

1. Obtain information from your school or public library and prepare a report on one of the following topics:

    Sir Alexander Fleming   **Plant Disease**

    Mushroom Growing   **Useful Fungi**

2. *Examining Mushrooms:* Obtain several large, fresh mushrooms. Draw and label stipe, annulus if present, cap and gills. Remove a single gill with scalpel and forceps. Care will be needed for this operation.

    Examine gill under microscope. Are spores present? Can you tell how they are formed? Draw and label what you observe.

3. *Making a Spore Print:* Using two mushrooms, carefully cut away the stipes as close to the caps as possible. Place one cap, gill side down, on a piece of white paper. Place the second cap on a piece of black paper. Cover each with a bowl and allow to stand for several days.

    At the end of this time remove bowls and carefully lift the mushroom caps from their papers. What appears on the paper? Make a drawing of your results.

How can you account for these markings? The spores of different mushrooms vary in color. Can you explain why it is best to use a white and a black background?

FURTHER READING

"Lichens." I. M. Lamb. *Scientific American,* October, 1959, page 144. The author explains the nature of lichens and how they are able to survive where few other plants can live.

Yellow Magic—The Story of Penicillin. J. D. Ratcliff. Random House, New York, N.Y. Describes the fortunate discovery of penicillin by Alexander Fleming and its subsequent large-scale production to heal the wounds of World War II.

"New Penicillins." Anthony H. Rose. *Scientific American,* March, 1961, page 66. Describes the chemist's attempt to produce new penicillins to meet the challenge of antibiotic-resistant strains of bacteria.

"The Fungus Gardens of Insects." Suzanne W. T. Batra and Lekh R. Batra. *Scientific American,* November, 1967, page 112. Some insects actively cultivate fungi, using them as food. A fascinating account of insect farmers.

"How Slime Molds Communicate." John T. Bonner. *Scientific American,* August, 1963, page 84. These peculiar organisms apparently "break up" for feeding, then recombine by "chemical communication" for reproduction.

15

Protists: Protozoa

Just as many algae may be considered plant-like protists, several phyla of organisms included in the Protist Kingdom may be described as animal-like. These are referred to as the *Protozoa.* Protozoa are single-celled organisms that lack chlorophyll and therefore depend on other living things for their food. Generally they are highly motile, moving about constantly in search of food. The term protozoa literally means "first animals" and these single-celled protists may indeed have been the forerunners of more highly specialized animals.

Kinds of Protozoa. There is no general agreement on the number of protozoan species. A figure sometimes mentioned by protozoologists is about 100,000. These are classified according to their method of movement. The phyla Rhizopoda, Ciliophora, and Sporozoa include most of them. Some members of the phylum Mastigophora that lack chlorophyll, like the trypanosomes, are also often included with the protozoa. Protozoa are widely distributed throughout the world in the sea, in rivers, lakes, and ponds. Some of them, including the entire phylum Sporozoa, are parasites that inhabit the bodies of the higher animals and man.

The simplest protozoa are little more than a tiny mass of cellular material that can move. Some protozoa have one or more whiplike extensions, called *flagella,* which are used to propel them through the water. Others have many extensions, called *cilia,* along the cell surface. Generally, cilia are shorter than flagella and much more numerous. Still other protozoa have no means of moving. The non-moving protozoa are all parasites. Some diseases of man, such as malaria, are caused by protozoa from this group.

Several kinds of protozoa build shells about themselves. One kind actually cements grains of sand together and carries this homemade house on its back. Other kinds secrete materials that harden into chalky shells that enclose the body. Countless numbers of such microorganisms are responsible for the formation of the chalky cliffs of Dover, England.

Protozoa that can produce light are said to be *luminescent.* Millions of such protozoa give the dark surface of the sea a shimmering, sparkling appearance. A ship passing through water containing luminescent protozoa leaves a glowing path at night.

Protozoa are found almost everywhere. The only requirements they seem to have are sufficient food and water. One fascinat-

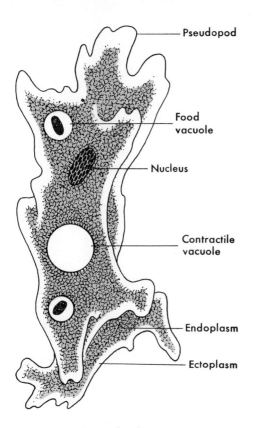

Pseudopod

Food
vacuole

Nucleus

Contractile
vacuole

Endoplasm

Ectoplasm

15–1 *Ameba proteus*

the plant material and pond water in a bowl and keep it at room temperature— about 70 to 75 degrees Fahrenheit is best. Keep the bowl in a place where there is little light, and don't let the temperature get too warm.

After the bowl has been allowed to stand for several days, examine the water very carefully with a microscope. Searching for amebae is like looking for a needle in a haystack. They are almost the same color as the water, so it is best to use a dark background. Look carefully along the sides and bottom of the bowl. Scrape some material from any submerged plants, a little at a time, and examine it. Amebae are only about 250 microns or one one-hundreth of an inch across. They have no definite shape. Their shape changes as they move about.

Prepared microscopic slides show the structures within Ameba more clearly. In preparing these slides, the amebae are stained to bring out structural detail. Usually, the nucleus stains more deeply than the surrounding cytoplasm. The cytoplasm consists of two well-defined areas: the *ectoplasm*, a clear, jellylike outer layer, and the *endoplasm*, the granular interior. The endoplasm contains the nucleus and *food vacuoles*, little bubbles containing food the organism has eaten. The nucleus may be stained with a contrasting color that makes identification easier. There are also *contractile vacuoles* that enlarge and contract, keeping the amount of water in the cell carefully regulated.

Ameba offers a wonderful opportunity for biologists to explore life in a very primitive form. All of the life processes are performed by Ameba's single cell.

MOVEMENT AND FOOD GETTING. Ameba constantly moves about in search of food. To do this, Ameba extends a part of its cell membrane in the form of a small lobe. Into this small lobe the endoplasm (granular cytoplasm) flows, making the lobe still

ing species lives in the body of the termite, the so-called "white ant" that eats wood and other cellulose products. In the digestive tube of the termite, the protozoa begin the chemical process that breaks down the wood into a compound the termite can use as a food. Without these protozoa, the termite dies.

Ameba

Where can you find protozoa? One species, called *Ameba proteus,* lives in pond water. Collect some of the larger pieces of submerged plant material from a pond, along with some of the water. If there are some pond lilies growing nearby, they are among the most likely plants for your search. Place

larger. The effect is to move all of the cell contents toward the new lobe. Thus, movement is accomplished by rolling the contents of the cell in the direction of motion. The lobes of the cell that are extended are called *pseudopods* (SUE-duh-podz). This name is appropriate since the term means "false feet."

In moving from one place to another, Ameba frequently comes upon food it can eat—small protozoa, bacteria, algae. It has no specialized area of the cell for taking in food. The method it uses to capture food is to extend pseudopods around the food particle and trap it within a food vacuole.

Digestion and Assimilation. After a food vacuole is formed, it gradually decreases in size as enzymes secreted from the surrounding endoplasm begin digestion of the food particles. The digested food is absorbed into the cytoplasm. There it is used to build more protein for growth. This process is called *assimilation.* Not all of the digested food is assimilated. Some of it is used to provide energy. Undigested food is pushed to the outside through an opening in the membrane.

Using Oxygen. As you recall, the process of using oxygen within the cell to produce energy is called *respiration.* Ameba requires small amounts of oxygen, which diffuses through the cell membrane into the endoplasm. There it oxidizes foods and produces energy. Carbon dioxide, the waste gas that results, diffuses to the outside.

The Contractile Vacuole. Water is constantly entering the body of Ameba. Some means of regulating the amount of water inside the cell is necessary. The contractile vacuole regulates water in Ameba. It enlarges and decreases in size as Ameba collects and periodically eliminates excess water. Within the water are wastes that accumulate in the cell. The elimination of these wastes that result from metabolism is called *excretion.*

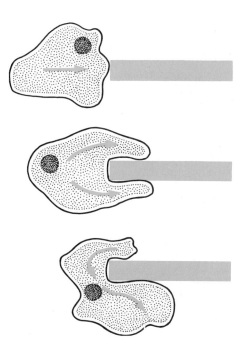

15–2 When a creeping Ameba touches a solid object, it draws back and turns away. The arrows indicate the flow of endoplasm.

Sensitivity. Can Ameba respond? Is it sensitive? The answer is yes. Even this tiny, shapeless mass responds to certain conditions in its surroundings. Ameba responds to food. It can even select its food to a certain extent. It seems to avoid tiny pieces of starch or salt that are fed to it. It avoids strong light and extremes of heat and cold. Even in this simple form of life, the important quality of *sensitivity* reveals itself.

Reproduction by Fission. Ameba reproduces every few days by *fission.* The cell becomes round in appearance, and the edge begins to pinch in on each side, dividing the cytoplasm into two parts. The nucleus, meanwhile, divides in two. Each half of the nucleus migrates to one end of the cell as Ameba divides to form two new cells. The entire process takes a little more than half an hour.

Although protozoa are generally quite small, at least one species has been found that is a comparative giant. This is a cousin of Ameba called *Chaos chaos*. This giant ameba is about one-quarter of an inch long and can be seen with the naked eye.

AMEBIC DYSENTERY. Most of the relatives of Ameba are free-living forms that dwell in lakes and streams. Some, however, are parasites that live in the bodies of animals. About a half-dozen are parasitic in man. Only one is harmful. This is *Entameba histolytica,* the cause of amebic *dysentery.* These parasites multiply in the intestine and attack the glands of the intestinal wall, causing bleeding. They also produce abcesses, and the general irritation causes diarrhea. Although amebic dysentery is more common in the tropics, a few cases continue to crop up in the United States.

Paramecium

If you have examined pond water looking for Ameba, you have probably already seen *Paramecium*, a common protozoan that resembles the imprint of a slipper. The toe is the posterior end.

Paramecium is not a slow-moving protozoan like Ameba. The individuals in a Paramecium culture move with speed and agility. The swiftness of their motion can be reduced by adding a drop or two of methyl cellulose to a small portion of the culture. It is then possible to observe tiny, hairlike cilia at the edge of the cell. The rhythmic beating of these cilia propels Paramecium through the water.

GETTING AND USING FOOD. Although the anterior end of Paramecium appears solid, it is not. In fact, it is somewhat funnel-shaped. If you watch the forward progress of the microorganism, you'll notice that it spirals or spins. As it does this, you can see that one side of the front end seems to overlap. Water is channeled by this side along

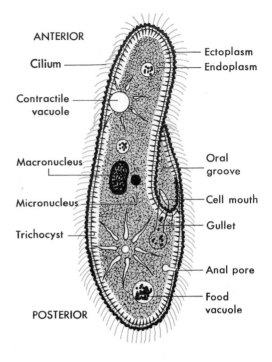

15–3 *Paramecium caudatum*

the *oral groove* into the cell mouth. There the food is forced into the *gullet* by the forward motion of the cell. When the organism is still, you may observe cilia along the oral groove that create a current of water leading into the gullet.

Just as in Ameba, a food vacuole is formed inside the cell membrane of Paramecium. The vacuole follows a definite path in Paramecium as it circulates around the cell, moving backward and circling around the nucleus. Finally, it arrives at the *anal pore* where the unused food is egested. During this circuit of the cell, enzymes digest the food. The food vacuole becomes smaller as the digested food diffuses into the cytoplasm.

NUCLEI, LARGE AND SMALL. A rather unusual thing about most paramecia is that they have two kinds of nuclei: one large, the *macronucleus,* and one small, the *micronucleus.* Experiments seem to show that the micronucleus is more important. When it is removed, the animal survives only a few days. We shall see that it also plays an important role in one of the reproductive processes of paramecia.

CO-ORDINATION OF PARTS. Protists do not have a nervous system. How then can Paramecium co-ordinate the action of its cilia so that it can swim so well? Careful examination of the base of the cilia has shown that there is a complex network of fibers connecting all of them to each other. Furthermore, when these fibers are cut, the ability to swim in a rhythmic manner is lost. Even in protozoa, we see the beginnings of a nervous system.

REPRODUCTION. We have already pointed out several ways in which Paramecium is more complex than Ameba. Its method of getting food, its ability to swim rapidly, its coordination, all seem to indicate that it is a more advanced form of life. When we consider how it reproduces, another advance is noted.

One method, fission, is the same as in Ameba. The large and small nuclei divide. The cell pinches in half, and two new cells thus form from the single parent. This is the common method of cell division.

A second method is called *conjugation.* Conjugation seems to depend upon the fact that there are several strains or sexes of paramecia. Biologists have not been able to identify external traits to tell the strains apart. For convenience, we shall call two of them *Strain A* and *Strain B.*

If a pure culture of Strain A is injected into a pure culture of Strain B, the individuals join in pairs. Each pair is united lengthwise at the oral groove where the cell membranes then dissolve. Material from each cell passes into the other. Meanwhile the large nucleus disintegrates. The small nucleus divides several times to form four nuclei. Three of the nuclei disintegrate. The fourth divides again, so that there are then two small nuclei in each mating cell. One of these migrates to the opposite mating cell and fuses with the nucleus there.

At this point the conjugating partners separate, and a series of nuclear divisions follows. Each member of a conjugating pair then reproduces by repeated fission. Conjugation thus results in the production of new individuals in which the nuclear material is derived from two parents. Conjugation is considered to be a primitive type of sexual reproduction.

15—4 Fission in Paramecium. When Paramecium reaches maximum size, the nucleus and the cytoplasm divide in half. This results in two daughter cells, each of which receives half the nuclear and cytoplasmic material of the parent cell.

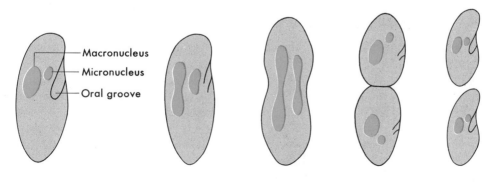

Macronucleus
Micronucleus
Oral groove

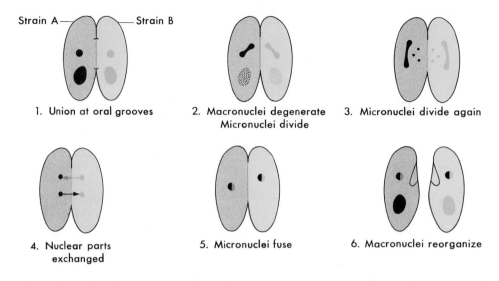

Strain A —— Strain B

1. Union at oral grooves

2. Macronuclei degenerate
   Micronuclei divide

3. Micronuclei divide again

4. Nuclear parts exchanged

5. Micronuclei fuse

6. Macronuclei reorganize

15–5 In conjugation, two paramecia of opposite strains join at their oral grooves and exchange parts of their micronuclei. After separation, each individual reproduces by fission. (See Figure 15–4.) No zygote is formed by conjugating paramecia.

TRICHOCYSTS. Embedded between the cilia in the cell membrane of Paramecium are rodlike structures called *trichocysts.* Under certain conditions, Paramecium can release the trichocysts, much like a salvo of thin darts. Some biologists believe that the release of these darts is a defense mechanism to protect Paramecium from its enemies. However, one protozoan, *Didinium nasutum,* continues to consume Paramecium even after being attacked by trichocysts. The function of trichocysts remains an unsolved problem.

African Sleeping Sickness

One of the common diseases of the African tropics, *sleeping sickness,* is caused by a protozoan called a *trypanosome.* Introduced by the bite of a *tsetse fly,* trypanosomes live in the blood. This parasite, which moves about by means of a flagellum, does not invade the red corpuscles. Instead, it swims among them and seems

to do no particular harm until it increases to large numbers.

After several months, the parasites invade the nervous system. They now swim in the fluid surrounding the brain and spinal cord. At this time the victim becomes depressed and begins to sleep far more than normal. Finally, the person becomes unconscious, sleeping all the time. Death eventually occurs.

The disease is spread by the tsetse fly, which draws in blood from an infected person. The parasites go through certain changes in the stomach of the fly. Then they migrate to the salivary glands and are ready to be injected into another victim.

There is great difficulty in controlling African sleeping sickness due to the fact that the parasite lives harmlessly in the body of many vertebrate animals, such as antelopes and cattle. Insect control, meaning direct attack upon the tsetse fly, seems to be the best means of keeping this disease in check.

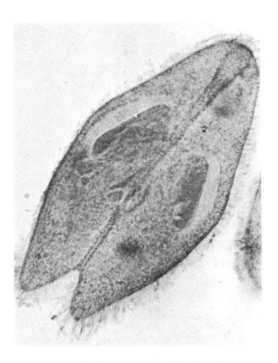

15-6 Two Paramecia in Conjugation

Malaria: A Worldwide Disease

One of the most widespread serious diseases in the world is *malaria*. Malaria is caused by a protozoan that is carried in the salivary glands of the *Anopheles* mosquito. The protozoan is injected into the blood stream of man when he is bitten.

The malarial parasite, *Plasmodium,* goes from the blood stream to the liver and remains for some time before returning to the blood stream. Having entered a red blood cell, it divides repeatedly to form as many as 36 new parasites. The blood cell is ruptured, and the plasmodia are released to attack new blood cells. In about ten days multiplication has produced such large numbers of parasites that as many as one-fifth of the red blood cells are destroyed each time a new release occurs.

The periodic release of the parasites into the blood stream produces a characteristic chill that lasts from 30 minutes to an hour. Accompanying the chill, but lasting much longer, is a violent fever that may reach 106° F.

Succeeding attacks occur at periodic intervals, depending upon the type of malaria. If an attack occurs every third day, it is called *tertian malaria*. If it occurs on the fourth day, it is called *quartan malaria*. There is much variation in the timing of the attacks.

If an infected person is bitten by an Anopheles mosquito, some of the protozoa are drawn into its body along with the blood. Sexual forms develop in the stomach of the mosquito and fertilization occurs there. Following a complicated series of changes, sporelike cells are formed that work their way to the salivary glands. There they can be injected into a human being.

The control of malaria depends upon several factors. One is the control of the Anopheles mosquito. Another is the treatment of the victim. Neither is easy. Direct attack upon the insect by use of killing sprays has proved to be the most helpful. Drugs for the treatment of malarial victims have improved greatly in recent years.

In 1955, the World Health Organization embarked on a campaign to completely eradicate malaria. The major strategy was to substantially reduce the Anopheles mosquito population by intensive spraying of DDT and other insecticides. In the fifteen years following 1955, the number of cases of malaria was reduced from a world-wide total of 350 million to fewer than 100 million. The number of cases continues to drop.

The reduction of Malaria cases has been hailed as a significant achievement. But many new problems have come about. DDT kills not only mosquitoes but many other organisms that are vital in the balance of nature. Birds have been killed by eating DDT-killed insects.

FEMALE ANOPHELES MOSQUITO

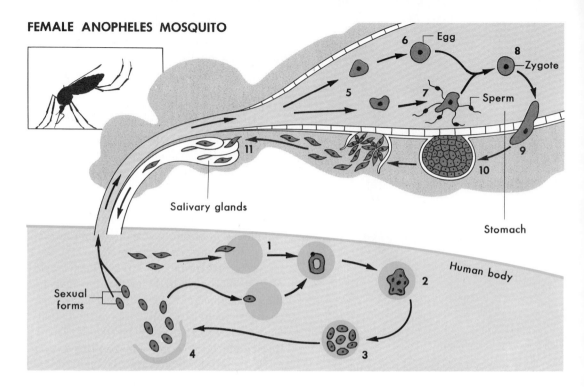

15–7 MALARIAL CYCLE. Plasmodia enter red blood cells (1) and form spores (2). Spores multiply in red cell (3), then break out and are released into blood stream (4). Some spores develop into sexual forms (5) taken in when mosquito bites. In stomach, sex cells form eggs (6) and sperms (7). Sex cells unite (8) and form wormlike zygotes (9) that penetrate stomach wall and cluster in capsules (10). Here zygotes multiply and form plasmodia, which migrate to the salivary glands (11) and are injected into the blood when mosquito bites man. Thus the cycle is completed.

DDT is a residual chemical. It remains unaltered in soil and runs off into waterways where it may be incorporated into organisms that are preyed upon by fish. The DDT persists in the fatty tissue of the fish and can be incorporated into human tissue when such fish are eaten. In areas where DDT has been widely used, it has been detected in human and cow's milk. In some countries, reduction of the malaria death rate has contributed to "population explosions" and consequent food shortages.

IMPORTANT POINTS

- Protozoa are animal-like protists. They may be the forerunners of the simplest forms of animal life. There are four phyla of protozoa, which are distinguished chiefly by the manner in which they move. Protozoa are found in the oceans and in ponds and lakes all over the world.

- Ameba is a simple protozoan found on submerged leaves and twigs in ponds. Lacking a definite shape, it moves about by extending pseudopods. The pseudopods are also used to engulf food in a food vacuole. Ameba absorbs oxygen and releases carbon dioxide through its cell membrane. Ameba reproduces by simple division, or fission. Amebic dysentery is caused by a protozoan closely related to Ameba.

- Paramecium is a slipper-shaped protozoan. Cilia propel Paramecium through the water with a rapid, twisting motion. Food is taken into the cell mouth of Paramecium and digested in a food vacuole. Unused food is egested through the anal pore. A primitive system of fibers coordinates the action of the cilia. Paramecium reproduces by fission and conjugation. The union of two strains of paramecia during conjugation is regarded as a sexual process.

- African sleeping sickness is caused by a trypanosome carried by the tsetse fly. The trypanosomes live in the blood stream of man in the early stages of the illness, but later invade the nervous system.

- Malaria is caused by the malarial parasite, Plasmodium. The parasite attacks the red blood cells of man, causing periodic chills and fever. Control of malaria depends upon controlling the mosquitoes that carry the parasites.

REVIEW QUESTIONS

1. What are the main characteristics of the protozoa?
2. Name two methods of movement used by protozoa.
3. How can Ameba be collected?
4. What two functions do pseudopods perform for Ameba?
5. Compare the shape of Paramecium with that of Ameba.
6. How does Paramecium move?
7. What is meant by saying there are two strains of paramecia?
8. Why is there some doubt about the function of trichocysts in Paramecium?
9. Distinguish between the cause and the carrier of malaria.
10. What is the cause of African sleeping sickness?

CHECK YOUR UNDERSTANDING

11. Why will the characteristics of the earliest protozoa that lived on the earth probably never be known?
12. Compare Ameba and Paramecium as to: shape, motion, food getting, egestion, reproduction.
13. What three reasons can you give to support the belief that Paramecium is a higher protozoan than Ameba?
14. Describe the process of conjugation in Paramecium.
15. What causes the periodic chills and fever characteristic of malaria?
16. What do you believe is the most effective way of controlling malaria?
17. What is the principal obstacle in controlling African sleeping sickness?
18. What reasons might account for the wide distribution of the protozoa on the earth?
19. Why does it seem reasonable to assume that animal life began in the form of single cells?
20. What tools of research have enabled man to gain some measure of control over both malaria and sleeping sickness?
21. How do the protozoa support the contention that the cell is the fundamental unit of life?

RESEARCH PROJECTS AND REPORTS

1. Obtain information from your school or public library and prepare a report on one of the following topics:

   Protozoa and Disease   **Protozoa Inhabiting Termites**

   Malaria   **Protozoa with Shells**

2. *Collecting Protozoa:* Protozoa are found everywhere in water. Extensive collections can easily be made. Take samples of water from quiet ponds and pools, especially those that are not too green. Drainage ditches usually contain many forms. Bring samples into the laboratory and examine them carefully under low power of the microscope. Some of your collecting bottles that appear to contain few, if any, specimens may eventually yield quite a number. Keep them in a warm place, about room temperature, and away from the sun. If you add some small pieces of dried leaves and hay, this will help to increase the numbers of protozoa.

3. *Experimenting with Culture Media:* If you want to try an investigation with some of the protozoa you already have, experiment with media of different types. Breakfast cereals are excellent to try. For example, boil a few corn flakes in about 200 cc of water, and use this as a culture medium. Report to your teacher how successful each of your trials was. Some, of course, will not work well, but failures often lead to success.

4. *Studying the Sensitivity of Protozoa:* Part of the problem of research is to devise methods for discovering things. How, for instance, would you test the sensitivity of Paramecia to light, to heat, and to certain chemicals? Draw up a plan for testing and submit it to your teacher for approval. Keep a careful record of the results you achieve.

FURTHER READING

How To Know the Protozoa. Theodore L. Jahn and Frances F. Jahn. Wm. C. Brown Co., Dubuque, Iowa. An excellent book for the student who wants to start collecting and identifying the protozoa.

"**The Clock of the Malaria Parasite.**" Frank Hawking. *Scientific American,* June, 1970, page 123. The life cycle of the protozoan that causes malaria is precisely timed to coincide with the best period of the day for infecting man.

"**Cilia.**" Peter Satir. *Scientific American,* February, 1961, page 108. The author discusses the working of cilia not only in protozoa, but in the cells of other living things as well. Fine electron microphotographs.

The Marvelous Animals. Helena Curtis. Natural History Press, Garden City, New York. The world of protozoa from Leeuwenhoek to the present. Well-written and illustrated.

UNIT FOUR

The Plant Kingdom

Sequoia NATIONAL PARK is located about 50 miles to the east of Fresno, California. In this park are the magnificent redwoods and sequoias. The sequoias are probably the oldest living trees. One of them, the General Sherman Tree, which measures more than 100 feet around its base, is believed to be about 3500 years old.

In Arizona, 500 miles southeast of Sequoia National Park, is the Petrified Forest National Monument. Here are found the petrified remains of trees that lived about 185 million years ago. The trees of the Petrified Forest have no living relatives, but they are distantly related to the huge redwoods of California. Both the redwoods and the "trees of stone" are conifers, or cone-bearing trees. The ancestors of the cone-bearing trees probably appeared on the earth more than 200 million years ago, but most of them are now extinct.

The conifers make up the great bulk of plants known as gymnosperms, plants that produce seeds with no protective covering. Among the common living representatives of this large group are the pines, spruces, and hemlocks. The gymnosperms were the first plants that developed seeds to reproduce themselves. This method of reproduction released plants from dependence upon water for fertilization.

More recent in the fossil record is the appearance of a different kind of seed plant. About 150 million years ago the first of the flowering plants appeared. The seeds of flowering plants are covered. These plants belong to the class of angiosperms. The angiosperms make up the great bulk of the plant kingdom, numbering over 250,000 species.

The seed plants, however, are latecomers in the evolution of the Plant Kingdom. Millions of years before the appearance of the conifers and flowering plants, simpler plants had gained a foothold on the land. Many biologists believe that the migration of plantlike organisms to the land was begun by the green protists. The first land plants probably evolved in the tidal pools so common along the edge of the sea. There, the green protists gradually became adapted to the dryness of the land. Hundreds of thousands of years elapsed before the pioneer protists evolved into plants that could tolerate the rays of the sun and the smaller amount of water the land provided. The oldest plant fossils are related to the mosses and ferns of today. The mosslike plants appear to have changed little from that ancient time. The fernlike forms evolved into the great variety of modern plants.

16

Mosses and Ferns
Primitive Land Plants

THE PLANTLIKE PROTISTS are water dwellers. They are products of the ancient seas when life first began and most of the planet was covered by water. As the land masses rose above the sea, primitive forms of green algae began the migration of organisms from the water to the land. New structures were required to survive in the new environment. Thousands of years passed before these new structures evolved through the slow process of change that marks the development of new species. Gradually plants appeared with specialized structures that enabled them to live on land.

The mosses and liverworts are believed to be among the earliest plants to invade the land in large numbers. Although some algae live on land, their numbers are few. The flowering plants, on the other hand, have become adapted almost exclusively to land dwelling. Between these two groups are the plants that might be considered amphibious. Such are the mosses and, to a lesser extent, the ferns. They live on the land and in the water. They are found in watery locations on the land, such as the swamps and the moist edges of brooks.

ANCIENT LAND PLANTS. Within the ancient rocks are found the imprints and remains of plants and animals. Botanists have found fossils of plants that are about 400 million years old. Essentially they are fernlike. Several were found in northern Scotland in the town of Rhynie. Others have been uncovered in Canada on the Gaspé peninsula.

In order for the first plants to survive, they had to absorb water from the soil and avoid losing it too quickly by evaporation in the sun's heat. They had to transport the water from one part of the plant to another. They had to have methods of reproduction that did not depend upon water alone. The ancient plants developed rootlike structures, primitive stems and leaves, and special water-conducting tubes. The reproduction of these first plants was adapted to prevent the reproductive cells from drying out.

Mosses and Liverworts

The simplest green plants that live mostly on land belong to the phylum Bryophyta. They are often found in the dimly lighted

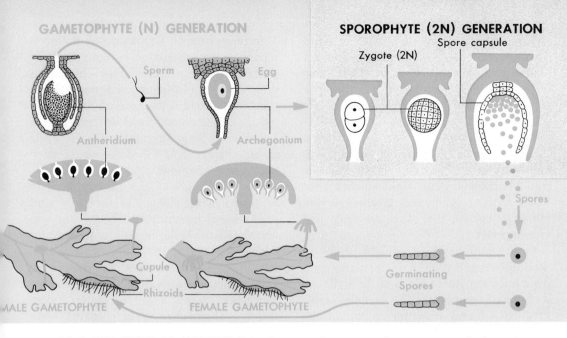

GAMETOPHYTE (N) GENERATION

Sperm

Antheridium

Egg

Archegonium

SPOROPHYTE (2N) GENERATION

Zygote (2N)

Spore capsule

Spores

Cupule

Rhizoids

MALE GAMETOPHYTE

FEMALE GAMETOPHYTE

Germinating
Spores

16—1 LIFE CYCLE OF MARCHANTIA, showing alternation of generations. Archegonia and antheridia may be separated from their stalks and observed under a microscope.

areas of the forest or in meadows along the margin of a stream. The *liverworts* have a flattened body that grows on moist rocks. Mosses have erect, stemlike bodies to which are attached organs that resemble leaves. At the base of the plant there are structures called *rhizoids* that absorb water from the soil.

Mosses and liverworts are the modern descendants of ancestors that invaded the land about 400 million years ago. Unlike the ferns, they did not develop special tissues for conducting water. They have remained small, growing close to the ground. The lack of any supporting tissue also prevented growth to any considerable height. Poorly adapted for living on land, they are not considered the forerunners of the ferns or of modern seed plants.

MARCHANTIA, A COMMON LIVERWORT. Liverworts are most frequently found in the shade of the forest, on the damp walls of caves, and on the moist rocks near a water-

fall. They rarely live far away from moisture, for they have little protection against drying by the sun.

Marchantia (mar-SHANT-e-uh) is a tiny, ribbonlike plant, about two or three inches long. Its flat body, or *thallus*, grows against the moist rock or ground. Its rhizoids grow beneath it and absorb water. The rhizoids also serve to hold the plant in place. If the environment is especially favorable and there are not too many competing plants of other types, the plants sometimes form dense mats.

Examination of a thin section of the thallus reveals tiny pores on the upper surface that permit air to enter. Internal air chambers are found just beneath the single layer of covering cells, the *epidermis*. The cells found immediately below these contain many chloroplasts, but their number decreases as we examine the lower layers of cells.

On the upper surface of the thallus tiny

cuplike structures, *cupules*, may be seen. These contain buds, or *gemmae*, that are attached by a short stalk to the bottom of the cupule. During heavy rain the gemmae are washed away from the parent plant and begin new ones.

SEXUAL REPRODUCTION OF MARCHANTIA. During most of the growing period, it is impossible to tell any difference between one Marchantia plant and another. But when sexual reproduction is about to begin, it is evident that there are male and female plants.

Both plants produce upright stalks at their growing tips. The male plants produce a flat structure on top of the stalk like a flattened umbrella. The female plants produce a round structure on top of the stalk that looks more like an umbrella.

On the flat surface at the top of the male stalks there are special male organs, the *antheridia* (ann-thuh-RID-eh-uh), in which sperms are produced. The stalks of the female plants bear corresponding female organs, the *archegonia* (are-ki-GO-ne-uh), on the lower surface of the umbrella-like head. The archegonium contains a single egg cell in its swollen base. When there is sufficient water, the sperm cells are released from the antheridia and swim to the egg cells in the archegonia. Here fertilization occurs and zygotes are formed.

The male and female plants, which produce the sperms and eggs, are called *gametophytes;* that is, plants that produce the gametes. Shortly after fertilization, the zygote divides repeatedly to form a small structure called the *sporophyte.* The sporophyte is the spore-producing structure of Marchantia. When the sporophyte is fully developed, it releases hundreds of spores into the air. These spores are carried by the wind some distance from the parent plant. They then begin the formation of new male and female plants when they germinate in a moist region.

ALTERNATION OF GENERATIONS. Botanists recognize two distinct generations of plants in the life cycle of Marchantia. The first of these is the *gametophyte*, or sexual generation. The second is the *sporophyte,* or asexual generation. Since these two generations follow each other alternately, the life cycle of Marchantia is said to demonstrate **alternation of generations.**

The significance of this alternation is to be found in the difficulties the early land plants faced in surviving when water was not abundant. Male gametes require water to swim to the egg. In the absence of water, the life cycle could not be completed. Plants that developed a spore-producing generation were able to scatter more widely. Their chances of survival were thereby increased.

The chromosome numbers in the sporophyte and gametophyte are related to each other in an unusual way. The cells of the sporophyte contain twice as many chromosomes as the cells of the gametophyte. For this reason the sporophyte is sometimes called the 2N generation, while the gametophyte is called the N generation. Thus, at the time of fertilization, two gametes, each containing N chromosomes, join to form the 2N zygote. The resulting growth of the zygote produces the 2N generation. At the time of spore formation there is a halving of the chromosome number. Each spore then contains the N number of chromosomes and produces the gametophyte or N generation.

MOSSES. Mosses are found in the meadows and pastures, as well as in the woods. Some live in the brighter sunlight in open fields. Some of them, like *Sphagnum,* grow in the swamps, while others are able to live on almost bare rock with little water. Some are able to survive the chill of the Arctic night, living in the barren northern stretches of Canada and Siberia. Others thrive in the heat of the tropics.

The chief value of mosses to us is their ability to retain water in the soil. The carpet of moss on the forest floor acts as a huge sponge that prevents the melting ice or heavy rain from washing the soil away.

Although these small plants seem to have erect stems that bear leaves, they do not have true stems or leaves. The stems do not have specialized tissues for conducting water. The leaves lack the typical structures found in the higher plants. Chloroplasts are present, as we would expect from the green color of the plants.

Moss Reproduction. Like the liverworts, sexual reproduction in the mosses is characterized by the alternation of a gametophyte with a sporophyte generation. The familiar plants are of two types: male (*antheridial*) and female (*archegonial*). It is rather hard to tell them apart, but the male plant has a flattened, flowerlike top. The cells contain the N number of chromosomes, and the plants are gametophytes.

After fertilization of the egg cell by the sperm, the zygote divides repeatedly to form a long stalk, or *seta,* on top of the female plant. This is the sporophyte or 2N generation. In the true mosses it is much more prominent than in the liverworts. The sporophyte is, in a sense, a parasite upon the gametophyte, because it absorbs its nourishment from it.

At the top of the seta a *capsule* develops. Spores are formed in the capsule that scatter the moss plants to new locations. A spore consists of but one cell. It is light and easily borne aloft by the wind. When it falls in a moist place, it germinates to form a threadlike structure called a *protonema.* The protonema closely resembles the filament of a green alga. For this reason, the mosses are believed to be descendants of the phylum Chlorophyta. Certain parts of the protonema send up vertical shoots that form the male and female plants. The life cycle is then repeated.

Sphagnum: The Bog Moss. In the spring, millions of bales of Sphagnum, or

16–2 LIFE CYCLE OF A MOSS. A significant difference between the gametophyte and the sporophyte is found in the chromosome number. Which generation has the haploid chromosome number?

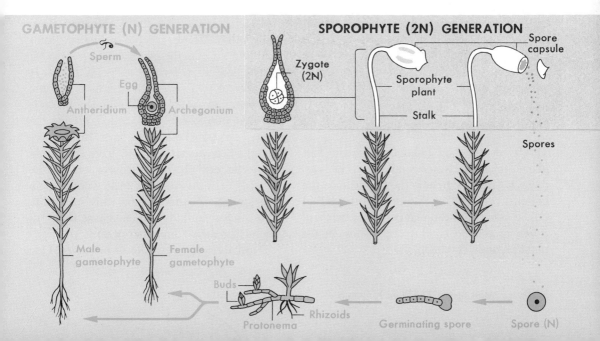

GAMETOPHYTE (N) GENERATION — SPOROPHYTE (2N) GENERATION

Sperm · Egg · Antheridium · Archegonium · Male gametophyte · Female gametophyte · Buds · Protonema · Rhizoids · Germinating spore · Spore (N)

Zygote (2N) · Sporophyte plant · Stalk · Spore capsule · Spores

peat moss, are sold for conditioning the soil in flower beds and for mulching shrubbery. Sphagnum grows in bogs where it forms a thick mat of vegetation. Its cell structure is such that it has the ability to absorb large amounts of water. In fact, it can absorb 200 times its own weight of water. This makes it very valuable to the gardener, as it helps to retain water in the soil.

Nurserymen find Sphagnum valuable in several other ways. Root cuttings start easily in it. Mixed with sand or clay, it makes a porous soil in which seeds germinate well. Because it holds so much moisture, it is often wrapped about the roots of seedlings and shrubbery before they are shipped to customers.

As Sphagnum grows, successive generations form a dense accumulation of organic material. The plants on top, together with a small amount of soil, gradually compress the plants below, which can be used as a fuel called *peat.* When peat has been compressed by great layers of material above it, chemical changes occur that result in the formation of brown coal or *lignite.* Although peat and lignite are low-grade fuels, they are valuable in those parts of the world where better fuels are not available. Ireland and the Scandinavian countries find them especially useful. A pound of peat yields about seven-tenths as much heat as the same amount of soft coal, yet gives twice as much heat as the same amount of wood.

Ferns: The First Vascular Plants

The ferns and their relatives were the first plants to have water-conducting, or *vascular,* tissues. So great is the importance the botanist attaches to this development that he includes all of the plants having *tracheal tubes,* or related conducting tissues, in the plant phylum Tracheophyta.

CHARACTERISTICS AND DISTRIBUTION. In addition to vascular tissues, ferns also possess true roots, stems, and leaves. Unlike the higher plants, however, they do not produce flowers or seeds. Reproduction is rather complex and involves alternation of generations.

Most of the ferns that live in temperate regions rarely grow more than six feet high. In the tropical rain forests of Central America, Ceylon, and Brazil, some tree ferns grow to 60 feet. Although most ferns send their roots into the soil, a few grow upon other plants, especially on tree trunks. In this case they are called *epiphytes* (EP-uh-fites). Epiphytes, however, do not obtain nourishment from the supporting plant.

PTERIDIUM: THE BRAKE FERN. Most of the fern plant that you can see is actually the leaf, for the stem of a fern grows underground and is known as a *rhizome.* The roots grow from the rhizome and bring soil water into the plant. The rhizome sends up new leaves with each new growing season. Since ferns live from year to year, they are said to be *perennial.* Like most of our common trees, they shed their leaves. A few species are evergreen.

The vascular system of the fern is best seen in a cross section of the rhizome. Two kinds of conducting cells can be observed: *xylem* (ZY-lem) vessels and *phloem* (FLOH-em) tubes. These are the principal fluid-carrying tubes in the plant.

The leaf of a fern is called a *frond.* It consists of two parts, the stemlike portion, or *stipe,* and the *blade.* Usually the blade is divided into small parts called *pinnae.* In some species the pinnae are further divided into *pinnules.* You have probably seen the curled young fronds, or "fiddleheads," of ferns growing in a woodland in the spring. The ferns have this unmistakable way of unfolding their leaves that distinguishes them from other plants.

Most ferns have two kinds of leaves. One

bears the reproductive structures, called *sporangia,* and is said to be fertile. The other kind of leaf is purely vegetative, having no sporangia. You may have noticed the marked difference between these two kinds of fronds in the cinnamon fern. In this species the fertile "leaves" are not even leaflike in appearance. Instead, they look like shaggy cinnamon sticks in the center of the normal fronds. On the other hand there are many ferns where the two kinds of fronds are almost identical.

LIFE HISTORY. The under surface of a fertile frond appears to have small brown dots on it. These are clusters of spore-producing structures, the sporangia. Each sporangium has a short stalk at the end of which there is a swollen capsule containing the spores. A special row of thickened cells throws the spores from the sporangium, scattering them widely about the parent plant. The familiar fern leaf is actually the sporophyte generation.

If the spores fall in a favorable location, they germinate. The structure they form is a thin, heart-shaped **prothallus,** the gametophyte. Unless you look very carefully, you will probably never see one. It is only about a quarter of an inch in diameter and lies flat upon the soil, sending tiny rhizoids into the ground. Among these rhizoids the male sex organs, the *antheridia,* begin to develop. When mature, the antheridia produce sperms that can swim in water. The female sex organs, the *archegonia,* develop near the notch of the prothallus. They are flask shaped just as in the mosses and liverworts. In the swollen base lies the egg cell.

If enough water surrounds the prothallus, sperms swim to the archegonia to fertilize the eggs. After an egg is fertilized, the zygote divides repeatedly. This begins the new sporophyte plant, which gradually emerges from the prothallus. At first a tiny leaf appears, and the root grows into

16–3 Sporophyte Generation of Fern

the soil. For a while the developing embryo plant is dependent upon the prothallus, but this dependence is short lived. The new sporophyte soon begins to make its own food. At this time the prothallus shrivels up. Eventually it disappears and is survived by the new fern plant. The new plant becomes the familiar clump of fronds seen in shady places.

In the ferns, as in the mosses, we see again an alternation of two generations of plants, the gametophyte and sporophyte, but the latter is now the prominent plant form. This is a further indication of the fact that the ferns are higher plants, for the sporophyte (2N) completely overshadows the gametophyte in the flowering plants, the most highly developed on earth.

LYCOPODIUM AND SELAGINELLA. These two groups of plants are closely related to the ferns even though they are commonly called *club mosses.* Their internal tissues and life histories are more fernlike than mosslike. That is why the botanist groups them with the Tracheophyta rather than the Bryophyta.

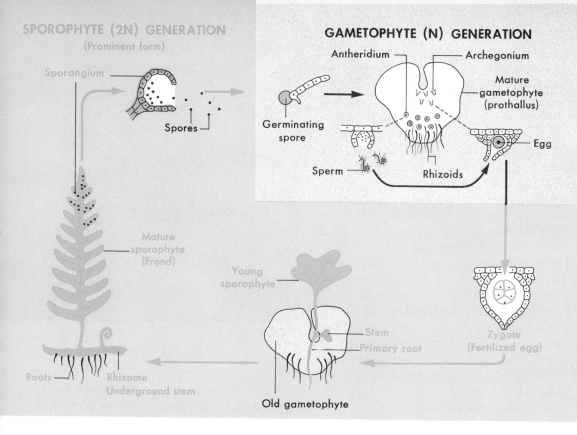

Sporangium

Spores

Mature
sporophyte
(Frond)

Young
sporophyte

Roots

Rhizome
Underground stem

Old gametophyte

GAMETOPHYTE (N) GENERATION

Antheridium

Archegonium

Mature
gametophyte
(prothallus)

Germinating
spore

Egg

Sperm

Rhizoids

Stem

Primary root

Zygote
(Fertilized egg)

16—4 LIFE CYCLE OF FERN. In the fern, the gametophyte is the dependent generation, and the sporophyte is independent. How is this situation different in mosses?

Another common name for *Lycopodium* is "ground pine," for it does resemble a pine seedling. Many species are evergreen and are widely used for Christmas decorations. *Selaginella* has been called the little club moss, for it is generally smaller than Lycopodium and grows rather close to the ground. Both of these plants reach a much greater size in the tropics than in temperate climates.

Two of the largest trees that flourished in ancient forests of 300 million years ago were relatives of the club mosses. They grew to 100 feet in some cases. The closest living approach to these ancient trees is the Joshua tree of Southern California. For some unknown reason these giants did not survive later upheavals of the earth's sur-

face. Their cousins, the club mosses, are probably descended from tiny species that grew at the base of their trunks millions of years ago.

HORSETAILS. This a strange name to give to a plant, yet you may be able to see a reason for it if you examine the sterile shoots. These appear later in the spring after the fertile cone-bearing shoots have emerged. The stems look somewhat like joined sections of tiny pipes. At each joint a whorl of smaller stems emerges giving the plant the appearance of a tail.

A common place to find *horsetails* is along a railroad embankment. They do not seem to require the moisture so necessary for most of their relatives. Some species do, however, grow in the shade.

One of the earliest signs of spring is the emergence of the slender reproductive shoots of the common horsetails. These grow a foot high in some cases and bear a distinctive yellow cone, which releases spores when mature.

The ancient relatives of the horsetails grew to enormous size. One species, *Calamites*, grew to a height of 60 feet. The trunk of Calamites was ringed with whorls of stems exactly like the present day plants. Sporangia also were grouped in the cone at the tip of the stem. Calamites and the present species of horsetails probably originated from a common ancestor.

FOSSIL FERN FORESTS. The first ferns appeared about 400 million years ago. The great fern forests did not appear until some 60 million years later. Geologists call this the *Carboniferous Period* in the history of the earth. It was during this period that great coal beds were formed.

Many fossils are found in the shale and slate of a coal mine. Beautifully preserved specimens reveal the kind of plants that lived at the time coal was formed. Even the most detailed study of the leaf and stem is possible. One of the most striking facts that these fossilized plants demonstrate is that the common plants of our day had not yet appeared. No fossils of maples, oaks, pines, flowers, or grasses are found. Instead, the dominant form of plant life was the fern and its relatives, the horsetails and club mosses. Fernlike trees grew to a height of more than 100 feet with six-foot trunks. Giant rushes, much like modern bamboo, sent their shoots 50 feet into the air.

The ferns grew everywhere. There were all shapes and sizes, and they intermingled with each other in a rich, lush growth that is characteristic of tropical jungles today. So completely did they dominate the vegetation of the period that it is sometimes called the Age of Ferns. Some were vines, some were trees, many were forms that do not presently exist.

16–5 The forest of the Carboniferous Period was dominated by mosses, large ferns, horsetails, and club mosses.

IMPORTANT POINTS

• When the first land masses rose above the ancient seas, green protists that had lived in the water began to invade the land. Prehistoric ancestors of today's mosses and ferns were the first plants to appear in great numbers.

• The mosses and liverworts were not as successful as the ferns and club mosses, for they did not develop a vascular system or woody tissue. Both of these are necessary for large plants. Hence, the mosses and liverworts remained small, while the ferns and their relatives grew to such heights that they dominated the vegetation of the Carboniferous Period. This was the time during which the great coal beds of the eastern United States were formed.

• The reproductive cycles of mosses and ferns exhibit alternation of generations, that is, the alternation of a gametophyte generation (N) with a sporophyte generation (2N). The gametophyte is the prominent moss generation. The sporophyte is the prominent fern generation.

REVIEW QUESTIONS

1. How did the absence of abundant water challenge the existence of the first land plants?
2. Name two places where liverworts, such as Marchantia, are likely to grow.
3. Describe the difference between male and female plants of Marchantia.
4. What is the difference between the gametophyte and sporophyte in terms of chromosome numbers?
5. What is the principal value of mosses in a forest?
6. List two uses for peat moss.
7. Why are no fossilized pine or maple trees likely to be found in coal mines?
8. Name two kinds of conducting cells found in ferns.
9. What significance do the small brown dots found on the lower surface of a frond have in the fern's reproductive cycle?

CHECK YOUR UNDERSTANDING

10. Compare asexual and sexual reproduction in Marchantia.
11. What is alternation of generations?
12. How is lignite formed?
13. How do fossils help us understand the development of modern plant life?
14. How did the ancient fern forests differ from the forests of today?
15. Compare the life cycle of the mosses with that of the ferns.
16. List three reasons why ferns are considered higher plant forms than mosses.
17. How did the rise of a sporophyte generation in land plants help them to survive?
18. What evidence might support the argument that mosses are related to the green algae?
19. What evidence supports a close relationship between the ferns and the seed plants?

RESEARCH PROJECTS AND REPORTS

1. Obtain information from your school or public library and prepare a report on one of the following topics:

Fossil Plants	**Giant Ferns of the Tropics**
Ancient Seas	**The Carboniferous Period**

2. *Collecting Non-flowering Plants:* Collect mosses and ferns in woodlands near home. You can dry them by spreading them carefully between layers of newspaper and putting a heavy object on top. Large pieces of blotting paper are even better. Your teacher may be able to supply you with texts that will help you identify your collection.

3. *Spore Identification:* If your interest is in using the microscope, make temporary slides of spores of different ferns and mosses. Examine them under low power, or high power if necessary, and make a series of sketches showing the differences in their appearance.

4. *A Non-flowering Terrarium:* Non-flowering plants that you collect may be kept in a terrarium. If you can bring some of the soil in which the plants were growing into the laboratory, they will probably do best. Try a layer of fine gravel underneath. A mixture of peat moss, sand, and loam in equal parts usually works well, if the original soil is not available. Cover the terrarium with glass so that the humidity is kept high.

FURTHER READING

How to Know the Mosses and Liverworts. Henry S. Conrad. Wm. C. Brown Company, Dubuque, Iowa. An illustrated key for the identification of these plant groups. Tips on collecting and preserving the plants are also given.

A Field Guide to the Ferns. Boughton Cobb. Houghton Mifflin Company, Boston, Mass. For the amateur collector there are illustrations and a key to permit identification.

The Forest. Editors of LIFE. Time, Inc., New York, N.Y. Chapter 2, Ancient Landscapes, in this volume of the LIFE Nature Library is a discussion of how plants invaded the land as revealed by fossil records.

CHAPTER

17

Seed and Root
The Growth of Plants

THE FIRST PLANTS that established themselves upon the land were especially dependent upon water. Even the ferns, more completely adapted to life on land than other ancient plants, require water for reproduction. Without water, the motile sperms cannot swim to the egg and fertilize it.

The plants that reproduce by seeds appeared rather recently. Their reproduction does not require water. The pollen they make is usually borne by the air or by insects to effect fertilization. Furthermore, during the time the seed is formed, ample food is stored in it. This enables the seed to begin its growth without being directly dependent upon the parent plant. The development of this kind of reproduction seems to have made the seed plants well adapted for life on the land.

The Kinds of Seed Plants

The seed plants are divided into two large classes, the *gymnosperms* and the *angiosperms.* Gymnosperms are the older plants and are considered more primitive than the angiosperms.

GYMNOSPERMS: NAKED SEEDS. Practically all of the existing gymnosperms belong to the order of *conifers.* Most of them are familiar trees, such as the pine, the cedar, spruce, hemlock, and fir. The name conifer means cone-bearing. More commonly, however, conifers are called evergreens because they remain green throughout the year.

The cones of the evergreen are of two types: pollen cones and ovulate, or seed, cones. Of the two, the ones you have probably seen are the seed cones because they are woody and thick. Pine seed cones are often heaped on the burning wood of a fireplace to give off a fresh pine odor. The pollen cone is smaller, but may be easily seen in the spring when covered with yellow pollen.

The seeds of the gymnosperms are the separate sections of the seed cone. Although they contain a supply of food to sustain the young plant when the seed germinates, they are naked in that they are not covered by any protective layers.

ANGIOSPERMS: FLOWERING PLANTS. The number of species of flowering plants is greater than that of all the other species of

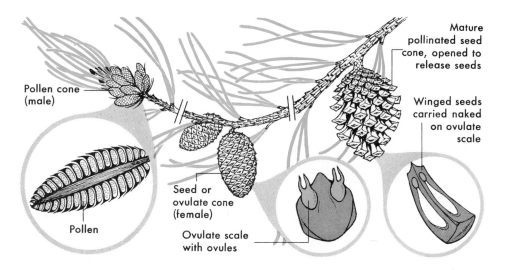

17–1 Conifers, such as pines, have seeds in ovulate cones. The air-borne pollen from pollen cones eliminates the necessity of water during fertilization.

plants combined. They are the food crops of the farmer. They are the trees of our great hardwood forests: the oak and the maple. They are the fruit trees also. They are the common plants of our homes and of our gardens. They are the grains of our great farmlands.

The distinguishing feature of the angiosperms is the flower. The flower produces the seed and the fruit. In these plants the seed is not naked, as in the gymnosperms, but has a protective covering. Angiosperms are also the only plants that produce fruits.

The Seed

The seeds of different plants vary in many ways, but they have certain characteristics in common. Each seed contains the young plant, the *embryo*. In some seeds the embryo looks like a miniature plant, completely equipped with tiny roots and leaves. Other seeds contain embryos that would never be recognized as immature plants.

Each seed also contains a supply of stored food. This stored food consists of proteins, fats, and carbohydrates. The presence of these stored materials in concentrated form is the main reason why man makes use of so many seeds for food. A seed also has a protective *seed coat*. This enables it to resist adverse conditions until it can sprout.

THE CORN GRAIN: A MONOCOTYLEDON. Botanists divide the angiosperms into two subclasses, the *monocotyledons* (mon-o-cot-ih-LEE-dunz) and the *dicotyledons* (dy-cot-ih-LEE-dunz). We can see one of the reasons for this division by comparing the seeds of these two groups.

If a grain of corn is soaked in water and cut down the center into two halves, it will appear as shown in Figure 17–2. The outer protective covering is readily identified. On the inside more than half of the grain is composed of stored food in the form of starch. This is the **endosperm.** Endosperm can be tested for starch by adding a drop of dilute iodine solution and observing how the color changes to a dark purple.

In the lower part of the grain is an irreg-

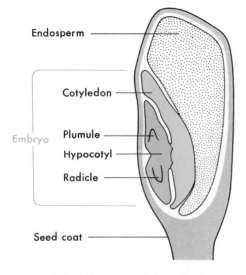

Endosperm

Cotyledon

Embryo

Plumule

Hypocotyl

Radicle

Seed coat

17–2 Structure of Corn Grain

ular section. At first glance it appears to be made of parts that bear no resemblance to a plant. This is the embryo. If it is examined with a hand lens, a tiny, rootlike structure is revealed at the bottom. This is the primitive root, or *radicle.* Just above it is the *hypocotyl* (HI-puh-cot-ul), the primitive stem. Above this is the *plumule,* the part of the embryo that will produce the first upward shoot of the new plant. Surrounding the plumule, hypocotyl, and radicle is the *cotyledon,* the primitive seed leaf.

In some seeds the cotyledon looks like a true leaf, but in a corn grain it does not. Because the grain contains only one cotyledon, corn is classified as a monocotyledon (or monocot). Monocots have marked differences in structure from plants that have more than one such seed leaf.

THE BEAN SEED: A DICOTYLEDON. When we examine a bean seed that has been soaked overnight in water, an entirely different arrangement of the main parts of the seed is observed. After the removal of the seed coat, we observe that

there are two halves. These are the cotyledons. They are quite different in appearance from the single one found in the corn grain. Since there are two of them, the bean is classified as a dicotyledon (or dicot).

Between the two halves of the dicotyledon rests the small plant. Two delicate leaves make up the plumule. The rootlike structure is the radicle and above it is the hypocotyl. These last two parts are practically indistinguishable, but differ in function. The radicle forms the root, whereas the hypocotyl forms part of the stem.

The stored food in the bean is concentrated in the very well developed cotyledons. It consists mainly of starch, fat, and some protein. There is no endosperm. The endosperm has been absorbed by the growth of the embryo.

DORMANCY OF SEEDS. Most seeds require a period of rest, or *dormancy,* before they can start the growth of the new plant. Many of them will not sprout unless they have been chilled almost to freezing for several weeks or months. During this dormant period, some of the stored food is

17–3 Structure of Bean Seed

Hypocotyl

Radicle

Plumule

Seed coat

Cotyledon

Embryo

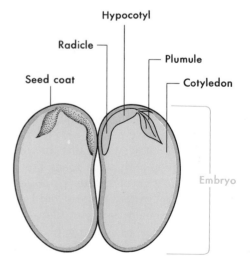

used up, and changes involving enzymes occur. Other factors, such as the thickness of the seed coat, amount of water, and the presence of certain soil bacteria, affect the length of the dormant period.

The period of dormancy varies widely. In some plants, such as the pea, the willow, and the poplar, the seeds can grow almost as soon as they are formed. In other plants, several months or years must elapse. In one case the seeds of a lotus plant, recovered from a Manchurian bog, produced plants after a period of dormancy in excess of 400 years!

Germination: The Plant Emerges

The sprouting of the seed and establishment of the new plant is called *germination*. Unless conditions are proper for a particular seed, it will not germinate.

THE CONDITIONS FOR GERMINATION. The conditions essential for germination vary to a certain extent, but we can recognize certain ones that seem to be general. Following the necessary period of dormancy there must be: (1) sufficient water, (2) an adequate supply of oxygen, and (3) the proper temperature.

The chain of events that occurs once germination has begun is largely chemical. The common medium in which the chemical reactions occur is water. Hence, without water the seed cannot sprout. The enzymes that are necessary to change the stored food into usable chemical forms in the seed require water. Water is also necessary as a medium for transporting these foods to the parts of the embryo as it begins to grow actively.

Growth also requires energy, and the production of energy occurs as a result of oxidation. If a supply of oxygen is not available to the seed, it will not sprout. Like other organisms, seeds vary in the amount of oxygen they need. Well-aerated soil is better for the germination of seeds because there is more oxygen present in it.

The enzymes that control the growth of the plant have very limited temperature ranges in which they can operate. The seed, therefore, has limited temperature ranges in which it can germinate. There is some variation, however. Peas will germinate in the early spring not long after the frost is out of the ground. Other seeds, like corn and beans, require a warm soil before they will sprout. Generally, seeds sprout when the temperature is about 70° F.

THE BEAN SEEDLING: DICOT GERMINATION. After the absorption of sufficient water starts the chemical reactions necessary for the growth of the seed, the radicle lengthens, breaks through the seed coat, and emerges into the soil. The food that supplies the energy for this initial growth comes from the cotyledons. The radicle soon branches into lateral roots, which absorb the water so necessary for the plant.

Meanwhile, the hypocotyl arches as it grows and draws the remainder of the seed out of the soil with it. The seed coat is lost in the process. By drawing the cotyledons from the soil rather than pushing them upward, the delicate growing tip of the plant is protected.

The rapid digestion of the stored foods in the cotyledons continues to provide the energy for the growth of the plumule. The tiny leaves of the seed now expand quickly to form the first green, functional leaves of the plant. Meanwhile, the cotyledons become much smaller as their food supply is exhausted. With the growth of leaves, with the expansion of the stem, and with the development of the root system, the plant is now independent.

THE CORN GRAIN: MONOCOT GERMINATION. Although the sprouting of a grain of corn is similar to the growth of the bean seedling, there are some differences. After the radicle has broken through the seed coat, it forms the root system. At almost the same time, the plumule also breaks through the seed coat and starts the formation of the stem and leaves of the plant. Since it is pushed directly upward through the soil, the sensitive growing tip would be injured if it were not protected. There is, however, a protective cap that is pushed ahead of it.

As in the bean seedling, the stored food provides the energy for growth until the plant becomes self-supporting. The endosperm contains the food for the corn grain. The starches in the endosperm must be converted into sugars by enzymes. When digestion is complete, the simpler food materials are transferred by the single cotyledon to the growing tips of the radicle and the plumule.

As the radicle continues to grow, it forms the fibrous root system characteristic of grains and grasses. The plumule forms the long, tapering leaves of the corn plant. The rest of the grain remains below the ground and decays.

The Plant Body

Now that we have seen how a seed germinates, we have an idea of four of the main parts of the typical plant. Two others develop as a result of later growth. The six parts of the plant are:

1. **The seed:** Provides for the development of the new plant and is able to endure adverse conditions.
2. **The root:** Absorbs water and dissolved mineral salts for plant growth. Also stores food and anchors the plant.
3. **The stem:** Transfers soil water and manufactured organic materials to other parts of the plant. The stem also supports the plant and stores food.
4. **The leaf:** Carries on the process of photosynthesis and makes the organic compounds necessary for the life of the plant.
5. **The flower:** Reproduces the plant by starting the formation of the seed and fruit.

17–4 Germination of Bean Seed. In typical dicot seeds, such as bean seeds, the cotyledons push through the soil, spread apart, and permit the plumule to develop.

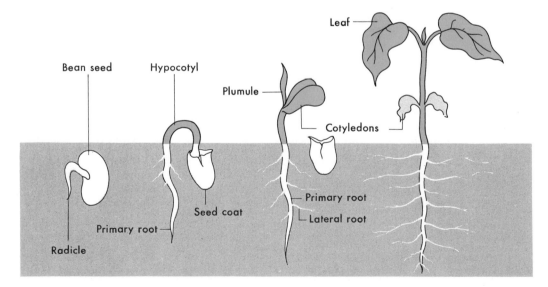

Leaf

Bean seed   Hypocotyl

Plumule

Cotyledons

Seed coat

Primary root

Lateral root

Primary root

Radicle

6. **The fruit:** Contains the seeds and the means for scattering them.

PLANT TISSUES. The names of plant tissues are different from the names of animal tissues. We shall mention here only the more important ones. Early in the growth of the seedling the following tissues can be identified:

1. **Epidermis:** The covering tissues. In most cases cells of the epidermis do not permit water to enter the plant, but certain specialized ones do.
2. **Parenchyma:** The most common type of plant tissue. It consists of thin-walled cells that give rise to all of the other types. The parenchyma (puh-REN-kuh-ma) is abundant in the growing tips of the root and stem.
3. **Xylem:** One of the two conducting tissues in the plant. It consists of several cell types. There are two of these of special interest: the *vessels,* hollow tubes that carry water, and the *wood fibers,* strong cells that support the plant body.
4. **Phloem:** The second conducting tissue. It consists of sieve tubes that carry nutrients and phloem fibers that give the plant added strength.
5. **Cambium:** The tissue that provides for the growth of the plant in width. It forms the xylem and phloem.

THE GROWTH OF THE PLANT. Most of the growth in length occurs at the tip of the root and stem. You can show the method of growth by marking the root and observing it. Mark a bean seedling's root at intervals of 1/16 inch with India ink. If you examine the root a day later, you find that the sections close to the tip have grown considerably. The sections farther back have grown very little. A similar area of active growth occurs in the tip of the stem.

The older parts of the root and stem are located far back of the growing tips. Here, growth occurs in width only and is con-

17–5 Germination of Corn Grain. In monocot seeds, such as the corn grain, the single cotyledon remains below ground and helps in absorption of food from the endosperm.

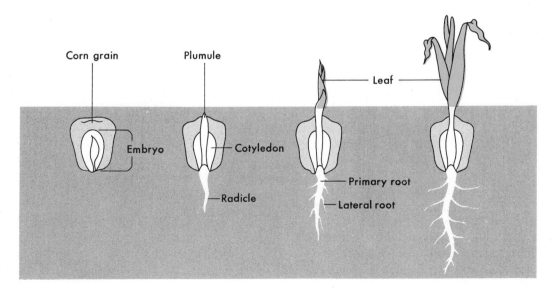

Corn grain

Plumule

Leaf

Embryo

Cotyledon

Primary root

Radicle

Lateral root

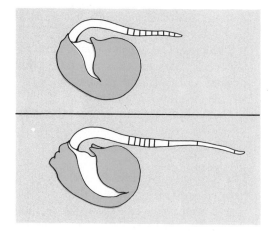

17–6 Obtain a lima bean that has sprouted well and mark the root tip in sixteenth-inch sections. Use a bristle or hair dipped in India ink. Do not harm the root or it will not continue to grow. After marking the root, place the seedling on moistened blotting paper in a Petri dish. Cover the dish. Examine the root tip a day later, then several days later. What can you conclude about growth at the tips of roots?

trolled by the *cambium,* a thin layer of cells that retains the power of active division.

The Root

Plants that became established upon land had to have some means of obtaining water. Even plants that live in open meadows require large amounts of it. The percentage of water in plants varies a great deal. In some plants, water may be as much as 95 per cent of their total weight.

The well-developed roots of flowering plants provide an ample supply of water. These plants have become especially adapted to extract the small amount of water that exists in the thin layer of the soil where they live.

THE ROOT HAIRS OF THE RADISH. The first organ of the plant that emerges from the seed coat is the root. If some radish

seeds are allowed to germinate on moistened blotter paper, another significant observation can be made. Within a day or two, not only has the root emerged, but very fine threads grow from its side. The fine threads are projections of the epidermis called *root hairs.* Their main function is to absorb water and mineral salts from the soil.

GROWTH REGIONS OF THE ROOT TIP. Careful study of the young root tip of the radish will reveal more about the growth of the plant. The botanist can prepare very thin slices of such a tip by cutting it on a microtome. The thin slices of tissue are stained with dyes to bring out details that would not otherwise be visible.

17–7 Longitudinal section of root tip showing internal structure and regions of growth.

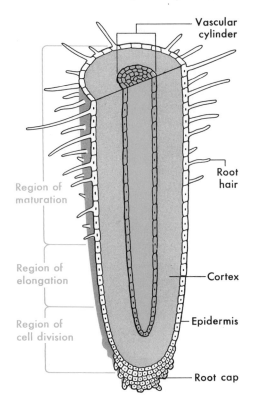

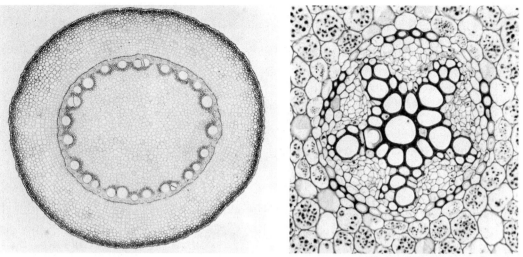

Carolina Biological Supply Company

17–8 In cross section the vascular cylinders of monocot (left) and dicot (right) roots are seen to differ in their tissue organization, although the same tissues are present. The dicot section here gives a closer view of the surrounding cells of the cortex.

At the very end of the root tip is an area of loose cells, the *root cap*. This cover protects the delicate growing tip as it is pushed between the rough particles of soil. As the cells of the root cap wear away, they are replaced by other cells from the layers of the root immediately behind them.

Just behind the root cap is the region that contains rapidly dividing cells. If the cells are properly stained, many of the stages of mitosis may be seen. These active cells are very small, thin-walled, and full of cytoplasm. The entire region, measuring about 1/16 of an inch in length, is called the *region of cell division*.

A little farther back the cells become longer. The change from short cells to longer ones is gradual. There is no clear line where the change occurs. Because the cells become longer in this particular area, it is called the *region of elongation*. Its total length is about ⅛ of an inch.

Approximately ¼ of an inch from the root tip, the permanent tissues of the root begin to form. Here the cells are not all alike. Some cells are beginning to form the central conducting tubes that carry water and develop thickened walls. Other cells retain their thin walls and are used for food storage. This is the *region of maturation*, the area in which the unspecialized cells mature and become specialized. It is also called the region of root hairs, for this is where the root hairs originate.

PERMANENT ROOT TISSUES. In a thin cross section of a young root that has been stained to bring out details, three main areas can be observed.

1. **Epidermis:** A single layer of cells that surrounds the root. In some regions you may see root hairs growing from these cells. The root hairs increase the surface area available for the absorption of water and dissolved minerals from the soil. The epidermis, therefore, has the function of absorption as well as that of protection.

2. **Cortex:** Several layers of thin-walled cells that frequently contain prominent starch grains. In many plants, the cortex is the main storage region for food and water. The cortex also serves to transport water and dissolved minerals from the root hairs to the vascular cylinder.

3. **Vascular cylinder:** The main water conducting region of the root. It is surrounded and protected by a thickened *endodermis,* usually one cell thick. In the center of the root is a group of wide cells with thick walls, the *xylem vessels.* In a dicot root cross section they form a star. In the notch of each arm of the star are separate bundles of *phloem vessels.*

The xylem and phloem vessels give the region its name (the term *vascular* refers to small vessels). They are channels for conducting water and dissolved foods throughout the entire plant body. Xylem vessels transport soil water upward. Phloem vessels generally conduct manufactured foods down, although some studies show that they may conduct in either direction.

Root Hairs and Osmosis. Root hairs are formed very soon after the seed has begun to germinate. These outgrowths of the epidermis are specialized for the purpose of absorbing water for the plant. But how does the process of water absorption occur?

Osmosis occurs when molasses is placed inside a cellophane sac and immersed in water. The water molecules outside the sac are in a constant state of motion according to kinetic theory. As a result of their motion, they pass through the cellophane and accumulate on the inside. More of them remain inside the sac than are able to escape; thus, the volume of fluid inside the sac increases.

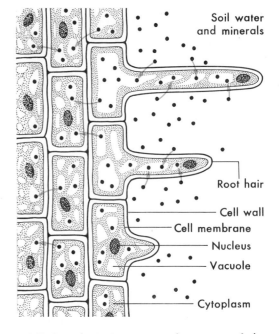

Soil water and minerals

Root hair

Cell wall

Cell membrane

Nucleus

Vacuole

Cytoplasm

17–9 Root hairs increase surface area of the root. Soil water and dissolved minerals pass through cell membrane of the root hairs into the vacuoles of epidermal cells.

The movement of the water molecules through the cellophane is probably due to pores that exist in it. The pores are believed to be large enough to permit water molecules to pass in either direction. Molasses (sugar) molecules, on the other hand, are much larger than water molecules and cannot pass through the pores. It is important to realize that the *water molecules move from a region where they are more concentrated to a region where they are less concentrated.* The water thus moves down a *concentration gradient* in much the same way that a ball rolls downhill. The cellophane acts like a selective membrane for it permits water to move in and out, but restricts the movement of molasses.

Thin films of water surround soil particles in which root hairs grow. This water corresponds to the water outside the cellophane sac. Adjacent to the cell wall of the root hair is the cell membrane, a selective or *semipermeable membrane.*

Inside the membrane are the molecules that make up the cell contents. Many of these are large organic molecules similar to the molasses molecules. The result is very much the same: the water molecules on the outside of the cell bombard the membrane, pass through, and find it difficult to get out.

Although there is movement of water molecules in and out of the cell, more remain inside than are able to leave. Because there is a greater concentration of water molecules outside the cell than inside, the water molecules move down the concentration gradient. The large organic molecules cannot escape from the cell because their size does not permit them to move through the small pores in the selective membrane.

FROM EPIDERMIS TO XYLEM. The root hair cells are part of the epidermis. The presence of water there does not help the plant unless it can be further distributed. The accumulation of water in the epidermis, however, causes it to diffuse, cell by cell, into the cortex. In each case the movement of the water is from cells where there is a higher concentration of water to those where the concentration of water is lower. The soil water thus moves into the vascular cylinder to the xylem vessels. These, in turn, carry the water upward to all parts of the plant.

SOIL AND MINERAL SALTS. Although the soil is often considered lifeless, hundreds of species of organisms live in it. These organisms, principally monerans and protists, are generally microscopic. The activities of bacteria, fungi, and algae change organic and inorganic materials into compounds useful to plants.

You have probably seen fungi growing upon fallen branches and on the trunks of trees. As the branch becomes soft, it breaks up into small particles that become

part of humus. *Humus* is the organic part of the soil formed by decaying plants and animals. Acids formed during the process of decay act upon the inorganic particles in the soil. The action of these acids changes many insoluble compounds into soluble ones that are then dissolved in soil water. Many of these compounds are essential for plant growth. Compounds such as nitrates, phosphates, and sulfates are called mineral salts. *Mineral salts* occur naturally as part of the earth's crust. The interaction of soil microorganisms with soil particles produces changes of vital importance to the growth of plants.

Biologists have discovered that the elements found in mineral salts can be divided into two groups. In the first group are those elements required in large quantities by plants. In this group are nitrogen, sulfur, phosphorus, potassium, calcium, and magnesium. In the second group are the so-called *trace elements.* Trace elements are needed in such small quantities that they had been undetected in plants for many years. This group includes iron, copper, manganese, zinc, boron, and molybdenum.

The analysis of a plant's mineral salt requirements has been made by growing them in culture solutions rather than in the soil. Small plants are grown in containers having soil water of known chemical composition. The soil water is mixed in the laboratory to provide a specific mineral salt "diet" for the plant. The results of many such experiments provide information about the essential elements needed for plant growth. In the case of the trace element molybdenum, for example, a concentration of only one part per billion parts of water is satisfactory. *Hydroponics* is the growth of plants in mineral salt solutions.

ACTIVE TRANSPORT AND PINOCYTOSIS. The movement of mineral salts into the root cannot be explained by diffusion or osmosis. As we explained previously, mineral

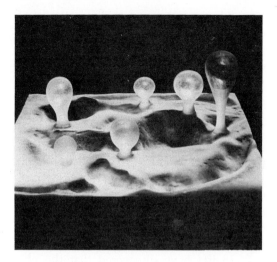

17–10 Inner surface of cell membrane model shows bulb-like involutions, which may pinch off and resemble bubbles in the cytoplasm.

salts form charged particles called *ions* when they are dissolved in water. (See pages 95–96.) The ions often move in a direction opposite to both an electrical and concentration gradient. In the alga *Nitella,* for example, the concentration of potassium ions (K^+) is one thousand times greater than in the water surrounding it. The movement of ions in a direction opposite to a gradient requires energy. A boat may drift downstream with the current, but it must be propelled by energy to go upstream.

The movement of materials of any kind through the cell membrane by the use of energy is called *active transport.* Active transport occurs in a direction opposite to an electrical or concentration gradient. In 1954, T. J. Shaw of the University of Cambridge proposed that certain compounds are necessary in the process. He called them *carriers.* A carrier is a compound that transports a specific compound, or ion, across a cell membrane. A biological carrier is somewhat like a boat that carries passengers up-

stream against the flow of the current. The precise method by which active transport occurs is not yet clearly understood, and it is not accepted as a valid explanation by all biologists.

Another way in which substances may get into the cells of the root is by *pinocytosis* (pin-o-cy-TOE-suhs). Pinocytosis means "drinking by cells." The literal meaning is somewhat misleading, however, for the process is not as simple as drinking. Certain substances, notably proteins and salts, appear to induce the process. The steps in pinocytosis can be briefly summarized as follows:

1. An inducer molecule, such as a protein or salt, is first bound to the membrane of the cell.
2. The cell membrane folds inward at the point where the inducer molecule is bound, surrounding the inducing molecule and forming a small cup or channel.
3. The cup or channel works its way into the cytoplasm of the cell.

Pinocytosis is the only kind of active transport that has actually been observed through the microscope. The pockets and channels characteristic of the process have been seen in many kinds of cells. The channels are most common in cells having a high rate of active transport, especially those of the kidney. Experiments have also shown that when ATP, the high energy compound of the cell, is reduced in amount, or absent, pinocytosis does not occur. Apparently, the energy for the transport of materials through cell membranes depends upon the presence of ATP.

CELL MEMBRANES AND RESEARCH. Because the entry and exit of materials is fundamental to an understanding of cell physiology, the cell membrane has been studied intensively for many years.

In 1940, J. F. Danielli, a British biologist,

proposed a model of the membrane that was about 80 angstroms thick. An angstrom is equal to 1/100,000,000 of a centimeter. The core was made of two layers of fatlike molecules, each about 30 angstroms long, covered by a layer of protein on each side that was 10 angstroms thick. Although there has been some slight modification in the dimensions, this model seems to have been confirmed by pictures taken with electron microscopes.

Unfortunately, a static model, such as that proposed by Danielli, does not indicate the dynamic qualities of the cell membrane. One biologist has proposed a model like a bowl of spaghetti that is constantly being shaken. The pores in the membrane seem to change their positions as the molecules shift position.

One of the appealing factors in scientific study is the search for understanding. There are many areas in which the quest for basic explanations continues. The area of cell membrane structure and function is one of these. Closely linked to it is the subject of ion transport. Perhaps future research may provide us with a clearer understanding of how substances get into and out of cells.

RADIOACTIVE COMPOUNDS. Radioactive compounds, or *radioisotopes,* afford us an excellent opportunity to demonstrate that the roots absorb mineral compounds from the soil. The passage of radioactive compounds through a plant can be followed quite easily.

A small, vigorous plant, such as a bean, clover, or tomato, is removed from the soil with extreme care so that the roots are not injured. The soil is carefully washed from the roots, and the plant is placed in a test tube two-thirds full of water. A small amount of radioactive phosphate is then added to the water. A Geiger tube is positioned above a leaf, and a background count is made immediately. As the phosphate begins to arrive in the leaf, its presence is detected by an increase in the counting rate of the Geiger tube. It is easy to understand why these radioactive materials are called "tracers." In an experiment such as this, their movement to any part of the plant can be traced and the time interval measured.

IMPORTANT POINTS

● The seed plants are of two main types: gymnosperms and angiosperms. The cone-bearing evergreens are the principal representatives of gymnosperms. The flowering plants represent the angiosperms.

● The production of seeds is one of the most important characteristics of the modern plants. Depending upon the kinds of seeds they produce, we may further subdivide the angiosperms into monocots and dicots. These terms refer to the number of cotyledons the seed contains. All seeds contain an immature plant (an embryo) and stored food, and are protected by a seed coat.

● The growth of the seed produces the new plant. In order to germinate, the seed requires water, oxygen, and warmth. The first organ that is established is the root, then the stem and leaves.

● As the root pushes into the soil, its sensitive tip is protected by the root cap. Root hairs develop behind the tip and begin the absorption of water and dissolved minerals. From the root hairs, the water passes to the cells of the cortex, then into the vascular cylinder. There, the xylem vessels transport it to the leaves by way of the stem.

● The root is the principal organ for absorbing water and mineral salts from the soil. It also transports liquids to the stem, stores food, and provides an anchored base for the plant in the soil.

● Water and certain ions move into root hair cells as the result of concentration or electrical gradients. In the special case of water, the process is called osmosis.

● Certain ions and other substances move into cells against concentration and electrical gradients. This process is called active transport and appears to be due to the action of specific carriers.

REVIEW QUESTIONS

1. Make a list of five common conifers.
2. What is the chief distinction between a flowering plant and a gymnosperm?
3. What three principal parts make up a seed?
4. How would you describe the principal function of the two "halves" of a bean seed?
5. List the three conditions that are necessary for seed germination.
6. Why are root hairs formed soon after germination begins?
7. What part of the root is concerned with growth in length? in width?
8. How does water get into a root hair cell?
9. How can a radioactive compound be used as a tracer element to show that it is absorbed by the root?
10. How might the presence of a positive charge in a cell membrane affect the diffusion of ions into the cell?

CHECK YOUR UNDERSTANDING

11. How do the enzymes in seeds depend upon water? temperature?
12. List the four main growth regions seen in a lengthwise section of a root tip.
13. Compare the movement of water into the root hair cell with the movement of water into a cellophane sac containing molasses.
14. What three factors might prevent the entry of an ion into a cell?
15. What is the significance of taking a count of radioactivity above the leaf of a plant as soon as the radioactive material is placed in the water about the plant's roots?
16. Can you think of any reasons why the flowering plants have been the most successful plant forms?
17. How do enzymes control the germination of a seed?
18. Why is the endosperm completely lacking in the bean seed, but prominent in the corn grain?
19. A molecule is too large to penetrate the pores in a cell membrane. How might you explain its entry into the cell?

RESEARCH PROJECTS AND REPORTS

1. Obtain information from your school or public library and prepare a report on one of the following topics:

Giant Redwoods

Cereal Grains

Uses of Roots

Diffusion of Solutes

2. *Growing Seeds:* Several methods can be used to observe the growth of seeds. For small seeds try the following:

Cut a circular piece of blotter paper to fit in the bottom of a Petri dish. Moisten the paper thoroughly and insert it in the lower half of the dish, then place the seeds on top. Add the cover and keep the seeds in a warm place.

For larger seeds that won't conveniently fit in a Petri dish use a shallow jar and place some absorbent cotton on the bottom. Moisten the cotton and place your seeds on top. Don't cover the seeds with water. Cover the jar almost completely, but leave just a slight opening for air. Place your seeds in a warm place and observe them daily. Add water if necessary.

3. *Experimenting with Osmosis:* Get some collodion from your pharmacist and make your own experimental membrane. Pour about 15 cubic centimeters of collodion into the bottom of a clean 6-inch test tube, then swirl it about the sides of the tube slowly so that it forms a film over the entire inside of the tube. It will form a plastic coat that makes an excellent membrane. Pull the top of the film away from the tube after it has dried, and gently pour water between the film and the tube. This loosens it so that the entire plastic sac can be removed.

Experiment with different materials placed in the bottom of the sac in small amounts. Try raw egg white, molasses, and jelly. In each case place just a small amount in the sac, then lower it into a jar of clear water. Does water accumulate on the inside of the sac or not?

FURTHER READING

Plants for Man. Robert W. Schery. Prentice Hall, Inc., Englewood Cliffs, N.J. Discusses many of the uses man has found for plants, and shows man's dependence upon the plant kingdom.

"Germination." Dov Koller. *Scientific American,* April, 1959, page 75. An Israeli scientist discusses the factors that awaken a seed from dormancy and cause it to begin to grow.

"How Things Get Into Cells." Heinz Holter. *Scientific American,* September, 1961, page 167. The director of the Carlsbad Laboratory in Copenhagen explains the ways in which materials are able to get into the cell.

Plants and Civilization. Herbert G. Baker. Wadsworth Publishing Company, Belmont, California. Traces the relation between man and the plants he has used throughout history to maintain himself.

18

The Stem and Leaf

Let us return for a moment to our observations of the growth of the seed into a new plant. Hardly have the first roots extended into the soil before the plumule pushes the young stem above ground, bringing the delicate first leaves into the sunlight. Before the plant can continue to grow, water must be transported to all parts of the plant. Everything must be in readiness for independent functioning once the stored food in the seed has been used.

Food for continuing growth must now be produced by the leaves, the chief organs of photosynthesis. The water required for food making is taken from the soil by the roots and sent upward to the leaves by the stem. Foods manufactured in the leaves are then carried by the stem to all parts of the plant body. Thus, the stem links roots and leaves and serves as the plant's main organ for the distribution of water and food.

In addition to carrying fluids, stems have other functions. Stems have growth patterns which bring about a display of the leaves to sunlight. The arrangement of leaves on the stem determines the amount of sunlight they receive. Lower leaves often extend farther from the stem than the upper ones. In a crowded forest, a young tree tends to grow tall and slender. The same

tree growing where there is no crowding and light is plentiful does not grow so tall. Stems are sometimes modified for storage of food and water. The potato has an underground stem called a *tuber,* which stores starch. In cacti the green, tough stems are swollen with stored water. Photosynthesis occurs in the stems, and the leaves are reduced to sharp spines without the ability to make food. This prevents the loss of water by evaporation in the dry desert.

The Growth of Stems

The emergence of the plumule above the soil is the beginning of the stem. The root has a delicate tip in which very rapidly dividing cells produce its growth. The stem has a similar vigorous area of rapidly dividing cells at its tip. These are thin-walled *parenchyma cells,* which have the ability to differentiate into all of the cell types found in the mature stem.

Behind this area of rapidly dividing cells lies the section of the stem where the cells lengthen and develop thick walls. Here the conducting vessels are formed that carry water and sap. Eventually, they join with the same tissues in the root and form continuous conducting tubes from root to leaf.

The growing regions of the stem are very similar to those of the root. In summary, there are three distinct areas: (1) the area of active cell division, (2) the area of elongation where cells lengthen, and (3) the area of maturity where cells reach their final form.

Like the root, the stem grows in length from the tip only. The actively growing cells of the tip press upward, leaving the lengthening cells behind them. The cells at the tip are frequently only one-tenth as long as the larger cells in back of them.

PERMANENT TISSUES. An examination of the cross section of a dicot stem shows, first of all, the protective epidermis or outer layer of cells. Beneath it are the cells of the cortex, large and irregular, that sometimes contain stored food. In the center are the very large, soft *pith cells.*

Embedded in the cortex, and separating it from the pith, are the *vascular bundles.* Each bundle contains *phloem* tissue on the outside, *xylem* tissue on the inside, and *cambium* between them. The xylem and phloem are the conducting tubes of the plant body. Cambium is a special growth tissue.

XYLEM. The cell walls of xylem tissue are thickened by the addition of the woody substance *lignin.* This makes them very strong and also serves to waterproof them. In older trees the xylem makes up most of the bulk of the trunk and makes the wood of commerce.

Three types of cells are found in xylem. The first makes up the xylem vessels, or *tracheae.* The tracheae are water-carrying tubes with no cross walls. Some of the tracheae have ringlike thickenings on their walls and are called *annular vessels.* Others have spiral thickenings. Still others have

18–1 Three-Dimensional View of Dicot Stem, Showing Xylem and Phloem Tissues

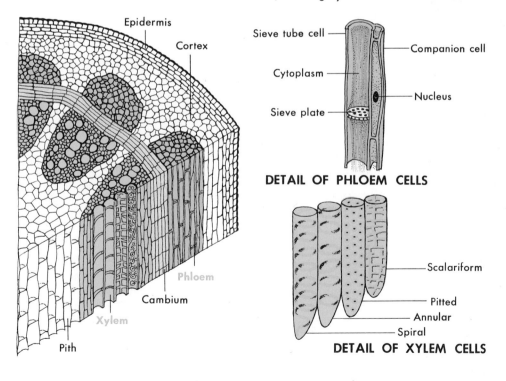

Epidermis

Cortex

Phloem

Cambium

Xylem

Pith

Sieve tube cell

Companion cell

Cytoplasm

Nucleus

Sieve plate

DETAIL OF PHLOEM CELLS

Scalariform

Pitted

Annular

Spiral

DETAIL OF XYLEM CELLS

pitted cell walls. Some even have a ladder-like arrangement. These are called *scalariform vessels.*

As well as vessels, xylem contains *tracheids* and fibers. The tracheids, like the vessels, can carry water. But since they have cross-walls, the water does not move as easily in them. The fibers are narrow, tough cells that, together with the tracheids, contribute strength and rigidity to the stem.

PHLOEM. The *phloem* tissue transports manufactured foods from one part of the plant to another. The use of radioactive "tracers" has shown that it also distributes mineral salts throughout the plant. Thus, phloem conducts materials both upward and downward.

Phloem consists of three types of cells: *sieve tube, companion,* and *fiber.* Sieve tube cells are long and thin-walled, having walls with tiny holes in them. These are called the sieve plates. Through sieve plates the sieve tube is connected lengthwise. Sieve tubes are composed of living cells with cytoplasm that extends through sieve plates and into the neighboring cells. The cytoplasm is thus continuous from one sieve tube cell to another.

The companion cells lie along the borders of the sieve tubes. Usually they form a single layer of short, thin-walled cells. Their cytoplasm is also continuous with the sieve tubes, extending into them through tiny, lateral pores.

CAMBIUM. This single layer of thin-walled cells separates the xylem from the phloem. It is the only growing tissue of the stem other than the tip. The cells of the epidermis, cortex, xylem, phloem, and pith lose their ability to divide. Cambium is the one exception. Its cells are full of cytoplasm and have very large nuclei. Cambium cells continue to divide throughout the life of the plant. It is the only tissue that retains the growing quality of the radicle and plumule that emerged from the seed.

The division of cambium cells produces growth in width. On the inside of the vascular bundle, lateral growth of the cambium makes more xylem tissue. On the outside it produces more phloem. The production of new xylem and phloem cells by the cambium is termed *secondary growth* to distinguish it from the cells produced by the growing tip of the stem. The cells produced by the tip of the stem are referred to as *primary growth.*

THE HERBACEOUS STEM. Plants that live only one year are called **annuals.** They are the common garden plants whose seeds must be sown each season. Their stems are soft and fleshy. Botanists group them together, calling them *herbs.* The erect position of the **herbaceous** (her-BAY-shus) stem is maintained by the stiffness of individual cells full of absorbed water.

Some plants have a life cycle that extends over two years. These are called **biennials.** Others live for many years and are called **perennials.** Among the latter are the trees. No matter how long a plant lives, its fundamental tissues are the same.

If you examine a young sunflower stem, you will notice that it consists very largely of soft pith cells. The vascular bundles do not form a complete ring, nor is the cambium continuous from one bundle to another. Later in the growing season, the growth of secondary tissues makes an almost continuous ring of xylem, cambium, and phloem. This same sort of growth occurs in the stem of a tree.

The Woody Stem

In contrast with the sunflower stem, let us look at the stem of a one-year-old tree seedling. Our first observation is that the amount of xylem is great. Furthermore, the xylem is arranged in a regular ringlike pattern and is, therefore, continuous. The wood will support the plant in its rapid upward

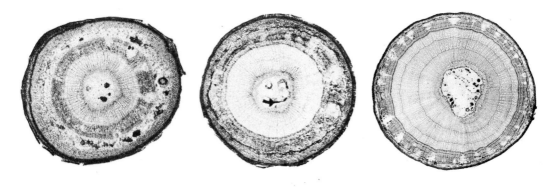

18—2 One-Year-Old Basswood   18—3 Two-Year-Old Basswood   18—4 Three-Year-Old Basswood

growth. The continuous cambium will provide for further lateral growth of the wood to increase the width of the supporting trunk. This will insure a solid foundation for the towering branches.

A roughened region under the epidermis marks the beginning of the *bark*. In older trees this will become so distinctive that you will be able to identify many of them just by examining this corky, external layer on the trunk.

ANNUAL RINGS. The growth of the cambium produces new xylem and phloem cells. The effect of this growth can be seen in the cross section of a three-year-old stem. Beginning at the center and counting outward, there are three distinct layers of xylem cells. Each marks the beginning and end of one season's growth. No such distinct regions of growth are found in the phloem.

The cambium does not produce identical xylem cells during the growing season. In the early spring, many wide vessels and few fibers are formed. This *spring wood*, which appears open and porous under the microscope, makes possible the rapid transport of large amounts of water. Later in the summer, when the rainfall is not so great, fewer vessels and more fibers are produced. The *summer wood*, which is denser and darker in color, gives the entire cross section a ringlike appearance that is easily distinguished from the spring wood by the naked eye.

The **annual rings** of trees can sometimes tell meteorologists interesting facts about the weather that existed centuries ago. Sup-

18—5 Annual growth rings may be seen on the surface of a stump or at the end of a log. Each ring has a layer of spring wood and a layer of summer wood.

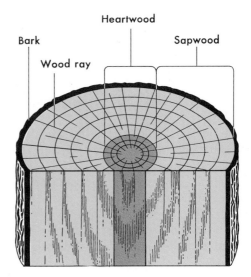

Heartwood

Bark

Sapwood

Wood ray

pose a 500-year-old tree is cut down, and it is found that the ring formed 400 years ago is very small. It can thus be established that the region in which the trees grew experienced a drought that year.

HEARTWOOD AND SAPWOOD. As the tree adds new xylem each year, the inner cells are squeezed and become filled with resins and oils to a point where they can no longer conduct water. This inner portion is called *heartwood.* It can be distinguished from the outer layer of *sapwood* by its darker color. The pith cells in the center of the young stem are crushed by this growth so that they are no longer visible in an old tree. Although it is useless for conduction, the heartwood gives strength to the tree. Also, because of its hardness and the beauty of its grain, it is used for furniture.

The outer, newer wood surrounding the heartwood is able to conduct water, hence its name, sapwood. However, with each year of growth, more sapwood is changed into heartwood. In this way the amount of heartwood gradually increases while the sapwood remains about the same. The great amount of sapwood in young trees makes them unsuitable for good lumber.

BARK AND CORK. The production of an outer, woody bark is just as characteristic of trees as the growth of the annual rings of xylem. Toward the end of the first season's growth a special layer of cells begins to appear in the *cortex* just beneath the epidermis. This is the *cork cambium.* It will produce new cork cells throughout the life of the tree.

The walls of the cork cells contain a waterproofing material that prevents the loss of water by the stem. As the tree grows in diameter, the cork layer splits and becomes roughened. The bark of a tree does not consist of cork alone. Botanists also include in it the cells of the cortex and the phloem that lie immediately beneath the woody cork.

THE PINE STEM. Practically all that we have said about the growth of woody stems thus far is true of trees like the pine, fir, and spruce. The gymnosperms form annual rings, adding a new layer of xylem each year. In this way, the age of the giant redwoods in California has been determined. Some have lived for several thousand years.

Two differences, however, distinguish the gymnosperms from other trees. First, the xylem consists of tracheids only. There are no vessels or fibers. In cross section, the pine presents the appearance of many box-like cells in its xylem. There are no vessels with rounded tubes. Second, the phloem contains no companion cells.

Running through the pine stem there are numerous *resin ducts.* The ducts run up and down as well as crosswise. So far, botanists are not agreed on the function or usefulness of the resin to the plant.

Amber, from which jewelry is often made, is a resin that has hardened into a glassy material over a period of thousands or even millions of years. Occasional pieces of amber have been found that contain preserved insects embedded in them. These furnish valuable information about

18–6 Millions of years ago, insects became trapped in the sticky resin of a pine tree. The resin later turned into amber, and the insects were preserved intact.

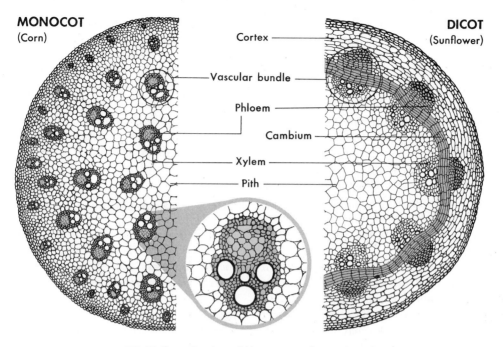

MONOCOT
(Corn)

DICOT
(Sunflower)

Cortex

Vascular bundle

Phloem

Cambium

Xylem

Pith

18—7 Cross Section of Monocot and Dicot Stems

life in the past, since insects are not usually found in fossil form because their bodies are too soft. The insects in amber became trapped in the sticky resin of gymnosperms growing millions of years ago.

The Monocot Stem

The stems of *monocots,* such as lilies, grasses, grains, palms, and bamboo, are different in certain respects from those of *dicots*. These differences may be seen in the corn stem.

Instead of being organized into definite, circular patterns, the vascular bundles of corn are scattered. No exact pattern can be observed. Most of the stem is composed of thin-walled parenchyma cells, the pith.

If you examine an individual vascular bundle, you will note that the arrangement of xylem, phloem, and air spaces gives it the appearance of a "monkey face." (See

Figure 18–7.) Surrounding the entire bundle is an irregular layer of thick-walled, protective fibers. No cambium is present, and there is little growth in width. For this reason, monocots grow tall and slender. This will become apparent to you if you note that the top of a palm tree is almost as wide as its base. The hardening of the fibers on the outside of the palm produces a tough rind, but the trunk does not develop a bark.

The Rise of Water in Stems

The rise of water in stems may be as rapid as 30 inches a minute. In a tall tree the water may rise 150 feet in an hour. Since the flow of water upward is opposed by the downward pull of gravity, biologists have sought for many years to understand how it takes place. At present there is no generally accepted explanation, but there are several interesting theories.

ROOT PRESSURE. You will recall that the root hairs absorb water from the soil by *osmosis*. The absorption of soil water by millions of root hair cells is thought to create a pressure that forces water into the xylem vessels, then pushes it upward. Direct measurements of this root pressure indicate, however, that it is not sufficient to raise water very high.

CAPILLARITY. A simple experiment will serve to show another factor that is important in the rise of water in stems. When a lump of sugar is placed in a dish that contains a small amount of ink, the ink rises to color the sugar.

The explanation for this will be clearer if we do somewhat the same thing with a set of capillary tubes. These are short lengths of glass tubing in which the inside diameter varies. The smallest tube may have a diameter 1/10 as great as the largest. When the ends of the tubes are placed in ink, the ink rises highest in the tube with the smallest diameter.

The rise of fluid in narrow tubes is *capillarity*. Since the vessels of the stem are very fine capillary tubes, water has a tendency to rise in them. However, the effect of capillarity alone is not great enough to explain the rise of water in tall trees.

THE COHESION THEORY. Physicists have known for a long time that the molecules of a liquid, such as water, are held together by strong forces. This property is known as *cohesion* (koh-HEE-zhun). Its effect is to make a long, thin column of water behave like a wire of amazing strength. A force applied at one end of the column can pull the entire column upward.

The leaves of a tree release extremely large quantities of water daily. As this water evaporates it exerts a pull upon the column of water contained in the xylem vessels. It is as though someone were tugging vigorously at the upper end of a strong thread, except that the thread is made of water. The powerful forces of cohesion hold the thread together in the tiny capillary tube and keep it from breaking.

Experiments have shown that the cohesive force of water is 100 times greater than is needed to hold a column of water together in the highest trees. Thus, the pull exerted by water evaporating from the leaves is another important factor causing water to rise in plants.

Origin and Form of Leaves

Even before a bean seed germinates, the first leaves have been formed. These are tucked between the cotyledons ready to emerge from the soil as soon as the root system is established. Without manufactured food from leaves, the plant cannot survive very long. During the period of early growth the new leaves must commence their activity or the plant perishes.

LEAF GROWTH. With the continued growth of the plant, new leaves arise in one of several ways as a result of stem growth. Just behind the growing tip of the stem, tiny buds shoot out laterally to form leaves attached to the main stem of the plant. Near the end of the growing tip are the lateral buds, which form the lateral branches of the stem. As branches grow sidewise, their growing tips also form in the manner just described.

Although roots and stems are permanent plant parts, leaves grow for a short time only. In many species, they drop off with the approach of winter, and new leaves grow in the spring.

LEAF SHAPE. Although there is much variety in the shape of leaves, there are likenesses in many of them. Except for the needles of conifers, most leaves consist of a flat *blade* containing numerous *veins*. Leaves are attached to the stem by a stalk, or *petiole* (PET-ee-ohl).

The shape of the blade often serves as an

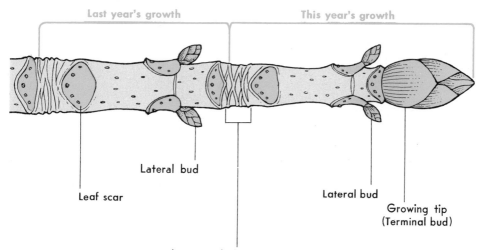

Last year's growth · This year's growth

Lateral bud

Leaf scar

Lateral bud

Growing tip
(Terminal bud)

Bud scar made by last year's terminal bud

18—8 Origin of Leaves on Horse Chestnut Twig

identifying character. For different plants there are different shapes. The taxonomist uses terms that are descriptive of the general leaf outline. Thus, *cordate* leaves are heart-shaped, *ovate* leaves are egg-shaped, and *lanceolate* leaves are spearlike.

The edge of the blade is also different in many leaves. In some the edge is almost smooth; in others it is saw-toothed. The margins of oak and maple leaves have deep indentations that form *lobes.*

18—9 Oak Leaf Showing Lobed Pattern

LEAF VEINS. Petioles support the blades and hold them in a position to receive light. The fact that they vary in length prevents the leaves from shading each other. The petiole is the extension of the stem's vascular tissue into the leaf. In the petiole are found the conducting tissues, xylem and phloem. These tissues are extended as veins in the blade. The veins of the leaf spread out from the point where they enter the blade at the petiole. The arrangement of the veins in the leaf is known as *venation.*

A fundamental distinction between monocot and dicot plants is seen in the venation of their leaves. Monocots, such as the grasses, have the main veins running parallel to each other. Dicots have veins that branch again and again to form a network. Thus, monocots have *parallel venation,* and dicots have *netted venation.*

AUTUMN AND THE FALL OF LEAVES. An early sign of autumn and the approach of winter is the changing color of leaves. The normal green gives way to yellow, brown, and red.

Although the green color of the leaf ap-

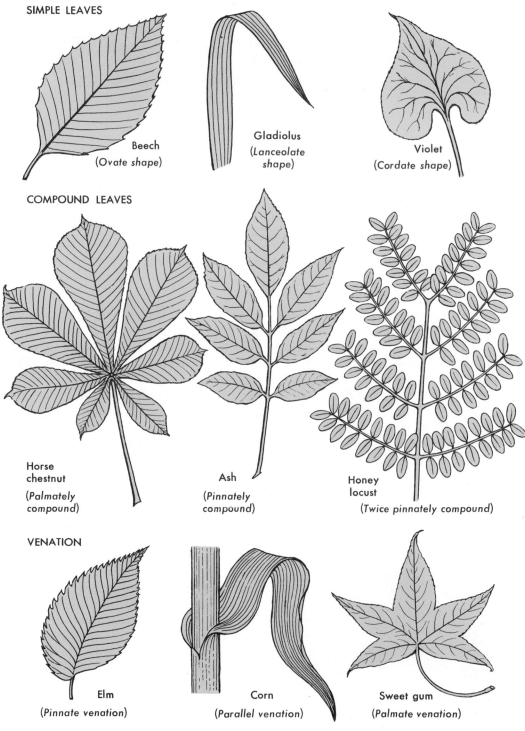

SIMPLE LEAVES

Beech
(*Ovate shape*)

Gladiolus
(*Lanceolate shape*)

Violet
(*Cordate shape*)

COMPOUND LEAVES

Horse chestnut
(*Palmately compound*)

Ash
(*Pinnately compound*)

Honey locust
(*Twice pinnately compound*)

VENATION

Elm
(*Pinnate venation*)

Corn
(*Parallel venation*)

Sweet gum
(*Palmate venation*)

pears to be a pure pigment, two yellow pigments are associated with it. At the end of summer the production of chlorophyll slows down, and more is destroyed than manufactured. As a result, there is soon not enough green to mask the yellows that are always present.

The red colors that appear in autumn are not always present in the leaf, as are the yellows. While the method by which the red color is formed is not well known, it is believed that the reduction in the amount of light and the lowering of the temperature are mainly responsible.

Contrary to popular belief, frost is not necessary for leaves to change color. Cool temperatures do aid the change to the bright foliage of autumn, however.

Trees that shed their leaves at the end of a single growing season are known as *deciduous* trees. Trees that retain their leaves for several growing seasons are known as *evergreens.*

Leaf fall in deciduous trees is accomplished by the development of an *abscission layer* located at the base of the petiole. In the autumn, the material that holds the cells of the abscission layer together begins to soften. The blade sags, but is still held to the stem by the vascular tissue. Rain, wind, and the action of frost finally cause the leaf to drop off. The wound is covered by a layer of cork cells, thus preventing the loss of water.

Internal Structure of the Leaf

The internal tissues of the leaf are similar to those found in the stem and root. There is the *epidermis* (ep-ih-DER-mis), or covering tissue, on the upper and lower surfaces. Between the epidermal layers is the *mesophyll* (MEZ-uh-fill). Among the cells of the mesophyll run the veins of vascular tissue that bring the water and minerals and take away the compounds manufactured in the leaf.

THE EPIDERMIS. The epidermis, a single layer of thin-walled cells, covers the entire leaf surface. Viewed from above, the cells are rather irregular in shape, but from the side they appear as regular rectangles. On the upper surface a thin, waxy layer above the epidermis protects the underlying tissues from injury and from excessive loss of moisture. This noncellular coating is the *cuticle.* Except for certain specialized cells, there are no chloroplasts in the epidermis.

STOMATA. Numerous tiny openings called *stomata* are found in the epidermis. Generally, stomata are much more numerous in the lower epidermis than in the upper. Each stoma is formed by two *guard cells* shaped like links of sausage. As the two ends of the guard cells press firmly together, their curvature produces a space between them. The guard cells are the only epidermal cells that contain chloroplasts.

18–11 When water is plentiful, the guard cells expand and the stoma opens.

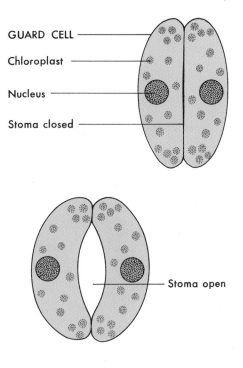

GUARD CELL

Chloroplast

Nucleus

Stoma closed

Stoma open

If some of the water is taken out of the guard cells, they will begin to collapse. The ends will not press firmly against each other, and the opening between them will close. This is the way the guard cells control the size of the stoma. The opening and closing of the stomata regulates the exchange of water vapor and other gases between the interior of the leaf and the atmosphere.

THE MESOPHYLL. Between the upper and lower epidermal layers is the mesophyll. In the typical leaf, the mesophyll is composed of two layers, the *palisade layer* and the *spongy layer.*

1. *Palisade layer.* The palisade layer is usually one or two cells thick. It is quite compact with few air spaces between the cells. The cells are arranged like rows of bricks standing on end. This arrangement gives the layer its name. Within the palisade cells are a great many chloroplasts, the green, oval bodies so important in photosynthesis. In some leaves there may be as many as 50 to 70 chloroplasts in each palisade cell.

2. *Spongy layer.* Between the palisade layer and the lower epidermis is the spongy layer. This layer is not nearly as compact as the palisade layer. The cells are irregularly shaped and are loosely arranged. Between the cells are air spaces that lead to the stomata. The cells contain fewer chloroplasts than the palisade cells.

THE VEINS. The veins are the endpoints of the vascular system that extends from the roots, through the stem, to the leaves. They are the conducting tubes for food and water.

Since the veins branch and rebranch many times in the blade of the leaf, you may see a cross section or a longitudinal section of a vein in any section of the leaf you study. Around the vein is a sheath of thick-walled cells that gives it strength and helps support the blade. Within the sheath are the xylem and phloem cells, which conduct water and sap. The xylem cells are above the phloem cells and nearer to the upper epidermis.

18–12 Internal Structure of a Leaf

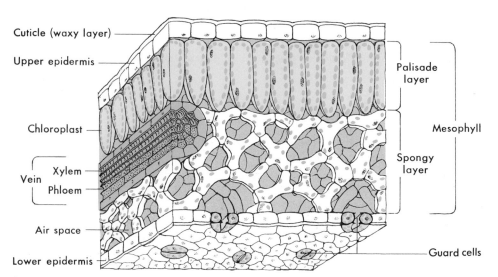

Cuticle (waxy layer)

Upper epidermis

Chloroplast

Vein — Xylem

Phloem

Air space

Lower epidermis

Palisade layer

Mesophyll

Spongy layer

Guard cells

The veins of the leaf branch into many smaller veins in the mesophyll. The cells of the mesophyll thus obtain minerals and water brought to them by the xylem. The phloem takes food from the mesophyll cells and transports it to other parts of the plant.

Leaf Functions

The principal functions of the leaf are photosynthesis, respiration, and transpiration. Because of its importance, we will review here some of the main facts concerned with photosynthesis.

PHOTOSYNTHESIS. The leaf uses two very abundant substances in the process of food making: water (H_2O) and carbon dioxide (CO_2). The water is absorbed from the soil by the root hairs and is transported by the xylem vessels into the petiole and blade of the leaf. The carbon dioxide enters the leaf from the air by way of the stomata.

Chemical reactions cannot occur without energy. The source of the energy required for photosynthesis is light. Without the chlorophyll found in the chloroplasts of the leaf, photosynthesis cannot occur. Chlorophyll is the catalyst that makes the chemical process possible. The process of photosynthesis is often summed up in the following equation:

$$6 CO_2 + 12 H_2O \xrightarrow[\text{Chlorophyll}]{\text{Light}}$$
$$C_6H_{12}O_6 + 6 O_2 + 6 H_2O$$

SYNTHESIS OF CARBOHYDRATES, PROTEINS, AND FATS. Plants build elaborate molecules using the relatively simple glucose molecule as a starting unit. Thus, the more complicated carbohydrates, proteins, fats, and vitamins are constructed from the principal product of photosynthesis. Some of the synthesis of these foodstuffs occurs in the leaf.

Since the leaf is generally very thin, it seldom acts as a storage organ. Usually, the glucose is transported to the root, stem, fruit, and seed where it is converted into more complex foods, then stored there.

Some starch is made directly in the leaf during the daytime. However, most of the starch that is formed during daylight in the leaf is again converted into glucose at night for distribution throughout the plant.

The leaf and the root seem to be the main organs in which amino acids are formed. Amino acids are the principal building blocks that form proteins. Protein molecules are generally insoluble in water and are formed directly in the tissue that uses them. Amino acids are transported to the site where proteins are formed. This can occur in any cell of the plant body.

RESPIRATION. Respiration occurs continually in all living cells. Plant cells oxidize glucose and use the energy released to carry on their life functions. Thus, plants absorb oxygen and give off carbon dioxide. The exchange of these gases takes place principally through the stomata of the leaf. The summary equation for aerobic respiration of glucose is as follows:

$$C_6H_{12}O_6 + 6 O_2 \longrightarrow$$
$$\text{glucose} \quad \text{oxygen}$$
$$6 CO_2 + 6 H_2O + \text{Energy}$$
$$\text{carbon} \quad \text{water}$$
$$\text{dioxide}$$

TRANSPIRATION. Plants take in much more water than they use for growth. Most of the water absorbed is eliminated. The process of eliminating water vapor from the plant is called *transpiration.* Because of the very large number of stomata, it is through these that transpiration principally occurs. For example, the lower surface of the apple or orange leaf may contain as many as 250,000 stomata per square inch.

Behind the stomata are the air spaces of the spongy layer. Water evaporates rapidly from the cells in this layer, passes quickly through the stomata, and escapes. Since the

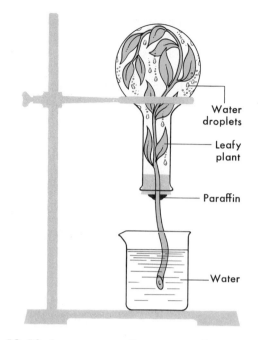

Water droplets

Leafy plant

Paraffin

Water

18–13 Apparatus to Demonstrate Transpiration. How would you set up a control?

supply of water to these cells is continually replenished by the veins, the loss of water is continuous unless the stomata close.

Many factors, such as temperature, humidity, amount of light, and wind, affect the rate of transpiration. The kind of plant is another important factor. Some desert plants lose hardly any water at all. The average plant, however, transpires a large amount of water each day. For example, an apple tree gives off about 96 gallons of water daily. A stalk of corn loses about two gallons of water in the same period.

If water is transpired too rapidly, the amount of fluid necessary to keep each cell in a swollen condition is not present. When all the cells in the plant shrink from lack of water, the entire plant becomes soft and flaccid. This condition is known as *wilting*.

The process of transpiration affects our environment by increasing water vapor in the atmosphere. Since growing plants are systems of ducts that carry soil water to the air by way of the leaves, they play a considerable role in the *water cycle*. Calculations for the United States, for example, indicate that as much as 25 per cent of the rain water that seeps into the soil is returned to the atmosphere by the leaves of plants. In heavily forested regions, the transpiration carried on by thousands of trees actually influences the climate.

Unusual Leaves

The thin, tapering needles and the flat, overlapping scales of the conifers do not look much like the leaves of the deciduous trees, but their internal structure is similar.

The leaves of most conifers remain on the tree three years or more. They are not lost in the late autumn. The tree retains its green appearance even with the arrival of snow. The larch, a deciduous conifer, is an exception to this, shedding its leaves as other shade trees do.

INSECT TRAPS. Plants that "eat" insects are among the most fascinating in the world. The leaves of these plants are adapted to capture insects. It is believed that these *insectivorous plants* obtain nitrogen compounds from the insects they eat. They digest their victim's proteins, thus adding to their supply of nitrogen. Nitrogen is often deficient in the soil where these plants grow. Three species of insectivorous plants are common along the eastern coast of the United States: the *pitcher plant*, the *sundew*, and the *Venus's-flytrap*.

In the pitcher plant, the leaves are modified into a tube or "pitcher." Insects fall into the tube, which usually contains water at the bottom. Escape is practically impossible because the inside of the pitcher is lined with numerous small spines that point downward. Eventually, the insect falls to the bottom of the tube.

Milestones In Biology

Melvin Calvin
(1911–   )

No CHEMICAL PROCESS in the scheme of life is more fundamental than photosynthesis. Without it, the world would be a barren place devoid of most of its plant life. Without it, animals would have no source of food. Yet, until recently, the chain of chemical events in photosynthesis was not understood. Much of the credit for analyzing the process is given to Melvin Calvin, a professor of biochemistry at the University of California. Calvin has spent at least ten years trying to explain the complicated chemistry of green plants. In 1961, he was awarded the Nobel Prize in Chemistry.

As a result of his work, Calvin has brought closer the day when the world may expect to produce an almost unlimited supply of food. The consequences of his research may be more far-reaching than the discovery of atomic energy. **The New York Times** stated on November 3, 1961, that he ". . . traced the highly complicated and exceedingly rapid steps taken by nature in creating starches and sugars to supply energy foods for all living things." If these rapid steps can ever be duplicated in the laboratory, the world's food shortages may end.

Calvin's early training was in the field of biochemistry. He is also an expert in radiobiology, the technique of using radioactive isotopes in biological research. In 1941, he discovered a method of extracting oxygen directly from the atmosphere.

Practically all of Calvin's postwar research has been concentrated upon photosynthesis. He recalls that one of his first real insights came to him while waiting for a traffic light to change. Why not start and stop photosynthesis by turning a light on and off in the laboratory? He tried the technique upon the simple alga Chlorella. Instead of "feeding" it ordinary carbon dioxide, however, he used radioactive carbon dioxide containing "tagged" carbon. He was then able to identify eleven intermediate compounds between the raw materials and the finished product glucose.

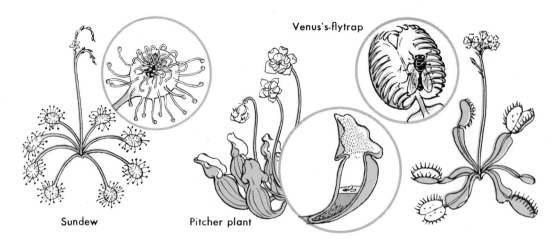

18–14 In some plants the leaves are adapted to capture and digest insects.

Sundew   Pitcher plant   Venus's-flytrap

Sundews are common among the pine barrens of New Jersey. The name is descriptive of the tiny, glistening droplets upon the slender tentacles on the leaves. The droplets are sticky and snare insects that crawl over them. Other tentacles slowly encircle the victim, while enzymes begin the process of digestion.

The swiftest insect-catching plant is the Venus's-flytrap. The leaf consists of two hinged halves. At the margins of the leaf numerous spines interlock when the leaf is closed. When an insect, attracted by a sugary solution, crawls over the opened leaf, the leaf closes in less than a second. The insect is then trapped within the cage formed by the two halves of the leaf. The indigestible parts fall out later when the leaf opens. The Venus's-flytrap grows naturally only in North and South Carolina. Because of the great interest in this curious plant, it is often cultivated in greenhouses.

IMPORTANT POINTS

● Stems transport water and foods to all parts of the plant body. As in the root tip, stem growth occurs at the end, except for lateral growth regulated by the cambium.

● Vascular bundles of woody seedlings form a complete ring by the end of the first year and add a ring of new xylem each year thereafter. Monocot stems have bundles of vascular tissue scattered in the pith.

● The rise of soil water to the tops of tall trees has not been successfully explained by botanists. Several factors, such as root pressure, capillarity, evaporation pull, and cohesion, seem important.

- Leaves are the principal food making organs of plants. Their distinctive features often serve to identify the plant.

- Leaves typically consist of petiole and blade. Some leaves are in the form of scales or needles. The veins branch in characteristic fashion.

- Leaves have three tissues: epidermis, mesophyll, and vascular cells. Stomata are the pores through which gas exchanges occur. The mesophyll contains palisade and spongy cells that have chloroplasts for food making.

- Leaves manufacture glucose by photosynthesis. They also make the more complex molecules of starches, proteins, and fats. Other leaf functions are respiration and transpiration. During transpiration, excess water is released as vapor through the stomata.

- The leaves of certain plants are equipped to capture insects. Insectivorous plants include the pitcher plant, the sundew, and the Venus's-flytrap.

REVIEW QUESTIONS

1. What are the main functions of stems?
2. Why are the lower branches of a stem often longer than the upper ones?
3. What are the main functions of xylem and phloem tissue?
4. What is the function of cambium in stem growth?
5. Why are the vessels in spring wood larger than those in summer wood?
6. Explain how the age of a stem can be determined.
7. What main function do practically all leaves have in common?
8. How do the stomata regulate the exchange of gases in the leaf?
9. What role do stomata play in respiration and transpiration?
10. What environmental factors affect the rate of transpiration?
11. Why are most leaves unsuitable for the storage of foods?

CHECK YOUR UNDERSTANDING

12. Name and describe the tissues in a vascular bundle.
13. What differences in growth are shown by monocot stems when they are compared with dicot stems?
14. What three theories explain the rise of water in stems?
15. Beavers girdle trees by chewing several inches into the bark all around the trunk. No matter how thick the trunk is, the tree dies after it has been girdled. Explain.
16. What is the significance of the fact that palisade cells are richly supplied with chloroplasts?
17. How do mesophyll cells obtain soil minerals?
18. How does transpiration play a role in the water cycle?
19. What reasons would you give for expecting that the roots of insectivorous plants are not well developed?
20. Can you suggest any way that radioactive tracers might be used to find out if mineral salts are absorbed directly into the leaf?
21. Most cacti have very few stomata. What advantage does this provide?

1. Obtain information from your school or public library and prepare a report on one of the following topics:

   Why Leaves Change Color   Tree Identification by Leaves

   Insectivorous Plants   Deciduous and Evergreen Forests

2. *Conduction in Stems:* Place a stalk of leafy celery in a beaker containing about 1 inch of water colored with red ink. Examine the stalk after several hours. Can you explain the coloring in the veins of the leaves? Cut a stalk several inches above its base. Can you see the vascular bundles? How are they arranged? What factors explain conduction in this experiment?

3. *Collection of Winter Twigs:* Make a collection of ten twigs from different trees during the winter season. Identify as many of them as possible with the aid of a tree identification manual. You can verify your identification by collecting leaves from the same trees in the summer.

4. *Leaf Experiment:* Start several bean seedlings in a mixture of sawdust and soil. Select four that are about the same size. Remove one of the first leaves from two of them. Leave the other two intact. Compare the growth of those that have had one leaf removed. Keep all other conditions the same.

5. *Leaves Need Light:* Start some bean seedlings in soil. When they seem to have a good start, separate two or three from the others, and try to grow them in a completely dark closet for several days. Compare them with the other seedlings that are allowed to grow in light. Keep the conditions of growth the same except for light, as far as possible. Can you test the leaves from the seedlings grown in darkness for starch? What are your results?

FURTHER READING

Dragons in Amber. Willy Ley. Viking Press, New York, N.Y. Chapters 1 and 2 tell how amber is formed and how "fossilized" insects contained in amber assist the scientist in determining the nature of ancient life.

The Plants. Frits W. Went and the editors of LIFE. Time Incorporated, New York, N.Y. Chapter 4 gives an excellent description of the forces that move water in the plant.

"Carnivorous Plants." Walter Henricks Hodge. *Illustrated Library of Natural Sciences*, Volume I, page 559. Perhaps no plants in the world are more fascinating than those that eat insects.

"How Sap Moves in Trees." Martin H. Zimmerman. *Scientific American*, March, 1963, page 133. Aphids are used to investigate the flow of food through phloem tissue.

CHAPTER

19

Flowers and Fruits

THE APPEARANCE of plants that reproduce by forming flowers is fairly recent in the history of life. That is why we refer to them as "modern plants." They seem to be the most successful land plants, and one of the reasons for their success is their ability to reproduce without the presence of water.

You will recall that water plays an important role in the reproduction of the mosses and ferns. Without it they cannot complete their life cycle. But the flowering plants became adapted to living in extremely dry places. The flowers of the desert cacti are perhaps among the most beautiful ever seen. The flower is thus an important organ that enables plants to live successfully on the land.

The Typical Flower

The function of the flower is to reproduce the plant. To accomplish this, the flower must produce fruits that contain seeds. We have already described how seed growth makes new plants. The production of seeds depends upon certain processes that occur in the flower. Without flowers seeds are not produced, and without seeds no new plants are grown.

ACCESSORY ORGANS. While there is really no such thing as a typical flower, there are certain floral parts that appear very commonly in most flowers. Among these "typical" floral parts are the brightly colored *petals.* Petals are not really essential for the production of seeds. Many flowers get along very well without them. In most flowers, however, petals are a means for attracting insects. All of the petals together are called the *corolla.*

On the outside of the petals many flowers have small, leaflike parts called *sepals.* These, too, are not essential parts of the flower. The sepals collectively are called the *calyx* (KAY-liks). They are mainly protective and, together with the petals, cover the inner organs while the flower is still in bud. The sepals and petals make up the *perianth.*

ESSENTIAL ORGANS. Within the protecting petals are the two organs of the flower that are essential for making seeds: the *stamens* and the *pistil.* The stamens, which are the male reproductive organs, bear pollen on their tips. In the center of the flower

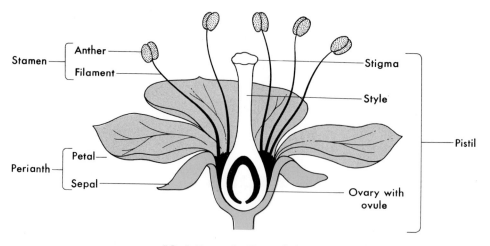

19–1 Parts of a Typical Flower

is the pistil, which is the female reproductive organ.

A single stamen consists of a stalk, or *filament,* that supports an **anther** at its top. Anthers are shaped differently in various plants. In some they are almost spherical. In others, they are very slender, pointed lobes balanced delicately atop the filament. The anthers make the pollen, which is usually found upon them when they are ripe.

The pistil has a swollen base, the **ovary,** in which the tiny, seedlike **ovules** are found. The ovules eventually become the seeds of the plant. Above the ovary is the *style,* a stalk upon which rests the **stigma.** The stigma has a sticky surface that receives pollen grains.

Types of Flowers

To a botanist a flower having both pistil and stamens is a *perfect flower.* If it has both the male and female reproductive organs, it is perfect in a reproductive sense. Such a flower may not have all the parts necessary to make it complete. A *complete flower* has all four of the main floral parts—calyx, corolla, stamens, and pistil. If any of these is lacking, it is an *incomplete flower.* Note that a complete flower is also a perfect flower. An incomplete flower may be perfect or imperfect.

An *imperfect flower* has either stamens or pistils, but not both essential organs. It may have stamens and have no pistil. In this case it is called a *staminate flower.* On the other hand, it may have pistils, but lack stamens. Then it is called a *pistillate flower.* The common Christmas holly is an example of a shrub that produces staminate flowers on one plant and pistillate flowers on another. The staminate plant does not produce berries.

The two types of imperfect flowers may be borne on the same plant or on different ones. There are many trees and shrubs, like holly, that bear the male (staminate) flowers on one plant and the female (pistillate) flowers on another. One of the most interesting is the date palm, which has been cultivated by farmers of the Middle East since ancient times. In order to produce fruit, the male flowers were cut and placed among the female flowers, a method still in use today.

PARTS OF A FLOWER

Name of Part	Description	Function
Sepals	Usually small, green, leaflike Occasionally brightly colored	Protection
Petals	Mostly brightly colored, leaflike	Protection Insect Attraction
Stamens		
Anther	Tip of the stamen	Forms pollen
Filament	Stalk of the stamen	Supports anther
Pollen	Mostly yellow, like dust	Contains male repro- ductive nucleus
Pistil		
Stigma	Sticky, top portion of pistil	Receives the pollen
Style	Stalk of the pistil	Supports the stigma
Ovary	Swollen base of pistil	Contains the ovules
Ovules	Small structures in the ovary	Contain egg nucleus

Many plants produce both types of imperfect flowers on the same plant body. One of the most familiar examples of this is corn. Many of the trees—the oaks, beeches, walnuts—and the members of the squash family are of this type. In corn, the staminate flowers are formed on the top of the stalk where the wind can easily scatter the pollen. The pistillate flowers are formed lower on the stalk and are distinguished by the silk at the end of the cob. The ear of corn is the fruit formed by the ripened pistillate flowers. Each strand of silk is the stigma and style of a flower.

REGULAR FLOWERS. It is very common to find that the number of sepals and petals on a flower is constant. For a given species of plant, the floral parts and their arrangement serve as major identifying characters. Monocot flowers, like those of the lily family, usually have three petals and three sepals. In dicots, the usual number of floral parts is five or some multiple of five. When each of the sepals is like the others and the petals are all the same, the flower is said to be *regular*.

In some cases, the petals are fused to form a tubelike structure, but the flower still maintains its very regular appearance since the parts making the tube are symmetrical. In many of the regular flowers, the stamens will be of the same number as the petals. Sometimes the number is doubled or tripled.

IRREGULAR FLOWERS. Some flowers do not have petals that are alike. A common exam-

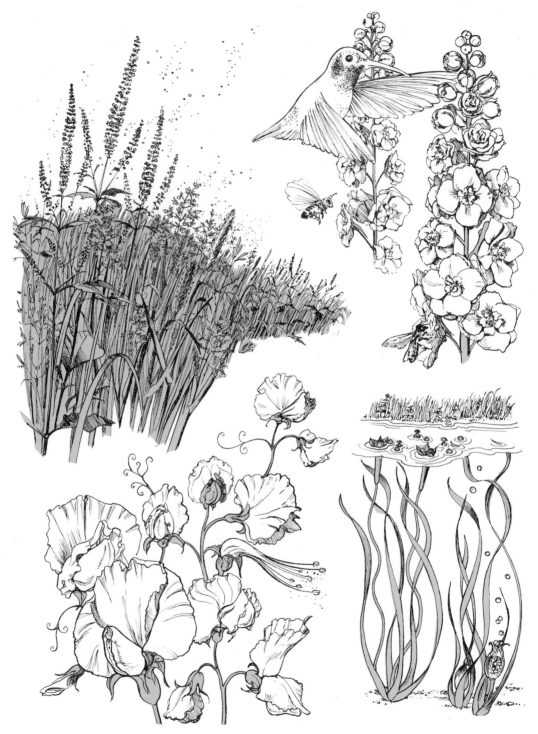

ple is the snapdragon. Here the petals are formed in such a way that if we could cut the flowers in two, each half would look the same as the other. We say that such a flower has *bilateral symmetry* and describe it as being *irregular*.

FLOWERS OF THE COMPOSITE FAMILY. Many wild flowers, such as the daisy and dandelion, have relatives—zinnias, marigolds, and asters—that are cultivated in our gardens. All of these plants belong to a group of dicots called the **composite,** or sunflower family.

The composites form the largest and most successful family in the entire plant kingdom. There are over 20,000 species distributed throughout the entire world. What is unusual about them is that the flowers are exceptionally tiny and are grouped together in one head. A daisy blossom, for example, is made of a hundred or more individual flowers.

If we carefully separate these individual flowers, we will find that they are usually of two distinct types. The *disk flowers* have a tubular corolla. The *ray flowers* have a broad corolla, which resembles a petal. Some composites are composed of one type or the other. Frequently, both types are found on the same floral head. In the daisy, the disk flowers form the central area, while the ray flowers are the white "petals" that surround it.

Pollination

If a cross section of an anther is examined under the microscope, it is found to contain four chambers in which the pollen is formed in great numbers. These are the *pollen sacs.*

Each pollen grain from a certain species of plant has a precise shape and pattern. In gladiolus, for example, the pollen has the appearance of rice grains, tapered at each end. In other plants the grains may

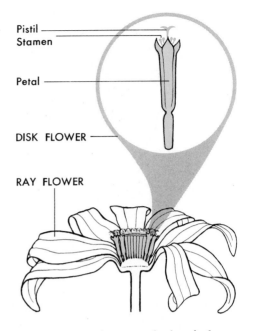

19–3 Composite Flower. In the head of a composite flower, such as the black-eyed Susan, petal-like ray flowers are arranged around a cluster of tubular disk flowers.

be spherical, often with characteristic markings or with spines.

Pollen grains can be compared with the sperm cells of animals. Within the pollen grain are the chromosomes that carry the traits of the parent plant. In the same way, the sperm cells carry the traits of the male animal. The number of chromosomes in the nuclei of the pollen grain is one half that found in the cells of the root, stem, and leaf. When the pollen grain is mature it contains two nuclei: the *generative nucleus* and the *tube nucleus.*

THE IMPORTANCE OF POLLINATION. Reproduction in flowers is a sexual process. It results when two reproductive nuclei, the egg and the sperm, unite. The sperm nucleus is produced by the growth of the pollen grain. Before a pollen grain can grow,

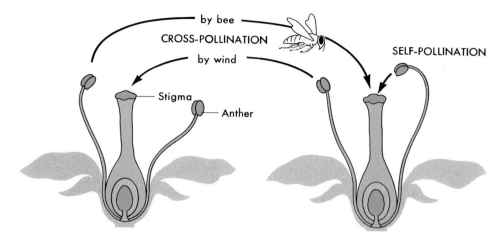

by bee
CROSS-POLLINATION

by wind

SELF-POLLINATION

Stigma

Anther

19—4 Self-Pollination and Cross-Pollination

so that the sperm can meet and unite with the egg, the pollen must be placed upon the stigma of a flower. The transfer of pollen from the anther to the stigma of a flower is called *pollination.* Without this process, the union of egg and sperm could not occur, and no seeds would be produced.

KINDS OF POLLINATION. When the pollen is ready for distribution, the pollen sacs open by splitting along their entire length. The pollen is released to the outside. There are many ways in which the pollen reaches the stigma. Wind, water, insects, and animals may effect the transfer.

In many perfect flowers the stigma is close to the anthers and the transfer of pollen to the stigma of the same flower can be easily accomplished. This is *self-pollination.* Where the plant bears only imperfect flowers, pollination can occur only by the transfer of pollen to a stigma on a different flower. This is termed *cross-pollination.* It is important to note that cross-pollination must occur between flowers of the same species, or a very closely related species, in order to be successful.

Some perfect flowers are so constructed that self-pollination cannot easily occur.

The style may be rather long, or the stigma may not be ripe to receive the pollen when it is produced. In some cases the anther ripens after the stigma has already received pollen from a different flower.

AGENTS OF POLLINATION. You may have watched bees flying from flower to flower in search of nectar. This sweet liquid is formed by tiny glands at the base of the petals. It is a powerful attraction for the bee.

As the worker bee thrusts her body among the petals, she is dusted with pollen from the anthers. If you examined her under the microscope, you would discover that her body is covered with pollen dust. As she goes from one flower to another, then, pollen is transferred from her to the stigmas, causing cross-pollination. Hummingbirds, moths, and butterflies are other animals that pollinate flowers.

Many of the flowers that bloom in the early spring are found on trees. You have probably missed seeing most of them because they are not bright and showy as are summer flowers. Frequently, the spring flowers do not have sepals or petals. Many of them achieve pollination by the wind.

The grains and grasses are also pollinated by the wind.

The staminate flowers of corn are borne high on the stalk. This arrangement is an advantage for wind-pollination. Plants that are wind-pollinated usually produce a great amount of pollen. Frequently, the pollen grains have air sacs that enable them to float in the air.

Some flowering plants that grow in water release their pollen on the surface so that it floats to other flowers and brings about pollination. Other aquatic plants, such as the water lily, raise their flowers above the surface, where they are pollinated by wind or insects.

Man frequently acts as the pollinating agent when he produces new varieties of plants. In this case, immature anthers are clipped from the flowers to be pollinated. This prevents self-pollination. Pollen secured from the flower to be cross-bred is then dusted upon the mature stigma.

The Formation of Seeds

The pistil is the female organ of the flower. At its base is the swollen ovary in which the ovules are produced. If we remove the pistil of a large flower like the tulip or gladiolus and cut through the ovary, the ovules are easily seen. They appear much like the small eggs of insects. The ovules are produced on separate stalks within distinct chambers of the ovary.

THE DEVELOPMENT OF THE OVULE. Each mature ovule has several protective cell layers about a large, central *embryo sac.* It is within this sac that the plant embryo will form. The *egg nucleus* is located at one end of the sac along with two other nuclei whose function is not clearly understood. Two *polar nuclei* are found in the center of the embryo sac. At the farther end are three other nuclei that later disintegrate. The number of chromosomes in the egg nucleus and in the polar nuclei is half the number of chromosomes in all the other plant cells except pollen.

GROWTH OF THE POLLEN TUBE. Soon after a pollen grain reaches the stigma it begins to germinate, much like a seed sending its root into the soil. Instead of a root, the pollen grain grows a *pollen tube,* which penetrates the style and grows downward toward the ovule. At the tip of the tube, a *tube nucleus* can be seen. Farther along the tube, the *generative nucleus* divides into two *sperm nuclei.*

FERTILIZATION. The pollen tube continues its growth toward the embryo sac containing the egg cell. As it reaches the ovule, the tube enters the end where there is a small opening in the protective layers, the *micropyle.*

19–5 Vertical section through the style and ovary, showing pollen tube entering the ovule.

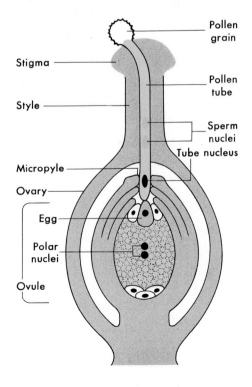

Upon entering the embryo sac, the pollen tube bursts, releasing the sperm nuclei. One of these unites with the egg nucleus. The other unites with the two polar nuclei, forming the *endosperm nucleus.* The union of the sperm nucleus with the egg nucleus is called *fertilization.* Meanwhile, the pollen tube nucleus has disintegrated, playing no role in fertilization.

Fertilization marks the beginning of a new generation of plants, for without it seeds are not formed. The chromosomes from two *gametes,* or reproductive nuclei, are combined. Fertilization produces the great variety of plant forms that now exist on the earth.

DEVELOPMENT OF THE EMBRYO. Fertilization is the beginning of the formation of the seed. The zygote now begins to divide

and redivide until it forms the embryo. This consists of the cotyledons, or seed leaves, the plumule, or primitive shoot, and the radicle, or primitive root.

While the fertilized egg is forming the embryo, the endosperm nucleus divides repeatedly to form the endosperm of the seed. In many cases the endosperm forms the largest portion of the seed. In others the embryo absorbs most, or all, of the endosperm, usually storing the food in the cotyledons. This is the case in the lima bean.

The Development of Fruits

The fertilization of the egg cell in the embryo sac is responsible for the development of the *fruit.* Fruits, in most cases, do not develop without fertilization. In the next chapter, you will learn about the effect of plant hormones upon the growth of the root and stem. The same chemicals effect fruit formation through the growth of the ovary wall. Fertilization seems to increase the amount of these hormones in the tissues surrounding the embryo sac. Within a few days the fruit is growing rapidly.

The ovary wall is the floral part that most often enlarges to produce fruit. In some plants, other parts of the flower may also fuse with the ovary to form fruits. A fruit, then, is usually defined as a ripened ovary. In plants where the ovary encloses but a single seed, the fruit and seed may be confused. This is true of the corn and other grains, which are actually fruits containing a single seed. In most other cases, many seeds are found within the fruit, as in watermelon and cantaloupe. Since fruits vary widely in structure, depending on the flowers that produce them, botanists classify them in different categories (see table on page 303).

FLESHY FRUITS. We usually think of fruits as being soft, fleshy, and edible. Oranges, apples, peaches, pears, apricots, grapes, and cherries all belong to this cate-

19–6 A seed, such as a corn grain, is a ripened ovary with one ovule. A tomato is a ripened ovary with many ovules (seeds).

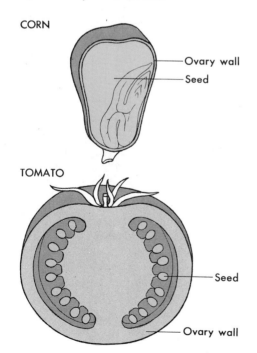

CORN

Ovary wall
Seed

TOMATO

Seed

Ovary wall

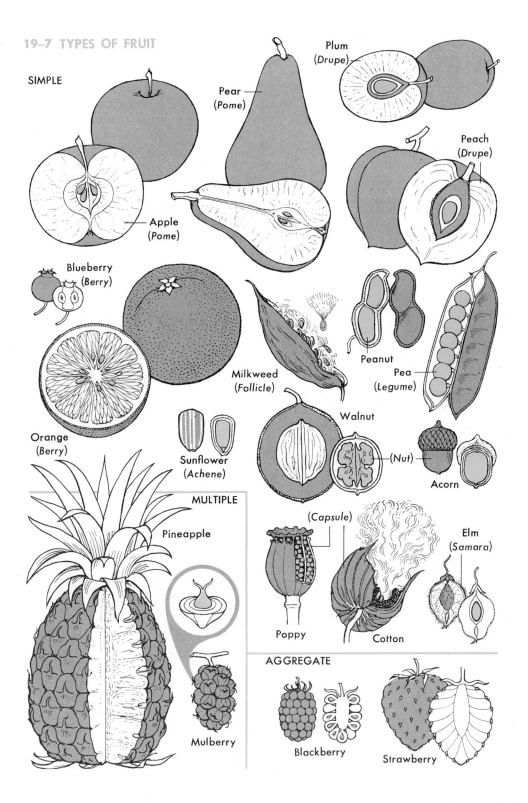

SIMPLE

Pear
(*Pome*)

Plum
(*Drupe*)

Apple
(*Pome*)

Peach
(*Drupe*)

Blueberry
(*Berry*)

Peanut

Milkweed
(*Follicle*)

Pea
(*Legume*)

Orange
(*Berry*)

Sunflower
(*Achene*)

Walnut

(*Nut*)

Acorn

MULTIPLE

Pineapple

(*Capsule*)

Elm
(*Samara*)

Poppy

Cotton

Mulberry

AGGREGATE

Blackberry

Strawberry

gory. But it would be a mistake to assume that all fruits are like this. Many fruits are very hard and dry.

POMES. Apples and similar fruits, such as pears and quinces, are known as *pomes*. The thickened, papery "core" contains the seeds. The "core" is that portion of the fruit that is produced by the wall of the ovary. The flesh of the pome is derived from the base of the sepals and petals, at the point where they have become joined about the ovary wall.

DRUPES. Some fruits, like peaches, have a fleshy outer layer within which is a hard stone. Sometimes they are called stone fruits, but botanists call them *drupes*. Plums, apricots, olives, and cherries belong to this group.

BERRIES. While the tomato is not commonly called a fruit, it does contain seeds. The fleshy pulp of the tomato is the modified ovary wall of the flower. It is an example of the kind of fruit botanists call a *berry*. When one considers all the members of this group, they appear as rather a strange assortment. Included here are the citrus fruits—oranges, lemons, limes, grapefruit—as well as grapes and blueberries. Generally, the ovary wall is rather soft and fleshy with the seeds scattered in the center. One of the largest berries is the eggplant. Some of the unusual varieties, such as the citrus fruits which have a skin or rind, are given special names; but it is easiest to think of them as modified berries.

AGGREGATE FRUITS. When a flower contains a number of pistils, each ovary may develop into a fruit. If the fruits adhere to each other, they produce a type of fruit like the raspberry. This is really a number of very tiny drupes that form a cluster, and for this reason it is called an *aggregate fruit*. Other similar fruits are the blackberry and strawberry.

MULTIPLE FRUITS. Multiple fruits may resemble the aggregate fruits in general appearance, but closer examination will show that each tiny unit has developed from a separate flower (rather than from one flower that has a number of pistils). The mulberry, Osage orange, and pineapple are fruits that develop in this manner.

DRY FRUITS. Many fruits produced by plants are different from the fleshy varieties we have just described. Their water content is much lower, and they are described simply as *dry fruits*. Many dry fruits split when ripe and thus scatter their seeds. These are *dehiscent*. When the dry fruit does not split, it is *indehiscent*.

Some of the dehiscent fruits are a rather common sight. One of them is the milkweed pod, or *follicle*, which opens along one side only. You have probably seen the seeds emerging from a ripened milkweed pod as it dries and opens.

Another common dehiscent fruit is the *legume*. The lima bean and string bean, along with all the other members of the pea family, produce seeds in a pod that opens on two sides.

The *capsule* is a dry, dehiscent fruit that contains many seeds that have developed from a compound ovary. Some capsules scatter their seeds through tiny openings. The action in this case is somewhat like a pepper shaker shaken by the wind. Other capsules will exhibit different devices that release their seeds.

A sunflower seed is an example of an *achene*, which is a single seed in a single ovary. Most of the composite family of plants produce dry, indehiscent fruits of this type. The grass family, including the cereals, produces seeds called *grains* that are like achenes.

The fruit of the maple tree is an example of the winged fruit that is called a "key," or *samara*. The elm, ash, and *Ailanthus* have similar winged fruits. Another indehiscent fruit, which has a very hard external covering, is the *nut*. It, too, is similar to the achene, except that it is much larger. Acorns,

TYPES OF FRUITS

Types	Descriptions	Examples
SIMPLE		
Fleshy		
Pome	Fleshy, edible layer formed by receptacle at base of calyx	Apple, Pear
Drupe	Outer fleshy layer encloses an inner stony layer	Peach, Plum
Berry	Fleshy ovary wall contains many seeds	Tomato, Orange, Blueberry
Dry, dehiscent		
Follicle	Podlike: splits along one side	Milkweed
Legume	Podlike: splits along two sides	Beans, Peas
Capsule	Many seeds in an ovary of many chambers	Poppy, Cotton
Dry, indehiscent		
Achene	Ovary becomes papery Contains one seed	Sunflower
Grain	Ovary wall fused with seed	Corn, Wheat
Nut	Ovary wall woody or stony Contains one seed usually	Acorn, Walnut
Samara	Winged seeds	Maple, Elm
AGGREGATE	Cluster of drupelets formed from separate pistils of same flower	Blackberry, Strawberry
MULTIPLE	Ovaries of many flowers fuse	Mulberry, Pineapple

chestnuts, and walnuts are good examples. Some of the large seeds that are commonly called nuts, however, are not classified as nuts by botanists. An almond, for example, is not actually a nut, but the seed of a fruit related to the peach.

19–8 ADAPTATIONS FOR SEED DISPERSAL

BY WIND

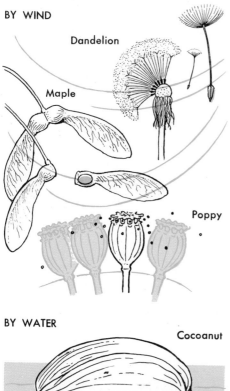

Dandelion

Maple

Poppy

BY WATER

Cocoanut

Lotus

BY ANIMAL

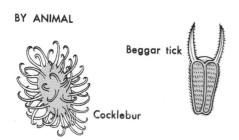

Beggar tick

Cocklebur

Seed Dispersal

Without some means of scattering its seeds, the parent plant would soon be crowded by its own seedlings growing about it.

Wind. The seeds of some plants are hardly larger or heavier than dust. When the wind blows, such seeds are borne aloft to some new location that may be much more favorable for growth. Even heavy seeds may be wind-scattered. Tufts of silky hairs may support the seed until it descends to the soil far from the parent plant. The winged fruits of certain trees scatter their seeds in the same manner.

Water. Water is a common means for scattering seeds. Whenever the seed is buoyant enough to float, it can be waterborne. In the tropics, coconuts often drift down rivers to the sea. Ocean currents then transport them over long distances. The seeds of many plants are normally carried along in the currents of streams.

Animals. The soft juicy flesh of pomes and drupes is eaten, but the hard parts containing the seeds are discarded, and thus scattered widely. Other fruits may be eaten by animals, but the seeds are not digested. Some animals, like the squirrel, store seeds and nuts in large quantities in many places. This, too, scatters them.

Mechanical devices, such as hooks and stickers, also provide the means for scattering seeds. The fruits of the cocklebur and burdock have sharp spines, which stick to the fur of animals and clothing of man. Although this may be a nuisance to us, it is an effective way of scattering the plant's seeds.

Growing Useful Fruits

Edible fruits are a valuable crop. Man, therefore, has sought ways to hasten their production and improve their quality. Fruit trees are not grown from seed. Instead, the farmer grows them from *cuttings,* pieces of the stem or root of selected plants. The cuttings may be planted in the soil or, more often, they are grafted to older plants. These techniques of *vegetative propagation* shorten the growing period required for fruit production. Furthermore, cuttings from superior plants produce fruit of the same high quality year after year.

GRAFTING. The attachment of a cutting from one plant, usually a stem, to a second related plant is called *grafting.* Grafting is generally most successful with trees and woody shrubs. The grafted cutting, called the *scion,* does not form roots, but becomes fused to the rooted plant, called the *stock.* The fused scion does not lose its characteristics. Thus, a lemon scion grafted to an orange stock will bear lemons.

There are a number of ways in which grafts can be made. One principle generally governs the way in which it is done. For the graft to be successful, the cambium of the stock and scion must be placed in contact with each other. In setting a graft, a nurseryman makes certain that the cambium layers are against each other. He then covers the exposed tissues with grafting wax. This keeps the parts in position and protects the plants until they have grown together. The cambiums fuse, producing new xylem and phloem, thus uniting the two plants permanently. In some cases, a bud scion is grafted to a stock, but the principle is essentially the same.

For the graft to be successful, the stock and scion must be closely related species. Grafting a new apple variety to an old apple tree is easily accomplished. Even pear twigs can be grafted to an apple stock. A single

19–9 Grafting and budding are methods of artificial vegetative propagation. The scion (shown in color) continues to produce the same type of fruit after grafting.

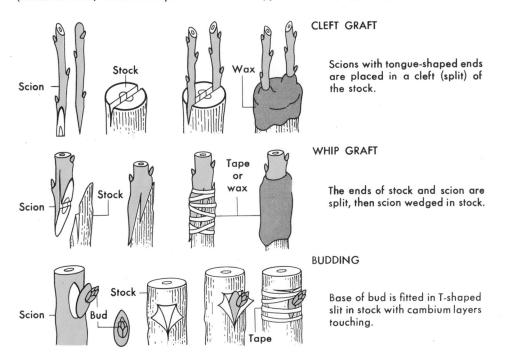

CLEFT GRAFT

Scions with tongue-shaped ends are placed in a cleft (split) of the stock.

WHIP GRAFT

The ends of stock and scion are split, then scion wedged in stock.

BUDDING

Base of bud is fitted in T-shaped slit in stock with cambium layers touching.

orange stock has had lemon, grapefruit, and lime twigs grafted to it. But the grafting of an apple twig to an orange tree is not successful. Grafting experiments with monocots are generally unsuccessful. Can you give a reason why this is so?

Some of our most valuable fruits have been produced by grafting. The original tree that produced seedless navel oranges was found growing in a monastery garden in Bahia, Brazil. The ovary of this fruit fails to produce seeds. Cuttings of the tree were imported into the United States in 1870. From them has come the Washington navel orange, one of the most widely cultivated varieties in California.

Fruit trees are usually propagated by grafting since the characteristics of the parent tree remain unchanged. In the case of seedless oranges, the grafted buds produce fruits that do not contain seeds. Apples that are juicy and sweet can be grafted on older, sour apple trees. The grafted stem produces sweet fruit. Most sweet oranges are propagated by a grafting process in which the buds are grown upon the rooted stocks of sour orange trees.

ADVANTAGES OF VEGETATIVE PROPAGATION. Plants grown from seeds usually exhibit great variation. This is due to the combination of traits from each parent by the process of fertilization. Seeds that are produced by chance combinations of sperm and egg cell do not breed true. The sexual process of seed formation results in variety. Biologists believe that this has advantages under natural conditions.

Vegetative propagation, however, is an asexual process. No seeds are involved. Plants grown from cuttings or grafts are exactly like the parent. For the nurseryman interested in propagating a variety of known value, this has great worth. A superior plant can be grown again and again unchanged. Bartlett pears, Delicious apples, pineapples, and bananas have the same high quality each year. All are produced by vegetative propagation.

IMPORTANT POINTS

• The flower is the reproductive organ of the plant. It produces the fruit within which are the seeds. Although many flowers have sepals and petals, these are not essential for the production of the seed. The stamen and pistil are the essential male and female floral parts.

• Flowers are of many types. Some are staminate (male); others are pistillate (female). Complete flowers have all four floral parts—calyx, corolla, stamens, and pistil. Perfect flowers have both stamens and pistil, but need not have the other parts. Composite flowers consist of two kinds of flowers, ray and disk.

• Pollination is the first step in the formation of seeds. Pollination is often accomplished by the following agents: insects, wind, water, and some birds.

● When the pollen germinates after being transferred to the stigma, it forms a tube that grows down to the ovule. Here, within the embryo sac, fertilization of the egg takes place. The zygote, or fertilized egg, then forms the embryo of the seed. Meanwhile, the fruit begins to develop. The fruit is a ripened ovary.

● Fruits are of two main types: fleshy and dry. Many are important foods for man. After eating them, men and animals scatter the seeds. Some dry fruits open and discharge their seeds.

● Wind, water, and animals are agents for dispersing seeds over large areas, giving individual plants a greater opportunity to survive.

● Valuable fruits are grown commercially by vegetative propagation. The process of grafting saves time. The use of superior cuttings insures high quality fruit from season to season.

REVIEW QUESTIONS

1. Why are flowers important from the standpoint of plant development?
2. Name and describe briefly the male and female parts of a flower.
3. Why are stamens and pistils called the "essential" parts of a flower?
4. Why cannot a staminate holly plant produce berries?
5. Why does pollination precede fertilization?
6. Name three agents of pollination.
7. How is fertilization related to the development of fruit?
8. List three ways in which seeds may be scattered.
9. A flower contains petals, sepals, and stamens. Which of the following terms would *not* describe it: imperfect, staminate, complete?
10. Why is cross-pollination characteristic of staminate and pistillate flowers?

CHECK YOUR UNDERSTANDING

11. What factors might prevent self-pollination in a perfect flower?
12. Describe the series of changes that occur in the pollen grain immediately after pollination.
13. List the events that occur just prior to and just after fertilization.
14. What is the significance of the endosperm nucleus?
15. Describe the series of changes that occurs after fertilization, resulting in seed and fruit formation.
16. There is a short-lived generation in the development of a seed plant. Can you explain what it is and what happens to it?
17. Identify the parts of the gametophyte generation in a flowering plant.
18. What reasons can you give to support the argument that wind pollination is more important than insect pollination?
19. Why is a peach orchard grown from grafted peach stock, not from seeds?
20. Compare the reproductive cycle of ferns and angiosperms with respect to their dependence upon water.
21. Suppose an orchard owner discovered a new variety of large, sweet apple that happened to be seedless. How could he develop future crops of this valuable fruit?

RESEARCH PROJECTS AND REPORTS

1. Obtain information from your school or public library and prepare a report on one of the following topics:

   Grains: Our Most Important Fruits   **Producing Seedless Fruits**

   Insects As Agents of Pollination   **Artificial Pollination**

2. *Flower Collection:* Try to make your collection varied by seeking some of the less showy species. Collect from trees as well as the garden and meadow. You can press and mount your specimens in much the same manner as leaves.

3. *Growth of Pollen Tubes:* If you have some fresh pollen, you can experiment with the concentration of sugar that will make the grains grow pollen tubes. Prepare some agar or gelatine in a Petri dish, and add a weighed amount of sugar before it has gelled. Make several such preparations, varying the amount of sugar. Shake a few grains of the same kind of pollen on each dish, and observe them for several days. Don't be discouraged if all fail. Try other concentrations until you are successful.

4. *Ovary Structure:* When you make a collection of flowers you may want to make a comparative study of the arrangement of ovules in the ovary. Some are attached to the wall, but others are attached to the central core. Use a sharp razor blade, and cut through the ovary to discover what arrangement each of several flowers has. Make sketches to support your observations.

FURTHER READING

How To Know the Spring Flowers. Mabel J. Cuthbert. William C. Brown Company, Dubuque, Iowa. Many illustrations and a botanical key help the beginner learn the spring flowers.

Plant Propagation. John P. Mahlstede and Ernest S. Haber. John Wiley and Sons, Inc., New York, N.Y. Discusses vegetative methods of plant propagation used in agriculture.

Field Book of American Wild Flowers. F. Schuyler Mathews (Revised by Norman Taylor). G. P. Putnam's Sons, New York, N.Y. An illustrated pocket guide to many of the wild flowers of the country.

"Pollen." Patrick Echlin. *Scientific American,* April, 1968, page 81. The exquisite architecture of pollen grains is shown by the scanning electron microscope.

20

Plant Growth and Behavior

GROWTH is a primary characteristic of life. Yet there are times in the life of every organism when growth almost ceases. The mature seed is a resting stage in the life of a plant, but with the spring of the year, it begins to grow.

Many factors controlling plant growth are like those that control animal growth. Many are quite different. Plants are much more responsive to light. Scientists have changed plant growth patterns by regulating the amount of light they receive. Thus, they have produced chrysanthemums in the spring and Christmas poinsettias in June.

In this chapter we shall examine some of the factors that control plant growth. We shall also see how some of these factors enable plants to respond to changes in their environment.

Environmental Factors in Plant Growth

If two plants of the same species are grown in different environments, they become quite different in size, shape, color, amount of foliage, and other features. Of the environmental factors that affect plant growth, light, moisture, and temperature are especially important.

INFLUENCE OF LIGHT. Light, the basic source of the plant's energy, dominates all other factors in plant growth. Without light, photosynthesis is stopped. The kind of light that a plant receives, its intensity, and its duration also affect the growth of the plant.

Seedlings grown in darkness have long, thin, and very fragile shoots, which are yellowish and lacking in chlorophyll. An onion bulb that sprouts in darkness has some of the same characteristics. When they sprout in the dark, potatoes send out pale, white shoots with tiny yellow leaves.

Plants grown in shady places tend to show the same characteristics as plants grown in total darkness. The stems are taller and the leaves are noticeably thinner. This knowledge has been useful to tobacco growers. Tobacco plants are often grown under long strips of cloth. The shaded plants produce the broad, thin leaves essential for making fine cigars. Nurserymen use similar methods to protect young plants from the heat of the summer sun.

THE KINDS OF LIGHT. By means of a prism, visible light can be separated into a continuous band of colors called its *spectrum*. One end of the spectrum is red, and the other end is violet. In between are

20–1 Shaded tobacco plants produce the broad thin leaves required for fine cigars.

orange, yellow, green, blue, and indigo. The rainbow is composed of these same colors.

Scientists have conducted tests to determine if plants are more sensitive to one part of the spectrum than to another. They have found that the blue-violet area is more important for growth than the red area. The full spectrum is best for normal growth.

DURATION OF LIGHT. Have you ever wondered why hollyhocks bloom in the summer and asters bloom in the fall? Scientists have discovered that the number of hours of daylight to which a plant is exposed determines when it will bloom. Individual species of plants vary in their reaction to long or short periods of light. Hollyhocks bloom in summer when days are long. Asters bloom in the fall when the days are short.

What happens if we lengthen the plant's day by using artificial light? If we extend a summer-blooming plant's day by exposing it to artificial light after sunset, the plant blooms long before its usual time. If fall-blooming plants are covered with a black

cloth during the late summer afternoons, they bloom earlier. The response of plants to varying periods of light is called *photoperiodism*.

Biologists now classify plants on the basis of their photoperiods. Thus, some are called short-day plants, others long-day plants, and still others, intermediate plants. Short-day plants include goldenrods, poinsettias, ragweeds, and most of the asters. Long-day plants include the iris, red clover, spinach, and certain varieties of strawberries. The length of day seems to have little effect upon intermediate plants, such as beans, roses, tomatoes. Even these, however, have limits to their photoperiods. If some types of tomatoes are exposed to more than 19 hours of light for a period of several weeks, they die.

MOISTURE AND TEMPERATURE. Plant growth is dependent upon light because light is needed for photosynthesis. Water is also required for growth. With little water, the plant is likely to be stunted, having a thick stem and small leaves. With excessive water, the plant tends to become very soft and may not develop root hairs.

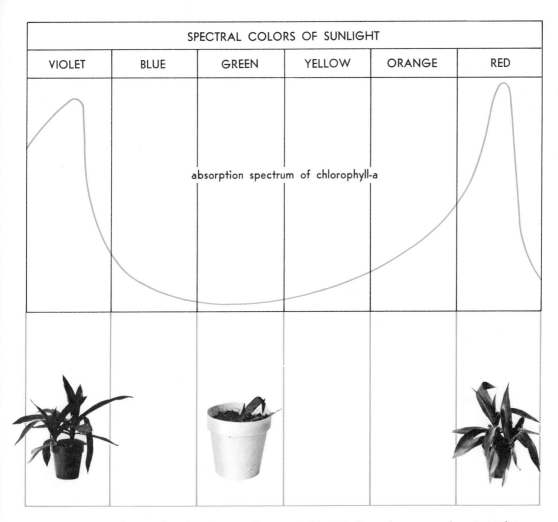

SPECTRAL COLORS OF SUNLIGHT					
VIOLET	BLUE	GREEN	YELLOW	ORANGE	RED

absorption spectrum of chlorophyll-a

20–2 According to the absorption spectrum of chlorophyll-a, plants grow best in violet light and red light, poorly in green light. Plants pictured here illustrate this fact.

The intensity of light is related to the temperature at which plants grow. It is somewhat difficult to separate the one factor from the other. However, we know that tropical plants do not thrive in cooler climates. Plants that grow high on the sides of tropical mountains are often the same as their relatives growing in cooler latitudes. This indicates that temperature, rather than light intensity, is the factor actually dominating their growth.

Plant Hormones

Plants, like animals, secrete growth-regulating *hormones.* In plants, certain of these hormones are called *auxins.* The fact that plant cells contained growth-regulating substances was first established by the Danish botanist Peter Boysen-Jensen in 1910. Biologists had guessed that some growth substance was present in the tips of stems and roots. The Dutch botanist Frits Went

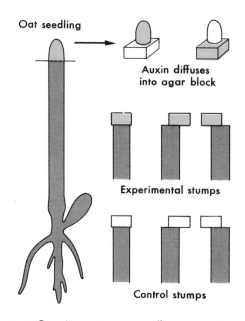

Oat seedling

Auxin diffuses into agar block

Experimental stumps

Control stumps

20–3 Germinate six oat seedlings in a flower pot filled with moist soil. When shoots are about 2 cm high, slice about 3 mm off the tip of each shoot. Place three of the tips on small blocks of agar. After two or three hours, discard the sliced tips. Place one of the agar blocks on the stump of a cut shoot so that the entire surface is covered. Place a second agar block on a stump so that only the right half of the stump is covered. Place a third block on the left half of a stump. For controls, cover the remaining stumps with agar blocks that did not have tips resting on them. Observe and record the growth of the shoots for the next two days. How did the agar blocks obtain their ability to affect the growth of the stumps?

thought that this substance might diffuse out of a stem tip cut from the plant. He cut off a tiny piece of an oat seedling's tip and placed it upon some gelatin. After several hours he placed the gelatin carefully on one side of the tipless seedling. This side grew faster than the other side, indicating that some substance from the gelatin on the seedling's tip stimulated the growth of the cells underneath it.

Since the time of Went's experiment in 1926, many other facts have been learned about plant hormones. The hormones are now classified as either *accelerators* or *inhibitors*. Accelerators promote plant growth; inhibitors retard it. The relative amount of one kind of hormone or the other determines whether the plant grows rapidly or lies dormant. Plant growth accelerators include the auxins, cytokinin, and gibberellin. *Dormin* is the only known inhibitor at the present time.

THE GIBBERELLINS. About the time of the investigation of auxins, Japanese botanists had discovered an unusual disease of rice. The Japanese called it the "foolish-seedling disease." The stems of the rice plants grew very long when infected by a certain fungus. The growth substance was extracted

20–4 The top row of holly cuttings was treated with the auxin indolebutyric acid, the bottom row remained untreated. The growth acceleration caused by the auxin is evidenced by the thick root growth in the treated cuttings.

from the fungus in the 1930's and given the name *gibberellin* (jib-er-EL-in). In practically all of the plants tested with gibberellin, a remarkable increase in stem length occurred. Certain plants increased their length as much as six times. Imagine marigolds growing five feet tall!

Research into the presence and effects of gibberellin did not attract much attention in the United States until the 1950's. Samples of the extract from the fungus were obtained from Japan. The effects of gibberellin were then widely studied. Its chemical structure was analyzed. Chemists produced gibberellin in the laboratory. Different gibberellins have been discovered, all closely related in chemical structure. Were the gibberellins in the same chemical family as the auxins? The answer is no. Since 1960, gibberellin has been found in almost every part of the plant. It seems likely that this hormone occurs in all the higher plants. The relation between the auxins and gibberellin in regulating plant growth has not yet been clarified.

COCONUT MILK AND CYTOKININ. Biologists have been studying the way plants grow by using tissue culture methods. The technique is similar to the methods employed by bacteriologists. First, the needed minerals and nutrients are added to a gelatine-like substance and water is added. The mixture is sterilized and then poured into sterile flasks. As it cools it hardens, or "sets." A piece of plant tissue is then placed on the growth medium in the flask. By changing the minerals or nutrients, or substituting one for another, biologists can determine the chemicals necessary for plant growth.

A group working at the University of Wisconsin on tissue cultures discovered an unusual fact. Although a piece of tobacco stem was supplied with all the necessary minerals and nutrients, as well as auxin, its cells would not divide. But when some coconut milk was added to the plant cul-

ture medium, the tobacco cells divided and grew. What did the coconut milk contain that made stem tissue cells divide? When the researchers finally found the answer to that question, it proved to be most interesting. The chemical in coconut milk was related to one of the four nitrogen bases that make up the DNA molecule. The growth hormone in coconut milk was a derivative of adenine. It belongs to a new family of growth hormones biologists call *cytokinins*. In the proper concentration, cytokinin was able to cause a few parenchyma cells from a tobacco plant to produce a complete plant.

DORMIN, THE INHIBITOR. In 1965, researchers at the University of California discovered a chemical that caused cotton bolls to drop from the plant too soon. The same chemical also seemed to prepare the buds on trees for winter. Its chemical name is so long that it was given the name *dormin* by some biologists. Dormin retards or slows down plant growth. In this respect its action is the opposite of the other plant hormones we have been describing. Experiments with duckweed cultures have shown that dormin stops growth in concentrations as low as one part per million. Cytokinin was then added to the duckweed cultures in a concentration of one part in ten million. The cultures resumed their growth! The conclusion from these experiments seems to be that dormin and cytokinin provide "stop and go" signals for the growth of the plants.

AGRICULTURAL USES OF SYNTHETIC HORMONES. Many *synthetic auxins* are widely used in agriculture to assist the farmer. The type of effect depends upon the kind of plant treated and also upon the concentration of the synthetic auxin.

When a weak solution of synthetic auxin is sprayed upon stored potatoes, it prevents them from sprouting. The same solution sprayed upon pineapples causes them to

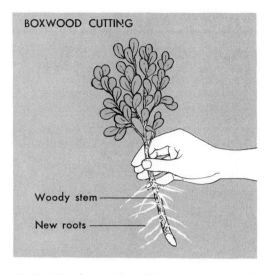

BOXWOOD CUTTING

Woody stem ———

New roots ———

20–5 After being dipped in a hormone solution and placed in moist sand, a boxwood stem develops a thick growth of roots.

flower several weeks earlier. Applied to fruit trees, it prevents the dropping of fruit before it is ready to be picked.

Synthetic auxins have also helped in the propagation of plants from cuttings. Evergreens like holly and yew are normally difficult to grow from cuttings. However, when the lower end of the cutting is dipped into a solution of auxin, root growth is stimulated (see Figure 20–4).

Of great importance was the discovery that auxins could also cause death by accelerating growth. The weed-killer 2,4–D, a hormone-like chemical, has been used extensively because its proper application causes a considerable rise in the metabolic rate of certain broad-leafed weeds. This increase in metabolic rate causes plant starvation and death.

Plant Tropisms

The reactions of plants are extremely slow. Like the hour hand of a watch that moves so slowly the eye cannot see it, the plant slowly pushes its roots into the soil, slowly turns its leaves to the sun, and slowly twists its stem upward in large spirals.

Plants do not have nerve tissues. They respond to *stimuli* by *tropisms.* A tropism is a turning away from a stimulus or a turning toward a stimulus. A tropism is referred to as *positive* when the movement is toward the stimulus. When the movement is away from the stimulus, the tropism is *negative*.

GEOTROPISM: THE RESPONSE TO GRAVITY. When a farmer plants seeds, he does not have to place each one so that its root will grow downward. The seed extends its root downward into the soil no matter in what position the seed has been planted. If it is sown in the "wrong" position, it grows upward a short distance, makes a half turn, and then grows down. If the seed is now removed from the soil, inverted and replanted, its roots will turn and grow downward once again. These effects are caused by the force of gravity.

The reaction of roots to gravity is called *geotropism.* If we consider the growth of a seedling, we note that the root grows down, but the stem grows up. The root's response is positive geotropism. The stem's response is negative geotropism, since it grows away from the direction of the force, rather than toward it.

Experiments have shown that only the tip of the root is able to respond to gravity. If the root tip of a seedling is cut off, the root "loses" direction. Such a seedling, placed on the surface of the soil, does not turn downward and penetrate the soil. A normal seedling, however, will turn.

Plant physiologists believe auxins may regulate this growth response of roots. In a vertical position the amount of auxin in the root tip cells is evenly distributed, but when it is placed on its side, the auxin becomes more concentrated on the lower side. In the root, excessive auxin slows the growth of cells in the region where it is

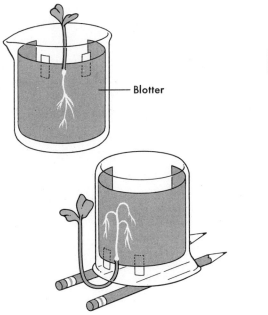

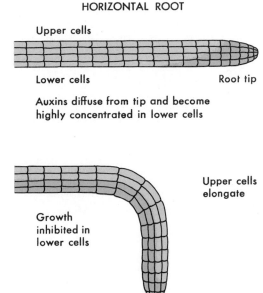

HORIZONTAL ROOT

Upper cells

Lower cells   Root tip

Auxins diffuse from tip and become
highly concentrated in lower cells

Growth
inhibited in
lower cells

Upper cells
elongate

20–6 Positive and Negative Geotropism. Will a plant grow upside down? Try it and see. Place a blotter around the inside of a beaker and fasten it with tape as shown. Germinate a radish seed near the top between the blotter and the glass. Keep the water level in the beaker just below the seed. When the plant's leaves grow above the rim of the beaker, remove the water and invert the beaker over two pencils. Keep the blotter moist for several days and observe the growth of the stems and roots.

20–7 How Auxins may Control the Direction of Root Growth. When the root is in a horizontal position, auxins in the root tip diffuse back and accumulate in the lower layer of cells. This high concentration of auxins inhibits the growth of the lower cells. The lower concentration of auxins in the upper layer of cells stimulates cell growth and causes the cells to elongate. The unevenness of the growth in the upper and lower layer of cells results in the turning of the root downward as illustrated.

highly concentrated. This makes the lower cells grow shorter, the upper cells longer. Uneven growth on the two sides of the root causes it to turn downward.

In the stem the concentration of auxins stimulates the cells to greater growth. Thus, when the young stem is in a horizontal position, its lower cells receive more auxin and grow longer. This causes the stem to turn upward.

At first glance these results in stem and root appear contradictory. However, experiments have shown that the same con-

centration of auxin that slows cell growth in the root may stimulate growth in the stem.

THIGMOTROPISM: THE RESPONSE TO CONTACT. The response to contact or touch is called *thigmotropism*. Although most plants do not react immediately to contact, there are some that twine around objects they touch. The best known plants of this type are the climbing species—peas, grapes, pumpkins, cucumbers—that produce *tendrils*. A tendril is a modified stem or leaf that may coil about a support in a few minutes. In other

20–8 A mimosa plant exhibits a dramatic response called thigmotropism. The plant is shown here before being touched (left) and after being touched (right). The reaction is accompanied by the release of water pressure in the cells at the base of the leaflets.

cases, tendrils coil gradually by slow growth. At least one plant is so responsive to touch that it reacts almost immediately to it. This is the sensitive plant *Mimosa pudica.* When the leaf is touched, its leaflets fold inward and the entire leaf droops rapidly. After a short time, the leaf resumes its original condition.

PHOTOTROPISM: THE RESPONSE TO LIGHT. The response to light is called *phototropism.*

It seems to be characteristic of the stem and leaves, but the roots are affected very little. The blue end of the spectrum is more important than the red end in producing this reaction.

Auxins are believed to be responsible for phototropism. Experiments have shown that auxins in the tip of the stem accumulate on the shaded side of the plant. This side then grows longer than the lighted side, resulting in a bending toward the light. Phototropism causes the leaves to be so arranged that they are exposed for maximum absorption of the sun's energy.

HYDROTROPISM: THE RESPONSE TO WATER. Although it is believed that roots of plants

20–9 Phototropism. Grow a young radish plant in a flower pot. When the plant has grown two or three inches high, cover it with a large paper cup that has a hole cut out of one side. Place the setup on a sunny window sill with the hole facing into the room. Observe how the stem grows through the hole and then bends toward the window. Why is it mistaken to say the plant is "seeking light"?

PLANT TROPISMS

Tropism	Stimulus	Example
Phototropism	Light	Stems and leaves
Geotropism	Gravity	Roots and stems
Thigmotropism	Contact	Stems of beans and peas
Hydrotropism	Water	Roots

grow toward water, it is not easy to explain why they do so. Yet, many of the breaks in water mains are due to the growth of tree roots into them. One explanation for the seeming responsiveness of roots to water is simply that they grow faster when water is present. In most plants, the response to water, *hydrotropism,* is not as strong as their response to gravity and their response to light.

IMPORTANT POINTS

- Plants react by growth and movement to certain factors in their surroundings, such as light, moisture, and temperature. The most important of these environmental factors is light. In the complete absence of light, plants grow tall and spindly and fail to develop chlorophyll.

- Under conditions of natural light, the growth pattern of many plants is influenced by the photoperiod, that is, the number of hours of daylight to which they are exposed. Plants are classified as short-day plants, intermediate plants, and long-day plants according to the number of daylight hours they require before they will bloom.

- The growth and movement of plants is controlled by certain internal substances called hormones. Auxins, gibberellin, and cytokinin promote plant growth. Dormin retards growth. Auxins may either stimulate or slow down cell growth. Synthetic auxins have given man new ways to alter the growth of useful plants. Gibberellin, which is a growth substance released by a fungus, causes plants to grow extremely tall.

- Plants respond to factors in their surroundings by growth movements called tropisms. Tropisms are classified as positive or negative according to whether the movement is toward or away from the stimulus.

• Plants exhibit positive and negative tropisms. Geotropism is the response of roots to gravity. The response of stems and leaves to light is called phototropism. Thigmotropism is the response of certain plants that are sensitive to touch or pressure. The response of roots to water is called hydrotropism.

REVIEW QUESTIONS

1. What is the general appearance of a seedling grown in darkness?
2. Why is tobacco grown in the shade?
3. How do the different colors of the light spectrum affect plant growth?
4. What is meant by photoperiodism?
5. Name several short-day and long-day plants.
6. What are auxins and what are their functions?
7. What are synthetic auxins and how are they used in agriculture?
8. What are gibberellins and how were they discovered?
9. Name three plant tropisms and give an example of each.

CHECK YOUR UNDERSTANDING

10. How can fall-blooming asters be made to bloom during summer?
11. What practical uses can we make of the knowledge of a plant's photoperiod?
12. Why do tropical mountain plants often have the same characteristics as plants growing in the temperate zones?
13. How does a weed killer like 2,4–D work?
14. How may cutting off a root tip prevent its continued growth in a downward direction?
15. How is the responsiveness of roots to water explained?
16. Describe several ways in which auxins increase man's food supply.
17. Some people believe that roots seek water and that climbing plants seek upright objects upon which to support themselves. Do you think there is any truth in these beliefs? Can you offer more scientific reasons for this type of plant reaction?
18. A vacant field near a deserted factory became overgrown with ragweed. It was noticed that the ragweed plants growing close to the building bloomed earlier than those in the open. Can you give a possible explanation for this?
19. Since light is essential for photosynthesis, how can we explain the growth of seedlings in total darkness?
20. Food plants are constantly being transferred from one part of the world to be grown in another. In many cases these transplantations are unsuccessful although soil conditions, temperature, and rainfall are similar in both places. Can you suggest a possible explanation for these failures?

RESEARCH PROJECTS AND REPORTS

1. Obtain information from your school or public library and prepare a report on one of the following topics:

   Auxins in Agriculture   **Plant Tropisms**

   Auxins in Ornamental Plants   **Plants That Thrive in Shade**

2. *Negative Geotropism in Stems:* Germinate seedlings in separate test tubes filled with moist absorbent cotton. Be sure that the seeds are well embedded in the cotton. Allow seedling shoots to grow about 2 inches above the lips of the test tubes. Select 3 of the test tubes and clamp them to a ring stand in the following positions: (1) upright, (2) horizontal, and (3) upside down. After several days note the direction of growth of the young stems. To learn if this is a reaction to light, repeat experiment in total darkness.

3. *Phototropism in Stems:* Plant some soaked beans or corn kernels near the surface of clean sand in small flower pots. Place several small pots under a box that excludes all light. Place several other pots under a box in which a slit has been cut at about the level of the pots. Set the boxes in a place where light can enter the slit. Examine the germinated seeds after four or five days, and compare the directions in which their young stems are growing. Can you explain this difference in direction? Why do the stems grow upward in the completely darkened box? What tropism explains the bent stems? What tropism explains the straight stems?

FURTHER READING

Hormones and Horticulture. G. Avery and E. Johnson. McGraw-Hill Book Company, Inc., New York, N.Y. Discusses the many practical uses of growth regulators in plants.

Great Experiments in Biology. Mordecai L. Gabriel and Seymour Fogel, Editors. Prentice-Hall, Inc., Englewood Cliffs, N.J. On pages 148–152, Frits W. Went describes how he isolated auxins from the oat seedling. This experiment, performed in 1926, is now regarded as a milestone in the study of plant physiology.

Plant Hormone Experiments. Turtox Service, Leaflet #54. This pamphlet may be obtained from General Biological Supply House, Inc., 8200 S. Hoyne Avenue, Chicago, Illinois. Directions are given for making cuttings and using root hormones to root them. Experiments with gibberellic acid, the chemical that produces giant plants, are also described.

"The Control of Plant Growth." Johannes van Overbeek. *Scientific American,* July, 1968, page 75. Discusses the way plant growth is regulated by promoting and inhibiting hormones.

Invertebrate Animals

ANIMALS that have a backbone are called vertebrates. The vertebrate species comprise only about one-twentieth of the known species of animals. Far more numerous are the invertebrates, animals that do not have a backbone. Many of the invertebrates live in profusion in the depths of the sea, while others live in streams and brooks upon the land. Still other invertebrates, like the insects, have become adapted to life upon dry land.

Biologists believe that invertebrates appeared earlier than the vertebrates. The first of the invertebrates were probably similar to the single-celled protists so numerous in the waters of the earth today. The earliest of these first living cells were so soft that no fossil remains have been found to give direct evidence of their existence.

Through the millions of years that followed the appearance of the first animals, a vast number of different animal forms has evolved. Biologists do not know what caused the amazing variety of animal forms, but at present there are more than a million known types.

In the following chapters we shall examine the simplest forms of animal life and attempt to trace the development of more complex species. The chapter arrangement is not meant to indicate that each phylum developed from the animals in the preceding phylum. Where relationships are fairly well established, we shall try to show what the line of development may have been.

CHAPTER

21

Metazoan Life Begins

Biologists have always been fascinated by protozoa. Within these single celled protists are performed all the functions necessary to sustain an organism and enable it to reproduce.

Unlike the protozoa, the members of the animal kingdom consist of many cells. Thus, the term *Metazoa* is often used to describe them. Metazoans are more complex than the unicellular animal-like protists. Since the direction of evolution is often from the simple to the complex, it seems logical to assume that the metazoans developed from some ancestral protistan stock. However, the exact protistan ancestors of the modern metazoans may never be known.

Fossils of many of the invertebrate metazoans have been found in rocks 550 million years old. The simpler metazoan animals probably appeared upon the earth several hundred million years earlier.

Metazoans range in complexity from animals of but a few hundred cells to those consisting of trillions of cells. Usually, these cells are not alike. Some are especially fitted for movement; others specialize in reproduction; and still others transmit nerve impulses. Specialization of cells results in a higher level of efficiency.

The advantages of specialization are easily understood if we compare civilized and primitive man. In a primitive society man existed at a low level of efficiency because he performed all of his tasks by himself. He became a jack-of-all-trades, building his shelter, making his clothing, fashioning his weapons, hunting, and cooking his food. A modern civilization has its specialists. The farmer, the baker, the carpenter, the tailor are highly skilled workers. Their cooperation increases the efficiency of the entire community.

We may regard the metazoan animal as a community of cell specialists that perform their separate tasks efficiently and thus benefit the entire organism.

Among the Metazoa there is a great range in complexity. The sponges are very simple forms of life. The vertebrates are highly specialized. We shall begin our study with the simplest forms and advance to the more complex.

The Sponges: Living Filters

The sponges were once believed to be plants. Some people thought they were non-living because they exhibit no motion. They appear to possess none of the characteristics of animals.

There are about 5000 species of sponges. For most of them man has found little use, since their skeletons are hard and abrasive. Although the majority of sponges live in the sea, about 150 species live in fresh water. Usually, they are found attached to the floor of the sea, to rocks, or to shells. Some sponges are found on piling or the backs of crabs.

The English biologist Robert Grant first identified sponges as animals. More than a century ago he observed that there is always a current of water flowing through a living sponge. By using dyes in a series of experiments, Grant noted that water goes into very small pores on the sides of sponges and then emerges from larger openings. The pores have since been used to give the phylum of animals its name, **Porifera,** which means "pore bearers." Through these pores a continuous stream of water brings the food the animals require. The food is filtered from the water. The sponges are thus living filters, extracting the materials of life from the water in which they live.

LEUCOSOLENIA: A SIMPLE SPONGE. The sponges are the simplest metazoans. They seem to have formed a side branch in the evolution of life that did not lead to the development of more advanced invertebrates. The loose collection of cells that makes up their bodies is held together by a tough skeleton. The simplicity of their structure is best shown by examining one of their members, *Leucosolenia.*

Leucosolenia is a tiny, yellow sponge that lives in small, branching colonies attached to submerged rocks along the edge of the sea. The individuals are shaped like vases. The outer wall contains numerous microscopic pores through which water continually enters the body. These are called *incurrent pores.* The water then continues out through the top of the vase, the *osculum.* The current is caused by special flagellated cells that line the inner cavity. Called *collar cells,* they have a loosely fitting projection about the cell where the flagellum emerges.

Just as the cilia of Paramecium create a

21–1 Leucosolenia, a simple sponge, has a saclike body with an inner layer of flagellated collar cells. These force water carrying food and oxygen into the body cavity.

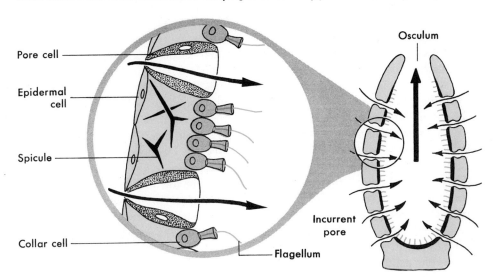

current of water that forces food into its gullet, so the flagella in the sponge draw the water into it. Even a small sponge may draw in as many as 30 gallons of water each day. The collar cells ingest the food—tiny plants and animals that float or swim by. The food is then digested and passed to other cells.

Specialization of cells in the sponges is not very pronounced. Between the outer, flattened cells and the inner, collar cells there is a nonliving jellylike material that joins the cells together loosely. In it there are wandering cells that resemble amebae. Coordination of body function is performed by these unspecialized cells. Although sponges do not appear to have nerve tissue or sense organs, they can respond to certain stimuli.

If you were to examine a tiny piece of a sponge under the microscope, you would see many small needles sticking out of the body, especially near the osculum. These needles, or *spicules,* are the parts of a very primitive kind of skeleton. In Leucosolenia, the spicules are made of calcium carbonate. Calcium carbonate is the same material found in marble and limestone. The shape of the spicules and their chemical composition are used as the basis for subdividing the sponges into classes.

REPRODUCTION IN SPONGES. One method of reproduction common to many invertebrates is *budding.* Budding is an asexual process in which a tiny animal grows from the side of the parent. Buds may remain attached to the parent, or they may separate and begin life as new individuals.

Many fresh-water sponges reproduce by forming internal buds called *gemmules.* These are little more than tiny sacs containing numerous sponge cells enriched with food. The wall of the sac, which is thick and protective, enables the cells within to survive dryness and frost. During unfavorable conditions, the gemmules escape from the parent sponge. When favorable growth conditions occur again, the gemmules open and the cells form a new sponge.

Sponges have no special sex organs. Certain cells become specialized as eggs. Others form sperms. In certain species, the eggs may be fertilized by sperms from the same sponge. In other species, the eggs are fertilized by sperms produced by another sponge. The fertilized egg divides and forms a larva, which is able to swim because it has flagella. The larva swims away from the parent, attaches itself to some submerged object, then divides repeatedly to form a young, new sponge.

REGENERATION. The lower forms of animals have the remarkable ability to regrow an entire organism from small pieces torn from the parent. Biologists use the term *regeneration* to identify this process. Regeneration is common in the invertebrates and many of the lowest forms regenerate to a great extent.

An experiment illustrates the ability of sponges to regenerate. A sponge is torn into small pieces and strained through fine silk cloth into a dish of sea water. Within a few days, the separated cells reunite and begin the formation of a new sponge.

Sponge "farmers" use regeneration to produce more sponges. Just as a farmer plants seeds, so the sponge fisherman "plants" small pieces of sponge on the ocean floor. Although growth is sometimes quite rapid, a period of several years is usually required before the sponge reaches marketable size.

SPONGE DIVERS. You have probably read about men who make their living by searching for sponges at the bottom of the sea. Sponge diving was known to ancient peoples. History records the use of sponges by the Greeks and Romans for a variety of household tasks—cleaning, bathing, and painting.

In the deep waters near the Philippine Islands, sponges made of silica, or glass, are found. One of these is Venus's flower basket, whose lacy skeleton is a thing of beauty. Since the quantity of silica found in sea water amounts to one part in 65,000, a sponge of this type must draw in a ton of water to build a single ounce of skeleton!

The coves that abound in the West Indies, Florida, and the Gulf of Mexico are ideal places for sponge growth. Here, glass-bottomed boats are sometimes used to seek them out, and divers cut them from the ocean bottom. Later, the sponges are set in the sun to rot the fleshy covering. They are then washed, bleached, and sorted. The tough skeleton of these sponges is made of *spongin,* which is porous and able to soak up a great deal of water. This is the part that is shipped to market as the sponge of commerce. Although the use of synthetic sponges has made serious inroads into the industry, the durability of natural sponges makes them more desirable for many tasks.

Hydra: A Simple Coelenterate

The tropic ocean floor, viewed through a glass-bottomed boat, is a fairyland of animal life. Brilliant corals shaped like ferns, furrowed domes, and leafless trees grow almost everywhere. Dazzling pink and yellow anemones wave their petal-like tentacles, fatal traps for unwary fish. Filmy jellyfish drift by like glass umbrellas, sometimes in clusters of several hundreds. Delicate sea fans wave lazily in the gentle currents. All of these animals are *coelenterates* (sih-LENT-uh-rates). Numbering about 9000 species, practically all of which live in the sea, coelenterates are believed to be the ancestors of higher invertebrate forms.

The phylum Coelenterata consists of animals that are composed of two distinct tissue layers: *ectoderm,* or outer tissue, and

21–2 **Common Bath Sponge**

endoderm, or inner tissue. Each animal has a distinct mouth surrounded by tentacles. The general body plan is best shown in a typical representative, the *Hydra.*

Two distinct forms are found in the coelenterates. One is the *medusa* (muh-DOO-suh), or jellyfish pattern; the other is the *polyp,* or tube pattern. Hydra is a polyp form. Though common, Hydra is exceptional in its phylum because it lives in fresh water. One end is adapted for attaching itself to rocks, stones, and plants. This is the *basal disc.* Hydra lives in quiet lakes, reservoirs, and slow-moving streams where it can stretch its body to full length, extending its tentacles to catch food. Most Hydra are less than an inch long, resembling a thin piece of thread somewhat frayed at one end. The frayed end consists of the tentacles, extensions that look like arms. At their base is the mouth.

NEMATOCYSTS, STINGING CELLS. Like all other members of this phylum, Hydra has tentacles equipped with numerous stinging cells, or *nematocysts.* These highly specialized cells contain tightly coiled threads that can be released by a trigger attached to their base. One kind of stinging cell contains a poison that is injected into the prey.

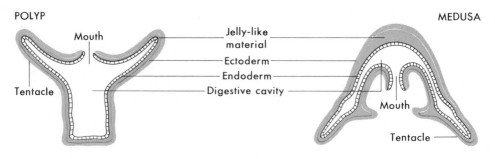

POLYP

MEDUSA

Mouth

Jelly-like material

Ectoderm

Endoderm

Digestive cavity

Tentacle

Mouth

Tentacle

21–3   Body Plan of Medusa and Polyp. Medusa is basically an inverted polyp.

The gentle movement of the Hydra's tentacles in the water is completely deceiving. As a tiny worm swims by and stimulates the stinging cells, there is sudden activity. The worm's body is riddled with poisonous darts. The tentacles then encircle the prey and force it into the mouth.

Jellyfish tentacles have similar stinging cells. The stings are quite painful, but not as painful as those of bees or wasps.

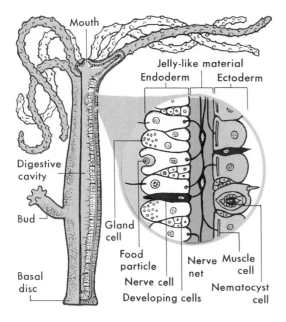

21–4   Hydra has a polyp-type body plan.

Mouth

Jelly-like material

Endoderm   Ectoderm

Digestive cavity

Bud

Basal disc

Gland cell

Food particle

Nerve cell

Developing cells

Nerve net

Muscle cell

Nematocyst cell

MOVEMENT. The ability of an animal to move depends upon the presence of muscle cells, which are able to contract. Such cells are found in Hydra, another evidence of the fact that it is a more specialized animal than the sponge. Movement also requires coordination. This is accomplished by nerve cells that form a nerve net throughout the entire body. Nerve cells mark a distinct advance in the development of higher invertebrates.

The cooperation of muscle and nerve cells permits Hydra to move quite easily in several ways. One method is to slide or glide along the object to which it is attached. Special cells on the basal disc enable it to do this. Another, more rapid method is somersaulting. Hydra bends over, attaches its tentacles to a solid object, releases its base, then flips over to its base again. This is somewhat like a boy doing handsprings. In still another method, Hydra "walks" along on its tentacles.

GETTING AND USING FOOD. Hydra obtains its food by stinging its prey and forcing it into the mouth. Once inside the digestive cavity, the food is acted upon by enzymes secreted by special gland cells in the endoderm. Digested food is absorbed by the lining cells and passed on to other cells of the body. Food that cannot be digested is passed out of the mouth as waste. Oxygen for respiration is obtained by diffusion from the surrounding water. Liquid wastes that accumulate within the cells are eliminated by diffusion.

REPRODUCTION. Coelenterates can reproduce by budding. You will often notice buds on living or preserved specimens of Hydra. Sometimes the bud is only a small swelling on the side of the animal.

Sex organs, which are clearly developed in Hydra, appear as swellings on the side of the animal. The sex organs that develop nearer the mouth are the testes which produce sperm cells. The lower swellings are ovaries, which produce the egg cell. The formation of the sex organs usually occurs in the autumn. When the sperm cells are released, they swim toward the egg. Only one sperm is needed to fertilize the egg. Following fertilization, the zygote, or fertilized egg, divides several times, then drops from the parent and lies dormant over the winter. In the spring, the zygote develops into a new animal.

Some species of Hydra produce both testes and ovaries on the same individual. This bisexual condition is called *hermaphroditism* (her-MAF-ruh-dite-iz-um) and is quite common among the invertebrates. Hermaphrodites are both male and female. In other species, the sexes are separate.

Like the sponges, Hydra can regenerate. If cut into a number of pieces, each piece grows into a complete animal. Pieces as small as one six-thousandth of an inch have produced complete animals. Biologists have also turned Hydra inside out like the finger of a glove. When this was done, the two layers of cells were reversed, but not for long. The cells of the ectoderm and endoderm migrated in opposite directions, restoring the original body condition.

Kinds of Jellyfish

Although we identified Hydra as a coelenterate built on the plan of a tube with ten-

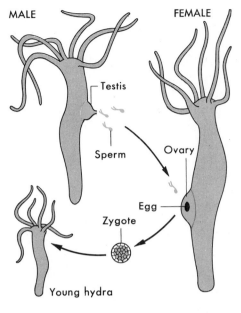

21–5 Sexual Reproduction in Hydra

tacles at the top, many of its relatives are *medusas,* or jellyfish. You may have seen jellyfish at the seashore swimming slowly along like animated umbrellas. Their tentacles trail from the edge of the umbrella. Some jellyfish are smaller than the head of a pin. Others, like the giant *Cyanea* of the North Atlantic Ocean, may grow to be more than seven feet in diameter. Tentacles more than 100 feet long trail from this gigantic jellyfish, which weighs almost a ton!

Many of the coelenterates produce both polyps and medusas in their life cycle. The forms are so dissimilar that it would not be easy to relate them unless they were observed to produce each other. This alternation of a polyp and medusa stage is similar to *alternation of generations.* Alternation of generations is well demonstrated in the colonial coelenterate Obelia.

AN OBELIA COLONY. Although many relatives of Hydra live in the tropics, *Obelia* lives in the cooler seas, attached to rocks, piers, pilings, and even to large seaweeds. It resembles a tiny leafless plant, for it has many branching polyps on an uneven stem. Obelia is not soft and elastic like Hydra, but is erect and encased in a transparent covering secreted by the ectoderm.

Examination of the Obelia colony reveals many individual polyps that are of two distinct types: *feeding polyps* and *reproductive polyps*. The feeding polyps exhibit a hydra-like structure and they are equipped with numerous tentacles. Digested food is circulated throughout a common body cavity, which extends through the entire colony.

The reproductive polyps are completely unlike Hydra. They contain a central stalk on which medusa buds develop. When the buds reach maturity, they break loose from the colony, escaping through the opening in the polyp, and swim away.

The tiny medusa is like a miniature umbrella with a ring of tentacles around the rim. From the center of the umbrella hangs a tube that leads into the digestive cavity. The cavity branches into four canals that reach to all parts of the body.

The medusas are either male or female. The sex organs release the eggs and sperm into the sea where fertilization occurs. The zygote develops into a larva that swims about for a short time, then settles to the ocean bottom. There it divides to form a young polyp, which produces an entire colony by budding.

The medusa marks the beginning of the sexual stage in the life cycle of Obelia. The colony of feeding and reproductive polyps is the asexual, or budding, stage. Thus, in this alternation of generations there are not only two kinds of individuals, but also two kinds of reproduction, as follows:

$$polyp \longrightarrow medusa \longrightarrow polyp$$
(asexual)   (sexual)   (asexual)

AURELIA. Most of the larger jellyfish are grouped together as a separate class of coelenterates. Practically all of them exhibit alternation of generations. In most, the medusa stage is much larger than the polyp stage, which in some cases is lacking. The general body plan is like the medusa of Obelia.

Aurelia is one of the larger jellyfish, ranging in size from two inches to a foot in diameter. Its body is a delicately tinted, almost transparent blue. Frequently, large schools of them are seen at sea swimming slowly by means of gentle body contractions.

These jellyfish differ from the medusas of Obelia in having long projections that resemble tentacles near the mouth. These *oral arms,* of which there are four, have stinging cells that can paralyze small ani-

21–6 In the life cycle of **Obelia**, sexual and asexual reproduction alternate. Free-swimming larva develops into an attached polyp, which grows by budding into a colony of polyps without separation. The reproductive polyps in the colony bud off sexual medusas.

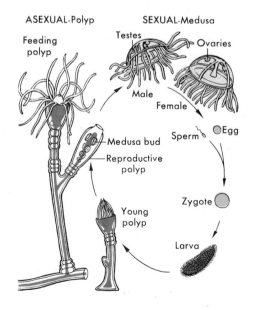

ASEXUAL-Polyp

Feeding polyp

Medusa bud

Reproductive polyp

Young polyp

SEXUAL-Medusa

Testes

Ovaries

Male

Female

Sperm

Egg

Zygote

Larva

mals. The oral arms then sweep the food into the mouth. The margin of the bell, or umbrella, is fringed with numerous short tentacles. Light-sensitive eye spots are scattered at eight separate indentations along the margin.

The sexes of Aurelia are separate. Fertilization is effected by the entrance of the sperm into the digestive cavity of the female. The fertilized egg develops into a swimming larva after its release from the parent. It sinks to the bottom of the sea and forms a polyp somewhat like Hydra in appearance. After several months, however, the polyp produces young medusas that grow into adult jellyfish.

THE PORTUGUESE MAN-OF-WAR. One of the deadliest of the coelenterates is *Physalia,* commonly called the "Portuguese man-of-war." It is often found in the Gulf Stream drifting northward from Florida. Its large, gas-filled float shimmers with beautiful blues, pinks, and violets, and is topped with a vivid red, sail-like crest. This striking animal trails a dangerous jungle of tentacles, some of which may be 40 feet long. So powerful are its stinging cells that they paralyze large fish and have even proved fatal to man.

The Portuguese man-of-war is a very complex colony of highly specialized individuals. Some are used for reproduction only. Others are clusters of feeding polyps, and still others are feeler polyps. Feeler polyps are food catchers equipped with especially powerful stinging cells. The long tentacles of the feeler polyps capture fish, then curl upward to deliver the fish to the feeders. The feeders then enclose the fish in elastic digestive sacs. The large float, which can be a foot long, is believed to be a special medusa that can no longer swim. The crest of the float acts somewhat like a sail that pushes the animal through the water as it is propelled by wind and ocean currents.

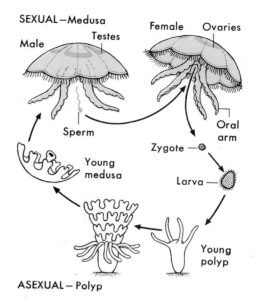

SEXUAL—Medusa

Male — Testes

Female — Ovaries

Sperm

Young medusa

Zygote

Oral arm

Larva

Young polyp

ASEXUAL— Polyp

21–7 Life cycle of Aurelia is similar to that of Obelia. The free-swimming larva develops into a small attached polyp. The young polyp grows and buds off male and female medusas, which are generally about six inches across. In Aurelia, the medusa is the dominant form.

21–8 This photograph illustrates the transparency of the medusa stage of Aurelia.

Walter Dawn

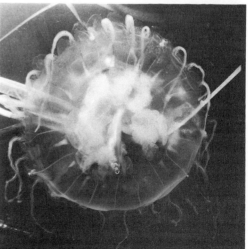

Walter Dawn

21–9 The hard limestone skeleton of coral is a commodity useful to man.

Corals and Anemones

For thousands of years the work of tiny coral polyps has built islands that dot the seas of the world. Wake Island, the Marshalls, Bermuda, the Bahamas, and the Fiji islands are but a few of them. Thousands of lesser islands made of *coral* are found in the tropical seas.

Coral polyps are tiny creatures that resemble smaller, squatter hydras. Each polyp secretes a hard limestone skeleton around its body and lives within its self-made stone house. Nearby polyps do the same thing, cementing their houses together. The result is a growing mass of limestone extracted from the sea. In the course of centuries, large masses of coral are thus produced. Growing from the floor of the sea, the masses produce coral reefs that are a serious hazard to ships. Coral islands are produced when the coral reef is elevated, as in volcanic action, or when the level of the sea is lowered.

Coral polyps live even in colder seas, but their greatest activity is confined to seas where the water temperature seldom drops below 70 degrees Fahrenheit. Most of their reef building occurs in a 3000-mile belt that circles the equator. Coral polyps, however, cannot live at depths greater than 150 feet. It has been found that they harbor algae, which increase their oxygen supply. The depth at which the coral polyp can live, therefore, is limited by the algae (and the depth at which the algae can live is limited in turn by their requirement of sunlight for photosynthesis).

Several theories have been suggested to explain the three kinds of coral reefs that are common in the tropics. In the *fringing reef*, the coral grows along the submerged shore of an island. If the island were to sink gradually into the sea, the distance between it and the reef would increase, forming a *barrier reef*. In this case, a deep channel of varying width exists between the reef and the island. A continuation of the sinking process causes the central island to disappear. However, since islands sink slowly over a period of centuries, the

21–10 Like coral and Hydra, the sea anemone does not have a medusa stage.

Walter Dawn

upward growth of coral results in a fringe of coral encircling a central lagoon. This is an *atoll*. According to some biologists, the sinking of the island caused these reef formations. However, other biologists believe that some reef formations were caused by the lowering of the sea level.

Coral is useful to man as a building material. Houses, streets, even airstrips are constructed from it where it is plentiful. Since many forms of coral are beautifully colored, they are often used for ornaments. The red coral of the Mediterranean is so hard that it is carved into jewelry and is known as "precious coral."

THE SEA ANEMONE. This coelenterate, a larger relative of the coral polyps, is noted for its flowerlike appearance. The *anemone* resembles a greatly enlarged Hydra with a thick, muscular body. At the top of the stout body, there are dozens of short graceful tentacles. The swaying mass of delicate tentacles gives the animal the appearance of an underwater flower. The anemones are the largest of the polyps, sometimes growing seven inches tall.

IMPORTANT POINTS

• Animals are many-celled and are called metazoans. In animals, certain cells become specialized for definite tasks. The sponges and coelenterates are the simplest forms of metazoan life.

• Sponges are a loose aggregation of cells held together by a skeleton. Essentially, they are living filters, extracting food and oxygen from the water. Their skeletons are made of calcium carbonate, silica, or a softer material called spongin. They reproduce asexually or sexually and have great powers of regeneration.

• Coelenterates consist of two distinct layers of cells. They have a digestive cavity open at one end forming a mouth. Tentacles and stinging cells are found in all forms. Common forms include Hydra, jellyfish, anemones, and corals.

• Like sponges, coelenterates reproduce asexually and sexually and are able to regenerate. Alternation of generations is common in this phylum. The free-swimming jellyfish is a sexual generation, which produces eggs and sperms. The fertilized egg gives rise to a polyp, which is asexual and reproduces by budding. The polyp produces free-swimming jellyfish, thus completing the cycle.

• Coral polyps are among the few animals that actually alter the geography of our planet. Billions of corals, growing over periods of millions of years, build important structures classified as fringing reefs, barrier reefs, and atolls.

REVIEW QUESTIONS

1. What are the advantages of cell specialization?
2. How do sponges obtain food?
3. Give an example of the sponge's great power of regeneration.
4. What are sponge skeletons made of?
5. What features do all coelenterates have in common?

6. How does Hydra get its food?
7. Give an example of regeneration in Hydra.
8. Describe the two ways in which Hydra reproduces.
9. Why may jellyfish be dangerous to swimmers?
10. Why are sponges referred to as loosely organized metazoans?

CHECK YOUR UNDERSTANDING

11. What is the difference between a polyp and a medusa?
12. What advances in structure do coelenterates show over sponges?
13. Describe alternation of generations in jellyfish.
14. In the Obelia colony, what is the difference between the feeding polyps and the reproductive polyps?
15. Explain the theories of formation of fringe reefs, barrier reefs, and atolls.
16. Explain why a sponge, resting almost motionless on the ocean floor, is considered an active animal.
17. Compare alternation of generations in coelenterates with alternation of generations in mosses and ferns.
18. Why do shallow tropical seas afford the greatest variety of coelenterate life?
19. How is it possible for coelenterates, which are slow-moving, to prey upon rapidly-moving forms of life?
20. What is meant by the phrase "a metazoan is an organized community of cells"?

RESEARCH PROJECTS AND REPORTS

1. Obtain information from your school or public library and prepare a report on one of the following topics:

   Australia's Great Barrier Reef   **Sea Anemones**

   Portuguese Man-of-War   **Sponge Fishing**

2. *Collecting and Examining Hydras:* With a little care and patience, living Hydras may be found. Collect submerged weeds from a pond or lake. Place them in a quart jar of clean pond water and examine by holding the jar up to the light. Hydras are ⅛ to ½ inch in length and can be seen with the naked eye. Several trips may be necessary before you are successful.

   Hydras may be kept in the laboratory in a dish of pond or aquarium water. **Note:** *Do not use tap water.* Keep in a cool place. With a little skill, you can take up a single Hydra from your dish with a pipette. Place it in a drop of water on a clean slide and examine under the low power of the microscope. If your school has a microprojector, Hydra can be shown to the entire class.

3. *Regeneration in Hydra:* Place a Hydra in a shallow dish containing pond water. With a sharp razor cut the Hydra transversely. Cover the dish to prevent evaporation. Prepare several more specimens the same way. Leave the dishes for ten days at room temperature or slightly cooler. At the end of ten days, examine the halves of the animal.

4. *The Geography of Coral:* With the aid of an encyclopedia and other reference books, locate several coral islands and reefs. What are the latitudes of your coral formations? Is there a relationship between coral locations and ocean currents?

FURTHER READING

A Guide to the Sponges of Eastern North America. M. W. de Laubenfels. University of Miami Press, Miami, Fla. A useful guide for the amateur as well as the professional sponge collector.

"**The Enigma of the Coral Isles.**" Editors of LIFE. *The Wonders of Life on Earth.* Time, Inc., New York, N.Y. Chapter 12 is a beautifully illustrated account of the role of coral in the community of the sea.

"**The Portuguese Man-of-War.**" Charles E. Lane. *Scientific American*, March, 1960, page 158. Interesting account of how this beautiful but deadly jellyfish captures its prey.

"**Corals as Paleontological Clocks.**" S. K. Runcorn, *Scientific American,* October, 1966, page 26. Calculations indicate that half a billion years ago, the earth had more than 400 days per year. Growth markings on fossil corals may provide the rate at which the days became longer and less numerous per year.

CHAPTER

22

Flat, Round, and Segmented Worms

THE ANIMAL PHYLA we have studied so far do not represent advanced stages in the development of life. The organs and systems, so common in the higher animals, have not yet appeared.

In the flatworms an important structural advance is seen. This is a third cell layer, the *mesoderm,* which is found between the ectoderm and endoderm. The mesoderm is the tissue that forms the muscles; hence, it gave rise to animals that could move about more swiftly. With increased activity came better coordination and better information about the animal's environment. The first specialized sense organs appear and the development of a central nervous system begins in the flatworm.

The roundworms show certain further advances. The food tube is better developed and a crude circulatory system is present in some forms.

In the segmented worms the development of organ systems is most pronounced. The lowly earthworm is really very complex. There are many ways in which its internal organization can be compared with that of higher animals.

Many of the animals that belong to these three phyla are free-living forms that dwell in streams, ponds, or in the soil. Others, however, are parasitic in plants and other animals, including man. Their parasitic characteristics make them among man's worst enemies.

Platyhelminthes: Flatworms

If there is a cold, spring-fed pool in your neighborhood, you may be able to collect *Planaria,* a representative of the flatworms. Place a small piece of raw beef or liver in the water at the edge of the pool. The worms will collect on the meat. You can then transfer them to a bottle.

APPEARANCE AND MOVEMENT. Near the eyespots, the typical planarian has two projections that look like ears. Its long, flat body is somewhat freckled in appearance. It cannot swim freely in water, but glides over the surface of rocks and stones.

After you have observed a planarian for some time, several things become clear. It has a definite *dorsal* (upper) and *ventral* (lower) surface. The eyespots are located

22–1 Planarian

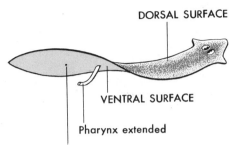

DORSAL SURFACE

VENTRAL SURFACE

Pharynx extended

Genital pore

Walter Dawn

22–2 The branching of the flatworm intestine is clearly indicated in the triclad, a relative of Planaria.

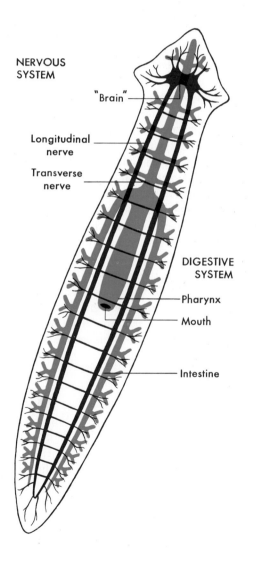

NERVOUS SYSTEM

"Brain"

Longitudinal nerve

Transverse nerve

DIGESTIVE SYSTEM

Pharynx

Mouth

Intestine

on the dorsal surface. The ventral surface is the side pressed against the object to which it clings. Furthermore, it has one end that is propelled forward all of the time. This is the *anterior* (front) end and contains the eyespots. The other end is called the *posterior* end.

FEEDING. The planarian's mouth is not located on its head. The opening into the food tube is a muscular *pharynx* (FAR-inks) located on the ventral surface about halfway between the head and tail. The worm presses its body against the object it wants to eat, then extends the pharynx from the mouth. After being torn into small pieces, the food is sucked into the tube.

The pharynx leads into a digestive system that has several branches. One of these extends forward. Two branches extend backward to the posterior end. The cells that line the digestive tract take in the food particles, forming food vacuoles much like Ameba. After the food has been digested, it is absorbed and diffuses to all the cells of the body.

THE NERVOUS SYSTEM. Planaria has a more highly developed nervous system than Hydra and other coelenterates. One evidence of this is the development of sense organs, such as the eyespots. Another is the organization of the nerve cells into two clumped areas in the head. The two nerve centers are sometimes referred to as the "brain" of the animal. From the two nerve centers separate nerve cords extend backward along the sides of the animal. The nerve cords are interconnected by lateral branches, which resemble the rungs of a ladder.

The specialized cells of the eyespots enable a planarian to respond to light, but it is not able to see in the same sense that we do. The earlike extensions near the eyespots are believed to be sensitive to chemical substances dissolved in water. This enables the worm to find food quickly.

EXCRETION AND REPRODUCTION. Planaria is the first animal we have studied that has systems for excretion and reproduction. These systems are not complicated, but they indicate a distinct advance over the coelenterates. The excretory system is composed of branching tubules that gather water and liquid wastes from all parts of the body. Scattered along the sides of the tubes are ciliated cells called *flame cells*,

which assist the movement of the fluids toward pores that lead to the outside.

Some planarians reproduce both asexually and sexually. In asexual reproduction, the animal undergoes fission by pinching into two. The head and tail ends then grow the parts they lack and two complete planarians result.

Sexual reproduction usually takes place during the spring and summer months. Both male and female reproductive organs are found in the same planarian. Although the worms are hermaphroditic, self fertilization does not occur. Instead, two planarians join at the *genital pore* and exchange sperms in order to fertilize each other's egg cells. After the mating individuals separate, each planarian discharges a capsule containing zygotes that develop into new planarians.

REGENERATION IN PLANARIA. Like the sponges and Hydra, Planaria has the ability to regenerate mutilated parts. If a planarian is cut in half, the pieces produce new animals. The anterior portion regenerates the new animal more quickly than does the posterior portion. In some kinds of planarians, the posterior end will not regenerate the head region. So pronounced is Planaria's ability to regenerate, that two-headed planarians can be produced by making an incision along the head's midline. In this manner, some biologists have been able to produce many-headed planarians.

The Parasitic Flatworms

The phylum Platyhelminthes consists of three main classes. One of the classes includes all of the free-living forms. The other two classes contain species that are entirely parasitic. All members of the phylum are similar in many ways to Planaria, the representative flatworm.

Since flatworm parasites are dependent upon their host for food, they usually have

22–3 If a planarian is cut in half, each half will regenerate the missing portion and will restore the normal proportions.

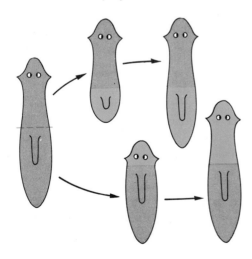

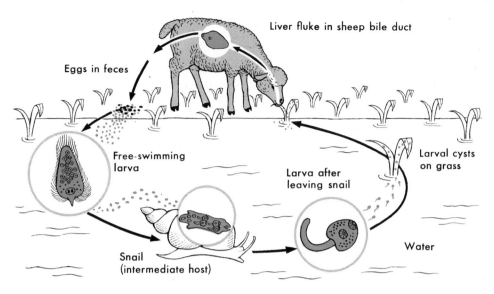

22—4 Life History of Sheep Liver Fluke

hooks and suckers for clinging to the host while absorbing food. Flatworm parasites produce huge numbers of eggs. The chances for survival are not great unless some of the new individuals can locate new hosts.

THE SHEEP LIVER FLUKE. This flatworm parasite of sheep is about an inch long and is shaped somewhat like a tiny leaf. Located at the base of the "leaf" are two suckers, which enable the liver fluke to attach itself to the walls of the bile duct, a tube leading from the liver. It then moves up the bile duct into the liver where it feeds upon blood. An attack by large numbers of liver flukes may be fatal.

The life history of the liver fluke is an interesting example of the dependence of parasites upon intermediate hosts. The eggs, which are produced in large numbers, are eliminated in the *feces,* or waste matter, of the sheep. Water is necessary for the survival and development of the fertilized eggs. In a swampy pasture they produce free-swimming larvae that infect certain snails. The snail is thus the intermediate

host. In the snail's body changes occur in the fluke larvae that result in the production of other larvae. These escape from the snail and form *cysts* on blades of grass. When a sheep eats the infected grass, the cycle starts again.

Poor sanitary conditions are responsible for the spread of certain parasitic flukes among humans. One such human parasite, the Chinese liver fluke, has two intermediate hosts, the snail and the fish. Eating raw fish introduces this fluke into man.

THE TAPEWORM. The largest intestinal parasite of man is the tapeworm, which may attain a length of more than ten feet. The head, or *scolex,* has hooks and suction discs that fasten it securely to the intestinal wall. Links, or *proglottids,* are produced behind the scolex. Each link contains a male and female reproductive system that can produce hundreds of eggs.

The tapeworm is so completely parasitic that it doesn't have a digestive system. It simply absorbs digested food from the intestine of its host. An infected person not only suffers a loss of food to the parasite,

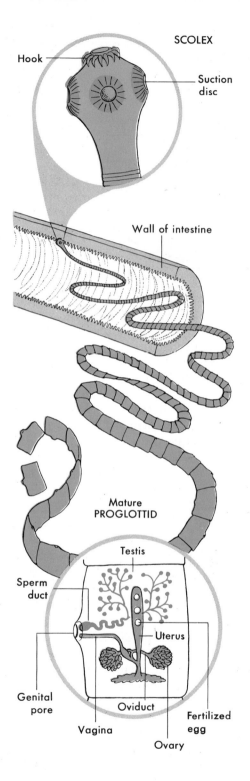

SCOLEX

Hook

Suction disc

Wall of intestine

Mature PROGLOTTID

Testis

Sperm duct

Uterus

Genital pore

Oviduct

Vagina

Fertilized egg

Ovary

but he may even develop anemia. The latter condition results from the poisonous substances produced by the tapeworm.

Mature proglottids, containing hundreds of fertilized eggs, are eliminated in the feces of an infected person. Where sanitation is lacking, the food of cows or pigs may be contaminated by these eggs. In the intestine of a pig or cow the eggs develop into embryos with hooks. These embryos bore through the intestinal wall into the blood stream and become widely distributed in the muscles of the animal's body. There they form cysts and grow into bladder worms, developing the characteristic head of the mature worms.

If infected pork or beef is eaten without being thoroughly cooked, the bladder worms pass into the digestive tract of the new victim. The cyst dissolves, and the scolex attaches itself to the new host. Tapeworm infection is less frequent than it once was because of better sanitary conditions and the inspection of meat by government agencies.

Nematoda: Roundworms

Worms with round bodies—not divided into rings or segments—are grouped in the phylum Nematoda. The worms in this phylum show a structural advance: a continuous digestive tube that extends from the anterior to the posterior of the body.

Most of the roundworms are very small, some being microscopic, but a few do grow quite large. Among these is the guinea worm, common in Africa, India, South America, and the West Indies, reported to attain lengths of three or four feet. In areas where sewage disposal is poor and filtered drinking water is not available, infection by the guinea worm is frequent.

22–5 Tapeworm, a Parasite in Man. Each section produces thousands of fertilized eggs.

Walter Dawn

22–6 Ascaris, A Parasitic Roundworm

ASCARIS: AN INTESTINAL PARASITE. This is one of the largest and most common roundworm parasites in the world. Physicians have estimated that in some parts of the United States thirty per cent of the population may be infected by *Ascaris*. Largely spread through poor sanitation, Ascaris infection is used by some health authorities as an index of sanitary control.

In Ascaris the sexes are separate. The female, which is much larger than the male, may grow seven inches to a foot long. The mouth opens into the digestive tract, a simple straight tube that leads directly to the anus. The external body plan is very simple. The two pointed ends of the worm are almost identical. Beneath the tough *cuticle* there is a layer of muscle that runs lengthwise. These muscles enable the animal to draw its body up in a thrashing mo-

tion that is characteristic of many of the roundworms.

The reproductive system is especially well developed. The males produce sperm cells in a *testis* that is a long, coiled tube. The ovaries of the females produce about 200,000 eggs each day. The eggs are fertilized in the *oviducts*, which consist of two coiled tubes and lead from the ovaries to a single tube that opens to the outside. As the egg passes down through the oviduct it is covered by a hard protective shell. The eggs pass into the intestine of the infected person and are then eliminated.

Contaminated food or water may introduce the tiny eggs into the new host. Two factors are responsible for the success of the parasite: the extremely large number of eggs and the ability of the eggs to resist adverse conditions.

The developing larvae hatch in the intestine of the new victim and burrow into

22–7 LIFE CYCLE OF ASCARIS. Eggs in contaminated food and water reach intestine and hatch into larvae (1). The larvae bore through intestinal wall, enter the blood, and are carried to the lungs (2). In the lungs, the larvae grow and are then coughed up or crawl up the windpipe into the mouth (3), are swallowed, and return to the intestine (4). Female worm produces eggs that pass out with feces (5) and may be introduced to another host.

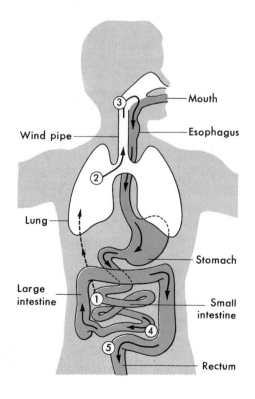

Mouth

Wind pipe

Esophagus

Lung

Stomach

Large intestine

Small intestine

Rectum

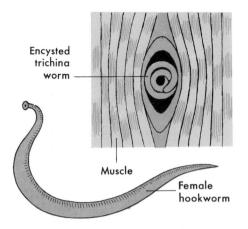

Encysted
trichina
worm

Muscle

Female
hookworm

22–8 Parasitic roundworms, such as hook-worm, cause widespread disease in man.

blood vessels of the intestinal wall. Once there, they can be transported to any organ of the body. They usually infect the lungs, journeying up the windpipe and down into the food tube again. During this period they have grown larger. In the intestine the adults reach such a large size that they often block the passage of food.

The larvae attack both the lungs and intestine. Coughing and difficult breathing are common. Nausea and intestinal distress often occur. Cyanine dyes have simplified the treatment of infected persons. These dyes cut off the oxygen supply from the tissues of the worms, causing their death.

TRICHINA: THE PORKWORM. In contrast with Ascaris, *trichina* (trik-EYE-nuh) worms are very small. Surveys indicate that in the United States one person in six probably suffers a mild infection at some time during his lifetime. Severe infections of trichina worms may cause death.

Infected pork is the common source of infection. The trichina larvae exist in cysts in the muscles of the pig. Cooking the meat thoroughly will destroy them. When undercooked pork is eaten, the cysts are dissolved in the intestine and the larvae

are released. The larvae may become adults and produce young in several days. At this point the parasites become highly dangerous because they burrow upward through the tissues of the chest. About five per cent of the cases of *trichinosis* are fatal. In most cases, the larvae simply burrow into the muscles of the body, where they form cysts and do no further harm.

Several methods of controlling trichinosis have proved successful. The most satisfactory one is to cook pork thoroughly. Another concerns the feeding habits of pigs. If these animals are not fed contaminated food, they do not harbor trichina worms. When pigs are properly fed, and untreated garbage is eliminated from their diet, trichinosis is drastically reduced. Treating infected pork with gamma radiation has also proved to be very effective in killing the larvae. Pork kept in a deep freeze for a period of two weeks is generally considered safe.

ELEPHANTIASIS. Elephantiasis is a tropical disease in which the limbs become greatly enlarged. The skin hangs in heavy folds, reminding one of the elephant. The grotesque appearance of victims of the disease is caused by *filaria* worms that clog the lymph ducts of the arms and legs.

The adult worms that cause elephantiasis may be two to four inches long. However, the larvae they produce are only one-hundredth of an inch long. The tiny larvae are sucked into the body of a mosquito when it bites an infected person. The infection of the next victim occurs after the larvae have developed within the body of the mosquito. The larvae continue their development in the newly bitten human host until they reach the adult stage.

HOOKWORM. In tropical countries the *hookworm* is considered one of the most damaging parasitic worms found in man. It is especially prevalent where people go barefoot and sanitary toilets are not used.

In such areas, as much as one-half of the total population may be infected.

The adult worms, which are about one-quarter of an inch long, live in the intestine. There they attach themselves to the wall and suck small quantities of blood, frequently causing anemia in the victim. The adult worms mate in the intestine of the host and produce thousands of eggs. These are passed out of the intestine in waste material, infecting the soil where proper sanitation does not exist.

The larvae develop from the eggs in the soil and are then ready to infect a new person. The worms gain entry into the body through the soft skin on the sides of the feet. The larvae then travel through lymph or blood vessels to the heart and from there to the lungs. They penetrate the lung tissue and enter the windpipe, eventually going up the windpipe, then down the gullet to the stomach and intestine.

In the control of hookworm, proper sanitation is most important. Wearing shoes is a simple preventive measure. Furthermore, since the worm is harbored in the intestine, it can be directly attacked by medicines.

Annelida: The Earthworm

The earthworm and its relatives are well-developed in many ways. They have a central nervous system. The digestive tract is specialized into several main parts. The system for circulating blood consists of organs and tubes. Animals of this phylum also have a *coelom*, or body cavity, an advance present in all the higher animals, but lacking in the lower ones.

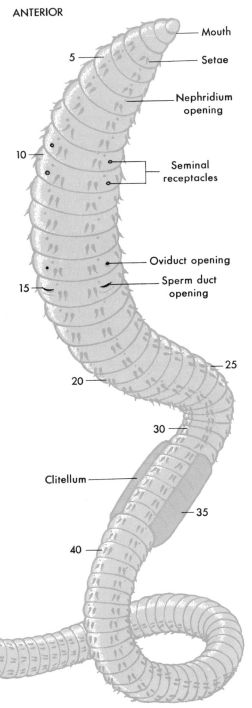

22–9 **External Structure of Earthworm**

ANTERIOR

Mouth
Setae
Nephridium opening
Seminal receptacles
Oviduct opening
Sperm duct opening
Clitellum
Anus
POSTERIOR

The most important characteristic of the phylum Annelida is the presence of rings, or segments, on the body. These are easily observed in the earthworm (see Figure 22–9). Dissection of any annelid reveals that the segments also exist internally. Segmentation is evidence of increasing specialization and development in animal life. All vertebrate animals are segmented. An example in the human body is the series of jointed bones that make up the backbone.

STRUCTURE AND MOVEMENT. The body of the earthworm is a long thin tube within a tube. The digestive tract is the internal tube. It is surrounded by several muscle layers that form the outer tube, the body wall. Between the tubes is the coelom. The outer muscle layers are covered by a thin layer of cells that secrete a thin, protective cuticle on the outside of the worm.

From the anterior to the posterior end, the body is divided continuously into more than 100 segments. For convenience, biologists usually number them so that internal organs can be located more readily. Thus, the mouth is located in the first segment. Segments 32 to 37 are swollen, forming the *clitellum* (kli-TEL-um), a structure used in reproduction. The openings of the oviducts appear on segment 14, and the openings of the sperm ducts are on segment 15. Internally, the segments are marked by *septa*, thin partitions that separate one segment from another.

The familiar crawling movements of the earthworm are caused by two external muscle layers: one circular, the other longitudinal. On the body's ventral surface are tiny bristles, or *setae*. The setae anchor the worm in the soil as it pulls itself along. They act somewhat like cleats on shoes.

EATING AND DIGESTING FOOD. Earthworms are most active at night. Anchoring themselves in their burrows, they extend the anterior part of the body outside in search of such food as leaves, roots, and soil particles. The food is sucked into the mouth by a muscular pharynx.

After passing through the pharynx and the *esophagus,* the food is stored temporarily in the *crop.* The earthworm has no teeth to grind its food into smaller particles. The *gizzard* is a thick organ that probably substitutes for teeth. Here the food is mechanically ground with the help of small particles of sand.

From the gizzard, the intestine of the worm extends in a straight tube to the anus. Digestion occurs in the intestine. Enzymes act upon the food chemically, breaking it

22–10   **Digestive System of Earthworm**

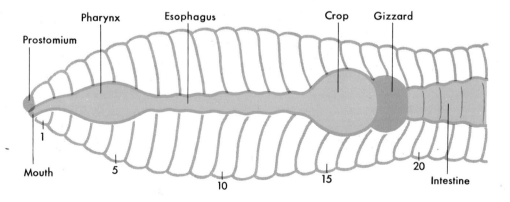

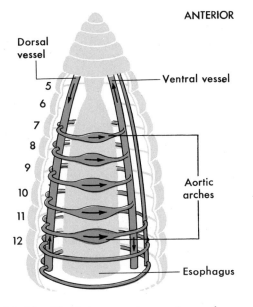

ANTERIOR

Dorsal vessel

Ventral vessel

5
6
7
8
9
10
11
12

Aortic arches

Esophagus

22-11 Circulatory system of earthworm, showing aortic arches around esophagus.

up into simple compounds that can be absorbed into the blood.

CIRCULATION. The blood circulates in a closed system of tubes throughout the body. Two of the principal blood vessels run the length of the intestine above and below it. These are called the *dorsal* and *ventral vessels.*

In segments 7 to 11, five pairs of "hearts" connect the dorsal and ventral vessels. Sometimes these are called *aortic arches,* a more appropriate name since the real "heart" of the worm is the dorsal vessel. The dorsal vessel is the pumping part of the system, forcing the blood forward to the anterior part of the body. The blood descends in the aortic arches to the ventral vessel, where it flows forward and backward to all parts of the body. The earthworm's blood is red, much like ours. The red pigment hemoglobin is dissolved in the liquid portion, however. In our blood, hemoglobin is contained in the red cells.

A well-developed circulatory system is

important in the advance of living things. Without it, the size to which an animal can grow is limited. Some methods must be available to supply all the cells with food and oxygen and to remove their wastes. These are main functions of the circulatory system.

EXCRETION AND RESPIRATION. Liquid wastes are transported by the blood to the *nephridia,* kidneylike tubes located in nearly all of the segments. Only the first three segments and the last segment lack nephridia. Each tubule has an opening that receives waste from the coelom. The wastes are then passed outside.

The earthworm has no organ system for obtaining oxygen. However, the skin is richly supplied with many tiny blood vessels just beneath the cuticle. Oxygen from the air passes into these vessels and is carried by the hemoglobin of the blood to all cells of the body. For efficient diffusion of gases, the skin must be moist. If the skin dries, the worm dies quickly. This method of obtaining oxygen indicates that the earthworm probably had ancestors that lived in water.

22-12 Excretory System of Earthworm

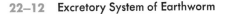

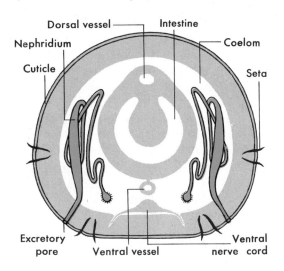

Dorsal vessel — Intestine
Nephridium — Coelom
Cuticle — Seta
Excretory pore — Ventral vessel — Ventral nerve cord

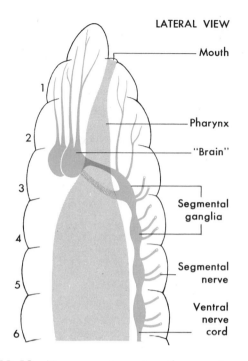

LATERAL VIEW

Mouth

Pharynx

"Brain"

Segmental
ganglia

Segmental
nerve

Ventral
nerve
cord

1
2
3
4
5
6

22–13   Nervous system of earthworm, showing ventral nerve cord and ganglia.

Nervous System. Although the earthworm is sensitive to light and touch, it does not have special sense organs. There are light-sensitive cells scattered through the skin. These cells enable the worm to distinguish between light and dark.

The sensory cells send nerve impulses into a nerve trunk, the *ventral nerve cord,* which runs along the ventral surface beneath the digestive tube. In each segment the ventral nerve cord is swollen into a *ganglion,* a slightly larger mass of nerve tissue. In the region of the pharynx, the ventral nerve cord branches about the digestive tube and unites above it to form the brain. Hardly larger than the other ganglia, the brain is not as important either in size or function as in the higher animals.

Reproduction. Like Planaria, earthworms are *hermaphrodites;* that is, they have both ovaries and testes. The ovaries

lead to oviducts, which open to the outside in segment 14. The testes store the sperm cells in the *seminal vesicles* until the sperm cells are released to the outside through two openings in segment 15. (See Figure 22–14.)

The exchange of sperm cells between two mating worms occurs during a process called *copulation.* Each worm receives sperm from the other. The sperm is stored in *seminal receptacles* until used in fertilizing the eggs.

After copulation the worms separate, each having sperms from the other stored in the seminal receptacles. Later the clitellum secretes a tube of mucus, which slips over the front of the worm. The tube receives eggs as it passes segment 14, and receives the other worm's sperm cells as it passes segments 9 and 10. Fertilization occurs inside the mucous tube. As the tube passes over the animal's front, each end

22–14   Reproductive System of Earthworm

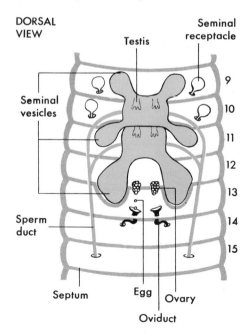

DORSAL
VIEW

Testis

Seminal
receptacle

Seminal
vesicles

Sperm
duct

Septum   Egg   Ovary
          Oviduct

9
10
11
12
13
14
15

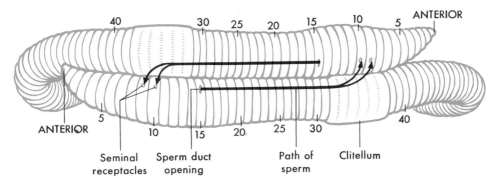

ANTERIOR

40   30   25   20   15   10   5   ANTERIOR

ANTERIOR   5   10   15   20   25   30   40

Seminal receptacles | Sperm duct opening | Path of sperm | Clitellum

22–15   Two Earthworms in Copulation

closes to form a capsule. The eggs develop into young worms within the capsule.

The ability of earthworms to regenerate is much less extensive than that of Planaria. Usually, only a few segments can be regrown from the anterior or posterior ends. As an animal becomes more specialized, it loses some of its ability to regenerate lost parts of its body.

EARTHWORMS AND AGRICULTURE. In the process of burrowing, earthworms swallow great amounts of soil from which they digest the organic material. The indigestible soil passes through their intestinal tracts and is deposited as "worm castings." This is of great significance to the farmer and to agriculture.

The great English naturalist Charles Darwin once calculated the effect of the earthworm's feeding habits. An acre of fairly rich soil may contain as many as 50,000 earthworms. In the course of ten years, they bring a layer two inches deep from the subsoil to the topsoil. This adds tremendously to the richness and fertility of farms and gardens. Darwin stated, "The plough is one of the most ancient and most valuable of man's inventions; but long before he existed the land was, in fact, regularly ploughed and still continues to be thus ploughed by earthworms. It may be doubted whether there are many other ani-

mals which have played so important a part in the history of the world as have these lowly organized creatures."

Sandworm

The *Nereis,* or sandworm, is a seashore cousin of the earthworm. It is inactive by day, living in burrows on the tidal flats. At night the sandworm ventures forth in search of food. Since it has a pair of strong

22–16   Sandworm

Walter Dawn

COMPARING PHYLA OF WORMS

Systems	Platyhelminthes	Nematoda	Annelida
Digestive	Pharynx and mouth.	Continuous digestive tube.	Mouth, pharynx, crop, gizzard, and intestine.
Respiratory	Diffusion. No system.	Diffusion. No system.	Moist skin.
Excretory	Tubules and flame cells.	Two canals. No flame cells.	Kidney tubules (nephridia).
Circulatory	None.	None.	Dorsal and ventral vessels and aortic arches.
Nervous	"Brain." Two nerve cords. Eyespots.	Two nerve trunks.	"Brain" and ventral nerve cord.
Reproductive	Hermaphroditic. Regenerate by fission.	Sexes separate.	Sexes separate. Some hermaphroditic.

jaws, the sandworm is better equipped to get its food than the earthworm.

Externally, the sandworm looks little like the earthworm. Its head is much better developed and has two pairs of simple eyes. On each side of the first segment are four pairs of tentacles. The body is flattened, not at all like the tubular construction of the earthworm. Each of the more than 200 segments bears a pair of fleshy outgrowths used in swimming and crawling.

Internally, the sandworm's organization closely resembles that of the earthworm. The major difference is in reproduction, for sandworms have separate sexes. The eggs and sperm are passed out of the body into the sea where fertilization occurs.

Leech

Leeches are among the best known segmented worms. Their habit of clinging to an animal and sucking its blood is made possible by the presence of two suckers: one anterior, the other posterior. The posterior sucker, which is much larger, is generally used to hold the leech to a rock or plant in a pond as it waits for its victim.

Once attached to its victim, the leech cuts the skin with its teeth and begins to draw the victim's blood. A substance called *hirudin* is injected into the wound to prevent the blood from clotting. The mouth and teeth are located in the center of the anterior sucker.

At one time, the practice of using the leech for blood letting was widely followed. The false notion that getting rid of bad blood would improve the patient's health was once widely held by physicians. Many physicians imported leeches from Europe for this purpose. Leeches survive several months on one meal of blood.

IMPORTANT POINTS

- The three phyla of worms show a series of structural advances in the development of metazoan life. The organ systems that begin in the flatworms continue in the roundworms and reach a fairly high degree of specialization in the segmented worms.

- In the flatworms the mesoderm, or third cell layer, is present. In the roundworms a continuous digestive tube appears. In the segmented worms a coelom, or body cavity, is observed. Segmentation is also an advance toward the higher forms of life.

- Flatworms may be free-living or parasitic. The free-living planarians are among the lowest invertebrates that have definite systems for digestion, excretion, and reproduction. They reproduce asexually by fission or sexually by exchanging sperm cells, since they are hermaphroditic. Planarians also show great powers of regeneration.

- Parasitic flatworms include flukes and tapeworms. Both of these parasites require more than one host to complete their life cycle. The liver fluke infects sheep as well as a certain species of snail. The Chinese liver fluke completes its life cycle by going from snail to fish to man.

- The tapeworm, the largest intestinal parasite that infects man, completes part of its life cycle in the cow or pig. Meat inspection to detect the bladder stage of the worms is an important method of preventing human contamination.

- Most roundworms are parasitic. Among the most serious roundworm parasites are Ascaris, trichina, hookworm, and filaria. Millions of people throughout the world are victims of mild to serious infection by these parasites.

- Hookworm disease is often prevalent in warmer climates where sanitary facilities are lacking, and people go barefoot. Trichinosis, which results from eating infected pork, is sometimes fatal. Because trichina worms are too small to be detected by meat inspection, the best preventive measure is thorough cooking of all forms of pork.

- Segmented worms are relatively advanced invertebrates. The earthworm exhibits considerable specialization in its organ systems. Within its body cavity are fairly well-developed digestive, circulatory, excretory, and nervous systems. Earthworms are hermaphroditic. During copulation, mating pairs exchange sperm cells.

REVIEW QUESTIONS

1. What evidence of increasing specialization is noted in Planaria?
2. Describe the method by which Planaria feeds.
3. In what way is the nervous system of Planaria advanced over that of Hydra?
4. Explain why the proglottids near the posterior of the tapeworm are larger than those near the head.
5. How does a tapeworm secure itself to the inside wall of the intestine?
6. What preventive measures may be taken against hookworm infection?
7. Why is the thorough cooking of all pork a wise health measure?
8. Trace the life cycle of the sheep liver fluke.
9. Trace the life cycle of the filaria worm.
10. In what ways are the sandworm and leech different from the earthworm?

CHECK YOUR UNDERSTANDING

11. Compare regeneration in sponges, planarians, and earthworms.
12. Describe several adaptations of the tapeworm for its parasitic mode of life.
13. Why is meat inspection unreliable as a control over trichinosis?
14. How do the organ systems of the earthworm indicate that it is a more specialized animal than other worms?
15. What is the role of the clitellum in earthworm reproduction?
16. Why would a free-living worm show more of the characteristics that are typical of a phylum than a parasitic worm?
17. Parasitic worms usually lay many more eggs than free-living worms. Explain why this is so.
18. Estimates indicate a higher incidence of trichinosis on a per capita basis in the United States than in Asia. Can you explain this fact?
19. Why are sheep less likely to become infected with liver fluke when they graze in pastures where there are no lakes and swamps?
20. The ideal parasite has been described as the one that does least harm to the host. Discuss this statement.

RESEARCH PROJECTS AND REPORTS

1. Obtain information from your school or public library and prepare a report on one of the following topics:

Meat Inspection	**Earthworms and Agriculture**
Hookworm Disease	**Filariasis**

2. *Anesthesia Experiments with Planaria:* Many small invertebrates need to be slowed down for study under the microscope. Some substances used for this purpose are alcohol, ether, and chloroform. You can try these on Planaria by adding very small amounts to the water in which you have isolated several worms. To give meaning to your work, be certain you know exactly how much of each test material you use. Keep accurate records. Make very dilute solutions of test materials and gradually increase their strength.

Don't be content with the usual anesthetics. Try dilute solutions of magnesium sulfate, sodium bromide, or other salts you may suspect have anesthetic properties.

3. *Reactions of Planaria:* Devise experiments to reveal the responses of Planaria to light, warmth, harmful chemicals, and mild electric shocks. Keep accurate records of your procedures.

4. *Collecting and Studying the Earthworm:* Earthworms are most easily collected at night when a steady rain has soaked the ground thoroughly. Well-kept lawns are a favorite hunting ground. Once captured, the worms can be kept for some time in a large container with soil, sphagnum, and leaf mold. This should be moist, but not soggy.

FURTHER READING

Parade of the Animal Kingdom. Robert Hegner. Macmillan Company, New York, N.Y. Many examples of the major phyla of animals. Contains much information on worms, related in an entertaining style.

"Worm Autobiographies." G. P. Wells. *Scientific American,* June, 1959, page 132. Describes unusual methods used to record the daily activities of certain marine worms.

"Filariasis." F. Hawkins. *Scientific American,* July, 1958, page 94. Discusses the parasitic worms that cause elephantiasis.

23

Echinoderms and Mollusks

A GREAT VARIETY of invertebrate forms developed in the ancient oceans. No two invertebrate forms are more different or more interesting than the two phyla discussed in this chapter: Phylum Echinodermata (e-ky-no-DER-ma-ta) and Phylum Mollusca.

The *echinoderms* are spiny-skinned animals, such as the starfish, the sea urchin, and the sea cucumber. The animals of this phylum, consisting of approximately 5000 species, are believed to be the forerunners of early vertebrates.

The *mollusks* represent the second largest of the invertebrate phyla, consisting of about 130,000 species. Many, like the oyster and clam, have a hard, protective shell. Others do not have an external covering. In all cases the body is very soft and well organized into organ systems. Many biologists believe that the mollusks are related to the segmented worms. This belief is based upon the fact that the early development of these animals is remarkably alike.

Here then are two phyla that mark the two main paths along which the more advanced vertebrates and invertebrates may have developed. The spiny-skinned creatures lead to the fishes. The mollusks lead to the insects.

Starfish: Phylum Echinodermata

Almost everyone has seen or heard of starfish. Even people who live hundreds of miles from the nearest ocean have seen dried, preserved specimens.

If a line is drawn from the anterior to the posterior end of an animal like the earthworm, the animal is divided into right and left halves that are exactly the same. Such animals exhibit *bilateral symmetry*. Unlike many of the other animals we have studied so far, the starfish does not have an anterior and posterior end. Its body is built on a circular, or radial, plan. From the center, where the mouth is located, five rays, or arms, extend outward like the spokes of a wheel. This kind of arrangement is called *radial symmetry*.

The polyps and jellyfish are similar to the starfish insofar as their symmetry is concerned. Because of this, biologists at one time grouped the coelenterates and echinoderms together. Now they are grouped in separate phyla.

EXTERNAL APPEARANCE AND STRUCTURE. The members of this phylum are called echinoderms because of their spiny skin. The latter part of the name refers to the skin, or dermis. The former part comes

23–1   Starfish   23–2   Sea Cucumber   23–3   Sea Urchin

from the Greek word *echinos,* meaning hedgehog, an animal about the size of a mole that has sharp spines like the porcupine. This spiny characteristic is better seen in the sea urchin than in the starfish.

Preserved or dried specimens of starfish give a false idea of their color. On the sea bottom or in tidal pools, starfish are variously colored. Some are a brilliant orange, some are purple, and some are pink.

Starfish walk on their rays in search of food. Embedded in the soft flesh are the skeletal plates made of a chalky material. The plates, which give the body form, project as spines and give the skin a rough appearance. Around the spines on the surface of the skin are tiny *skin gills,* hollow tubes used for breathing, and small pincers, which can be seen only with a hand lens. The pincers are used to prevent small organisms from collecting on the skin and to protect the skin gills.

Several openings can be identified on the dorsal surface. One is the *anus,* a tiny opening in the center of the body through which undigested food is eliminated. The other is a more prominent structure, the *sieve plate.* The sieve plate, which is a short distance from the center, draws water into the water vascular system. This system is responsible for the unique method of movement used by starfish.

The mouth is on the ventral surface and leads into the stomach. Radiating from the mouth are five grooves, each running along the entire length of a ray. Along the side of each groove are several rows of *tube feet* tipped with suckers. The hundreds of tube feet enable the starfish to walk on its rays at about six inches per minute.

The starfish has no well-developed sense organs. The tube feet probably serve as organs of touch. Also, at the end of each ray there is a small light-sensitive *eyespot.* The eyespots detect changing environmental conditions.

WATER VASCULAR SYSTEM. An unusual feature of the echinoderm is the canal system used to operate the tube feet. We have already mentioned the sieve plate, which admits water into the system. From the sieve plate, a central circular canal sends branches to each ray. These radial canals supply water to all the tube feet along the ventral groove of each ray. Forcing water into the tube foot causes it to expand and press the sucker against the surface on which the starfish is attached. The attachment and release of hundreds of tube feet provides the means for "walking."

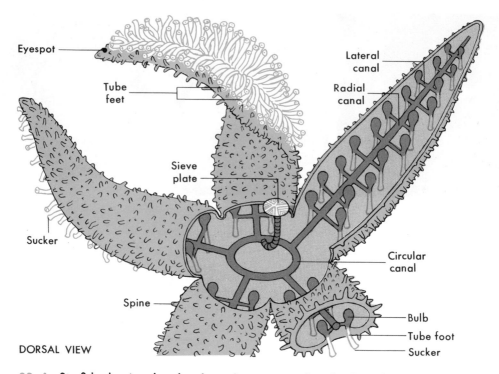

Eyespot

Tube
feet

Sieve
plate

Sucker

Spine

Lateral
canal

Radial
canal

Circular
canal

Bulb

Tube foot

Sucker

DORSAL VIEW

23–4 Starfish, showing dorsal surface of one arm, underside of another arm, and water vascular system in third arm. Two arms of the starfish have been removed.

FEEDING AND DIGESTION. Tube feet are also extremely important in feeding. Oysters and clams are the favorite food of starfish. As you probably know, oyster and clam shells are very hard to pry apart. Arching its rays about the clam, the starfish attaches its tube feet to the shell and begins to pull. If a continuous pull can be exerted long enough to cause the clam's muscles to become tired, its two half shells are drawn apart. The starfish then turns its stomach inside out and extends it into the clam. The starfish eats only the soft part of the clam, leaving the empty shells. When the clam has been digested, the starfish returns its stomach to the inside of its body. Some starfish are able to eat as many as ten clams or oysters in a single day.

Part of the reason for their huge appetite may be the presence of very large digestive glands in each ray. Large amounts of enzymes are secreted by these glands, which are connected directly to the stomach.

REGENERATION. Like many of the invertebrates we have studied, the starfish has amazing powers of regeneration. A ray that is torn off is easily replaced. A single ray with part of the central disc attached will grow four new rays, thus completing the animal.

Ordinarily, you would think that cutting a starfish into several pieces would kill it. This is what oystermen used to do when they discovered them in oyster beds. We know now that this only served to increase their number. Today, a different technique is used. Large mops of rope are dragged along the ocean bottom. The starfish attach themselves to the mops and are hauled in. Once ashore, they are removed from the mops and destroyed. In some regions oyster beds are treated with lime. This kills the starfish, but does not harm the oysters.

REPRODUCTION. Unlike the earthworm, which is hermaphroditic, the sexes of starfish are separate. The ovaries or testes that produce the eggs and sperm cells are paired, branching organs found in each ray near the base. Tremendous numbers of the gametes are shed into the sea water where fertilization takes place. An adult female may release over two million eggs in a two-hour period, and as many as 200 million in a single season!

The starfish has long been a favorite animal for *embryologists.* An embryologist specializes in the study of how an egg, after fertilization, develops into the immature animal, or embryo. Starfish egg and sperm cells are easily obtained and illustrate very clearly the early development of the fertilized egg. Many embryologists have spent a lifetime trying to learn what makes an egg develop into a certain form of animal, and are not yet certain. Much research is yet to be done in this field.

The beginning of the story of the embryo is fairly clear, however. The fertilized egg, or *zygote,* divides into two cells, then into four, and so on. After repeated divisions, a hollow ball of cells is formed, the *blastula.* Gradually, one side of the blastula grows inward and forms two layers of cells. This two-layered structure is the *gastrula.* Further division of the cells, along with considerable molding and shaping, produces a larva that exhibits bilateral symmetry. Later, however, the larva changes its shape into the familiar radial pattern of the starfish.

Relatives of the Starfish

An animal built on the same general plan as the starfish is the serpent star. The rays

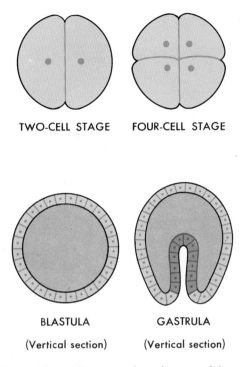

TWO-CELL STAGE   FOUR-CELL STAGE

BLASTULA   GASTRULA
(Vertical section)   (Vertical section)

23–5 These diagrams show how starfish zygote undergoes repeated cell divisions to form hollow blastula, which then invaginates to form two-layered gastrula.

of the serpent star are much more slender, giving it a snakelike appearance. The animal swims about by moving the rays in a writhing motion.

SEA URCHINS. The spiniest of all the echinoderms are sea urchins, sometimes referred to as "animated pin cushions." A *test,* or shell, surrounds the body with long spines protruding through it. In some species, the spines are an inch or more in length. Among the spines are still longer tube feet.

Although there are no rays, the body plan of the sea urchin is similar to that of the starfish. It crawls slowly on its ventral surface, mouth downward. Inside the mouth are five movable teeth. These teeth are controlled by a complicated part of their

23–6 Tests (dried shells) of sand dollars are often found without spines on beaches.

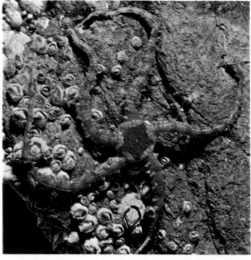

Walter Dawn

23–7 The arms of brittle stars will break off when the animal is grasped by an enemy.

muscular system. Sea urchins are scavengers living on organic material found in the mud and sand of the sea bottom.

The *sand dollar* is a close relative of the urchin that is flattened into a circular disk, resembling a large silver dollar. Its spines and tube feet are very short, giving it a furry appearance.

SEA CUCUMBERS. These fleshy, elongated relatives of starfish probably derive their name from their shape. The spiny plates found in other echinoderms are almost completely lacking. *Sea cucumbers* look very much like enormous fat worms. Along the side are five rows of tube feet. Around the mouth, the tube feet are modified to form tentacles that obtain food. In some species the tentacles are sticky and entangle small organisms that swim by.

The sea cucumber reacts in a curious way when disturbed. Some eject slime threads that entangle their enemies. Others can break their bodies in two by violent contraction. Others eject their internal organs, which later regenerate.

The sea cucumber is one of the echinoderms that is eaten by man. In parts of the Orient, the dried animal, called *trepang*, is used in soup.

The Clam: Phylum Mollusca

The single device that seems to have insured success in the fierce struggle for survival in the ancient seas was a hard, protective covering. The animals that could withdraw into the stony fortress of a shell enjoyed a tremendous advantage over those that could not. The waters of the earth were dominated for a time, some 400 million years ago, by giant relatives of the octopus and squid that were clad in shells. These ancient animals, called *nautiloids*, were sometimes 15 feet long. They are believed to be the largest invertebrates with shells that ever lived on earth.

Today, members of the phylum Mollusca do not all have a heavy coat of armor. Some have no external covering whatever. But the shell is so common a characteristic that most of them are referred to as shell-fish. The clam, the oyster, and the snail all have shells. The squid has a shell, too, but it is small and internal. The slug, a relative of the snail, gets along well without any shell. Another characteristic of the mollusks is the very soft body. In fact, the Latin word *mollis*, from which mollusk is derived, means soft.

The organ systems of the mollusks are generally well developed. In some forms, like the octopus, the eyes indicate clearly how advanced the nervous system has become. The class to which this animal belongs is considered the highest of all the mollusks.

GENERAL BODY PLAN. In some ways the clam is a typical mollusk. Its soft body is encased in two shells, or valves, hinged at the top and joined together by two powerful muscles. The front one is called the anterior adductor; the hind one is the pos-

terior adductor. If you have ever gathered clams on the beach, you know just how strong these adductor muscles are. When disturbed, the clam pulls its valves together so tightly one can hardly insert a knife between them.

Within the shells a thin *mantle* envelops the entire body. The mantle forms the shell in somewhat the same way that the bone cells of our body form bone. The space between the two folds of the mantle inside the shells is the *mantle cavity*. On the midline of the cavity the *foot* is suspended. On either side of the foot are the *gills*. Immediately above the muscular foot is the softer part of the body that contains most of the organ systems.

MOVEMENT, RESPIRATION, AND FEEDING. The clam moves by extending its foot into the sand and then pulling itself forward. The clam uses the same technique to burrow into the muddy sea floor to escape its

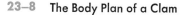

23–8 The Body Plan of a Clam

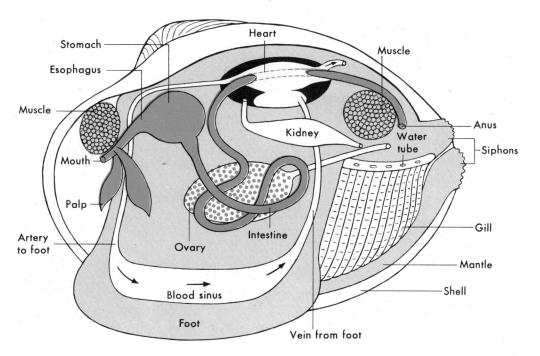

Stomach
Esophagus
Muscle
Mouth
Palp
Artery to foot
Ovary
Intestine
Blood sinus
Foot
Vein from foot
Heart
Muscle
Kidney
Water tube
Anus
Siphons
Gill
Mantle
Shell

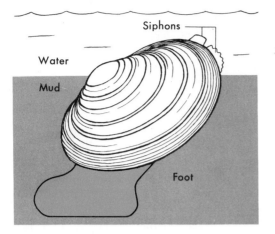

Water

Mud

Siphons

Foot

23-9 A clam burrows by extending a muscular foot. The foot tip swells, the muscles contract, and the clam is drawn downward.

enemies. The oyster, living under much the same conditions, cannot move at all.

Generally, the clam lies quietly on the ocean floor with its shell in a vertical position, partly covered by sand. The posterior end is held clear of the bottom to permit the entry and exit of water through the *siphons*. A continuous supply of water enters the ventral siphon, circulates through the mantle cavity, then passes out through the dorsal siphon. Some of the water enters the gills, which extract the oxygen the animal needs. Inside the gills, the water flows through a series of water tubes and is thus brought into close contact with the blood vessels. Oxygen dissolved in the water is absorbed by diffusion through the walls of the blood vessels. Carbon dioxide diffuses out of the blood into the water that finally leaves the body.

The water also supplies food. In the water are tiny algae, protozoa, and other food materials. Two tiny flaps, the *palps*,

23-10   LIFE CYCLE OF A FRESH-WATER CLAM

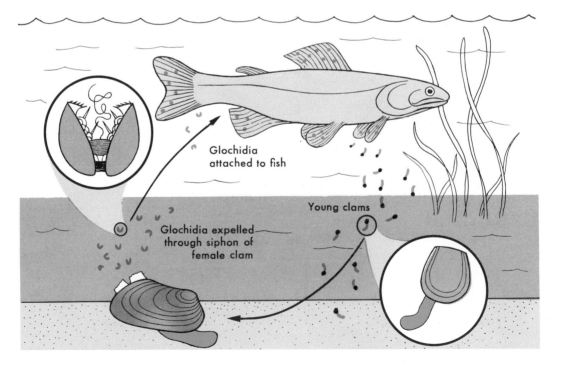

Glochidia attached to fish

Glochidia expelled through siphon of female clam

Young clams

direct food particles to the mouth. Much of the food material has been previously caught on the slimy surface of the gills and is directed toward the palps by the action of cilia. Digestion of the food occurs in the stomach and the long, coiled intestine. Undigested food is eliminated through the anus, which empties into the dorsal siphon.

BLOOD AND CIRCULATION. The clam's blood is not red. In fact, most of the invertebrates do not have red coloring material in their blood. The earthworm is an exception.

The clam's circulatory system consists of a tubular heart located high in the dorsal part of the body. It is interesting that the heart pumps the blood forward and backward at the same time. Arteries carry the blood to all parts of the body. In many places the blood flows into large blood sinuses, then is returned to the heart by veins.

As the blood passes to the various parts of the body it does many things. It receives oxygen from and gives off carbon dioxide to the gills. It also carries liquid wastes from the cells to the kidneys, a pair of small organs near the heart. The blood also makes locomotion possible by filling the large blood sinus in the foot.

REPRODUCTION. Like most water animals, the clam releases its sperm cells into the water where they can swim to the eggs. The sperm enter the siphon of the female and fertilize the eggs in the mantle cavity.

In some of the fresh-water clams an interesting larval form develops. After developing among the gills of the female, the lavae are expelled into the water, usually in the spring. At this time they become parasitic upon fish, attaching themselves to the gills and skin. The tissue of the fish grows around and protects them. At this stage they are called "blackheads." Meanwhile, the fish may swim many miles from the original beds where the young clams became attached to it. The effect, then, is to scatter the clams very widely. After a period of several weeks, the young clam releases itself from the fish, drops to the bottom, and grows into an adult.

SHELLS AND PEARLS. The mollusk shell, which is secreted by the mantle, consists of three distinct layers: (1) an outer horny, thin layer, (2) a thicker middle section made of calcium carbonate, and (3) an inner pearly layer. The inner layer, which has a shiny, colored surface, is used to make beautiful ornaments. Part of the fascination of collecting shells is to discover the variety of their form and color.

Occasionally, a foreign particle, perhaps a grain of sand or a tiny parasite, becomes lodged between the shell's mantle and pearly layer. The irritating particle stimulates the mantle to form a protective covering about it. After several years, the particle is covered and a pearl is formed.

The value of the pearl depends upon its size, luster, and shape. Many pearls found

23–11 **Stages in the Formation of a Pearl**

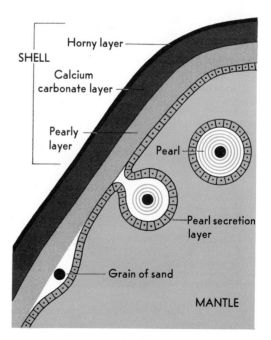

23–12 The variety of shell types found along the seashore are all composed of calcium carbonate secreted by the mantles of mollusks.

in mollusks are of little value since they are irregular. Most of the pearls of gem quality are produced by the pearl oysters in the Indian Ocean and in the waters off the coast of Japan. Pearl divers may open as many as a thousand oysters before finding a pearl of value. The ordinary oysters and clams of the coastal bays of the United States rarely produce pearls of any value. There are exceptions, however. One pearl produced by a fresh-water clam is said to have sold for $10,000.

Relatives of the Clam

Zoologists usually subdivide the mollusks into six classes. The more familiar forms are found in only three of them. The oysters, clams, mussels, and scallops are all covered by two shells and have a muscular foot shaped like a hatchet. The scientific name of this class is *Pelecypoda,* but they are more commonly called bivalves.

The snails and their relatives have only one shell, or none at all. They belong to the class *Gastropoda,* but their common name is univalve. The octopus, squid, and nautilus, which have tentacles or arms growing from the head region, belong to the class *Cephalopoda.*

SNAILS. One reason why the clams and oysters are not truly representative of the mollusks is that they do not have a clearly defined head region. The snail's head is identified by the tentacles and the mouth. Because of the large number of species of snails and their body plan, these mollusks are more typical of the phylum than either of the other classes.

The large foot extends out of the single-coiled shell. At the anterior end are the tentacles. On the tip of each tentacle is an eye, guiding the animal's forward movement. The mouth, on the ventral surface, is equipped with a row of horny teeth, the *radula,* used to scrape and tear food.

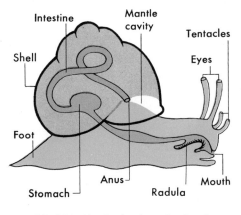

23-13   The Body Plan of a Snail

Aquatic snails breathe by means of gills, just like the clam. Land snails, however, take air into the mantle cavity, which then acts like a lung. To prevent their soft, moist bodies from drying, land snails retire into their shells and secrete a leathery door across the opening during a very dry season. The garden slug, a snail that has no shell at all, solves the problem of drying out by remaining under moist rocks.

The snail has a curious way of moving. By a wavelike motion of its foot, it glides over a path of mucus or slime that is laid down immediately ahead of it by a *slime gland.* In a sense, it builds a road directly ahead of itself. Its progress is slow—about two inches per minute.

THE SQUID. If you blow up a toy balloon and release it, it flies in a direction opposite to that of the escaping air. The balloon moves by jet propulsion. The squid and the octopus swim by the same principle. By forcing a jet of water out of its *funnel,* a structure located near the head, the squid swims with speed and agility. Since the funnel can be turned in different directions, the squid can swim in any direction. It moves backward to escape its enemies and forward to seize its prey.

The squid and octopus are "headfooted"

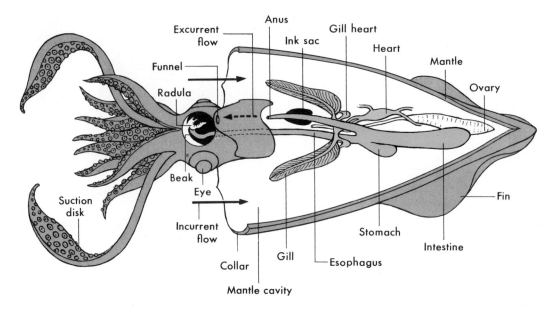

23–14 Longitudinal section of a common squid, showing organs in the mantle cavity. In many respects, the squid is more advanced than other mollusks. The sensory organs include two highly developed eyes capable of forming a distinct image.

mollusks. They belong to the class Cephalopoda, a group in which the foot and head region are together. Zoologists consider them the most highly developed of the mollusks, for they are extremely active and have highly specialized organ systems. All of them are characterized by arms in the head region. Most of the cephalopods are rather small. But the giant squids are known to reach a length of 50 feet and weigh up to two tons.

The head-foot of the squid is divided into ten arms, two of which are considerably longer than the others. The arms surround the mouth and grasp the food and force it into this opening. A sharp, horny beak tears the food so that it can be eaten more easily. Hundreds of round suction discs cover the arms enabling the squid to keep a firm hold upon its prey. The discs of the giant squid may be as large as coffee cups.

Few cephalopods have external shells. The outside of the body is protected by the hardened, muscular mantle. The end farthest from the mouth is flattened into fins which guide it in swimming. In the squid, the shell is reduced to an internal plate, called the *pen*. The forward edge of the mantle is separated from the head and fits around it, like a collar. Water enters the mantle cavity when the collar is loose. When the collar is tightened water is forced out of the funnel in a swift jet.

The squid, which leads the active life of the hunter, has a well-developed circulatory system. The heart pumps faster than in the sluggish clam. Another feature of the circulatory system is the presence of two *gill hearts* that pump the blood to the gills. This makes possible a higher rate of respiration than that in less active animals.

The nervous system of an active animal must be efficient. The eyes of the squid are not simple, light-sensitive organs like those in most other invertebrates. The eyes are complex "camera eyes" that form clear images in the same way as do the eyes of vertebrates.

The squid has several interesting ways of defending itself. Its skin contains numerous pigment cells of different colors: yellow, violet, and brown. The squid can control and mix the colors at will. This changes the color of the skin so that it blends into its background and "disappears." The squid confuses its enemies in another way. When attacked, it discharges an inky fluid from the funnel. The inky cloud serves as a "smoke screen" that permits the squid to escape. In Europe and Asia, where the squid is eaten, it is sometimes referred to as the "inkfish." The ink from the cuttlefish, a cousin of the squid, is a valuable artist's water color called sepia.

THE OCTOPUS. The common octopus is a small animal that lives among the rocks and tidal pools of the seacoast. It feeds upon clams, scallops, and small crabs. A large species feared by pearl divers is the giant octopus of the Pacific, reported to have a tentacle spread of 30 feet.

The female octopus has eight arms of equal length. The male uses a specialized arm, which may break off, to transfer sperm to the female during mating. The octopus has no internal skeleton like the pen of the squid. A horny case protects the

Walter Dawn

23–15 The Octopus. Large specimens are often dangerous to unwary divers.

brain, which lies just between the large eyes.

Like the squid, the octopus can defend itself by protective color changes and by squirting ink into the water. Experiments in a California marine laboratory showed that the ink of the octopus has an additional role. A moray eel, the major enemy of the octopus, required two hours to regain its sense of smell after it had been disabled by a blast of octopus ink.

IMPORTANT POINTS

• The echinoderms and mollusks mark two divergent paths along which animal life developed. The echinoderms are believed to be the forerunners of the vertebrates. The mollusks are related to the segmented worms and lead to the highest forms of invertebrates.

• Echinoderms are marine animals that exhibit radial symmetry as adults, but bilateral symmetry in the larval form. They include the starfish, the sea urchin, and the sea cucumber. All have tube feet controlled by a water vascular system. The tube feet are used for locomotion and as an aid in feeding. Echinoderms have separate sexes and most species have great powers of regeneration.

• Starfish are a serious pest, destroying millions of clams and oysters each year. To control their numbers, starfish are periodically caught and destroyed.

• Mollusks are more widely distributed than the echinoderms. They live in the sea, in fresh water, and on land. The foot, mantle, and the mantle cavity are typical structures in most forms. Many, like the clam and oyster, are sluggish. Others, like the squid and octopus, are active. Land snails and slugs must avoid drying in order to survive. Snails secrete a leathery flap across the shell opening.

• Most mollusks are used for food the world over. Man has found additional uses for the shells, as buttons and ornaments.

REVIEW QUESTIONS

1. How do echinoderms differ from other invertebrates?
2. How do the tube feet of the starfish enable it to "walk"?
3. Locate the sieve plate on the starfish and describe its function.
4. Why is the starfish considered a pest? How can it be controlled?
5. How do starfish regenerate?
6. What is the function of the mantle in the clam?
7. How does a clam move? obtain its food?
8. Describe the circulation of blood in the clam.
9. Describe several differences between the octopus and the squid.
10. What is the function of the inky discharge of the squid and octopus?

CHECK YOUR UNDERSTANDING

11. How does a starfish eat a clam?
12. Why are snails considered to be more representative of the phylum Mollusca than clams?
13. Describe locomotion in the snail.
14. Name two characteristics of the squid that enable it to be a hunter.
15. Why are cephalopods the most highly developed of mollusks?
16. Why do scientists know more about fossil mollusks than fossil worms?
17. Why are slugs and land snails usually more active at night than during the day?
18. Why do biologists study starfish embryology so intensely?
19. Much of Charles Darwin's theoretical work was based on studies of the numerous structural relationships that exist among all living things. An animal structure he was least able to explain was the eye of the squid. Why was this so?

RESEARCH PROJECTS AND REPORTS

1. Obtain information from your school or public library and prepare a report on one of the following topics:

Oyster Industry	**Pearls and Pearl Diving**
The Giant Squid	**The Sea Cucumber**

2. *Collecting and Observing Snails:* Snails may be collected on land and under water. Land snails are often attached to stones and logs, or they may be found in leaf mold on the ground. Aquatic snails attach themselves to rocks, sticks, or the stems of plants growing in ponds or streams.

Collected snails should be placed in jars with secure lids. Include some of the leaf mold or water from the place where they were found. Do not leave lids on jars longer than necessary. Do not stand jars in the sun.

Land snails may be kept alive in dampened leaf mold or in your school terrarium. If kept elsewhere, they may be fed on lettuce leaves. Aquatic snails should be placed in an aquarium. This affords an excellent place for you to observe them. As they glide over the glass, notice the wavelike movements of the foot. Notice the action of the mouth in keeping the glass clean. Which structure scrapes the algae from the glass?

3. *Shell Collecting:* If you live near the seashore, or go there for a vacation, you might want to make a shell collection. Many shells picked off the ocean floor at low tide are beautiful objects. You might want to arrange your shells (by gluing them to poster board) by color, size, or type. Often, shells of the same species of mollusks may be found in different sizes representing different ages. Arranging them by size (age) will sometimes show gradations in color.

Try to identify as many species as possible. This can be done with the aid of a shell collector's guide. These specialized books may be found in your school or public library. Well-illustrated simplified manuals can be purchased in department stores and hobby shops.

FURTHER READING

"The Moment of Fertilization." Robert D. Allen. *Scientific American,* July, 1959, page 124. Discusses the behavior of the sea urchin egg at the precise moment the first sperm cell penetrates the egg cell membrane.

"The Teredo." Charles E. Lane. *Scientific American,* February, 1961, page 132. Known as the shipworm, the Teredo is a mollusk that burrows in submerged wood, weakening it in the tunneling process.

"The Buoyancy of Marine Animals." Eric Denton. *Scientific American,* July, 1960, page 119. The cuttlebone of the cuttlefish acts much like the ballast tanks on a submarine, raising and lowering the animal in the water.

Sea Shells of the World. R. Tucker Abbott. A Golden Nature Guide, Golden Press, New York, N.Y. A guide for identifying better-known species of shells. Fully illustrated in natural color.

"Learning in the Octopus." Brian R. Boycott. *Scientific American,* March, 1965, page 42. Both man and the octopus appear to have short and long term memory systems.

CHAPTER

24

Animals with Jointed Legs

BIOLOGISTS KNOW that about 500 million years ago great changes occurred in the seas. At that time the warm seas swarmed with life, but the land was barren. Little is known of animal life before this time. The earlier animals had soft bodies and left few fossils. About 500 million years ago, however, hard-shelled animals appeared in the seas. These left fossil records in the ocean bottoms. Snails and other mollusks, spiny-skinned creatures resembling the starfish, tiny lampshells, all flourished in the warm seas, then perished, leaving their impressions in the rocks.

Among the animals in the tidal pools of a younger planet were the armored *trilobites,* which in some ways resembled the lobster. Most were only three inches long, but some measured a foot or more. Many shrimplike forms appeared as the first animals with jointed legs. All of them belong to Phylum Arthropoda, the most successful of all the invertebrates. The term *arthropoda* means jointed legs.

Although fossil records are incomplete, it is probable that ancient marine arthropods were the ancestors of the first land invertebrates. Just how this change from sea to land was made we do not know. But when the barren land became populated with primitive plants, animals became adapted to living there.

THE TEEMING WORLD OF LIFE. From the standpoint of numbers of species, the arthropods are by far the most successful animals in the world today. About 800,000 species are known. More are being discovered each year. The number of individuals in each species is very large.

No other phylum of animals has a wider distribution. Arthropods have been found in the upper levels of the highest mountains and in the lowest depths of the sea. Some live in fresh water lakes and streams. Others swarm over the land, and many are experts at flying. Many familiar animals, such as the crab, the spider, the grasshopper, the centipede, and the butterfly, belong to the arthropod group.

The Arthropod Body Plan

Why are these animals so successful? Perhaps we can discover some of the reasons in their structural organization. The body plan of all arthropods exhibits three important characteristics: *an external skeleton, jointed appendages,* and *segmented bodies.*

24–1 Fossil trilobite, a common marine animal that lived 500 million years ago.

EXTERNAL SKELETON. Like the very successful mollusks, the arthropods have an external body covering. In arthropods, however, the body covering, or *exoskeleton,* has the advantage of being jointed. The principal material found in the exoskeleton is *chitin* (KITE-en), a horny, flexible compound. Because chitin is insoluble in most common liquids, it provides a very effective covering. Where the skeleton is especially hard, it is usually found to contain calcium carbonate in addition to the chitin.

JOINTED APPENDAGES. The legs of such arthropods as insects, crabs, and centipedes show this characteristic very clearly. Other appendages, like the mouth parts and the antennae, are also jointed. Segmentation is a characteristic of the higher forms of life.

SEGMENTED BODIES. Most arthropods have the body divided into three parts: *head, thorax,* and *abdomen.* In some arthropods, however, there may be a fusion of body sections. An important characteristic to note is the extent to which the head dominates the other parts of the body. Most of the sense organs are located on the head. This is a logical adaptation in an active animal because it is important that information about the surroundings be relayed quickly. Since danger may lurk ahead, the active animal requires sense organs at the anterior end of its body.

24–2 Arthropods make up the largest and most varied phylum of animals. All have segmented body, jointed external skeleton, and six or more paired, jointed appendages.

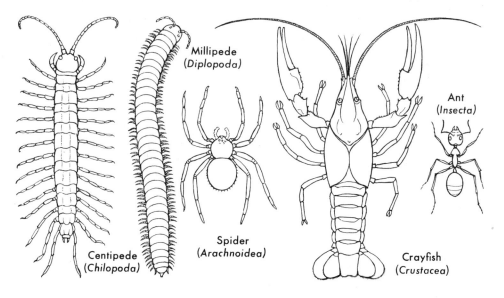

Millipede
(*Diplopoda*)

Ant
(*Insecta*)

Spider
(*Arachnoidea*)

Centipede
(*Chilopoda*)

Crayfish
(*Crustacea*)

EFFICIENT ORGAN SYSTEMS. The arthropod organ systems are among the most efficient in the entire animal kingdom. This makes it possible for them to be extremely active. Their digestive and respiratory systems release the energy that is required for an active life. Wastes and the by-products of metabolism are not allowed to accumulate, but are eliminated by the excretory system.

Centipedes and Millipedes

In the tropical forests of the West Indies and Central America lives an animal that resembles a caterpillar at first glance. You might also mistake it for a common earthworm. Or you might even think it is a centipede. Actually, it is none of these, but seems to be related to all of the animals mentioned.

Peripatus is such an interesting zoological puzzle that biologists do not quite know how it should be classified. It has some of the characteristics of the segmented worms, but it also exhibits some of the features of the arthropods. For many years Peripatus was thought to be a missing link between these two phyla of animals and was classified by itself in the separate phylum *Onychophora*. When you compare its appearance with that of centipedes, you can see several reasons for believing it might be one of the primitive ancestors of the arthropods. Today, however, many biologists regard Peripatus as an arthropod that evolved very early from an annelid ancestor. Onycophora, therefore, has been dropped as a separate phylum and established instead as a class within the phylum Arthropoda.

24–3 What important structural differences indicate that Peripatus is not very closely related to millipedes or centipedes? In what ways are the two animals similar?

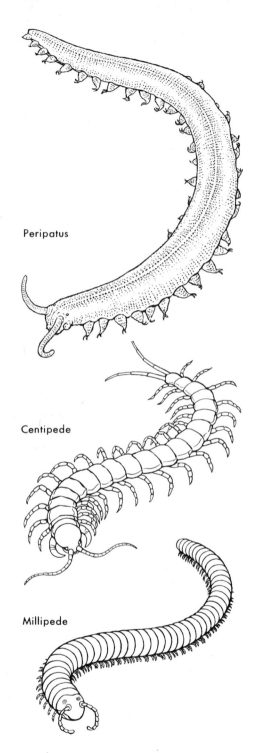

Peripatus

Centipede

Millipede

PHYLUM ARTHROPODA

Class	Characteristics	Examples
Onychophora	Wormlike body with weak segmentation. Two rows of clawed legs. One pair of thick antennae. Obtains oxygen through tracheae. Lives on land.	Peripatus
Chilopoda	Head and trunk of many segments. One pair of antennae. One pair of legs per segment. Obtains oxygen through tracheae. Lives on land.	Centipedes
Diplopoda	Body consists of head, thorax, and long abdomen. One pair of antennae. Two pairs of legs per segment. Obtains oxygen through tracheae. Lives on land.	Millipedes
Arachnida	Body consists of cephalothorax and abdomen. No antennae. Four pairs of legs. Obtains oxygen through tracheae, or book lungs. Lives on land.	Spiders, mites, scorpions, ticks
Merostomata	Body consists of cephalothorax and abdomen. No antennae. Cephalothorax and abdomen have six pairs of appendages each. Obtains oxygen through book gills. Lives in shallow coastal waters.	King crab
Crustacea	Body consists of cephalothorax and abdomen. Two pairs of antennae. One pair of legs per segment. Obtains oxygen through gills or body surface. Most live in water—a few live on land.	Crayfish, shrimp, lobster
Insecta	Body consists of head, thorax, and abdomen. One pair of antennae. Three pairs of legs and usually two pairs of wings. Obains oxygen through tracheae. Lives primarily on land.	Grasshopper, bee, ant, housefly

Centipedes. Centipedes have a rather flattened body with a pair of legs attached to each body segment. They are swift-moving animals and are frequently mistaken for insects.

Centipedes are hunters. Equipped with a pair of poison claws, they are able to paralyze their prey. The claws are hollow and connected to poison glands. Like most hunters, centipedes are active at night, seeking insects. In this respect they are beneficial to man.

Millipedes. Both the centipedes and millipedes resemble the segmented worms. In some ways the millipedes bear a closer resemblance to the worms. The body is rounded and appears to be built more on the tubular plan. The legs are generally short.

If we compare the legs of centipedes and millipedes, we discover outstanding differences. The body segments of centipedes have only one pair of legs, whereas each segment of the millipede has two pairs. Since the short legs of the millipede do not permit it to run swiftly, millipedes are defensive creatures. They have scent glands to protect themselves from their enemies. They secrete a fluid that is irritating to other animals that try to attack them.

Arachnids: Spiders and Scorpions

The numerous body segments of the many-legged arthropods do not appear in most other members of the phylum. The more advanced types reveal a body pattern in which many segments are joined together, or fused.

Spiders. The bodies of spiders exhibit far fewer segments than do the bodies of millipedes. The head and thorax of the *arachnids* are fused to form a single body region called the *cephalothorax* (sef-uh-loe-THOR-acks). Posterior to this is the abdomen, which is not segmented.

The distinguishing features of the spiders are their four pairs of walking legs, the small cephalothorax to which the legs are attached, and the large, rounded abdomen. In addition to the walking legs, spiders have another pair of appendages, the *pedipalps,* used as mouth parts and sensory organs. In the front of the mouth there is a pair of poison jaws. The bite of a spider can be irritating to man, but only the black widow spider is venomous enough to kill humans.

Black Widow Spider. The only spider in the United States venomous enough to fear is the black widow. The female is about one-half inch long and shiny black with a red hourglass marking on the ventral surface of the abdomen. The venom is strong enough to kill a person. In about one case in twenty death results from its bite. The victim usually has very severe pain and muscle spasms. Headache, dizziness, and nausea also result from the bite. Prompt medical treatment with an antivenin in-

24–4 The spider is an arachnid. What structural differences indicate that spiders are not closely related to insects?

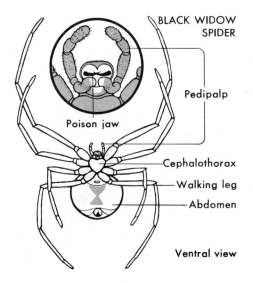

BLACK WIDOW SPIDER

Poison jaw

Pedipalp

Cephalothorax

Walking leg

Abdomen

Ventral view

24–5 Tarantula

creases the victim's chances of survival. Probably the best advice to give anyone about spiders is to avoid the small black varieties that resemble the black widow.

HUNTING SPIDERS. Not all of the spiders wait for their prey to come to them. Some of them are hunters. One of the best-known hunting spiders is the *tarantula,* a hairy giant of the spider world. Some tarantulas grow to the size of a man's hand. The trop-

24–6 Not all spiders make webs, but most have spinnerets to produce a fine thread.

ical species, called "banana spiders," sometimes enters a country on shiploads of bananas. Tropical tarantulas have been known to attack and kill small birds. Some tarantulas occur in the southwestern United States. They are not especially venomous.

SPIDER WEBS. One of the most interesting traits of many spiders is their ability to spin webs to catch their prey. Not all webs are alike. The web is characteristic of the kind of spider. Furthermore, the young spider spinning its web for the first time is not instructed in the way to do it. Somehow it manages to construct a web that is like the one its parents weave. Such behavior, apparently not learned, is called *instinctive* behavior.

The spider's silk is manufactured in silk glands located in the abdomen. The fluid silk is squeezed from the tip of the abdomen through three pairs of appendages called *spinnerets.* On each spinneret are large numbers of minute pores through which the fluid is passed. As the sticky material comes into contact with the air, it hardens into a fiber stronger than steel wire of the same diameter. Spider silk is 1/20th to 1/200th as thick as human hair. Because of its fineness and strength it is often used for cross hairs in optical instruments.

The construction of the web is interesting to observe. One kind of web begins with the formation of a horizontal bridge. From this a vertical line is suspended, much like a **T.** The center of the web is placed somewhere along the upright part of the **T,** and radial spokes are constructed from it to the outer edge. Then, beginning at the outside, the spider weaves the connecting strands that hold the spokes together.

When a fly is trapped in the web, its struggling apparently attracts the spider. Most spiders do not see very well. Their eyes are poorly developed. The buzzing of the fly's wings draws the spider near. The spider then encircles the victim with more threads or paralyzes it with its poisonous bite. One scientist reported that the vibrations of a tuning fork always attracted the spider's attention when the fork was held against the web.

SCORPIONS. These crablike animals have enlarged pedipalps on the end of which are pincers, or claws. At the tip of the narrow abdomen is a poison spine used to paralyze prey. Scorpions are found in the southwestern United States and in tropical areas farther south. A scorpion's sting is quite poisonous to man, although its effect is more severe in children than in adults.

Almost 350 million years ago giant water scorpions crawled along the muddy sea bottoms in search of their prey. A few were nine feet long. Most of them, however, were only several inches long.

THE HORSESHOE CRAB. If you have visited the eastern seacoast, you have probably seen a horseshoe crab washed up by the tide. It is called a horseshoe crab because of its shape. The horseshoe crab is sometimes classified as an arachnid, a relative of the spiders. Because of certain structural differences, however, many modern taxonomists assign the horseshoe crab to a separate class, *Merostomata*. They believe it to be a descendant of the same arthropod stock that produced the spiders and scorpions. To see it slowly plowing its way along the tidal sands is to be reminded of an armored tank. It uses the numerous pincers on its legs to seize sand worms.

Fossil ancestors of the horseshoe crab have been found that are millions of years old. When these are compared with present-day forms, it is remarkable how similar they are. Usually modern animals show considerable change from their primitive relatives. In this case, however, the horseshoe crab's heavy armor may have been so effective that it survived with very little change.

MITES AND TICKS. Mites and ticks are tiny, sometimes microscopic, relatives of the spiders. The body regions of mites and ticks are closely fused. They appear to be made of just one segment. Many are parasites upon plants and animals, feeding on plant juices or the blood or skin of animals.

Mites and ticks are known by various names: the feather mite, the red spider, the itch mite, the mange mite, the dog tick.

24–7 The horseshoe crab has flourished virtually unchanged for millions of years. What structural similarities indicate its relationship to spiders and scorpions?

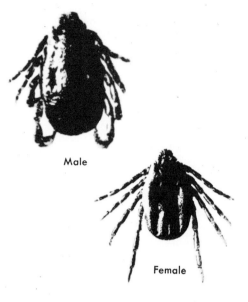

Male

Female

24–8 Texas Cattle Fever Ticks

One tick is the carrier of Rocky Mountain spotted fever, a disease that is often fatal to man.

Crustaceans: The Crayfish

The freshwater crayfish is a *crustacean* that is common in streams and ponds in the United States. Its large salt-water cousin, the lobster, is probably better known because it is so widely used as a sea food. Structurally, the crayfish and the lobster differ only in minor details. Both show the arthropod characteristics clearly.

EXTERNAL CHARACTERISTICS. The exoskeleton is thick and hard. The legs are clearly jointed. The body consists of two regions, the cephalothorax and the abdomen. The organ systems are well developed.

24–9 Body Plan and Internal Parts of Crayfish

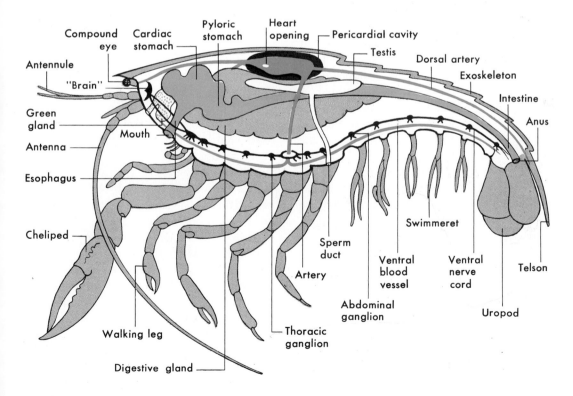

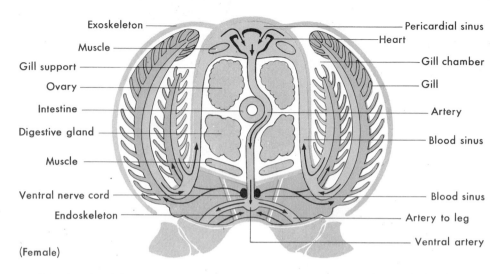

Exoskeleton — Pericardial sinus
Muscle — Heart
Gill support — Gill chamber
Ovary — Gill
Intestine — Artery
Digestive gland — Blood sinus
Muscle — Blood sinus
Ventral nerve cord — Artery to leg
Endoskeleton — Ventral artery
(Female)

24–10 Crayfish Cross Section, Showing the Arrangement of Gills in Gill Chamber

Attached to the cephalothorax are five pairs of prominent walking legs. The first pair is much larger than the others and bears stout claws. These are the *chelipeds* (KEE-luh-pedz), or claw feet. The second and third pairs have smaller claws. The fourth and fifth pairs have small spines at their tips.

The principal sense organs are located at the extreme anterior end of the animal. A pair of long *antennae* and a pair of short *antennules* extend the sense of touch and taste ahead of the crayfish, somewhat like a blind man using a cane to touch objects ahead of him. At the base of the antennae are the stalked *compound eyes*.

On the ventral surface not far from the extreme anterior is the mouth. It is surrounded by the mouth parts and is not easily located. A sturdy pair of *mandibles*, which resemble tiny teeth, are on the midline of the body. Two pairs of small finger-like projections, the *maxillae*, are on either side of the mandibles. The maxillae are continually beating. Slightly behind them are three pairs of larger appendages used in handling food. They resemble small fingers

and are used in much the same way. These *maxillipeds* also taste the food the animal eats.

The abdomen of the crayfish consists of six distinct segments and a terminal section called the *telson*. On the ventral surface of each segment is a pair of *swimmerets*. The first and second pairs of male swimmerets are much enlarged and are used for the transfer of sperm to the female. The same swimmerets on the female are much reduced in size. The swimmerets on the third, fourth, and fifth segments of the female are used for the attachment and development of eggs. The sixth pair of swimmerets is modified into broad plates or *uropods*, which, with the telson, form the main swimming organ. If you have ever tried to catch crayfish, you know that they swim backward very swiftly. This is accomplished by elevating the tail and quickly jerking it down under the abdomen. The resulting backward motion and the cloud of mud that is stirred up make the crayfish hard to capture.

GETTING AND USING FOOD. Crayfish feed on snails, small fish, tadpoles, plants, and decaying organic materials. The food is generally seized by the chelipeds and passed on to the mouth parts. The maxillipeds and maxillae then serve as fingers, holding the larger pieces of food until the mandibles tear them into small portions, which are then passed into the mouth.

From the mouth the food moves along a short esophagus into the stomach. Actually, the crayfish has two parts to its stomach. The first part, the *cardiac* stomach, is used mainly for storing and grinding food. In this part of the stomach is the *gastric mill*, a set of ridges that act as teeth. The larger, hard particles of food that cannot be ground smaller are ejected through the mouth. The finer particles are passed into the smaller *pyloric* stomach. A pair of large digestive glands just beneath the stomach secretes digestive enzymes. Although some digestion occurs in the stomach, much of it occurs in the glands themselves. Digested food is also absorbed there. The straight intestine serves mainly to collect undigested food for elimination through the anus, an opening found on the telson.

RESPIRATION. The crayfish obtains a continuous supply of oxygen from the water in which it lives. Special structures, the gills, are located in gill chambers lying just above the walking legs on each side of the cephalothorax.

Careful dissection of the exoskeleton exposes the gills to view. They look very much like wet feathers and are seen to be attached to the base of the legs. The movement of the animal, as well as the constant motion of the maxillae, creates currents of water that bathe the gills continuously. As the water passes over the gills, oxygen diffuses from it through these delicate structures into the blood.

CIRCULATION. If you have examined the gills of a fish, you know that they are bright red. The gills of a crayfish are not red because its blood is not red. Crayfish are real blue-bloods. Their blood contains *hemocyanin*, a pigment that gives the blood a blue-green color. This pigment carries oxygen from the gills to all parts of the body.

The heart is in the dorsal part of the body cavity near the hind portion of the cephalothorax. The chamber surrounding it, the *pericardial cavity*, is filled with blood. Arteries conduct the blood to the entire body. Instead of being returned to the heart by veins, the blood passes from the arteries into an elaborate system of *sinuses*. These

24–11 Diagram of Blood Flow in Crayfish. Blood from the pericardial cavity enters the heart through valvular openings, is pumped through arteries into open body sinuses, which drain into gills. From the gills the blood returns to the pericardial cavity.

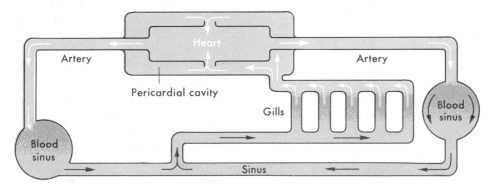

are large open spaces in the tissues. A system of valves in the arteries prevents the blood from flowing backward. All of the blood reaches the gills before being returned to the pericardial cavity where it is again pumped through the arteries by the heart.

In its circuit of the body the blood goes to the *green glands.* These are organs of excretion located in front of the esophagus at the base of the antennae. They perform a function similar to that of our kidneys, eliminating nitrogenous wastes and regulating the water content of the body.

REPRODUCTION AND GROWTH. There are distinct sexual characteristics in the male and female crayfish. The male's first two pairs of swimmerets are different from the first two pairs of the female. A seminal receptacle is located between the fourth and fifth walking legs of the female.

During copulation the male transfers the sperm cells to the seminal receptacle by

24–12 Crayfish eggs hatch on swimmerets, where the young remain for a month.

means of the modified swimmerets. Later when the female releases her eggs, the sperm cells fertilize them. This usually occurs several weeks after copulation. The fertilized eggs are attached to the female's swimmerets where the early development of the eggs occurs.

After several weeks the young larvae hatch and cling to the swimmerets where they continue their development. Periodically, they shed their exoskeleton, a process known as ***molting.*** This is necessary since the body is growing inside the covering and needs room to expand. The tiny crayfish cling to the female for several months until they become self sufficient.

Because they are encased in an exoskeleton, arthropods cannot grow without molting. Molting is more common, therefore, in the young than in the adults. You probably have heard of soft shell, or shedder crabs. These are crabs that have molted and have not yet grown a hard shell. It usually takes several days before the new exoskeleton becomes as hard as the old one. During this molting period, arthropods are practically defenseless and usually hide to escape their enemies.

SENSE ORGANS AND COORDINATION. The crayfish has sense organs that keep it well informed about its surroundings. Scattered all over the body are sensitive *setae,* tiny bristles that project through the exoskeleton and respond to touch. The animal can taste and smell with its mouth parts and antennules. At the base of the antennae are small sacs that serve as organs of balance.

The most highly specialized sense organs of the crayfish are the compound eyes, which are made of several thousand tiny units. In good light the units form a mosaic pattern, an image somewhat like that formed by making a picture out of separate tiles. The image formed, however, is not very sharp. Crayfish are nearsighted and do not see distant objects very well.

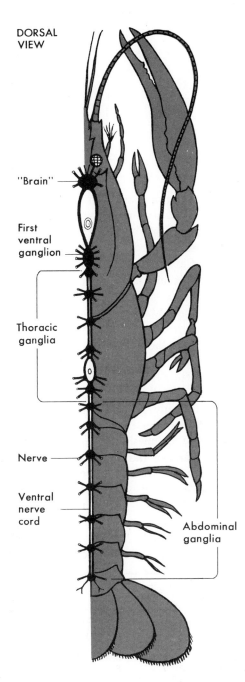

DORSAL
VIEW

"Brain"

First
ventral
ganglion

Thoracic
ganglia

Nerve

Ventral
nerve
cord

Abdominal
ganglia

24–13 Central nervous system of crayfish includes a large dorsal ganglion that forms a primitive "brain." The nerves then branch to the body from the brain and ventral nerve cord.

The nervous system is very similar in many ways to that of the segmented worms. Near the antennae is the "brain." Leading from it are two branches that encircle the esophagus and reunite beneath it as a large ganglion. The ventral nerve cord extends backward from this point as a double thread forming six ganglia in the thorax and six in the abdomen. Other smaller nerves branch from this central nervous system to many parts of the body. The coordination that this well-developed nervous system provides enables the crayfish to compete with other animals.

Other Crustaceans

Not all of the crustaceans are as large as the crayfish and lobster. Some are almost microscopic forms. Such are two animals that are very likely to turn up in a sample of pond water.

DAPHNIA AND CYCLOPS. *Daphnia* is sometimes called the "water flea," because it seems to hop about continuously. *Cyclops* is named after the mythical character with one eye because it has but one eye in the center of its head.

Emerging from the head of Daphnia are two large, multi-branched antennae. The swift movement of these appendages causes the "flea" to jerk its way about in the pond. The body is almost oval and transparent. The biologist can examine its inner workings as though it were made of glass. You can see its heart beating in ceaseless rhythm. You can even observe the movement of food along the digestive tract. Even its unborn young can be seen developing within the brood pouch.

Cyclops differs greatly from Daphnia in shape, its body being longer and tapered. It has two pairs of antennae. One pair is long and the other is considerably shorter. The females often carry a pair of egg sacs at the end of the abdomen.

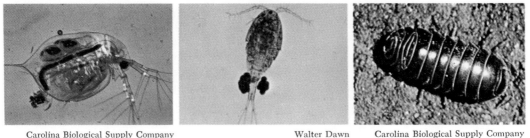

Carolina Biological Supply Company   Walter Dawn   Carolina Biological Supply Company

24–14 Daphnia   **24–15 Cyclops**   **24–16 Pill Bug**

Both of these crustaceans are common in fresh-water ponds. They also have many close relatives in the oceans. In both fresh and salt water these tiny crustaceans serve as food for small fish. They are thus an important link in the food chain that supports the higher forms of life. The floating collection of organisms that thrive in the surface waters is called *plankton*. Many of these organisms are microscopic, but the small crustaceans are an important part of the plankton community.

PILL BUGS. If you search diligently under rocks and rotting logs, you will probably turn up some pill bugs. These armored land-dwelling crustaceans curl up into a ball when disturbed. You will find these creatures only where it is quite damp, for they breathe by gills. Generally the body is oval and about one-half inch long. The exoskeleton is slate-grey in appearance. The pill bug is one of the few crustaceans that has adapted itself to living on the land.

EDIBLE CRUSTACEANS. Practically all of the larger crustaceans can be used as food by man, but only a few are actually eaten. Lobsters and crabs have been seafood delicacies for many years. Within the last twenty years, the shrimp has become the most important crustacean sold in the United States. Over 250 million pounds are marketed annually. The segmented abdomen is the only part of the shrimp that reaches your home. The anterior portion is chopped off before the animal is shipped. In many parts of the United States, where crayfish reach a good size, the anterior portion is also eaten.

IMPORTANT POINTS

- The animals with jointed legs and external skeleton, the arthropods, are the most numerous of all living creatures. Fossil remains of arthropods have been found that are over 500 million years old.

- At least one animal, Peripatus, resembles a connecting link between the segmented worms and the centipedes and millipedes.

- The spiders and their relatives—the scorpion, the mites and ticks—form one important class of this phylum, the arachnids. Arachnids are characterized by having four pairs of legs and only two body regions. Many of the spiders spin webs and have poison glands for paralyzing their prey. Most of them are not harmful to man.

- The crayfish is representative of the crustaceans, another large arthropod class. Its body is well protected by a thick exoskeleton. It is an extremely active animal with well-developed appendages, sense organs, and internal organ systems.

- Crustaceans are an important food for man. In the United States alone, millions of pounds of lobster, shrimp, and crab are consumed annually. In addition, the tiny crustaceans of the ponds, lakes, rivers, and oceans are a vital link in the food chain that supports animal life.

REVIEW QUESTIONS

1. List the three major characteristics of arthropods.
2. Where were trilobites found?
3. How are centipedes and millipedes different?
4. How many body segments do spiders have?
5. How does the young spider learn to spin a web?
6. How do the fossil ancestors of the horseshoe crab compare with present-day forms?
7. List three sense organs located on the head of the crayfish.
8. Why is molting necessary in animals with an exoskeleton?
9. What facts support the belief that the arthropods are the most successful animals in the world?
10. List five principal classes of the phylum Arthropoda and give one example of each.

CHECK YOUR UNDERSTANDING

11. What two reasons can you give for the success of centipedes as hunters?
12. How are the tarantula, the black widow spider, and the scorpion similar?
13. What characteristics of the crayfish illustrate the basic plan of all arthropods?
14. What are two functions of the digestive glands in the crayfish?
15. How is oxygen carried in the blood of the crayfish?
16. What evidence is there that the animals with exoskeletons had a tremendous advantage in the development of life on earth?
17. What arguments can you give to support the belief that the segmented worms and arthropods may be distantly related?
18. Why is instinctive behavior, such as spinning a web, difficult to explain?
19. In what ways does the crayfish show increased specialization of the nervous system?
20. Do you know of any crustacean that may have lived first in the water and then on land?

RESEARCH PROJECTS AND REPORTS

1. Obtain information from your school or public library and prepare a report on one of the following topics:

Scorpions	**The Black Widow Spider**
Spider Webs	**Shrimp Fishing**

2. *Collecting Arthropods:* Many of the arthropods are interesting animals to collect. Collection methods vary because some live in the water while others live on land. Many of the spiders are collected in the same way as insects, and we shall have more to say about that in the next chapter. Daphnia, which can be collected in ponds with a dip net, will live several days if kept in the original water.

3. *Egg Development of Cyclops:* If you discover a female Cyclops with egg sacs in a collection of pond water, isolate her in a separate container. With careful observation you should be able to see the development of the eggs.

4. *The Brine Shrimp:* You can observe the development of this interesting animal from its eggs. The dried eggs can be purchased at your tropical fish store or from a biological supply house. Make a solution of several tablespoons of salt in two quarts of water in a shallow agate pan or baking dish. Place about a hundred eggs in it and keep the solution at room temperature. Some of the eggs can be kept in a feeder ring to make them easily available for study. Within a day or two, move several to a slide ringed with vaseline and cover the preparation with a cover slip. You will then be able to observe the development of the egg without having it dry out.

FURTHER READING

Animals Without Backbones. Ralph Buchsbaum. University of Chicago Press, Chicago, Ill. Chapters 22 and 23 are beautifully illustrated accounts of the jointed-legged animals.

How To Know the Spiders. Benjamin J. Kaston and Elizabeth Kaston. William C. Brown Company, Publishers, Dubuque, Iowa. Almost three hundred American spiders may be identified by drawings and by the webs they construct.

"Spider Webs." Theodore H. Savory. *Scientific American,* April, 1960, page 114. Spiders lay out a drag line of silk behind them. Through the years of spider development, they have fashioned the drag line into many forms of webs.

"False Scorpions." Theodore H. Savory. *Scientific American,* March, 1966, page 95. Resembling tiny, tailless scorpions, there are some 2000 species of arachnids that have fascinating patterns of behavior.

CHAPTER

25

Insects
Foremost Invertebrates

Most of the invertebrates that we have studied so far live in the water. Insects, by far the largest group of animals, are land dwellers. They probably appeared on the land when it began to support the mosses, ferns, and flowering plants—perhaps some 350 million years ago. In the vast length of time since then, insects have developed adaptations for survival in a great variety of environments.

Insects outnumber all other forms of animal life. This single class of arthropods contains five times as many species as all the other animal phyla together. To say that man lives on a planet dominated by insects is not far from the truth.

Characteristics of Insects. Entomologists (biologists who specialize in the study of insects) regard insects as man's most serious competitor for food. Insects not only destroy crops, they also invade our homes as serious pests and spread disease. We are constantly seeking better means to control them.

Insects are an extremely varied class, but we can summarize their basic characteristics as follows:

1. Three body regions: head, thorax, and abdomen.
2. Three pairs of legs attached to the thorax.
3. Usually two pairs of wings attached to the thorax.
4. A single pair of antennae.
5. Usually a pair of compound eyes.
6. Breathe by spiracles (pores) and tracheae (air tubes).

The Grasshopper

Unlike the crayfish, which has a fused head-thorax, the grasshopper has a distinct head well protected by a heavy exoskeleton made of chitin. A pair of large compound eyes occupies much of the area along the dorsal and lateral surfaces. Between the eyes is a pair of antennae made of numerous segments, somewhat like a string of flattened beads. Slightly above each antenna and just between them are three simple eyes, or *ocelli*.

The grasshopper has mouth parts adapted for chewing grains and grasses. The jaws, or mandibles, look like two teeth. Un-

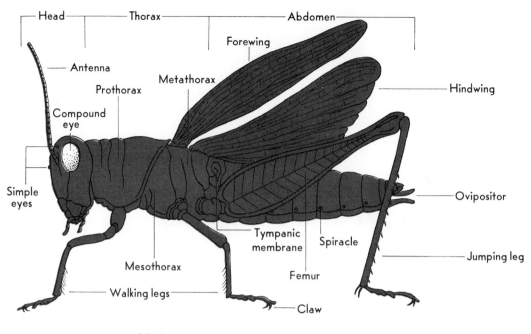

Head — Thorax — Abdomen
Forewing
Antenna
Metathorax
Prothorax
Compound
eye
Simple
eyes
Mesothorax
Walking legs
Tympanic
membrane
Spiracle
Femur
Claw
Hindwing
Ovipositor
Jumping leg

25–1   The Grasshopper—A Representative Insect

like our jaws, which work up and down, the jaws of a grasshopper work sidewise. Below the mandibles are the maxillae. The maxillae are smaller jaws that have a fingerlike *palp* attached to each of them. These smaller jaws assist in grinding the food. The palps are organs of taste. Covering these two pairs of jaws are an upper lip, the *labrum,* and a lower lip, the *labium.* The latter is flattened and acts something like a shovel, scooping food into the mouth. Like the maxillae, there are palps on each side of the labium.

THE THORAX: LEGS AND WINGS. The midsection of the grasshopper, as in all insects, is the thorax. It is clearly divided into three parts: the *prothorax,* the *mesothorax,* and the *metathorax.* The "collar" you probably have noticed on this insect is actually an extension of the prothorax that fits over the other two segments. One pair of legs is attached to each segment of the thorax. A pair of wings is attached to the mesothorax and to the metathorax.

Each of the legs consists of five segments. The first two pairs of legs are used for walking and for holding the insect securely upon the plants it eats. Hooks and spines on the legs assist them in the same way that spikes help a telephone man climb poles. The third pair of legs is quite different, being large and powerful and equipped with strong muscles. These jumping legs are so efficient that a grasshopper can jump 100 times its own length.

The two pairs of wings differ in structure and function. The forewings, leathery and rigid, are not used for flying, but serve as covers for the hindwings, which fold beneath them when the animal is at rest. The hindwings are thinner than the forewings and spread out like a fan for flying. Both pairs of wings are made of a thin *cuticle,* strengthened by a network of veins.

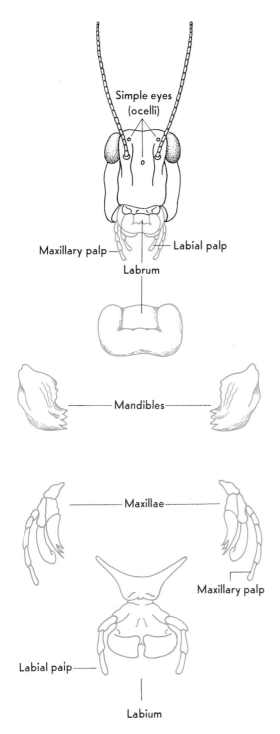

Simple eyes
(ocelli)

Maxillary palp —

Labrum

— Labial palp

— Mandibles —

— Maxillae —

Maxillary palp

Labial paip —

Labium

25–2 Front view of grasshopper's head. Separated mouth parts are enlarged.

THE ABDOMEN. The abdomen is the largest section of the insect's body. The abdomen of the female is especially large because she produces the eggs. Most of the eleven abdominal segments can be clearly seen. They are flexible in spite of their covering of chitin. The first segment contains the insect's ears, or tympanic membranes. The tympanic membranes are large, smooth areas just beneath the wings.

The extreme tip of the abdomen is somewhat more modified than the rest. The female has the last three segments shaped into a hard, egg-laying apparatus, the *ovipositor*. She uses its sharp points to dig holes in the soil in which to lay eggs. The tip of the abdomen of the male is rounded, not modified like the female's.

On each side of the first eight segments are the *spiracles*, or breathing pores. Two additional pairs of spiracles are found in the thorax. Microscopic valves in the mouth of the spiracle regulate the flow of air in and out. Closing the spiracles by any means causes the insect to suffocate.

DIGESTION AND EXCRETION. Have you ever noticed a child playfully command a grasshopper to "spit tobacco"? You may have been surprised that the insect did secrete a brown liquid. The child probably squeezed it so hard that some of its partly-digested food was forced out of its mouth. The "tobacco" is food and saliva that begins digestion through enzyme action.

After the food leaves the mouth it passes through the esophagus into a large storage compartment, the *crop*. Behind the crop is the muscular gizzard equipped with teeth that grind the food. When the food is sufficiently shredded, it is passed into the stomach. Six pairs of *gastric pouches* joined to the stomach secrete enzymes that continue to digest the food. There is no hard lining in the stomach such as is found in the crop and gizzard. Digested food can therefore be easily absorbed into the blood.

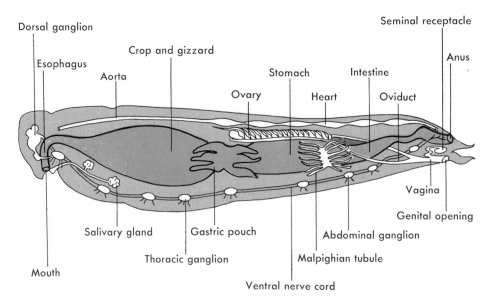

25–3 Internal Organs of Female Grasshopper

Undigested material is passed into the intestine to be given off as waste through the anus. Since the grasshopper seldom drinks water, most of the water in its food is absorbed into the blood through the walls of the intestine.

The excretory system is attached directly to the digestive tube. Located at the junc-

25–4 Respiratory System of Grasshopper

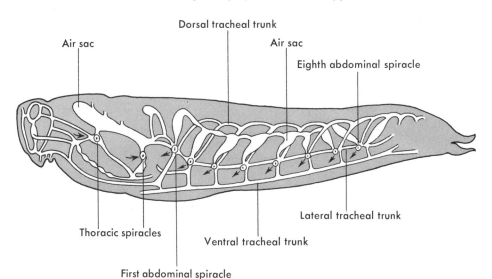

tion of the stomach and intestine are numerous threadlike structures called *Malpighian tubules.* Named after their discoverer, Marcello Malpighi, a famous Italian anatomist of the seventeenth century, these tubes are miniature kidneys. They hang in the body cavity and absorb nitrogen-containing wastes from the blood. The wastes are then concentrated and poured into the intestines to be passed out of the body with undigested food.

RESPIRATION. Insects are air breathers. Their respiratory system is adapted to make use of the oxygen in the atmosphere. The ability to obtain oxygen from the air is an important advance in animal development.

The breathing system of the grasshopper differs greatly from ours. The oxygen that enters our lungs is absorbed by the red cells of the blood and is circulated by them to all parts of the body. In the grasshopper, however, the oxygen is circulated throughout the body by a system of tubes, called *tracheae.* These are connected directly to the spiracles in the abdomen and thorax. The tracheae branch into still smaller tubes, the *tracheoles.* These in turn continue to form still smaller branches that are microscopic in width and lead directly to the cells.

In this type of system the blood plays no part at all in carrying oxygen. The tracheal network carries the oxygen to the cells and carries the carbon dioxide away. If you watch the abdomen of a living grasshopper, you will observe that it inflates and deflates as it breathes. Experiments have shown that the spiracles of the thorax inhale air while the spiracles of the abdomen let it escape.

CIRCULATION OF BLOOD. The blood of the grasshopper, which is colorless, contains dissolved food and a few amebalike cells. It is circulated by the pumping action of a heart located on the dorsal wall of the abdomen. Actually there is only one blood vessel in the entire body. The posterior region of this *dorsal blood vessel* is the heart we have just mentioned. The anterior part of the vessel is the *aorta.* Both ends of the vessel are open, and blood is pumped forward out the front.

From the anterior portion of the aorta the blood circulates into body spaces, bathing the internal organs. It then moves backward, finally entering small openings in the sides of the heart to be recirculated. This kind of system, in which there are no veins to return the blood to the heart, is called an open circulatory system. A closed circulatory system is one in which the blood is confined to tubes as it circuits the body. Circulation is faster in a closed system.

COORDINATION AND SENSE ORGANS. The grasshopper has a nervous system similar to that of the crayfish. The brain is located between the eyes and is similar to the other nerve clusters along the nerve cord. (See Figure 25–5 on the following page.) This is different from vertebrate animals where the brain is the largest mass of nerve tissue. Extending downward from the brain, the nerve cord loops around the esophagus and continues along the ventral surface of the body wall as a double thread. Along this ventral nerve cord are masses of nerve tissue called ganglia. The larger ganglia in the thorax control walking and flying.

Insects are capable of responding to a variety of stimuli. We have mentioned the palps as organs of taste. The paired *antennae* are organs of touch and smell. Tactile hairs scattered all over the body are also sensitive to touch. There are also sensitive ears and a pair of compound eyes.

The ears deserve special notice. The tympanic membranes are found on the first segment of the abdomen and are stretched drumtight over cuticle rings. They can respond to sounds too high-pitched for the human ear to perceive.

The compound eyes of insects are like those of the crayfish. The eye is like a win-

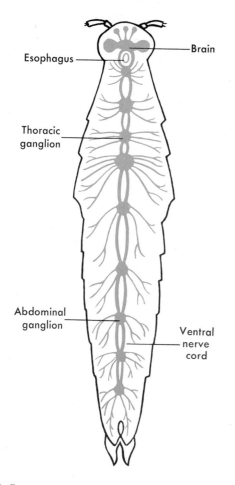

Esophagus — | — Brain

Thoracic ganglion

Abdominal ganglion

Ventral nerve cord

25-5 Nervous System of Grasshopper. A dorsal ganglion or "brain" and a chain of ganglia on the ventral nerve cord provide nerves to all parts of the insect's body.

dow made of hundreds of window panes. Each pane is six-sided and is capable of forming an image. Insects cannot focus upon near and distant objects. They are believed to be quite nearsighted. Objects at a distance become a faint blur. Some insects, like the horsefly and dragonfly, have compound eyes that cover much of the head and contain as many as 30,000 separate lenses. The simple eyes, the ocelli, are not believed capable of forming an image.

REPRODUCTION AND DEVELOPMENT. Male and female grasshoppers can be distinguished by the differences in the abdomen. The female is generally stouter. She also has a pointed egg-laying ovipositor at the tip of the abdomen. The male produces sperm cells in the paired testes. The genital openings at the tip of the abdomen release the eggs and sperm cells to the outside.

The production of eggs in grasshoppers has one unusual feature. The eggs are not fertilized until after a shell has formed around each one. The sperms fertilize the eggs by entering a special pore in the shell.

The female lays her eggs in the late summer or early autumn after she has mated with the male. At that time she stores sperm cells in a seminal receptacle. Here the sperm cells remain and are released to fertilize the eggs when they are laid. Several lots of eggs are laid at different times, about twenty in each lot. The female digs a hole in the ground with her sharp ovipositor and deposits the eggs there. The adults usually die several days after breeding.

If you have walked through the meadows in the spring, you may have seen the young grasshoppers, the *nymphs,* swarming in the fields ahead of you. They resemble the adult, but their body proportions are not the same. The head is especially large, and they are wingless. The nymphs are voracious feeders and grow quite rapidly. Periodically, like all arthropods, they molt to increase in size.

The Changing Lives of Insects

The development of the human infant into the fully grown adult is a gradual process. It is not marked by sharp changes from day to day. The development of many insects, however, is not gradual. In some species, sudden changes occur as they grow to be adults. Biologists use the term *metamorphosis* to describe the series of changes that oc-

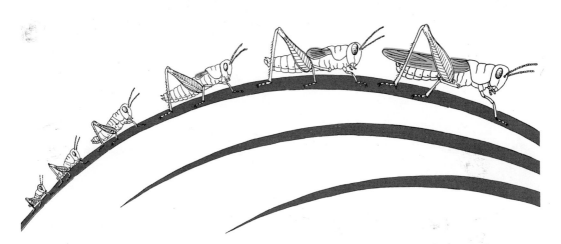

25–6 LIFE CYCLE OF GRASSHOPPER demonstrates incomplete metamorphosis. Eggs hatch into nymphs, which generally undergo five moltings before attaining adult size.

curs in animals. In the most primitive insects no metamorphosis occurs. The most highly developed forms undergo a complete metamorphosis. Between these two extremes are those insects that undergo a less dramatic change, which is called *incomplete metamorphosis.*

CICADAS. Many insects have a life cycle that is similar to that of a grasshopper. The egg hatches into a nymph that resembles the adult in most ways, but is not quite the same. Where the stages of growth are similar and the transitions abrupt, as in cicadas, dragonflies, and mayflies, the metamorphosis is called incomplete.

The cicada is a familiar insect whose buzz is often heard in the late summer. Its sound is produced by a pair of vibrating membranes operated by powerful muscles. The nymph is short and stout with powerful forelegs for burrowing in the ground where it spends most of its life. The exoskeleton of the nymph is often found in orchards in the late summer after the adults have emerged. The heavy, winged body of the "locust," as it is commonly called, is different from the nymph. The nymph of the "seventeen-year locust" spends from thirteen to seventeen years underground before emerging as an adult.

BUTTERFLIES AND MOTHS. Few changes in nature inspire as much wonder as the transformation of a caterpillar into a beautiful butterfly. The metamorphosis is complete. A complete metamorphosis consists of four distinct stages: *egg, larva, pupa,* and *adult.*

The adult female lays her eggs on plants that provide food for the developing young. The names of certain insects are taken from the food preference of the larva. Thus, the cabbage butterfly is so called because it lays eggs on cabbages.

The larva of the butterfly is commonly called a caterpillar. It resembles the segmented worms in some respects for its fat, round body consists of a head and thirteen segments. Three pairs of true legs are attached to the thorax. Five pairs of appendages that resemble legs, the *prolegs,* are found on the segments of the abdomen. The head has six simple eyes but no compound eyes. The mouth parts are adapted for chewing. Caterpillars are constantly eating, a fact that makes them serious plant

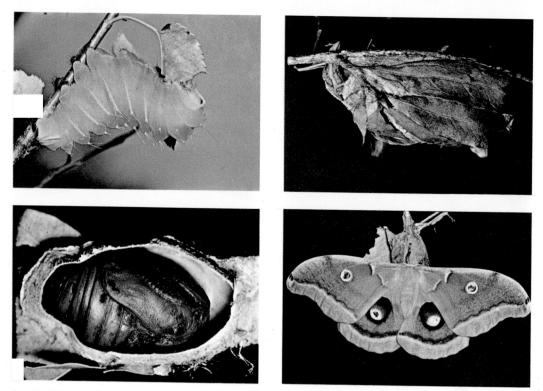

Carolina Biological Supply Company

25–7 Moth Metamorphosis. The caterpillar is the larval stage, feeding and growing the most rapidly. The pupal stage, encased within a cocoon, is the period of greatest transition. Note the developing antennae and wings on the exposed pupa (lower left). Last, the adult moth emerges. The female will lay eggs and the cycle will be completed.

25–8 Moths have fuzzy antennae and generally rest with their wings in horizontal position. Butterflies have thin antennae and generally rest with their wings folded back.

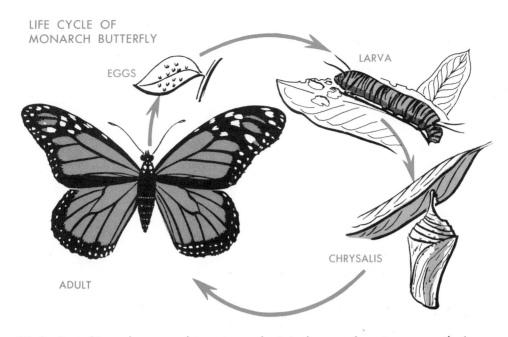

LIFE CYCLE OF
MONARCH BUTTERFLY

EGGS

LARVA

CHRYSALIS

ADULT

25–9 Butterflies undergo complete metamorphosis in the same four stages as moths (see Figure 25–7), except that butterflies pupate in a chrysalis rather than in a cocoon.

pests. Another important feature of the head is the *spinneret*, or silk apparatus, located near the labium.

One day the fully grown caterpillar attaches itself by a band of silk to a twig or leaf. The body is curled into a compact ball. The exoskeleton is shed and the pupa appears. It is the inactive, nonfeeding stage. In the moths, the pupa is covered by a silken *cocoon*. Although the pupa does not feed, the food reserves of the caterpillar stage are now transformed into the structures of the adult. Wings are formed. The mouth parts are changed from the chewing type to a tubelike *proboscis*, which can draw nectar from flowers.

Most of these changes occur during the winter months. In the spring the pupa molts and the adult butterfly emerges. At first the adult is moist and shrivelled. It rests for several hours while body fluids stiffen the wings.

25–10   Moth, Showing Coiled Proboscis

Chapter 25—Insects: Foremost Invertebrates   **387**

The changes that insects experience as they go through a complete metamorphosis have aroused much interest in recent years. Some biologists have identified certain insect hormones that regulate the orderly process of growth and change. Insect physiologists have been able to slow down, speed up, or prevent metamorphosis altogether in moths and butterflies by using these hormonal secretions.

FLIES, MOSQUITOES, AND BEETLES. Each of these insects also undergoes a complete metamorphosis. The details of growth are different in each case.

The adult fly lays about 500 eggs at a time on dunghills and garbage heaps. Within 24 hours the larvae hatch. They turn into small brown pupae after several intervening molts. In several days the adult fly emerges. The entire life cycle requires only two weeks.

The mosquito, on the other hand, lays her eggs in water. Almost any body of water is favorable: a pond, ditch, puddle, or even a rain barrel. The larva is called a *wriggler* from its peculiar twisting motion in the water. At the end of its abdomen there is a long tube through which it breathes air. To do this, the larva comes to the surface of the water and hangs upside down while extending its breathing tube into the air. This method of breathing makes it easy to kill the wrigglers. Spraying oil over the water suffocates the larvae.

After several weeks as a larva, the wriggler changes into the pupa. Unlike other pupas, which are inactive, the mosquito pupa swims about in a rotating or tumbling motion. It does not eat, however. From time to time it comes to the surface to breathe air through two tubes attached to its thorax. After a week it molts into the adult. Many species seem to require at least one meal of the blood of a warm-blooded animal before their eggs can develop. This makes them pests as adults.

You have probably seen the larvae of beetles in the soil. The *grubs* look like small, white worms with a head that is darker than the rest of the body. Not all grubs live in the soil. Some, like the Mexican bean beetle, feed upon a particular plant. The larva of the bean beetle is a woolly, yellow insect. Like the butterflies and mosquitoes, the beetles pass through a quiet pupa stage and eventually molt into the hard-winged adult.

The Honeybee

Probably no group of insects arouses man's curiosity more than the bees. They are among the most highly specialized of all insects. Bees are of great value to man because they collect nectar and pollen from flowers. This, in turn, leads to the fertilization of many flowers and the production of fruits.

ANATOMY OF THE BEE. The worker bee is one of the most well-adapted insects. Its mouth parts are not the simple chewing type of the grasshopper, nor the sucking type of the butterfly, but a combination of both. Its mandibles are used for chewing and shaping wax into the comb. Its maxillae and part of the labium form a sucking tube to draw in nectar.

Each pair of legs has special functions. On the first pair of legs are notches that remove pollen from the antennae. Long bristles on one of the lower segments serve as an effective pollen brush, which removes pollen from the front of the body. There is a similar pollen brush on the second pair of legs and also a wax spur to pick up wax. The hind leg has a triangular segment curved inward to form the *pollen basket*. Firm bristles form a sort of lid to hold the pollen in place. The swollen pollen baskets can often be seen as the bee moves from one flower to another. The segment just beneath the pollen basket has another pol-

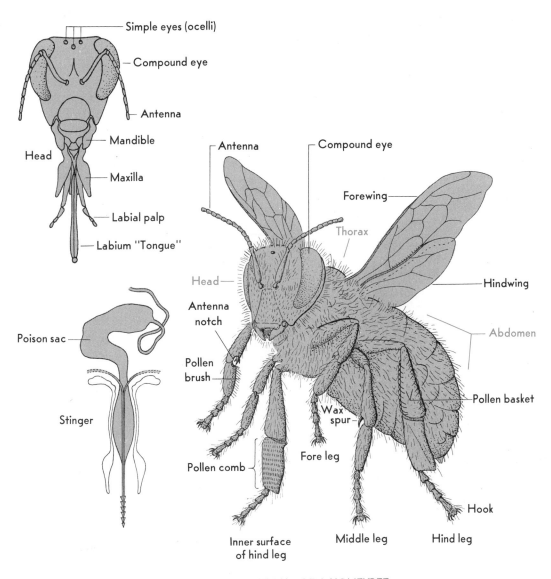

Simple eyes (ocelli)

Compound eye

Antenna

Mandible

Maxilla

Head

Labial palp

Labium "Tongue"

Poison sac

Stinger

Antenna

Compound eye

Forewing

Thorax

Head

Hindwing

Antenna notch

Abdomen

Pollen brush

Pollen basket

Wax spur

Fore leg

Pollen comb

Hook

Inner surface of hind leg

Middle leg

Hind leg

25–11 THE ANATOMY OF A HONEYBEE

len brush on the outside and ten rows of spines that form a pollen comb on the inside. Each pair of legs also has hooks on the last segment to help the bee hold securely to flowers.

The wings of the bee also have interesting modifications. The familiar buzzing sound is caused by the rapid motion of the wings, which vibrate about 400 times per second. Hooks join the two pairs of wings and keep them moving together at this great speed. The hooks are easily seen on the leading edge of the hindwing. They are clasped to a notch on the forewing in flight.

Internally, the bee has further interesting modifications. The *honey crop,* for example, is a device for making the nectar into honey. Associated with the pharynx are glands that make *bee milk,* a predigested food made from pollen. Along the ventral portion of the abdomen are the *wax glands.* These secrete wax on the under surface of the body. The wax is chewed into long ribbons to make the honeycomb. A tiny *scent gland* near the tip of the abdomen gives off a characteristic odor that seems to enable bees of the same hive to identify each other.

Located on the extreme tip of the abdomen is the *stinger,* a hollow dart with jagged edges. Glands associated with the stinger secrete an irritating fluid. When the worker bee attempts to withdraw the jagged dart, the stinger and its glands are usually pulled from the bee's abdomen. Within a day or two the bee dies.

THE BEE COLONY. The beehive's occupants may be considered one big family with a common mother, the *queen.* She is the only female in the hive capable of reproducing. She is larger than the *workers,* who are females but cannot lay eggs. There may be as many as 70,000 workers in one queen's family. Reproductive males, the *drones,* are also present in the colony. There are usually a hundred or more drones during the summer. In the winter there are no drones because the workers drive them out.

THE ROLE OF WORKERS. Although the queen is surrounded by royal attendants who feed her, she is in no sense a ruler. Actually, she is more like a captive who maintains the family by her enormous egg-laying ability. Queens may lay as many as 2000 eggs daily. The total weight of the eggs may be four times that of the queen. The queen is not permitted to leave the hive to get food. She is fed by the workers.

The queen does not take care of her young. Certain workers, usually younger ones, feed the larvae. For the first two or three days, all the larvae are fed with *royal jelly,* a substance secreted by the pharyngeal glands of the workers. At the end of this period, the workers supply the larvae of prospective drones and workers with a mixture of honey and pollen, sometimes called *bee bread.* The larvae of prospective queens are continued on their diet of royal jelly. It is this difference in feeding that produces a queen rather than a worker. The eggs that are laid are the same for each. Drones, however, hatch only from unfertilized eggs. Apparently the queen can control the numbers of males and females she

25–12   A bee colony has a queen, a few hundred drones, and thousands of workers.

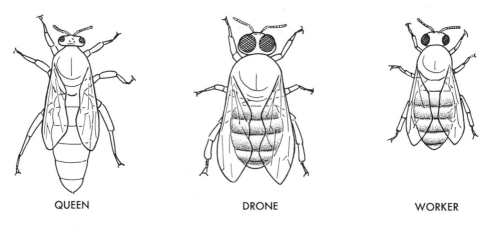

QUEEN   DRONE   WORKER

will have. She does this by laying either fertilized or unfertilized eggs at will.

During the summer months, all of the provisions for the winter must be stored. Food gathering is the job of the older bees. Visiting several hundred flowers, a worker will bring back almost its own weight of pollen and nectar. Upon returning to the hive, the stores are transferred to the parts of the comb used for this purpose. Younger workers are busy making new hexagonal cells out of the wax ribbons their wax glands supply. So great is the activity of the workers during the summer months, that their life span rarely exceeds six weeks.

BEE LANGUAGE. So many different activities are coordinated in the beehive that it seems that there must be some means of communication. The Austrian zoologist Karl von Frisch has indicated the means by which foraging bees tell other members of the hive where they may find good stores of pollen and nectar. A peculiar "bee dance" is performed by returning scouts. If the food is close, a round dance is performed. If the food is farther than 100 yards, a special tail-wagging dance is staged. The direction of the food is also indicated. Further clues as to the kind of pollen and nectar to seek are given by the scout who distributes samples.

The queen's attendants keep the colony informed about her presence by licking a secretion from her body. This secretion is then passed from bee to bee in the food the entire colony shares. If the amount of the

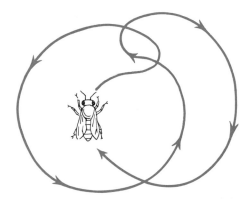

Round dance, in which foraging scout alternately circles to right and left, indicates food within 100 yards of hive.

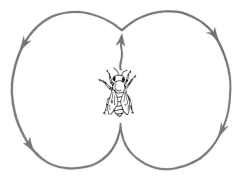

In tailwagging dance, the rate at which the bee completes the cycles indicates the distance to food. The straight portion of the dance indicates the direction.

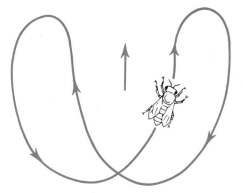

In the sickle dance, used by one variety of bee, the opening of the sickle indicates the direction of the food from the hive.

25–13 On returning to the hive, a foraging worker bee performs dance patterns to indicate to other workers the distance, direction, and richness of food supplies. In general, the dance pattern indicates distance and direction. Speed of dance indicates richness of the food supply. Workers at the hive join in the dance and then fly off to find the food.

secretion is reduced, the colony ~~.ckly~~ acts to produce a new queen.

Each colony of bees has a distinctive odor. This is apparently caused by the fact that they all eat the same food. If a strange bee enters the hive, the workers recognize the intruder by scent almost immediately and sting it to death.

MATING AND SWARMING. When a colony becomes too large, it prepares to divide by producing a new queen. The workers prepare several large cells in which the old queen lays eggs. The hatched larvae are then fed royal jelly to produce new queens. Meanwhile, the old queen is put on a diet to make her slim so that she can fly more easily. When the first of the new queens is almost ready, several thousand workers leave the colony with their old queen. This is called *swarming*. Scouts have examined new locations, and the new colony is established in one of them.

The first of the new queens to mature in the old colony seeks out the other developing queens and stings them to death. She is not harmed in the process because her stinger is not barbed like the worker's. The new queen mates within a week to ten days. She flies high into the air followed by the drones, one of whom mates with her. The drone dies shortly thereafter. The queen mates but once in her life and stores enough sperm cells for all of the fertilized eggs she will lay. Once she has returned to the hive she will not depart again unless swarming occurs a year or so later.

Ant Colonies

Ants are even more highly specialized in their activities and adaptations than are bees. In addition to the usual activities of foraging for food, storing the food and acting as nursemaids and attendants for the queen, some ants are further modified into the role of soldiers.

Ants have even become experts at farming. The spores of certain fungi are planted in a part of the nest. When the fruiting part of the fungus develops, the farmer ants bite small chunks off to be fed to the rest of the colony. Dairies are also kept in many ant colonies. Here are housed the ant "cows," insects of the *aphid* group. These aphids secrete a sweet, sticky "milk" on their abdomens that ants eat.

Certain species of ants overrun and conquer neighboring colonies. And when they prevail, they take "slaves." The slaves then undertake most of the menial tasks of the colony.

Ants do not build a wax comb like the bees. The storage of liquids is accomplished by some colonies by having certain workers become gorged with honey. Swollen to unusual size in the process, these "living casks of honey" secrete the sweet drops to other workers upon demand.

ORGANIZATION OF THE COLONY. Fundamentally, ants are organized like bees. Thousands of sterile workers perform the routine tasks of the colony. The queen, considerably larger because of her egg-laying duties, is the common mother of the family. She is carefully attended, like the queen bee. There are some males that are apparently produced at will by the queen from unfertilized eggs.

Unlike the beehives, there is considerable variety to the structures built by ants. Very primitive forms of ants do not bother to build nests. They live under stones and rocks. Some species build tunnels or galleries under the ground where they keep their young and store their food. Others build mounds made of soil, twigs, and leaves. Some tropical species construct nests suspended from trees by silken threads. The fire ant of southern United States builds mounds of earth to house its colony and packs the earth tightly so that the mounds become quite strong.

25-14 After the queen lays the eggs, they are tended through the larval and pupal stages by the worker ants of the colony. Shown here are the workers with the enclosed pupae.

ESTABLISHING NEW COLONIES. Although ants are wingless, they produce winged, fertile males and females at certain times. The winged males and females fly off and may mate several miles from the colony. The fertilized queens establish their colonies by burrowing in the earth and laying about a hundred eggs. Within several weeks each queen has a brood of workers to assist her. The colony then expands to a thousand or more in a few months. At the end of a year more winged individuals are produced and new colonies can again be established.

Termites

Termites, commonly called "white ants," are not classified in the same order with ants. This is because, structurally, termites are more primitive insects than ants, but their social organization is more advanced than that of any other group. The termite workers do not have the narrow "waist" where the abdomen joins the thorax. This is a characteristic of the ants. Furthermore, the antennae of termites are made of segments that look like beads. This is in contrast to the basal segment of the ant's antenna, which is longer than the rest and not at all like a bead.

TERMITE COLONIES. Perhaps the most unusual characteristic of the termites is their ability to use wood for many purposes. Termites are able to use wood as food. This is possible only because a mutualistic association exists between the termites and certain protozoans living in their digestive tracts. These protozoans secrete an enzyme capable of digesting the cellulose in the wood. Much of the wood, however, is simply used as a building material for the elaborate galleries the termites form within their nests. In the tropics, huge mounds of soil are cemented together by the saliva of these insects, thus forming the ten-foot skyscrapers of the termite world.

The variety of individuals in the termite colony is greater than in any other insect colony. Some biologists have identified as many as ten different kinds. There are three kinds of fertile males and females and two kinds of sterile workers or soldiers.

Within the termite colony, and closely guarded by soldiers and royal attendants, is the space set aside for the queen and king. After mating, the queen grows to an enormous size and lays eggs at the rate of one per second. In some colonies the queen is twenty times as large as a worker. Some colonies contain over a million termites. If anything happens to the queen, the colony produces new reproductive pairs within a day.

WORKERS AND SOLDIERS. In many termite colonies much of the work is done by the nymphs, immature individuals. In other cases, mature sterile workers perform the usual tasks of housekeeping. There is also a special soldier caste for protecting the colony. Like certain soldier ants, the members of this caste have enlarged mandibles. But the most interesting soldiers of all are members of the chemical warfare divisions.

These are called *nasutes*. They have snouts through which they secrete a sticky substance that effectively entangles the legs of their enemies. While they are attempting to untangle themselves, the victims are chopped to pieces. In spite of all this protection for the colony, many other kinds of insects are frequently found in the termite nest. The relationship that exists between them and the termites is not understood, but they are tolerated since they do no harm.

Carolina Biological Supply Company

25–15 Soldier termites guard the colony.

IMPORTANT POINTS

• Insects are the most numerous and successful of the arthropods. There are almost three-quarters of a million species of insects, more than the combined total of all other animals. This large number is subdivided into more than twenty orders based mainly on the structure of the wings and mouth parts.

• The grasshopper illustrates the major insect characteristics: three body regions, three pairs of legs, and one pair of antennae. Its two pairs of wings are typical for most, but not all, insects. Internally, the grasshopper has a tracheal network for respiration and an open circulatory system. Its nervous system is like that of the crayfish—it has a ventral nerve cord and well-developed sense organs.

• Most insects undergo either complete or incomplete metamorphosis. Growth and molting occur in the larval or nymph stages, but cease in the adult form.

• Many types of bees, ants, and termites are social insects, living in colonies of many related individuals of different structures and functions. They share the work of food getting, building, and caring for the young. The honey bee is among the most useful insects for it pollinates many important flowers. The termite is among the most destructive, often eating the foundations of wooden buildings.

REVIEW QUESTIONS

1. What are the three body regions of an insect?
2. Name and describe the mouth parts of the grasshopper.
3. What is the function and location of the tympanic membrane?
4. What are the principal parts of the digestive system of the grasshopper?
5. What is the function of the Malpighian tubules?
6. Describe the functions of the spiracles and the tracheae.
7. How do complete and incomplete metamorphoses differ? Give examples.
8. List three types of individuals in a bee colony.
9. If the queen bee dies, how is a new one produced?
10. What is the difference in function between wingless and winged ants?
11. Why is it incorrect to describe termites as white ants?

CHECK YOUR UNDERSTANDING

12. How do the spiracles regulate the intake and outflow of air in the insect body?
13. Why is it unnecessary for an insect's blood to carry oxygen?
14. List and locate five sense organs of the grasshopper.
15. Which stage of the butterfly's life cycle is the most destructive? Why?
16. How does the queen bee control the sex of her offspring?
17. What evidence exists to indicate that bees have a "language"?
18. List three differences in the social organizations of bee and ant colonies.
19. Why is it unlikely that insects will overrun the earth despite their high reproductive rate?
20. Why does an insect not drown if its head is immersed in water for a long time?

RESEARCH PROJECTS AND REPORTS

1. Obtain information from your school or public library and prepare a report on one of the following topics:

   Insects in Amber   **Insects and Disease**

   Locust Plagues   **Insect Behavior**

2. *Insect Collection:* An insect net is made from a wire clothes hanger shaped into a circle, and cheesecloth sewn into a bag. Any capped, wide-mouthed bottle serves as a killing bottle, with absorbent cotton soaked in lighter fluid as the killing agent. Place the insects in the jar as you capture them. Mount them a day later, using thin insect pins. Old cigar boxes are good display cases. If the wood is hard, use soft balsa wood as a base. Classification is aided with a book like *The Field Book of Insects*, by F. E. Lutz.

3. *Raising Insects:* These insects may be raised at home or in the laboratory:
   Fruit flies: Capture several flies and keep them in a jar with some grapes or pieces of banana. You can observe their entire life history. *Meal worms:* The larvae are kept in a jar with ground breakfast cereal. Pupae and adults will be formed.
   Cocoons: Collect the cocoons of moths in the fall, and keep them in a jar in a warm, humid place. The jar should be covered with cloth for ventilation.

FURTHER READING

The Insects. Peter Farb and the Editors of LIFE. Time Inc., New York, N.Y. The insect world is examined in terms of its impact upon man's world.
The Life of the Bee. Maurice Maeterlinck. Dodd, Mead & Co., New York, N.Y. A great classic in biology that describes the organization of the bee colony.
The Ants. Wilhelm Goetsch. University of Michigan Press, Ann Arbor, Mich. Discusses the many activities of the ant colony and its complex function.
"The Flight-Control System of the Locust." Donald M. Wilson. *Scientific American*, May, 1968, page 83. How the nervous system of the locust controls flying.

Vertebrate Animals

WHEN Charles Darwin explored the Argentine coastal plain in August, 1833, he found some remarkable fossils. Among them were the spine and jaw of two species of giant sloths more than half a million years old. Animals like these were unknown in South America at that time. To Darwin they presented no great mystery. The giant sloths must have lived years ago. He reasoned that parts of their skeletons had been preserved in the mud of the coastal strip. Many of Darwin's contemporaries did not agree with him, for the science of paleontology was just beginning. Debate over the significance of fossil discoveries was widespread. Darwin's theory of evolution, linking the life of the past with the present, had not then been formulated.

In April, 1958, a team of scientists from Harvard University and the Argentine Museum of Natural Sciences discovered one of the richest fossil deposits in the Western Hemisphere. Bones of fish, amphibians, and reptiles dating back 180 million years were uncovered in the Andes Mountains in Western Argentina. During the 125 years between the two discoveries, great strides had been made in interpreting the story of the fossils. Today, there is little doubt that such fossil beds as those in the Andes provide a view of the life of the past that can be obtained in no other way. The modern biologist marvels at the insight of Darwin who correctly predicted the importance of his few fossil discoveries.

Vertebrate animals have a bony skeleton, a fortunate circumstance in tracing their origins. Soft-bodied animals generally do not leave good fossils. Hard bones, however, make excellent fossils. The history of the vertebrate past is thus more completely preserved than that of any other group of animals. In the great deserts of Mongolia, South Africa, Utah, Wyoming, and Argentina, the pieces of a giant jigsaw puzzle are being found. They tell a story of the history of these highly organized animals. The story is far from complete. Yet it is complete enough to reveal the broad outlines of vertebrate development.

All of the vertebrate animals belong to the phylum Chordata. Within this phylum the vertebrates occupy the position of a subphylum, making up the great bulk of the total number of chordate species. All of the vertebrates have a backbone made of separate segments called vertebrae. Practically all of the animals kept in our homes as pets are vertebrates. All domesticated animals and beasts of burden are vertebrates. They are the most familiar animals.

CHAPTER

26

Vertebrate Development

Whence came the vertebrates? From what phylum did the vertebrate pattern emerge? The biologist is constantly asking questions such as these. He wishes to understand the continuity of life from the beginning. Partial answers sometimes have occupied a lifetime of work. The clues come from many sources: fossils, detailed anatomical study, chemical reactions of body fluids, growth and development of animals.

Some biologists have suggested that relatives of the segmented worms were the forerunners of the earliest vertebrates. The segmentation of the body and the likeness in blood systems seem to support this suggestion. Other biologists have pointed to the ancient armored fishes as being related to the horseshoe crab or the huge water scorpions of prehistoric times. There are many objections to both of these theories. The principal objection is that the nerve cord is in the wrong position. The chordates always have the nerve cord on the dorsal surface of the body, but both the annelid worms and the horseshoe crab have the nerve cord on the ventral surface.

Many biologists believe that the echinoderms are related to the simplest chordates

by some unknown ancestor. This sounds almost unbelievable at first because the starfish and its relatives are built on a radial plan. Vertebrates, on the other hand, have bilateral symmetry. But the larva of the starfish is different. It has bilateral symmetry. The larvae of certain echinoderms resemble those of the acorn worm, Phylum Hemichordata, so closely that experts have difficulty telling them apart. The development of the fertilized egg follows a strikingly similar pattern in both cases. The acorn worms appear to be closely related to the primitive chordates.

Chordate Characteristics

What characteristics do all of the chordates have that lead them to be classified together? In the first place all *chordates* have a flexible rod that extends along the entire body at some time in their life history. This is called a *notochord*. It gives the phylum its name. In the vertebrate animals the notochord is replaced by a backbone as the embryo develops. The second characteristic that all chordates possess is a series of paired slits, resembling the gill slits of fish. In many chordates, these slits are found only

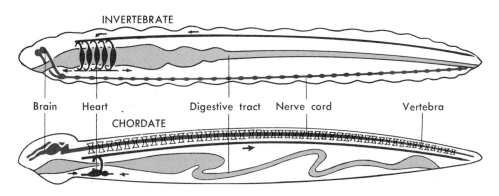

INVERTEBRATE

Brain   Heart   Digestive tract   Nerve cord   Vertebra

CHORDATE

26–1 Diagrammatic longitudinal sections of chordate and invertebrate bodies show characteristic placement of the nerve cord in relation to the digestive tract.

in the embryo. The third common characteristic is the presence of a *dorsal nerve cord*. At the anterior end of the body, the nerve cord is enlarged to form the brain. In the chordates the specialization and enlargement of the brain is carried further than in any other phylum.

The vertebrates make up most of the phylum Chordata. However, there are a few animals of this phylum that do not have backbones.

AMPHIOXUS: THE LANCELET. The fishes are believed to be the simplest of the vertebrates, but there are chordate forms that are even simpler. One of these is the fishlike form known as the lancelet or by its scientific name, *Amphioxus* (am-fee-AHK-sus). The lancelet usually measures about two inches long, prefers warm water, and is generally found in shallow seas. Although it is not a common animal, in some localities it is so abundant that it is collected like fish and sold in markets.

In place of a backbone the lancelet has a notochord. Just above the notochord a hollow nerve cord runs the length of the body. Also there are numerous gill slits along the sides of the pharynx.

26–2 The Anatomy of Amphioxus

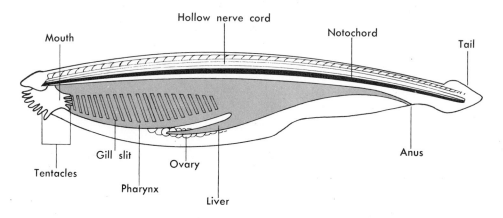

Mouth   Hollow nerve cord   Notochord   Tail

Tentacles   Gill slit   Ovary   Pharynx   Liver   Anus

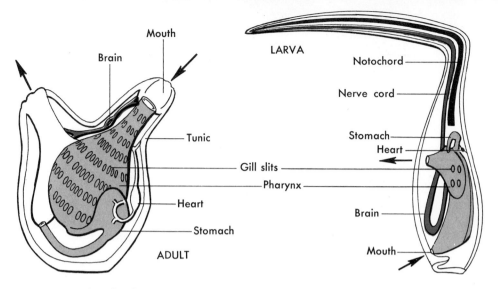

Mouth
Brain
Tunic
Gill slits
Pharynx
Heart
Stomach
ADULT

LARVA
Notochord
Nerve cord
Stomach
Heart
Brain
Mouth

26–3 Larval and Adult Forms of Sea Squirt. Can you explain why the larval form of this animal is said to be more characteristically chordate than the adult form?

The lancelet takes in food through its mouth along with sea water. The water is strained by the gill slits and the food particles removed. Around the mouth is a ring of tentacles. The nervous system is not well developed. There is no special brain tissue, and sense organs are lacking. The lancelet indicates what the ancestors of vertebrates were probably like.

THE SEA SQUIRTS. These are rather shapeless animals often found attached to rocks at the seashore. The body resembles a bag, the outer part of which is a tough, leathery tunic. It is from this that the group derives its name. There are two openings at the top of the body, and when the animal is irritated it forces water from them, hence the name *sea squirt*.

PHYLUM CHORDATA

Subphylum	Characteristics	Examples
Urochordata	Marine animals enclosed in cuticular tunic.	Sea squirts
Cephalochordata	Fishlike forms called lancelets. Notochord extends entire length of body and persists throughout life.	Amphioxus
Vertebrata	A vertebral column with a brain case.	Fishes, frogs, snakes, birds, man

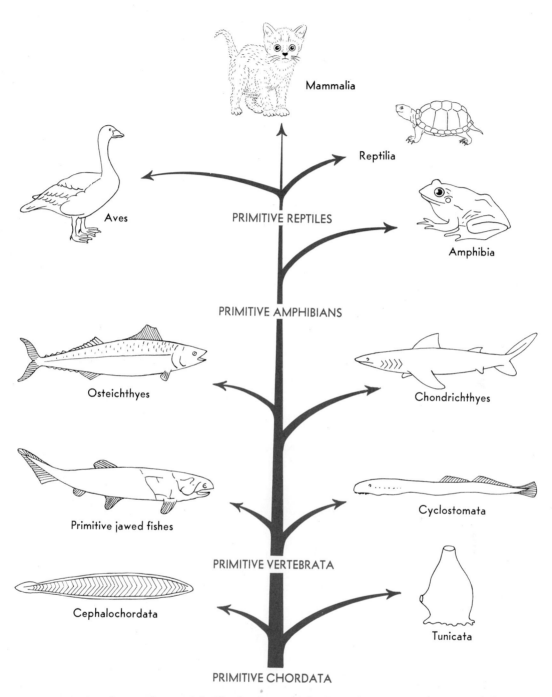

26–4 Family tree shows probable developmental relationship of animals of the phylum Chordata. Although superficially quite different, all have a tubular nerve cord dorsal to the notochord. All develop gill slits at some stage of their lives. In vertebrates, the embryonic notochord is replaced in adults by a vertebral column.

Sea squirts, or *tunicates,* were once thought to be mollusks. The adult shows little resemblance to other chordates except for gill slits on the pharynx. The larva, however, shows the three chordate traits clearly. It has a notochord and gill slits; its nervous system is a dorsal tube. During the transition from larva to adult the nerve cord and notochord disappear.

Kinds of Vertebrates

There are about 45,000 living species of animals with backbones. Only two other groups of animals rival them in numbers: the arthropods and the mollusks. Both of these groups have existed far longer than have the vertebrates.

CHARACTERISTICS OF VERTEBRATES. The backbone of *vertebrates* is made up of segments, the *vertebrae.* These give this subphylum its name. You can feel the projections of the vertebrae in your neck and between your shoulder blades. All the animals classed as vertebrates have a backbone made up of vertebrae.

The nerve cord of vertebrates runs through a hollow, protective tube of bone formed by successive vertebrae. No other group of animals has the nerve cord so well protected. In addition, the brain is larger and better developed. Furthermore, it is enclosed within a protective covering, the cranium. The sense organs are also well developed. The organ systems of vertebrates are well developed even in the primitive forms.

THE CLASSES OF VERTEBRATES. In the unfolding pageant of vertebrate life as it is revealed by fossils in the rocks, the ancestors of the fishes came first. The simplest vertebrate forms had no jaws. Others, such as the modern sharks, had a skeleton made of cartilage rather than bone. Still others had a skeleton made of bone, as do most modern fish. Some biologists believe that the earliest fishes were freshwater forms that later migrated to the sea.

26–5 In early embryonic stages, vertebrate animals resemble each other quite closely. This fact provides some evidence of descent from a common ancestor.

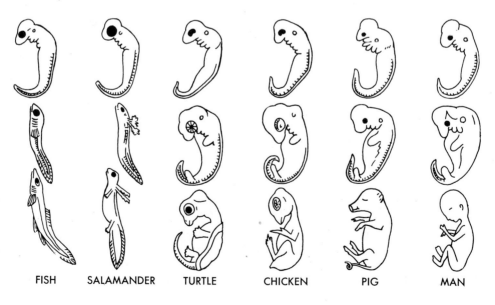

FISH   SALAMANDER   TURTLE   CHICKEN   PIG   MAN

CLASSES OF VERTEBRATES

Class	Characteristics	Examples
Agnatha	Fishes with a circular mouth. No scales, jaws, or lateral fins.	Lampreys, hagfish
Chondrichthyes	Fishes with skeleton of cartilage, jaws, and paired fins.	Sharks, rays, skates
Osteichthyes (Pisces)	Bony fishes with covered gills, paired lateral fins.	Mackerel, tuna
Amphibia	Cold-blooded animals. When young, breathe by gills. Adults have lungs as respiratory organs. Moist skin.	Frogs, toads, salamanders
Reptilia	Cold-blooded, lung-breathing vertebrates. Body covered by horny scales.	Snakes, lizards, crocodiles, alligators
Aves	Warm-blooded, lung-breathing vertebrates with feathers.	Birds
Mammalia	Warm-blooded, lung-breathing vertebrates with hair. Young nourished by milk from mammary glands of the mother.	Horse, cow, man

The history of the rocks shows that the next advance was the land invasion by the amphibians. The reptiles followed. The birds appear to be descended from reptiles. Finally, the mammals appeared. They, too, seem to have sprung from the reptiles.

The Development of Vertebrates

As long ago as 1828 the German biologist Karl Ernst von Baer recognized the remarkable likenesses found in different vertebrate embryos. He studied the development of the eggs of rabbits, dogs, and chickens.

One of the observations that interested von Baer was the presence of gill arches and gill slits in the chick embryo. Other investigators have since discovered that all the chordates have such structures at some period of their life. Even the human embryo passes through a period in which similar structures appear.

Von Baer believed that the presence of slits in the embryos of widely different animals suggested a common origin. His observations provided evidence to support the belief held by many naturalists that the present forms of life have come from very different forms in the past.

The special field of inquiry established by von Baer is now an important subdivision of biology known as embryology. Embryology is the study of the development of the young animal from the fertilized egg. Embryologists raise important questions and also provide us with many answers. Why, for example, do fishes and birds, elephants and mice, show resemblance in their embryonic stages? In raising this question embryologists have also supplied us with this important fact: the development of the vertebrates is basically the same. As we begin our study of the vertebrate classes, we shall try to show the similarity in the basic vertebrate pattern as they begin their lives.

FERTILIZATION: EGG AND SPERM CELLS. From the instant of fertilization, the plan of a developing animal is fixed. Within the egg and within the sperm lie the chromosomes that help determine the ultimate form of the organism.

The eggs of vertebrates are not all the same. They differ in the number and kinds of chromosomes. The number and kind of chromosomes in the cells of a certain species of animal is constant. It is not always possible to determine the number exactly, however. The number of chromosomes in the body cells of the horse is 60. The number of chromosomes in the reproductive cells, however, is always one half the number in the normal body cells. This is called the *haploid number*. The body cells have the *diploid number*. In the horse, therefore, the number of chromosomes in the body cells is 60, but in the egg and sperm cells only 30.

The sizes of egg cells vary a great deal. In most mammals the egg is roughly the width of a pinpoint. The hen's egg is much bigger. In addition, the hen's egg contains a greater supply of yolk for nourishing the chick. The eggs of mammals contain little, if any, yolk. In mammals, the supply of food comes from the body of the mother, where the young develop.

Sperm cells are generally much smaller than egg cells. The egg cell is often 100 times as large as the sperm. The microscopic sperm cell contains the chromosomes that transmit all the characteristics that the new organism will receive from the male parent. Studies with the electron microscope have shown that the sperm has a design far more intricate than the optical microscope had ever revealed. It is important to note that sperm cells contain the haploid number of chromosomes. Furthermore, they are *motile*. Generally, they have a whiplike tail to propel them about.

Two events are closely related when fertilization occurs. In the first place, the nuclei of the egg and sperm, which contain the haploid number of chromosomes, unite to form a nucleus containing the diploid number of chromosomes. This means that the original number of chromosomes peculiar to a certain species is restored during fertilization. The second event is the activation of the egg, which begins the formation of a new animal.

CLEAVAGE. Shortly after fertilization, the fertilized egg, or zygote, divides. Among mammals the fertilized egg usually divides into two equal parts. In some cases, as in the chick, where a large amount of yolk is present, only a portion of the egg divides. In the chick, this portion is called the *blastodisc*. The blastodisc is a small section of cytoplasm on the top of the yolk.

The first division is followed by a second, usually at right angles to the first. A third division of the egg, usually at right angles to the first two, follows. If we think of the first two as vertical divisions, the

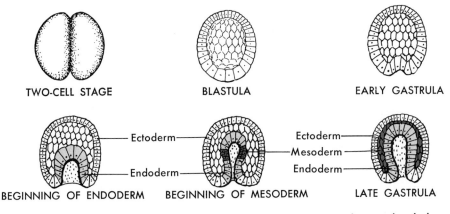

26–6 Cleavage and gastrulation in amphioxus, showing origin of ectoderm and endoderm.

TWO-CELL STAGE   BLASTULA   EARLY GASTRULA

BEGINNING OF ENDODERM   BEGINNING OF MESODERM   LATE GASTRULA

Ectoderm
Endoderm

Ectoderm
Mesoderm
Endoderm

third is then horizontal. The series of divisions that results in the formation of numerous cells from the zygote is called *cleavage*. The number of chromosomes in each of the cells is the diploid number typical of the body cells.

THE BLASTULA. As cleavage continues, more and more small cells are produced until a hollow mass of cells is formed. This is the *blastula*. The cavity within the blastula is called the *blastocoele,* or segmentation cavity. In the development of the chick, the yolk does not cleave to form a blastula. Instead, the blastodisc forms a flat plate of cells, the *blastoderm*. At this point in the development of the embryo, there is no clear indication of the specialization that will finally produce the animal.

THE GASTRULA. There is much variation in the manner in which the blastula is folded until it finally produces three distinct cell layers. Where the blastula is a hollow sphere, the outer cell layer simply grows in, just as you would press a rubber ball inward to form a cup of two layers. A third cell layer then grows between these. In spite of the variation, however, the end result is the same: three germ layers are produced. At this stage the developing embryo is called the *gastrula*.

The *ectoderm* is the outermost of the three cell layers and will form the outer layer of the skin and the nerve tissue. The *endoderm* is the innermost layer and will form the digestive and respiratory systems. The *mesoderm,* or middle layer, will form the great bulk of body tissue: the muscles, the skeleton, and most of the internal organs. Up to this point many of the invertebrates follow a similar plan of development. But as the embryo begins to form its organ systems, the plan followed by the vertebrates is quite different.

ORGAN FORMATION. The spherical gastrula begins the formation of the *neural tube,* the tissue that will become the central nerve cord. This structure first appears as a thickened series of cells on the outside of the gastrula in the form of two parallel ridges. These grow upward and toward each other. When they meet, a tube is formed. The anterior end of the neural tube forms the brain; the posterior end forms the spinal cord.

During the formation of the neural tube, the gastrula begins to grow to produce the elongated figure of the young animal. The point at which the many cells grew rapidly inward to form the gastrula will be the end of the digestive tract. Directly opposite is the area where the mouth will grow. Between these two points, the digestive tract will form a continuous tube. As the embryo thus begins to take form, a head region takes shape. It curls down towards the developing tail region. The growth of the tail also produces a curling effect, such that head and tail almost join. This is a widely characteristic pose of vertebrate embryos.

Another characteristic of vertebrate development is the early appearance of the head and the rapid growth of nerve tissue to form the brain. You have probably noticed the comparatively large head size of the young chick. In the earlier stages of growth, the head is proportionately larger.

Behind the head and brain, the blocks of mesoderm that are called *somites* begin to appear. In the developing chick they seem like crude vertebrae, much too large for the rest of the embryo at this stage. It is from these segments of mesoderm, however, that the vertebrae, other parts of the skeleton, and most of the muscles will eventually arise. The limb buds, which appear later, are projections that will form the arms and legs of man, the wings and legs of the chick. The animal begins to assume the shape it will have at birth.

DEVELOPMENT OF THE CHICK. The growth of the fertile hen's egg is one of the best examples of the pattern of vertebrate development. The embryo begins with the flat mass of cells, the *blastoderm*, on the surface of the yolk. The yolk is digested and assimilated to provide for the growth of the embryo. The blastoderm thickens and lengthens in the hind region to form the *primitive streak*. At this point, the embryo is about one-tenth of an inch long and hardly noticeable to the naked eye.

As the primitive streak lengthens and determines the center line of the body, two neural folds rise from its forward edges. These then grow towards each other and form the neural tube. Beneath the neural tube, the notochord develops, following the axis established by the primitive streak. The mesoderm has been steadily growing in size and begins to split into segmented blocks, the somites, which form the main parts of the muscular and skeletal systems.

Shortly thereafter the primitive heart starts beating. It doesn't look much like a heart in the embryo, but more like a crimson blob that beats steadily, signalling the beginning of a new life. Meanwhile, the head has been formed by a fold from the front of the embryo. The beginnings of the

26–7 These photographs indicate various stages in chick embryo development from 2 days to 21 days (hatching). The amnionic sac is most clearly evident in the 10- and 15-day photographs. Note the extent of the blood vessel network at 2 days and again at 5 days. What has happened to the embryo itself in this time? Where is the yolk at 21 days?

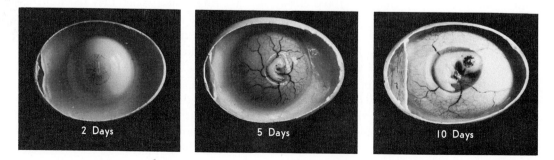

2 Days

5 Days

10 Days

brain, the sense organs, and the indentation that will be the mouth are clearly seen.

After several days of incubation, a network of blood vessels has spread over the yolk, bringing the embryo nourishment. The heart is beating steadily. The tail is forming. The head and eyes are clearly visible. There are gill slits along the side of the embryo's neck. The lateral buds that mark the position of legs and wings soon appear.

During this period, embryonic membranes enclose the embryo and protect it from injury. One of these membranes, the *amnion*, forms a watery sac in which the developing animal is suspended. In all of the higher vertebrates, this same kind of fluid protection is provided for the embryo. Thus surrounded, the chick continues to grow until it finally emerges from the egg.

IMPORTANT POINTS

• Vertebrates are animals that have a backbone made of vertebrae. All vertebrates belong to the phylum Chordata. Members of this phylum have a flexible rod, the notochord, along the dorsal axis of the body at some period of their life history.

• Closely related to the vertebrates are the chordates that do not have a backbone: animals like the lancelet and the sea squirt. They may be similar to the ancient forms from which vertebrates developed.

• There are seven classes of vertebrates. The first three are different types of fishes; the remaining four are the amphibians, reptiles, birds, and mammals.

• Embryology is that special branch of biology that deals with the development of embryos. The study of vertebrate embryos has revealed some remarkable likenesses that may suggest common origins in the past.

• The egg and sperm cell contain the haploid number of chromosomes that is restored to the diploid number when fertilization occurs. Fertilization begins the series of egg divisions known as cleavage. As cleavage continues, a hollow ball of cells, the blastula, is formed. Later, three primary tissue layers are produced, and the embryo is called a gastrula.

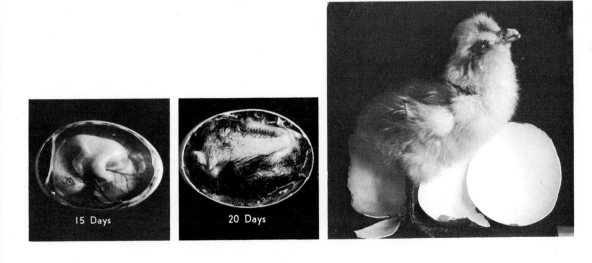

15 Days

20 Days

- The ectoderm produces the skin and nervous system. The endoderm produces the digestive and respiratory systems. The mesoderm forms the bulk of the muscles, bones, and internal organs.

- The development of the chick illustrates the pattern of vertebrate development. The primitive streak develops and forms a neural tube. Blocks of mesoderm form muscles and bones. Organs and limbs develop in an orderly progression.

REVIEW QUESTIONS

1. List two examples of animals that are chordates but not vertebrates.
2. What is the difference between a notochord and a backbone?
3. Give two reasons why Amphioxus is not classified as a fish.
4. Which vertebrates seem to have appeared on the earth first?
5. Do the mammals appear more closely related by descent to the birds or to the reptiles?
6. How did von Baer explain the presence of gill arches in the chick?
7. What structures in the reproductive cells seem to be the principal determiners of the ultimate form of an animal?
8. How would you distinguish between the blastula and gastrula?
9. Which of the three fundamental layers of the embryo forms the bulk of the adult organism?

CHECK YOUR UNDERSTANDING

10. List two factors that have contributed to the biologist's knowledge of the vertebrate past.
11. What three characteristics are found in chordate animals?
12. List the seven classes of vertebrates in the approximate order of their appearance on earth and give one example of each.
13. What evidence from embryology supported von Baer's contention that many vertebrate animals appear to have had a common origin?
14. What four main stages can be recognized in the development of the embryos of most vertebrates?
15. List the three fundamental tissues of the embryo and opposite each, name one structure or organ each tissue forms in the adult.
16. What is the significance of the development of embryonic membranes?
17. Why should the study of the embryos of invertebrates and vetebrates provide more significant clues to the origins of animals?
18. How do you account for the fact that the number and kinds of chromosomes are generally different in different species of animals?
19. Why do you think the head of the embryo develops so rapidly?
20. Suppose that the two cells formed by the first division of the fertilized egg were carefully separated. Describe how you would expect them to develop after such a separation.

RESEARCH PROJECTS AND REPORTS

1. Obtain information from your school or public library and prepare a report on one of the following topics:

   Karl Ernst von Baer   **Starfish Embryology**

   Hans Spemann and the Organizer   **Development of the Chick**

2. *Incubating Chicken Eggs:* You can study the development of a chick embryo if you can obtain some fertile eggs from a hatchery. You will need an incubator, but you can improvise one if your school doesn't have one. The main requirement is that your design produce a constant temperature of 103° Fahrenheit. A light bulb is a good source of heat. You'll have to experiment with different bulb sizes to get the best one to maintain just the right temperature. A dish of water must also be placed in the incubator to maintain moisture in the air. When you set the eggs, allow about four hours for them to warm up, then count the developing period from that time. Work out a schedule for opening the eggs, and consult your teacher about good technique. Keep records in the form of drawings of what you see.

3. *Frog Egg Development:* If you live near a frog pond, you can collect frog eggs and study their development. Keep a clump of the eggs in a small bowl and change the water daily, using fresh pond water. You can watch the development from day to day if you have a binocular microscope.

FURTHER READING

The Vertebrate Story. Alfred S. Romer. The University of Chicago Press, Chicago, Ill. Discusses the origin and development of the vertebrate classes with many exceptional illustrations.

"The First Heartbeats." James D. Ebert. *Scientific American*, March, 1959, page 87. Study of the chick embryo identifies the cells in the embryo that eventually form the heart and circulatory system.

"Feedback in the Differentiation of Cells." S. Meryl Rose. *Scientific American*, December, 1958, page 36. Discusses the experiments by which biologists seek to learn how the special cells of the animal are developed from unspecialized cells.

Principles of Development and Differentiation. C. H. Waddington. Macmillan Co., New York, N.Y. Discusses the relationship between genes and the developing organism.

"Mammalian Eggs in the Laboratory." R. G. Edwards. *Scientific American*, August, 1966, page 73. The growth of the eggs of rabbits and pigs in the laboratory enables the biologist to learn about the development of mammals.

CHAPTER

27

Fishes
Early Vertebrates

ALMOST 400 million years ago the animals that developed into modern fishes swam in the waters that covered Colorado and other western states. These were the *ostracoderms,* fishlike animals with bony plates. These odd animals had no jaws or paired fins. They had a few scales on their trunk and tail. The heavy plates on the head were their most outstanding characteristic. In the middle of the head many ostracoderms had a single nostril. Certain fishes that live today, the *lampreys* and *hagfishes,* bear a remarkable resemblance to the ancient ostracoderms, even though their external appearance is not the same.

There is evidence that the earliest vertebrates originated in fresh water. Some evidence is based upon the structure of the kidney, which seems designed for life in fresh water. Other evidence comes from fossil remains. The earliest fossils are mainly freshwater forms. Later fossils show an increase in the number of marine forms, indicating a migration to the sea.

About 100 million years after the appearance of the armored fishes, their descendants were so numerous that biologists have

called this period the Age of Fishes. Today, fishes are still the most numerous form of vertebrate life. Some 20,000 species are known. Additional species will no doubt be discovered.

Life in the sea is influenced by the dimension of depth. Pressure increases with depth. Certain species are adapted to different depths. The deep sea may be compared to an apartment house with different species of fish living on different floors. The tenants of the top floors find light and food abundant, especially algae, which thrive in sunlight. But the basement dwellers have no sunlight and little food. They swim about in a world of darkness. They feed upon each other, or upon the continual "rain" of material that falls from the inhabitants of the upper floors. Some are equipped with phosphorescent lights, which attract their prey or help them find mates.

There is great variety among the three classes of fishes. The simplest forms, the lampreys and hagfishes, have no jaws, no paired fins, and no scales. Then there are the sharks, skates, and rays, fishes that have skeletons made of *cartilage,* a substance

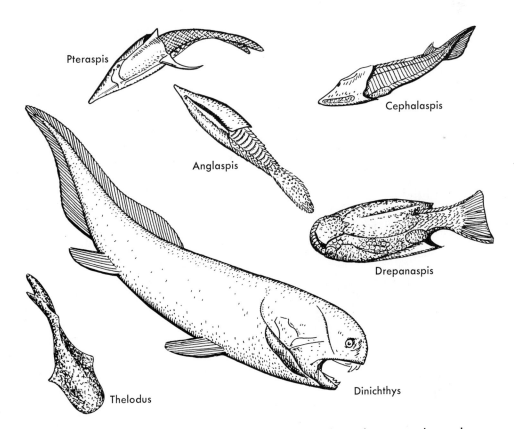

27-1 Extinct Fossil Fishes. Jawless, armored fishes, such as the ostracoderms shown, represent the earliest vertebrates. Dinichthys, which appeared later, was more advanced than the ostracoderms. He had large jaws and grew to a length of 30 feet.

softer than bone. The most advanced forms of fishes have bony skeletons.

Primitive Fishes

Certain present-day fishes that exhibit characteristics similar to those of ancient fishes are known as *primitive fishes*. The most important of these characteristics is a skeleton made of cartilage instead of bone. The primitive, or cartilaginous, fishes make up the first two classes of fishes, Agnatha (lampreys and hagfish) and Chondrichthyes (sharks, rays, skates, and sawfish).

Fishes with cartilaginous skeletons are a small group. Of the 600 species, most are confined to the warm tropical seas. They are the largest of the fishes. One species, the whale shark, attains a length of 50 feet. It is one of the largest of all vertebrates, second in size only to the whale. Some sharks, like the common dogfish shark of our Atlantic coast, rarely grow longer than 30 inches.

THE SEA LAMPREY. The adult lamprey is parasitic upon other fish. It is often confused with an eel, which it closely resembles. Unlike the eel, which is a bony fish, the sea lamprey has a skeleton made of cartilage. Its skin is smooth and slimy, entirely devoid of scales, colored brown or dark blue above and white below. There is

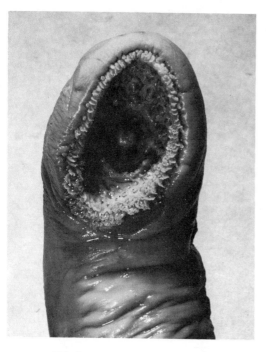

27–2 Mouth of Sea Lamprey

no distinct head, but a pair of eyes marks the head region. Between the eyes is a single nostril. The paired fins of bony fishes are absent. There are fins on the midline of the body near the posterior end. These form the dorsal fin and tail. Behind the eyes are seven pairs of *gill slits.*

The blunt mouth of the lamprey is its most prominent feature. It is circular and has no jaws. Within the mouth are horny teeth and a rasping tongue. The lamprey attaches itself to its victim, bores a hole in its body, and then sucks the blood from it. The lamprey has been known to kill another fish in as little as four hours.

Thriving in either fresh or salt water, the lamprey attacks many fish man uses as food. Sturgeon, cod, and mackerel are attacked in the ocean. Trout, carp, and white-fish are attacked in freshwater lakes and streams. The migration of sea lampreys into

the Great Lakes has had a disastrous effect upon lake trout. Between 1936 and 1948 the commercial catch in Lake Huron dropped from almost two million pounds to less than five thousand. Experiments have shown that an adult lamprey kills about 20 pounds of fish during its active feeding period.

Careful study of the lamprey's habits and life cycle pointed to possible methods of control. The lamprey, like the salmon, migrates from the ocean into freshwater streams to spawn. Those that live in the Great Lakes travel up tributaries to reproduce. The female lays about 60,000 eggs, which the male fertilizes with sperm. Then both adults die. In a few weeks the eggs hatch into small blind larvae that swim downstream into quiet water. Here the larvae make a burrow in the muddy bottom where they remain for almost five years. In their fifth year the larvae change into adults, which return to the lake and begin their attacks upon fishes.

The construction of mechanical and electrical barriers has proved quite effective in preventing the adults from going upstream to spawn. Other attempts at control are aimed at the developing larvae. The most promising method so far has been the use of a substance that kills the larvae of the lamprey but is almost harmless to other fishes.

THE HAGFISH. Like the lamprey, the hagfish is a round-mouthed, primitive fish. But it is even more destructive. It lives on the sea bottom, sometimes at a depth of more than 2000 feet. Its principal victims are cod and flounder. Fishermen often find in their nets fishes that have been partly eaten away by this parasite.

Hagfishes are similar to the lamprey in appearance. The mouth, however, is soft and four pairs of tentacles grow around it. The gill slits are also more numerous and are placed farther back along the body. An

27–3 Mouth of Hagfish

SHARKS. Some of the earliest ancestors of modern sharks appeared in the sea at a time when the giant fern forests flourished on the land. But they were not numerous, probably because the smaller fishes they now prey upon had not yet journeyed to the ocean basins.

Sharks are more advanced fishes than the lampreys. The skull and the vertebrae are better developed and the brain is enclosed in a *cranium*. The mouth is equipped with firm jaws containing numerous sharp, pointed teeth, usually curved backward. The teeth are loosely attached to the jaws, easily lost and easily replaced.

An important advance seen in the sharks is the development of paired fins. These are the *pectoral fins* behind the head and the *pelvic fins* near the anus. The development of these paired fins corresponds to the development of the paired limbs of the higher vertebrates. The appearance of paired fins in the sharks marks a great step forward in the vertebrate body plan.

The skin of sharks is very rough because of the presence of many *placoid scales.*

unusual feature of its life history is that the same individual that develops as a male, producing sperm cells, later functions as a female, producing eggs.

27–4 Dogfish Shark

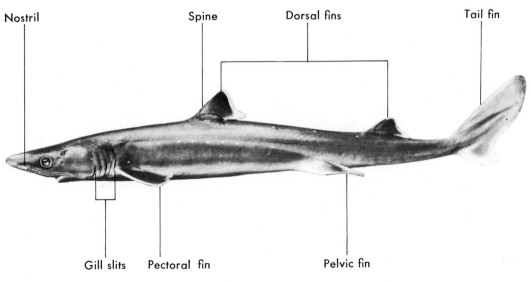

Nostril Spine Dorsal fins Tail fin

Gill slits Pectoral fin Pelvic fin

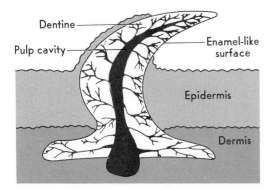

Dentine

Pulp cavity

Enamel-like surface

Epidermis

Dermis

27–5 Skin of shark is covered with placoid scales, the forerunners of true teeth. Over the jaws, these scales are modified into teeth, which point backward.

These are extremely hard scales built on the same plan as the teeth of higher vertebrates. Most of the scale is composed of *dentine* and is covered by a material like enamel. The teeth of the shark are made in the same way and are considered to be modified scales.

Sharks have a reputation as man-eaters, but this is a reputation deserved by only a

27–6 Sting Ray

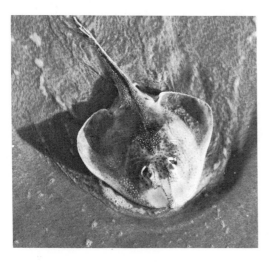

few species. Sharks feed upon smaller fishes, squids, and crustaceans. But the great white shark, a thirty-foot monster, does not hesitate to attack man. Large and aggressive though he is, the white shark would suffer by comparison with the sharks of long ago. Several reconstructed sharks appear to have been much bigger, with huge teeth, twice the size of the largest modern species.

SKATES AND RAYS. These relatives of the shark have flattened bodies. A further modification is the greatly enlarged pectoral fins, which give the appearance of wings. As these "wings" are waved in the water, the fish swims, or "flies." Skates and rays are generally bottom-dwellers, feeding upon mollusks and crustaceans. Both the mouth and gill slits are on the ventral surface. Several openings on top of the head behind the eyes lead clear water into the gills.

The *sting ray*, an inhabitant of warmer coastal waters, has a thin tail tipped with poisonous barbs. The sting ray lies half buried in the sand and feeds upon mollusks, which it crushes with powerful teeth. When disturbed, the sting ray lashes out with its tail and can inflict severe wounds. The barbs have even been known to penetrate leather shoes.

The *electric rays* have developed still another way of capturing prey. The muscles of the large fins have become modified to form electric generating organs. The sudden release of the electricity stuns their prey and enables them to seize it.

The *sawfish* is another ray that has enlarged pectoral fins for swimming. Larger than most rays. the sawfish attains a length of ten to twenty feet. But its outstanding characteristic is its enlarged snout, which is edged with sharp, pointed teeth. Swimming into a school of small fishes, it thrashes about with its "saw." The fishes it injures are then eaten.

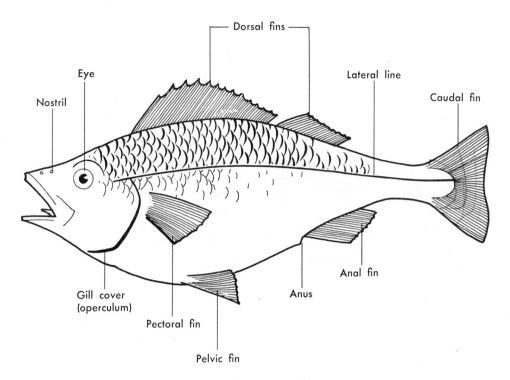

Nostril

Eye

Dorsal fins

Lateral line

Caudal fin

Gill cover
(operculum)

Pectoral fin

Pelvic fin

Anus

Anal fin

27–7 External Structure of Bony Fish

The Bony Fishes

Most of the familiar fishes have a skeleton made of bone. Many biologists refer to them as the "true" fishes to distinguish them from the more primitive, cartilaginous forms. The bony fishes are found in the oceans, lakes, and streams of every part of the world. They are the predominant form of vertebrate life, outnumbering all of the other classes.

EXTERNAL CHARACTERISTICS. The body of the typical fish consists of three parts: the head, trunk, and tail. These merge into a streamlined body that permits the fish to move almost effortlessly through the water. The body is covered with scales that overlap toward the rear, like shingles on a roof. Large numbers of *mucous glands* embedded in the skin secrete a slippery fluid that protects the fish against infection and also makes movement through the water easier.

Fins are typical appendages of fish. The dorsal fins are found on the back. The caudal fin is at the extreme end of the tail. The anal fin is on the ventral midline of the body. The paired pectoral and pelvic fins are found just behind the gill cover.

The mouth is at the extreme front of the head and has jaws that bear fine teeth. The mouth leads to the digestive tract and also permits water to enter the gills. The large flap on the side of the head just behind the eyes is the gill cover, or *operculum*. The typical gill slits of the lower fishes are not exposed in bony fishes. In front of the eyes are the nostrils, or *nares*. Unlike the nostrils of the higher vertebrates, these openings are used only for the sense of smell, not for breathing. There is no connection between them and the mouth.

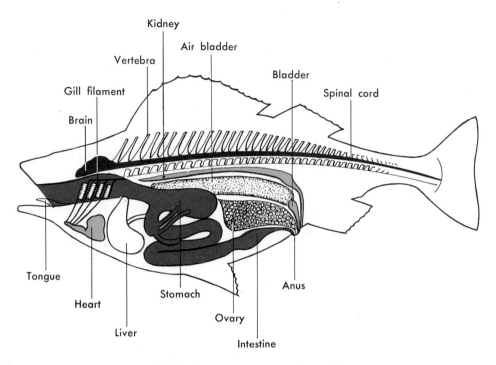

Kidney

Air bladder

Vertebra

Bladder

Gill filament

Spinal cord

Brain

Tongue

Heart

Stomach

Anus

Liver

Ovary

Intestine

27–8 Internal Anatomy of Bony Fish

SWIMMING. Have you ever watched a fish in an aquarium to see how it swims? A fish swims so easily that its slight movements are difficult to observe. The caudal fin is the most important one for propulsion. It pushes the fish forward as it is moved from side to side. The other fins are used for balancing and steering. The fins along the center line of the body keep the fish in an upright position.

The fish, like a submarine, needs ballast to adjust to water pressure at different depths. Its ballast tank is the *air bladder,* a large, thin sac filled with gas derived from the blood vessels. The fish can regulate the amount of gas in the sac. In deep water it is contracted; in shallow water it is expanded. If a fish from a great depth is brought up suddenly, the pressure drop causes the bladder to expand so rapidly that it forces the stomach out of the mouth.

THE SKELETON. The plan of the fish skeleton is the basic plan of the vertebrate body reduced to a simple form. Most prominent is the major axis of the body consisting of the numerous vertebrae. These form the backbone. The head derives its pattern from the shape of the skull, some parts of which are made of cartilege. Surrounding the internal organs are the ribs, bones that are attached to the vertebrae by connective tissue. There are no limbs, but the paired fins are believed to be the forerunners of the limbs of higher vertebrates.

DIGESTION. Big fishes eat little fishes, and little fishes eat littler fishes. But a limit comes where the smallest fishes must eat algae and protozoa, at least in part. There always seems to be some smaller insect, mollusk, or crustacean that even the smallest fish can eat. The mouth and teeth of fish indicate they are generally carnivorous, for the teeth are sharp and recurved for holding prey. The food is swallowed whole.

From the mouth the food passes through the pharynx, where the gill slits are located, into the short esophagus and then to the stomach. Here enzymes begin to digest the food. Digestion continues in the short intestine. Undigested food accumulates as waste in the intestine and is eliminated through the anus just forward of the anal fin.

CIRCULATION. Although the circulatory system of the fish is rather simple in comparison with that of higher vertebrates, it is considerably more advanced than in the invertebrate animals.

The blood is pumped through a closed system of blood vessels by the heart. This is a two-chambered organ in the ventral

portion of the body cavity just beneath the gills. The *ventricle,* the muscular pumping chamber, sends blood through the *ventral aorta* to the gills. The other chamber, the *atrium,* receives blood returning to the heart from all parts of the body. Valves in the heart control the flow of blood from the atrium into the ventricle. The blood contains red corpuscles and white corpuscles. The latter are like amebae. The heart itself is contained in a very thin, watery sac, the *pericardial cavity.*

After blood has been pumped to the gills to receive oxygen, it is distributed to the rest of the body by the *dorsal aorta.* This large artery, located just under the backbone, branches into smaller arteries that supply blood to the organs of the head, trunk, and tail. The arteries are further sub-

27–9 Diagram of Fish Circulation. A fish has a two-chambered heart, consisting of a ventricle and an atrium. Blood flows from ventrical to gills, where oxygen is absorbed and carbon dioxide is given off. Colored portions represent oxygenated blood.

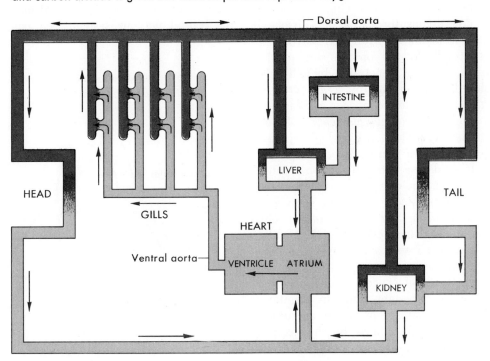

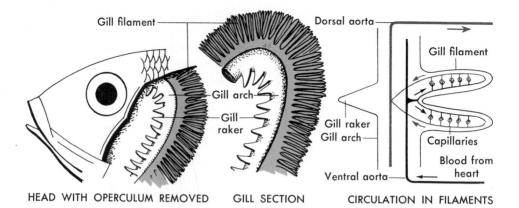

Gill filament

Dorsal aorta

Gill filament

Gill arch

Gill raker

Gill raker
Gill arch

Capillaries

Blood from
heart

Ventral aorta

HEAD WITH OPERCULUM REMOVED   GILL SECTION   CIRCULATION IN FILAMENTS

27–10 Gills of a Bony Fish. The operculum has been removed to show the gill parts. Enlargements show structural details and the flow of blood through gill filaments.

divided into a network of capillaries. The capillaries collect wastes from and bring food and oxygen to the individual cells. The blood now flows from the capillaries into the smallest veins, then into larger ones. Finally, they collect into one large vein that empties into the atrium.

GILLS AND RESPIRATION. Gills are special breathing organs for extracting dissolved oxygen from water. Most fish have four pairs of gills located on the side of the pharynx, which is penetrated by gill slits. Each gill is supported by a *gill arch*, a tough, curved structure made of cartilage.

A double row of *gill filaments* is found on each arch. These are richly supplied with blood. Their thin walls permit carbon dioxide to diffuse outward into the water. At the same time oxygen diffuses from the water into the blood. The inner surface of the gill arch contains the *gill rakers*. Gill rakers are straining devices that keep solid food particles from passing over the delicate gill filaments.

The amount of oxygen dissolved in the water is an important factor in maintaining fish in a stream or in an aquarium. Autotrophs supply much of the oxygen fishes need. Some oxygen is also dissolved

at the surface where the water and air meet. Aerating pumps in an aquarium keep the oxygen level high. When the supply of oxygen is inadequate, fishes suffocate.

THE NERVOUS SYSTEM AND SENSE ORGANS. The nervous system of the fishes is far more complex than that of the highest invertebrates. The brain and spinal cord make up the central nervous system. Ten pairs of

27–11 Diagram shows water movement over gills, out slits, and under opercula.

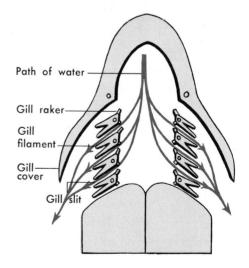

Path of water

Gill raker

Gill filament

Gill cover

Gill slit

cranial nerves emerge from the brain. A pair of spinal nerves arises from each segment of the backbone. The brain is small, but the principal parts found in the higher vertebrates are present.

The fish is well equipped with sense organs. The eyes have no eyelids. The eyes are kept moist by the water. Fishes seem to be somewhat nearsighted. The sense of smell is located in the nostrils, or *olfactory sacs*. The skin is responsive to touch. A small tongue enables the fish to taste its food. There is some doubt about the function of the ear, which is internal and not visible from the outside. There is evidence, however, that at least some fish can hear. One sense organ peculiar to the fish is the *lateral line*. The lateral line is a row of minute pits along the side of the body that responds to pressure changes and vibrations in the water.

REPRODUCTION AND DEVELOPMENT. With the approach of spring many fishes migrate to areas favorable for spawning. For freshwater fishes this may mean traveling from the deeper water of a lake to the more shallow streams. For some marine fishes it means migrating hundreds of miles to ancestral breeding grounds. Having arrived at the breeding site, the female lays thousands of eggs in the water. These are fertilized by the male who deposits sperm cells directly over them.

Some species show novel aspects of spawning behavior. The stickleback, for example, has an elaborate mating ritual. The male builds a nest of algal threads that are held together by a sticky kidney secretion. His color then changes to a bluish white with red spots on the belly. In his bright garb he performs a sort of dance to entice a female to lay her eggs in his nest. After a female has done so, he places sperm, or *milt*, over the eggs. It is the male who carefully guards the eggs until they hatch and the fry mature.

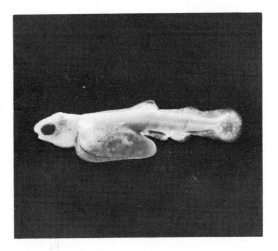

27–12 Yolk sac attached to the abdomen of young fish supplies nourishment until fish is capable of obtaining its own food.

Fertile eggs hatch into fishes in about one or two weeks. Much of the egg consists of yolk, and the development is somewhat like that of the chick. A tiny bit of cytoplasm develops into the blastodisc growing on top of the yolk. From this the embryo gradually takes shape as it grows around the yolk. When the young fish first hatches, part of the yolk sac still remains attached to it. Soon, however, it learns to find its own food and becomes independent. In this immature condition the young fishes are tasty morsels for animals that live in the water. They are eaten by the thousands. The few that survive are but a tiny fraction of the number of eggs fertilized.

FISH MIGRATIONS. The migration of fishes over long distances to spawn raises some interesting questions. Why do they do it? How do they know the way? Of special interest are the salmon and the common eel.

The Pacific salmon lives in the sea as an adult, but returns to freshwater streams to spawn. In the spring and summer millions of adults invade the coastal rivers where they battle swift currents to reach the gravel

27–13 The salmon has to fight upstream to return to the freshwater spawning grounds.

bottoms of the headwaters. Here they lay their eggs. The female scoops out a place in the river bed with her tail. The fertilized eggs are covered with bits of gravel to protect them. After hatching, the young fishes make their way down the river to the sea. The parents of some species die soon after spawning.

For commercial fishermen, spawning season is the time of the big annual catch.

During the peak of the migration, the salmon are so thick that they are netted by the hundred thousands. In Alaska, even the bears and their cubs sit by brooks during the salmon run and scoop them up in their paws. The amount of salmon caught on the Pacific coast amounts to about one-quarter of the total tonnage of fish marketed in the United States and Canada.

The common eel migrates from the freshwater streams of Europe and North America to an area south of Bermuda in the open sea. Although the eel is a common fish, its breeding habits were a mystery until the breeding place was discovered by Johannes Schmidt, a Danish naturalist. What impels the eels to migrate several thousand miles is still a mystery. It is known, however, that the breeding area is a spot in the ocean where the temperature and salinity of the water is greater at a depth of two hundred and fifty fathoms than elsewhere in the Atlantic.

The eels that undertake the long journey to Bermuda can usually be identified by color. In the autumn they become silvery, instead of their normal yellow-green. They also stop feeding. From Iceland, Norway, Sweden, from Canada and the United States—even from Egypt—these silvery eels travel to their appointed spot in the ocean. Once there, they breed two hundred and

27–14 American eels average three feet in length. Larger ones may reach six feet.

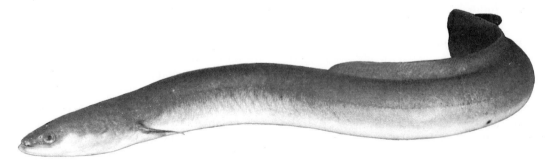

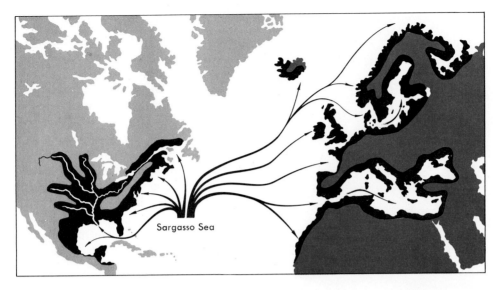

27-15   Migration of Eels from Southern Atlantic to North America and to Europe

fifty fathoms beneath the surface. Then they die. They do not feed on their long journey that takes many months. The transparent larvae that hatch from the fertile eggs swim near the surface and feed on the plankton. The European eels then travel eastward, riding the Gulf Stream across the Atlantic. They travel about a thousand miles a year and arrive along the European coast three years after their departure from Bermuda. At this stage the larvae are transformed into baby eels, called *elvers*. The elvers now enter fresh water streams and grow to maturity. It usually takes the large silvery females about twelve years to reach the stage where they migrate. The American eels do much the same thing except that the larvae swim westward and mature into elvers in about one year. Their journey from their spawning grounds is much shorter.

FISHES AND MAN. Throughout the entire world fishes are an important part of man's diet. They are an excellent source of proteins, minerals, and vitamins. Herring,

flounder, mackerel, cod, tuna, and salmon are but a few of the fish we eat. In countries where meat is not plentiful, fish are important in the national diet. Seafood accounts for most of the animal protein in the diet of the Japanese, for example. As the world's population grows, man's dependence upon food from the sea will undoubtedly increase.

The finest commercial fishing areas in the world are located in the North Atlantic and the North Pacific oceans. These areas supply 98 per cent of all the fish caught in the world. Along the coastal strips of the northern continents, the sea bottom slopes gently and forms the great fishing banks where vast schools of herring, mackerel, and cod abound. These have been commercial fishing grounds for centuries.

Man has other uses for fishes besides food. Oil from the liver of the cod is a rich source of vitamin D. Shark livers contain an abundance of vitamin A. Fish meal is used as fertilizer and pet food. Some fish, like the stickleback, have been used as labora-

27–16 Stocking a Stream with Trout

Fish Conservation. Fish are one of the many important natural resources that need protection for future generations. Many rivers that once teemed with fishes have become so polluted with industrial wastes, sewage, and garbage that the fish population has been reduced to the vanishing point in those rivers. The active cooperation of communities that use the stream can effect dramatic improvement. Pollution control and restocking have restored some streams to their original condition.

Even in the ocean, where one would expect an almost inexhaustible supply of fishes, serious problems have arisen as a result of poor conservation practices. For instance, polluted coastal rivers pollute in turn the bays and inlets. Overfishing by commercial interests has also reduced the fish supply. This problem has led to the establishment of international agreements. Such agreements have been in effect between the United States and Canada since 1924, when an International Fishery Commission was formed.

tory animals. Certain small fish eat mosquito larvae. Stocking lakes and streams with them has been an effective method of mosquito control.

27–17 A steplike fishladder enables fish to bypass power dam and return to spawning grounds. Passageways are also constructed near power dams to allow young to go down river to the ocean. At some dams, fish are provided with elevators.

SPORT FISHING. With the increase in the leisure time available to Americans, both fresh- and saltwater fishing are attracting millions of new sportsmen each year. Many of the game fish are stocked in local streams by state agencies. Millions of dollars are spent each year for rods, hooks, and lures. The money obtained from the anglers' license fees is used in part to rear young fishes in state hatcheries so that the restocking of streams can be continuous.

Forerunners of the Amphibians

Some fish breathe by lungs. One is native to Australia and is known locally as the *Barramunda*. It is a large fish that reaches six feet in length. Its African cousin lives along the Nile. A South American cousin is found in Paraguay. Each species lives in swamps and marshland, where wet seasons are followed by periods of drought. The nostrils of these fishes are modified to draw in air. The air bladder is used as a lung. During the dry season they dig burrows in the muddy bottom, being careful to construct a breathing pore to admit air. Then they become inactive and live on their

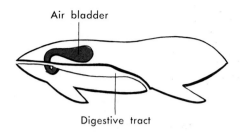

LUNGFISH

Air bladder

Digestive tract

27–18 Lungfishes have air bladders that open into the esophagus, as shown above.

stored fat until the rains create more swampy pools.

The lungfishes are believed to be survivors of several ancient species. Lunglike structures appeared early in the development of fishes. Furthermore, the very conditions that are suitable for the lungfishes today are believed to be the conditions that existed when their ancestors first appeared upon the planet. Alternate periods of drought and rain characterized the Age of Fishes. It was thus a great advantage for the fish to have lungs to breathe air when the water dried up.

27–19 Modern Lungfish. The earliest fishes probably lived in oxygen-poor water and had a lunglike accessory breathing organ, which later evolved into an air bladder.

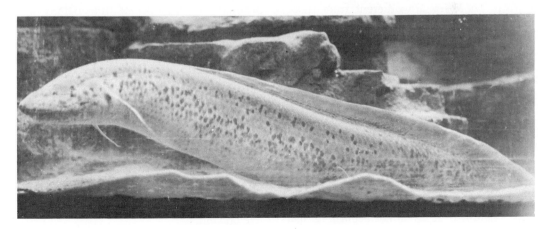

27–20 Coelacanth. This specimen was caught off South Africa in 1952. Dr. J.L.B. Smith, identifier of Coelacanth, is shown kneeling behind its head.

Although the lungfishes are believed to be somewhat off the main path that led to the development of the amphibians, one other characteristic they possess is noteworthy. Their fins are different from those found in most modern fishes. They contain a fleshy lobe within which are the typical bones of the higher vertebrates.

THE COELACANTH: A LIVING FOSSIL. If you saw a dinosaur charging down the street, you'd probably think you were dreaming. Yet, in the year 1938 a strange event occurred that was in some ways like the return of a dinosaur. A trawler working along the South African coast brought in a peculiar five-foot fish with large blue scales. J. L. B. Smith, a South African zoologist identified it as a *coelacanth*, a fish whose ancestry dated back to fossils 300 million years old. It was believed that fish like the coelacanth had become extinct 60 million years ago! Called lobefins from the peculiar construction of the paired fins, fish similar to these are believed to be the ancestors of all the land-based higher vertebrates. They were, in a sense, ancestral cousins of the lungfish. Even today they have a pair of outgrowths from the throat that resemble the lungs of ancient fishes.

Since 1938, about a dozen coelacanths have been caught off the east coast of South Africa. Scientists are busy studying these "living fossils" in hopes of gathering more information about how these strange fishes may have developed into animals that could live on land.

CLASSES OF FISHES

Class	Characteristics	Example
Agnatha	Poorly-developed, cartilaginous skeleton. No vertebrae. Exposed gill slits. Tail and dorsal fin; no paired fins. No jaws or scales.	Lamprey, hagfish
Chondrichthyes	Well-developed, cartilaginous skeleton. Uniform vertebrae. Exposed gill slits. Paired fins. Well-developed jaws. Scales present.	Shark, ray, skate, sawfish
Osteichthyes	Bony, well-developed skeleton. Uniform vertebrae. Gill slits covered by opercula. Paired fins. Well-developed jaws. Scales present with few exceptions.	Perch, trout, carp, mackerel

IMPORTANT POINTS

● The fishes are the simplest and most numerous vertebrates. Typically their streamlined bodies are covered with scales. They breathe by means of gills. They use fins for swimming.

● The primitive fishes have a skeleton made of cartilage and gill slits on the side of the head. Some of the simplest fishes have neither jaws, nor paired fins, nor scales. Most of the modern fishes have a bony skeleton, paired fins, and gill covers.

● Bony fishes have their skeleton, sense organs, and organ systems built on the same structural plan as the higher vertebrates. Biologists believe that the ancient fishes gave rise to the amphibians, the first vertebrates to live on land.

● Some fish travel many miles to reproduce. Salmon leave the sea to spawn in fresh water. Eels leave freshwater streams and travel several thousand miles to spawn in the ocean.

● Fishes are of great economic importance not only as food, but also as a source of vitamins and fertilizer. Sound conservation programs are necessary to insure their protection.

● One of the great events in the development of vertebrate life on our planet was the invasion of the land by the amphibians. The lungfishes and lobefins provide us with clues that help us understand how this event may have occurred.

REVIEW QUESTIONS

1. What are the major characteristics of the three classes of fishes?
2. How are lampreys controlled in the Great Lakes Region?
3. In what two ways are sharks more advanced than lampreys?
4. Why are paired fins important in the growth of the vertebrate body plan?
5. What functions do the gills perform in circulation?
6. Describe the migration of the salmon or the eel.
7. Why is the coelacanth referred to as a "living fossil"?
8. How are deep sea fishes different from those living near the surface?
9. What are three characteristics of bony fishes?
10. Trace the path of the blood in the circulatory system of a fish.
11. What are the three principal parts of the gill?

CHECK YOUR UNDERSTANDING

12. Fishes lay thousands of eggs. Why aren't the earth's waters overrun with them?
13. Discuss the importance of fish as a natural resource.
14. What lungfish characteristics may have led to the rise of amphibians?
15. What do biologists hope to learn from the study of the coelacanth?
16. Why do fishes like the sea horse that raise their young in brood pouches lay fewer eggs than most other fishes?
17. How would you explain the fact that practically all large fishes are carnivorous, and very small ones are largely herbivorous?
18. Why are the organs of deep sea fishes often ruptured when they are hauled rapidly to the surface?
19. Why is the density of a fish population likely to be high near the surface of the sea and sparse in its depths?
20. International agreements that regulate ocean fishing will probably become even more important in the future. Can you think of reasons for this?

RESEARCH PROJECTS AND REPORTS

1. Obtain information from your school or public library and prepare a report on of the following topics:

Man-eating Sharks	**Deep Sea Fishes**
Fish Conservation	**The Sea Lamprey**

2. *A Balanced Aquarium:* Your class or biology club may want to keep small fishes in a balanced aquarium. This may be easily done if certain rules are followed:
An aquarium measuring approximately 12 × 8 × 8 inches is very good for smaller fishes. Place about an inch of washed sand or gravel on the bottom. Fill the aquarium about two-thirds full of lake or stream water, preferably from the place where the fishes are caught. Add water plants. The best producers of oxygen are *Vallesneria*, *Elodea*, and *Myriophyllum*. Plants may be weighted or tied to small stones. Allow water to stand for several days.

Stock aquarium with small sunfish, perch, or minnows. Goldfish purchased from a pet shop may also be used. Do not use too many fishes. Six or seven should be enough. Add a few snails to keep the glass clear of algae. Stand aquarium in bright place. Direct sunlight will heat the water and kill the fish. Watch for a few days. Some of your fish may attack and eat others. These predators may be removed and replaced with more peaceful inhabitants. For a while your fishes will feed on the plants. Tiny bits of meat, insects, or small worms may be added. Prepared fish food may also be used. Fishes thrive better when fed sparingly.

3. *Maintaining Tropical Fish:* Tropical fish require more care than other kinds of aquarium fish. However, you might like to rear and observe guppies and Japanese medakas, which can be maintained with little extra effort. Although tropical, neither of these fish requires rigid temperature control. Guppies can even withstand occasional low temperatures. Both may be purchased in pet shops.

    Guppies: Guppies can be fed prepared commercial foods. They are interesting because they are live bearers. The young, which are smaller than rice grains, dart about with great agility. When you have a brood of "fry," remove the adults to a second tank lest they eat most of the young.

    Japanese Medakas: Medakas need live food in order to reproduce. If fed on Daphnia, the female will produce a batch of eggs daily. Try to remove these eggs (they are attached to the female) with a camelhair brush, and place them in a glass dish. The eggs are clear and the development of the embryos may be observed through a dissection microscope. Make a series of drawings of the day-to-day embryonic development.

4. *Circulation of Blood in the Fish's Tail:* The caudal fin of a small goldfish offers an excellent opportunity to study the circulation of blood in a living animal. Wrap the fish in moistened absorbent cotton or paper toweling and place on the stage of a microscope. The exposed tail is placed between two glass slides and positioned in the center of the hole in the stage. Use the low-power objective and focus carefully upon the thin membrane between the rods of cartilage that support the fin. Write a description of what you see.

FURTHER READING

Kamongo. Homer W. Smith. Viking Press, New York, N.Y. An absorbing novel about an expedition in search of a lungfish, written by a zoologist.

The Fishes. Editors of LIFE. Time, Inc., New York, N.Y. A well written and beautifully illustrated account of the fishes of the world.

Old Fourlegs: The Story of the Coelacanth. J. L. B. Smith. Longmans, Green and Co., New York, N.Y. A fascinating account of the capture of the first living coelacanth by the scientist who identified it.

"Electric Fishes." Harry Grundfest. *Scientific American*, October, 1960, page 115. Electric fishes are known to generate up to 500 volts with enough current to electrocute their prey in some cases.

"The Hagfish." David Jensen. *Scientific American*, February, 1966, page 82. This primitive animal has four hearts, can tie itself into a knot, and can live for months without feeding.

28

The Amphibians
Invasion of the Land

JUST AS PLANT LIFE is believed to have originated in the warm ancient seas and spread to the land, so animal life spread from the water and finally conquered the land.

The first vertebrates that lived on the land were the amphibians. Most amphibians known today start life in the water. Later they are able to live on the land. Some of the more common amphibians include frogs, toads, and salamanders.

At least two very important factors helped the first amphibians to survive upon the land. First, they had the ability to breathe air. Second, they had a means of locomotion other than fins. Closely related to the lungfish, they had lungs and short, stubby legs.

What was the nature of the earth at the time amphibians appeared? Geologists tell us that it was a period of great upheaval. New continents arose as a result of titanic forces within the earth's crust. Vast inland seas were created in which animal life was trapped. Periods of drought followed, and the seas shrank. Many animals perished. But those that had legs and could breathe air emerged from the water to seek another place to live. The amphibians could slither through the drying ooze of the muddy bottoms while animals like fishes were trapped. Although they were the pioneers on the land, the amphibians were only partially adapted for their new role. They still had to keep their skin moist, and they were dependent upon the water for reproductive processes. Except for the change from paired fins into stubby legs, the earliest amphibians resembled the lobe-finned fishes.

Kinds of Amphibians

The earliest amphibians appeared about 350 million years ago. However, they did not reach their greatest development until millions of years later. Unlike today's forms, many of the fossil amphibians were quite large; some were eight feet in length. They are believed to have spent most of their lives in water. The swampy environment seems to have been ideal for these first amphibians. On their tail was a dorsal fin, a remnant of their fish ancestry.

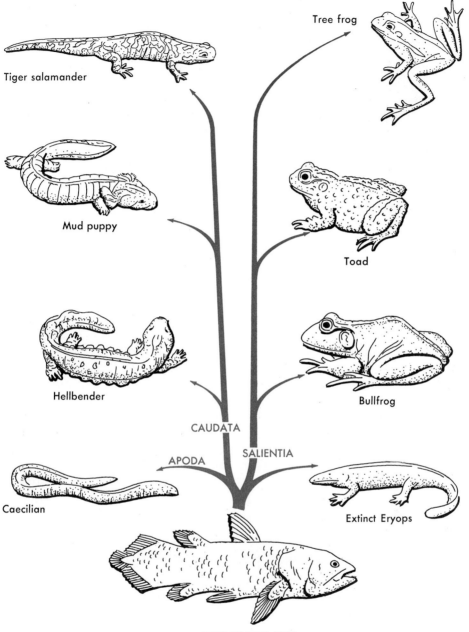

Tree frog

Tiger salamander

Mud puppy

Toad

Hellbender

Bullfrog

CAUDATA

APODA   SALIENTIA

Caecilian

Extinct Eryops

LOBE-FINNED FISH

28—1   PROBABLE ORIGIN OF AMPHIBIANS

28–2 Eusthenopteron, a lobe-finned fish of 350 million years ago, had a lunglike air bladder and could crawl on land. The amphibian Diplovertebron, a probable descendant of lobe-finned fishes, had limbs structured like those of land vertebrates.

MODERN AMPHIBIANS. The amphibians reached a period of great success, then declined. Many of the larger forms became extinct. It is interesting to note that ten of the original thirteen orders of amphibians are extinct. Only three orders survive today, but their representatives are numerous in many parts of the world. Two of the three orders are especially numerous in North America. These are the *tailed forms,* like the salamander, and the *tailless forms,* like the frog and toad. The third order (Apoda) consists of wormlike inhabitants of the tropics.

One of the most important characteristics of the amphibians is their dependence upon water for breeding. Most forms mate and lay their eggs in water. The larvae that hatch from the eggs resemble fishes in certain ways, but gradually they undergo changes that convert them into land-dwelling forms. This two-stage life cycle, one aquatic and one terrestrial, is the main reason for calling these animals amphibians, for the name means "having two lives." This metamorphosis of the amphibians from a water-dwelling to a land-dwelling animal is one of the most interesting events

ORDERS OF AMPHIBIA

Order	Characteristics	Example
Apoda	Body slender and wormlike. Lack feet. Usually found in the tropics.	Caecilia
Caudata	Two pairs of legs. Tailed. Larvae usually aquatic.	Salamanders, newts
Salientia	Jumping form. Tailless. Hindlegs larger than forelegs. Larvae usually aquatic.	Frogs, toads

you can observe. In a few short days you can watch the gradual unfolding of a drama that marked the progress of animal life from the water to the land.

THE SALAMANDERS. Most modern salamanders rarely reach more than a foot in length. They resemble the ancient amphibians in having a tail and four legs. In the adult stage the relationship with the fishes is difficult to establish. The skin of the salamander is not scaly, but smooth and moist. Some biologists take this as an indication that salamanders are degenerate forms that have changed considerably.

As you would expect, salamanders live in a watery environment. The humid undergrowth of the temperate forests, particularly near small lakes and streams, seems to be especially suitable for their growth. They cannot live in the tropics. Although they are quite numerous in North America, few are found in Africa below the northern coastal strip. Australia has none.

You may have seen a red salamander scurrying along the edge of a pond or stream near your home. This is one of the commonest forms in the United States. At this stage it is called the red eft. Later, when it returns to the water to mate, it changes appearance. The dorsal surface becomes olive green with black dots. Along each side there is a row of crimson spots. Now it is more commonly called the spotted newt. The young are different from the adults. They are quite small and breathe by means of gills. As they grow older and larger, their gills are replaced by lungs, and the color changes to red.

Like the red eft, many of the salamanders are brightly colored. The tiger salamander is orange and black when adult. It is common in the United States. The spotted salamander of southern Europe is yellow and black.

UNUSUAL SALAMANDERS. The *axolotl* is a peculiar salamander from Mexico. It swims like a fish, has fins on its back and tail, and breathes by means of large external gills. It has apparently lost the ability to change into an adult and even breeds in the larval form. In the latter part of the 19th century, however, German biologists from the Uni-

28–3 Spotted Newt. Larvae spend about two months in water, then spend about two years on land as red efts. When efts return to water they change into spotted newts.

Red eft (larva)

Spotted newt (adult)

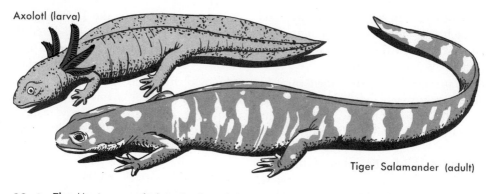

Axolotl (larva)

Tiger Salamander (adult)

28–4 The Mexican axolotl is the larval form of the tiger salamander. Metamorphosis from the larval to the adult form is under the control of the thyroid gland.

versity of Freiburg discovered that a meal of beef thyroid soon enabled the Mexican axolotl to change into an adult. When it turned into an adult, it was found to be a tiger salamander!

Salamanders rarely get very large, but along the Mississippi Valley lives the grotesquely flattened hellbender, an amphibian that grows to a length of almost two feet. Another large American salamander is the mud puppy, but like the axolotl it does not become an adult. Some of the salamanders have limbs that are so small as to be almost unnoticeable. In this condition they

28–5 The mud puppy has large external gills and spends its entire life in the larval form.

MUD PUPPY

resemble eels. One American form, the "Congo eel," may grow three feet long. In Japan, however, lives the giant of all salamanders, a relative of the "Congo eel" that reaches a length of six feet.

A few of the salamanders found in this country have been discovered by *speleologists* (spee-lee-AHL-uh-justs), scientists who study caves. The species found in caves are blind, and their skin is almost without color. This is in sharp contrast to their relatives who live above ground, many of whom are brightly colored.

FROGS AND TOADS. The tailless amphibians, the frogs and toads, are widely distributed and highly specialized. Two characteristics clearly mark them as advanced forms: the leaping legs and the smaller number of vertebrae in the backbone. Fossilized amphibians have as many as thirty vertebrae in the backbone, not including the tail, whereas the toad has only nine.

Toads are similar to frogs in structure, but their skin is much rougher. The skin of the toad produces a bitter secretion that protects it from its enemies. Turtles, birds, and snakes that prey upon toads are somewhat discouraged by the taste.

The tougher skin of the toad enables it to live farther from the water than the

28–6   The American Toad

28–7   Tree Frog

frog. But it must still remain in rather cool, damp places. More active at night, it feeds upon worms, insects, and slugs, which it catches by flipping out its sticky tongue. During March and April the adults journey to a local pond where they mate. The females lay eggs in long strands of gelatine.

The bullfrog, *Rana catesbiana,* is the largest American species, attaining a length of eight inches. Its legs are considered a delicacy and taste like veal. An even larger frog, *Rana goliath,* lives in Africa. This rare form is reported to be a foot long. It is said to be able to eat a rat with one gulp.

Trees seem remote from water, the favorite spot for frogs. Yet one genus, *Hyla,* lives in trees in many parts of the world. Tree frogs are small creatures, with pads on their toes that permit them to grasp the tree surfaces. A common characteristic is the huge vocal sac that enables them to produce sounds worthy of a much larger animal. Some males are able to enlarge the vocal sac to a size greater than the head. One species that lives in the Canary Islands, China, and Japan is capable of changing its color from green to white, to yellow, then to dark brown, in a matter of seconds.

The Frog: A Representative Vertebrate

The common leopard frog is often used in the biology laboratory to study the organ systems of the higher animals. Since the anatomy of all vertebrates is similar, a study of lower animals helps in understanding the human body. By studying frog anatomy, we can learn a great deal about the structure and function of our own bodies. All of the organ systems of the frog have their counterpart in man.

EXTERNAL ANATOMY. A frog lying quietly at the surface of the water near the edge of a pond is difficult to observe. The green skin of its back blends with nearby plants. Its pale underside is an effective camouflage against an enemy looking upward from the bottom of the pond. The large head is joined directly to the trunk—there is no neck. The short forelimbs have only four toes and serve mainly to balance the animal

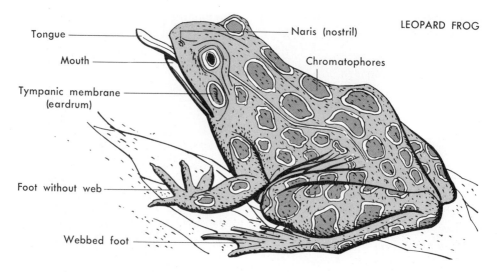

Tongue

Mouth

Tympanic membrane
(eardrum)

Foot without web

Webbed foot

Naris (nostril)

Chromatophores

LEOPARD FROG

28–8 The common leopard frog has round spots and greenish legs and sides. It also has a pair of light lines running from the eye back along the sides.

when it is resting. The hindlegs have five webbed toes and are much larger and more powerful than the forelegs. They provide the thrust for leaping on land. The same kicking motion is used in the water to effect a swift swimming stroke. As soon as they are disturbed, frogs swim to the bottom and swirl up a protective screen of mud.

Two of the sense organs are prominently placed. The eyes protrude from the top of the head, an adaptation that permits the frog to float at the surface of the water and see above it. The *tympanic membranes,* or eardrums, are flat circular plates in back of the eyes. There are no external ears.

A pair of nostrils admits air into the mouth. The nostrils are located on the dorsal surface on the front of the head. This location permits the frog to breathe air while floating on the surface.

The skin of the frog resembles that of higher vertebrates in structure. It consists of an outer epidermis and an inner dermis. Two kinds of glands are found in the dermis. The *mucous glands* are quite numer-

ous and secrete a slimy material that makes the frog very slippery. The poison glands secrete a bitter substance that discourages the frog's enemies from eating it. *Chromatophores,* or pigment cells embedded in the skin, allow the frog to change color and blend with its background. The skin is not joined closely to the muscles of the body wall beneath it. Instead, there are large *lymph spaces* immediately beneath the connective tissue at the base of the dermis. Lymph is a colorless fluid similar to blood except that it contains no red cells. The skin and muscles are joined together by partitions of connective tissue called *septa.* The skin is thus similar to a loose-fitting suit that is stitched to the frog's body along these partitions.

THE SKELETON. The bones of an animal tell a great deal about its total structure as well as its habits. This explains how scientists are able to reconstruct animals from fossilized bones.

The vertebrate skeleton consists of two major parts: the *axial skeleton* and the *appendicular skeleton.* The axial skeleton consists of the skull and the backbone. The appendicular skeleton consists of the paired appendages or limbs. The skeleton is the basic framework of the body. It provides for the attachment of muscles and for the protection of internal organs.

The bony case, the *cranium*, that protects the brain is narrow and flattened, for the brain is not large. At the back of the cranium is a large opening through which the spinal cord joins the brain. On either side of the opening are projections that fit into the first pair of vertebrae. On the sides of the cranium are the large orbits of the eyes. The *maxillary* bones that form the upper jaw are on the side of the head, and beneath them are the *mandibles*, the bones of the lower jaw.

An unusual feature of the frog's skeleton is the small number of vertebrae; there are only nine. Most vertebrates have about twenty-four. There is a very long extension on the last vertebra called the *urostyle*. There are no tail vertebrae, as in most other chordates. Each vertebra has two basic parts: the *centrum,* the bony base, and the *neural arch,* a loop of bone through which the spinal cord passes.

The *pectoral girdle* supports the forelegs. The *pelvic girdle* supports the hindlegs. Both girdles are attached to the vertebrae. Together, they form the appendicular skeleton. The bones of the forelimb and hindlimb have a remarkable resemblance to each other and to the appendages of man.

MUSCLES. Attached to the skeleton are the muscles of the body that control the frog's movements. All the skeletal muscles are voluntary; that is, they are controlled at will by the frog. One of the easiest muscles to locate and study is the *gastrocnemius,* the large muscle in the back of the shank. Its *origin,* the place where it begins, is on the lower part of the thigh. The connective tissue that surrounds it is gathered into a tendon. This is the *tendon of Achilles,* which slips over what would be our heel. Its *insertion,* the place where it is attached

28–9   THE SKELETON OF A FROG

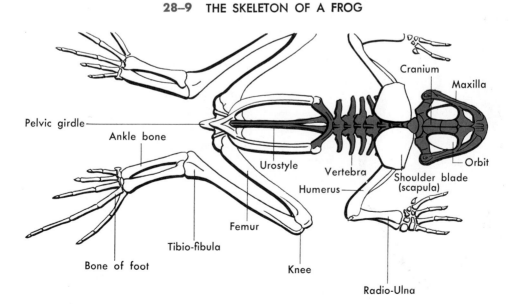

Pelvic girdle

Ankle bone

Bone of foot

Tibio-fibula

Femur

Knee

Radio-Ulna

Urostyle

Vertebra

Humerus

Shoulder blade (scapula)

Cranium

Maxilla

Orbit

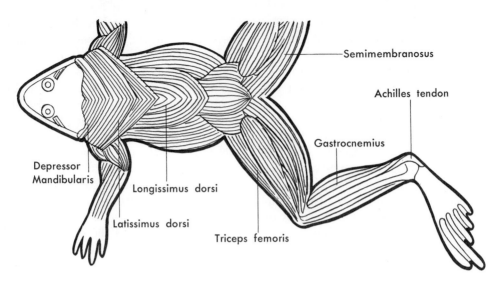

28–10 THE MUSCLES OF A FROG

Semimembranosus

Achilles tendon

Gastrocnemius

Depressor Mandibularis

Longissimus dorsi

Latissimus dorsi

Triceps femoris

to the part to be moved, is on the lower surface of the foot. When the gastrocnemius contracts, it bends the leg and extends the foot.

28–11 Internal Structure of Frog's Mouth

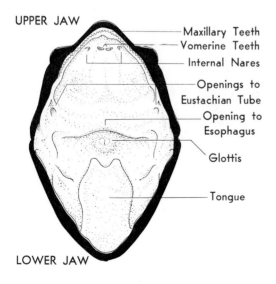

UPPER JAW

Maxillary Teeth
Vomerine Teeth
Internal Nares
Openings to Eustachian Tube
Opening to Esophagus
Glottis
Tongue

LOWER JAW

FOOD GETTING AND DIGESTION. Frogs and toads prefer a diet of living insects. A frog captures insects with its tongue, which is attached to the front of the lower jaw and folded backward. The tongue is sticky and can be flipped out quickly to snare unwary victims. Flies, mosquitoes, and even grasshoppers are thus captured and swallowed whole. Because they eat insects, frogs and toads are valuable to man and should be protected.

The mouth cavity of the frog is quite large, extending from one side of the head to the other. On the edge of the upper jaw there are fine teeth. The roof of the mouth also has two small groups of *vomerine teeth*. An opening at the back of the mouth leads the food into a short *esophagus* that opens into the large stomach. Here the food is stored and acted upon mechanically and chemically. The *pylorus*, the valve at the end of the stomach, regulates the passage of food into the intestine. After it has been moistened by mucus in the

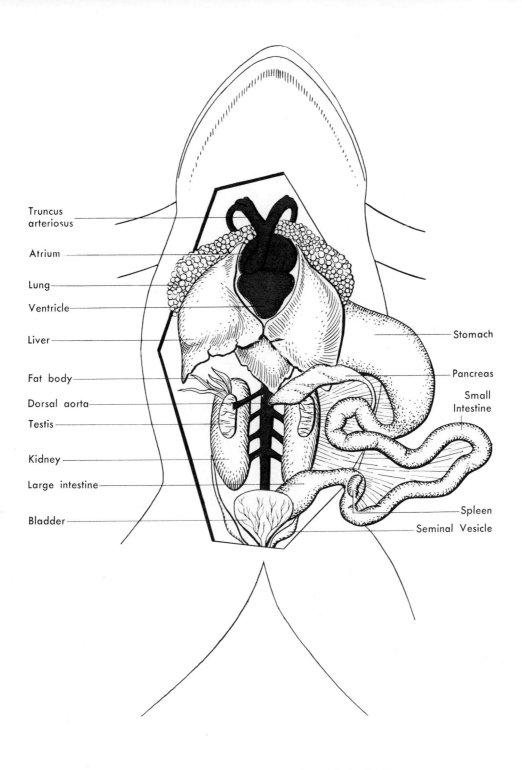

Truncus arteriosus

Atrium

Lung

Ventricle

Liver

Fat body

Dorsal aorta

Testis

Kidney

Large intestine

Bladder

Stomach

Pancreas

Small Intestine

Spleen

Seminal Vesicle

28–12 THE INTERNAL ORGANS OF A FROG

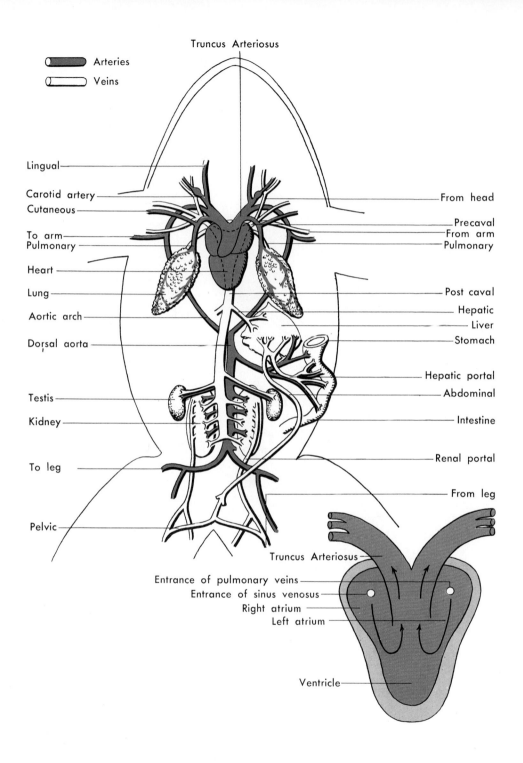

Truncus Arteriosus

Arteries
Veins

Lingual
Carotid artery
Cutaneous
To arm
Pulmonary
Heart
Lung
Aortic arch
Dorsal aorta
Testis
Kidney
To leg
Pelvic

From head
Precaval
From arm
Pulmonary
Post caval
Hepatic
Liver
Stomach
Hepatic portal
Abdominal
Intestine
Renal portal
From leg

Truncus Arteriosus
Entrance of pulmonary veins
Entrance of sinus venosus
Right atrium
Left atrium

Ventricle

28-13   THE CIRCULATORY SYSTEM OF A FROG

stomach and acted upon chemically, the food is in a semiliquid condition as it enters the intestine.

Two very important digestive glands, the *liver* and the *pancreas*, are associated with the small intestine. The liver is a large, red-brown organ that makes *bile*. This is passed to a storage area, the *gall bladder*, a small sac located among the lobes of the liver. A duct or tube carries the bile from the gall bladder to the intestine. Bile prepares fats for digestion. The pancreas is a small, flat gland that lies in the supporting tissue between the stomach and the small intestine. Usually colored yellow, it is not easily seen. Pancreatic secretion is carried to the bile duct, and thence to the intestine. This secretion contains several important digestive enzymes.

The small intestine of the frog is rather short, having only a few loops. Here is where most digestion occurs. The fats, carbohydrates, and proteins are split into simpler molecules and absorbed into the blood. Undigested material accumulates in the large intestine, a shorter, wider tube. The extreme end of the intestine, the *cloaca*, receives liquid waste from the kidneys in addition to the unused food.

THE BLOOD AND HEART. Frog's blood consists of a liquid portion, the *plasma*, within which are the blood cells. Plasma is mostly water containing dissolved salts and proteins. The red blood cells, *erythrocytes*, are oval and somewhat larger than human red blood cells. They also contain a nucleus, a structure that is usually absent in the red cells of mammals. The white blood cells, *leucocytes*, are less numerous than the red. They are of different types and all contain nuclei. *Spindle cells* are also present in frog blood. They release *thrombin*, a chemical that begins the complex process of clotting.

The blood is carried to all parts of the body through a complex system of vessels.

The main parts of this system are the three-chambered heart, the arteries, the veins, and the capillaries. Arteries carry blood away from the heart; veins carry it back to the heart. Between the two are the microscopic capillaries that bring the blood in contact with all the cells of the body.

As in man, the heart is the pump that maintains circulation in the frog. There are two atria, right and left. The right atrium receives blood from most of the body through the large vein called the *sinus venosus*. The left atrium receives blood returning from the lungs. Both atria lead into the single ventricle, which is the main pumping part of the heart. This is a thickly muscled chamber in contrast to the thin-walled atria. Leading from the ventricle is a large artery, the *truncus arteriosus*, which is the main distribution trunk for the entire circulatory system.

ARTERIES OF THE BODY. As the truncus arteriosus emerges from the ventricle it branches almost immediately to the right and to the left. Each branch in turn forms three separate arteries: the *carotid*, the *pulmocutaneous*, and the *aortic arch*. The carotid supplies blood to the head. The pulmocutaneous carries blood to the lungs and skin. The aortic arches give off branches to the shoulder and forelimb before uniting to form the dorsal aorta. This is the principal artery of the body, supplying almost all of the internal organs, including the stomach, intestine, liver, and pancreas. Other branches of it supply the kidneys before it subdivides to send branches to the hind limbs.

VEINS OF THE BODY. All of the returning blood is brought into the sinus venosus and the right atrium by three principal veins: two *precaval veins* from the head and fore-limbs and one *postcaval vein* from most of the rest of the body. In addition, the *pulmonary veins* bring blood that is rich in oxygen to the left atrium.

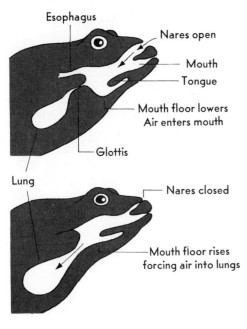

Esophagus

Nares open

Mouth

Tongue

Mouth floor lowers
Air enters mouth

Glottis

Lung

Nares closed

Mouth floor rises
forcing air into lungs

28–14   Breathing Movements of Frog

Two special parts of the venous circulation are worthy of attention. These are the capillary beds in the kidneys, known as the *renal portal system,* and those in the liver, known as the *hepatic portal system.* In the kidneys, veins bringing blood from the hind limbs divide into capillaries and wastes are removed. In the liver, veins from the digestive tract form a capillary net that later unites as the *hepatic veins.* The liver is important in regulating the amount of certain materials in the blood. The hepatic portal circulation permits the liver to exercise control over the blood chemistry. This control is necessary for the blood to function properly.

RESPIRATION. The lungs of the frog are paired, thin-walled sacs that are connected by the *bronchi* to the voice box, or *larynx.* This is a tiny cavity just behind the *glottis,* the opening in the mouth. In the voice box are the vocal cords that make the croaking sound so often heard in the spring.

The continuous gulpings of the frog are his breathing movements. Air is pulled in through the external nares by lowering the floor of the mouth. The nares are then closed, and the floor of the mouth is raised. This forces the air through the glottis and bronchi into the lungs. Air is expelled from the lungs by the contraction of the muscles of the body wall.

The thin walls of the lungs are richly supplied with blood vessels. These subdivide into microscopic capillary nets that surround the smallest units of the lung, the *alveoli* (al-VEE-oh-li). The diffusion of oxygen into the red blood cells occurs here. The waste gas, carbon dioxide, also diffuses from the blood into the air sacs. The blood, thus enriched with oxygen and freed of carbon dioxide, is circulated to all parts of the body to supply the requirements of individual cells.

Although the lungs would seem to be the principal organs used for breathing, the frog can survive long periods without them. During the long winter months when the frog is safely hibernating at the bottom of a pond, its skin serves as its only organ for

28–15   Respiratory Organs of Frog

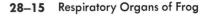
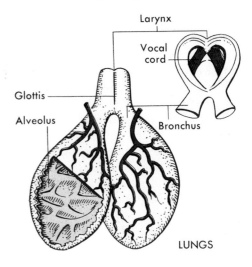

Larynx

Vocal
cord

Glottis

Alveolus

Bronchus

LUNGS

obtaining oxygen. The body covering is richly supplied with blood vessels, and the exchange of oxygen and carbon dioxide can occur either in air or in water.

Another auxiliary method of breathing is by simply pumping air in and out of the mouth cavity. Here the exchange of gases occurs through the mucous membrane lining of the mouth.

THE KIDNEYS AND EXCRETION. On each side of the backbone, pressed closely against the dorsal body wall, are the kidneys. These red-brown organs are the principal means of excreting liquid wastes that accumulate in the blood. Both the dorsal aorta and the renal portal vein keep the kidneys richly supplied with blood.

As the blood circulates through the kidneys, organic waste matter such as *urea,* mineral salts, and water are extracted from it. The filtering occurs in thousands of tiny *renal corpuscles* that make up the kidney. Thus, the blood leaving the kidney through the renal veins has had much of its waste material removed.

In the renal corpuscles tiny droplets of the waste accumulate as *urine.* This is passed through collecting tubules to the *ureters,* small ducts that carry it to the cloaca. Urine may be stored in the urinary bladder and voided later, or voided immediately through the cloacal opening.

THE NERVOUS SYSTEM. The higher forms of animal life require a better developed nervous system to coordinate the more complex systems of the body. Careful study of the frog enables one to understand the functions performed by our own nervous system.

The frog's brain is protected by the cranium as well as by two membranes, the *dura mater* and the *pia mater.* Also surrounding the brain and acting as a shock-absorbing medium is the *cerebrospinal fluid.* The same protective membranes are also found in man.

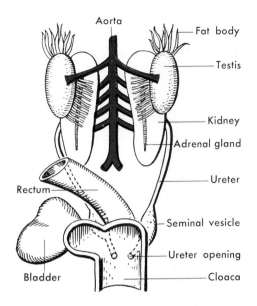

28–16 Urogenital System of Male Frog

The brain has two large *olfactory lobes* at the anterior end (see Figure 28–17). These receive sensations of smell from the nares by way of the olfactory nerve. Two large *cerebral hemispheres* indicate that the frog is capable of a certain amount of intelligent action. They are much larger than those of the fish. There are also two large optic lobes connected by optic nerves to the eyes. Behind the optic lobes is the *cerebellum,* used to co-ordinate muscle activity. The widened *medulla* lies just beneath the cerebellum and connects to the spinal cord. Most of the remaining cranial nerves orginate here.

The eyes, ears, and nostrils are the specialized sense organs. The eyes are similar to man's, but the lens is not adapted to view objects near and far. The nostrils contain the nerve endings that are sensitive to smell. The ear serves two purposes: hearing and maintaining balance. The *auditory nerve* carries impulses from the ear to the brain. The nerve endings that respond to touch and heat are found in the skin. Those

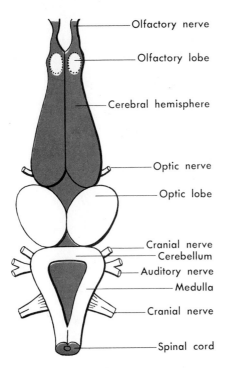

| | Olfactory nerve |
| Olfactory lobe |
| Cerebral hemisphere |
| Optic nerve |
| Optic lobe |
| Cranial nerve |
| Cerebellum |
| Auditory nerve |
| Medulla |
| Cranial nerve |
| Spinal cord |

28–17   Dorsal View of Frog Brain

that respond to taste are on the tongue and in the lining of the mouth.

REPRODUCTION. The mature female frog can easily be distinguished from the male. She has a much thicker abdomen because she produces thousands of eggs. Dissection of the female reveals large egg masses in the ovaries surrounded by coiled oviducts. The ripe, black eggs are released by the ovaries into the body cavity, but eventually enter the oviducts. As they pass down the oviducts a mass of jellylike material is secreted about them so that when they are laid in the water they have a thick coating.

The *testes* in the male frog produce the sperm. Each testis is a small organ found on the ventral surface of the kidney. The sperm cells pass into the kidney through small tubes, then follow the ureter to the cloaca. Both the eggs and sperms pass to the outside through the cloacal opening.

FROM FERTILE EGG TO FROG. The mating call of the frog is a familiar sound that heralds the spring. At this season of the year the female deposits several hundred eggs in the water. The male places sperm over them immediately. The black color of the eggs allows them to absorb heat from the sun. The jelly covering causes them to stick to each other and to cling to pond grasses and weeds.

Fertilization begins the process of cleavage, the cell divisions that eventually produce the blastula. Cleavage of the entire egg occurs, not just a small portion as in the chick. The early gastrula has two cell layers, the ectoderm and endoderm; the mesoderm appears later. The primitive streak appears along with the neural folds that will produce the nervous system.

The elongation of the embryo is the first indication that the tadpole will soon take shape. Gradually the yolk cells are absorbed. The head, the trunk, and tail of the tadpole emerge, and soon it hatches. It is fishlike, breathing by external gills. Its tail seems to have a continuous dorsal and ventral fin. It has a two-chambered heart and no limbs. It has a long, coiled intestine for digesting the plants it eats. Soon, however, it begins the metamorphosis that converts it into a frog.

The external gills disappear first, being covered by an operculum, and are replaced by internal gills. These, in turn, are replaced by lungs. Limb buds appear as swellings under the skin. The hindlegs emerge first, then the forelegs. Meanwhile, the tail is absorbed, its tissues apparently being converted into limb materials. The mouth and the entire digestive tract undergo great changes. The tadpole is quite active while these major changes occur.

In some frogs the transition from tadpole to adult takes several weeks. The tadpole of the bullfrog may remain in that stage a year or more.

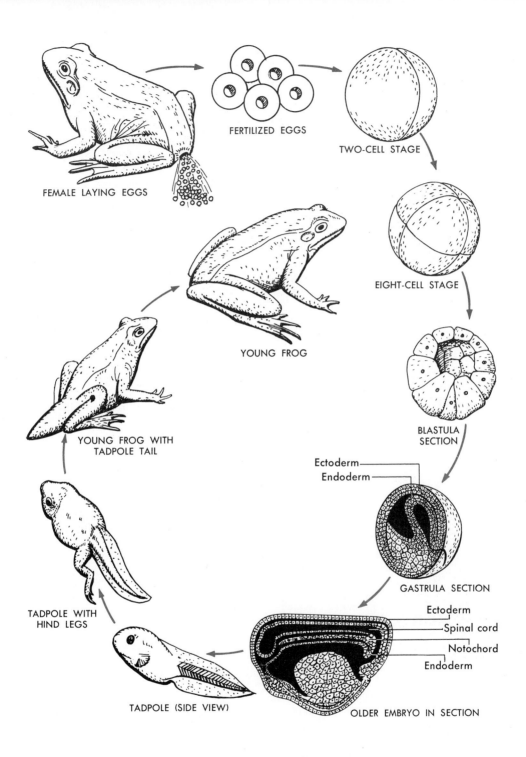

FERTILIZED EGGS

TWO-CELL STAGE

FEMALE LAYING EGGS

EIGHT-CELL STAGE

YOUNG FROG

BLASTULA
SECTION

YOUNG FROG WITH
TADPOLE TAIL

Ectoderm
Endoderm

GASTRULA SECTION

TADPOLE WITH
HIND LEGS

Ectoderm
Spinal cord
Notochord
Endoderm

TADPOLE (SIDE VIEW)

OLDER EMBRYO IN SECTION

28–18   LIFE HISTORY OF THE FROG

IMPORTANT POINTS

• The amphibians were the first vertebrates to live upon the land, but they were not perfectly adapted to it. They seem to have been related to the lobefins and lungfishes. Modern amphibians, especially the frog, are far removed from their primitive relatives who first slithered from one pool to another on the ancient earth.

• Modern amphibians that live in North America are usually one of two types: tailed forms like the salamanders and newts, or tailless forms like the frog and toad. Generally, amphibians mate and spend their larval period in water. Later, they pass through a metamorphosis and become adapted to the land.

• The frog is a widely used laboratory animal. Its organ systems are representative of the basic plan found in many vertebrates, including man. Careful study of its structure and physiology is an excellent preparation for understanding the human body.

• The imperfectly adapted amphibians were successful for many years, but changing conditions led to their decline. Today, they are a small class of animals. The animals that followed them were better suited for drier conditions.

REVIEW QUESTIONS

1. What conditions existed on the earth at the time of the appearance of the first amphibians?
2. Give two reasons why many biologists believe the amphibians are related to the fishes.
3. Does the frog or the salamander resemble the ancient amphibians more closely?
4. What peculiar developments are found in amphibians that spend their lives in caves?
5. Why is the frog a popular animal for laboratory study?
6. How do frogs capture living insects?
7. What regions of the frog's body are supplied with blood by the dorsal aorta?
8. In what three ways can a frog breathe?
9. In what two ways is the frog's brain protected in addition to having a cranium?
10. How may the male frog be distinguished from the female?

CHECK YOUR UNDERSTANDING

11. What are the principal differences between the three orders of amphibians?
12. List three unusual salamanders and briefly describe why they are considered unusual.
13. What two adaptations of the frog's skin help it escape its enemies?
14. What is the distinction between the axial and the appendicular skeletons?
15. How does a biologist distinguish between the origin and the insertion of a muscle?
16. What are the four main parts of the frog's circulatory system?
17. Discuss the absorption of oxygen in the alveoli of the lungs.

18. Summarize the changes that occur as the tadpole becomes an adult.
19. How is the toad's dependence upon water for mating and early development interpreted by the biologist?
20. How might the frog's ability to breathe through its skin be an evidence of its evolution?

RESEARCH PROJECTS AND REPORTS

1. Obtain information from your school or public library and prepare a report on one of the following topics:

   Ancient Amphibians   **Cave Salamanders**

   The Axolotl   **Tree Frogs**

2. *Amphibians in a Terrarium:* If your school is maintaining a woodland terrarium with mosses and ferns growing in it, you will be able to keep salamanders and toads in it too. Small animals survive best, and only a few should be kept at a time. Be sure to catch some live insects for them to feed upon, but if these are not available, try tiny pieces of liver or hamburger. If you keep frogs, place a small dish containing water at one end of the terrarium.

3. *Tadpole Development:* Tadpoles are fine laboratory animals that can teach you many things. You can watch their development from day to day as they change into adults. Keep them in an aquarium that has sufficient plant material growing in it so that they have enough to eat. Watch for the development of the hind legs, then the front legs. Meanwhile, if you are very careful, you can examine the way the blood circulates through the tail by wrapping a tadpole in moistened cloth and examining the tail under the microscope.

4. *Frog Respiration Through the Skin:* Place a healthy frog in a gallon pickle jar that has been completely filled with water. Don't leave any air space at the top and screw the lid on securely. Watch the floor of the frog's mouth, and observe his reactions. Leave him in the water from fifteen minutes to a half hour, then remove the lid. How did he breathe in the meantime?

FURTHER READING

Salamanders and Other Wonders. Willy Ley. Viking Press, New York, N.Y. Describes some of the peculiar stories that are told about these unusual amphibians.

Living Amphibians of the World. Doris M. Cochran. Doubleday & Co., Inc., New York, N.Y. Discusses the coloration, distribution, courting, mating, and breeding habits of a wide variety of amphibians.

Handbook of Frogs and Toads. Albert H. Wright and Anna A. Wright. Comstock Publishing Associates, Ithaca, N.Y. Describes all the species of these amphibians found in America.

"How a Tadpole Becomes a Frog." William Etkin. *Scientific American,* May, 1966, page 76. The investigation of the tadpole developing into a frog brings the biologist face to face with some of the most fundamental problems of biology.

29

Reptiles and Birds

Aʟᴍᴏsᴛ 300 million years ago, while the amphibians were still crawling from one drying pool to another, the reptiles became the first animals fully adapted to life on dry land. They eventually gained full control of the land and overran the earth.

During the Age of Reptiles gigantic dinosaurs roamed the planet. On a younger, warmer earth, covered with marshes and fern forests, they were the most numerous land vertebrates. About 60 million years ago the dinosaurs disappeared, leaving only their fossilized bones as reminders of their existence. Their descendants, the modern reptiles, consist of some 6000 species. Among them are the turtles, lizards, snakes, alligators, and crocodiles. Most live in the warm parts of the world.

Some biologists have called birds "glorified reptiles." The term recognizes that birds evolved from reptilian stock. Even a casual inspection of birds today reveals traits that persist from their reptile ancestors: their claws, the scales on their legs, their sharp, turtle-like beaks.

Birds are thought to have begun their descent long before the great age of dinosaurs ended. Exact records of the first birds are scarce in the history of life recorded in the rocks. The bones of birds are fragile and make poor fossils. Their feathers are especially difficult to fossilize and are preserved in only a few of the early forms.

Dinosaurs

About 1820, workers in an English slate quarry discovered some large bones and teeth embedded at a depth of forty feet. One bone, almost three feet long, measured ten inches in circumference. William Buckland, a British geologist, examined these strange fossils, and declared, "The vertebral column and extremities much resemble those of quadrupeds . . . the teeth show the creature to have belonged to the order of Saurians or Lizards."

Buckland named the animal *Megalosaurus,* or "giant reptile." Baron Cuvier, the French zoologist, estimated the animal to have been more than forty feet long. The first of the giants had been found.

Thousands of dinosaur fossils have since been found in all parts of the world. In the United States alone the dinosaur beds of Wyoming, Utah, and Montana have yielded fossils that have enabled man to reconstruct many prehistoric forms.

29–1 The ichthyosaur, shown with its young, was an inhabitant of the sea. Requiring support for his great weight, the brontosaurus (upper right) spent most of his time in the shallow waters of lagoons and marshes. A more slender relative of the brontosaurus, but measuring about twenty feet longer, was the diplodocus (lower left). One of their contemporaries was the allosaurus (lower right), a carnivorous land dinosaur.

Dinosaurs ranged in size from one to eighty feet in length. Some were giant vegetarians that could stretch their long necks to browse on leaves high above the ground. Others were flesh eaters that ran swiftly. Some were armored with huge, horny plates that protected them from the swift predators. Still others had large, flat snouts lined with more than 2000 teeth. A few forms had large, leathery flaps of skin that enabled them to fly.

As the land became crowded, many dinosaurs returned to the warm seas. There they swam, their legs replaced by flippers, and preyed upon the abundant fishes. For over 100 million years the planet was dominated by these ancient reptiles.

BRONTOSAURUS, THE THUNDER LIZARD. One of the best-known dinosaurs is *Brontosaurus*. Measuring eighty feet from head to tail, he stood fifteen feet high at the shoulders. A long, thin neck supported a small head. The name of this dinosaur suggests that the earth thundered when he walked. Actually, Brontosaurus probably did little walking on the dry land. He was so heavy that he spent most of his time in marshes and lagoons where his great weight was partly supported by the water.

Brontosaurus was a vegetarian who ate soft water plants. Unlike the flat teeth of modern plant-eating animals, the teeth of the Brontosaurus were pointed. They could be used only for tearing pieces of plants, which were then swallowed whole.

Brontosaurus had a poorly developed brain, no larger than your fist. He also had a second "brain" at the base of his spine that was about twice the size of the one in his head. This was probably a large relay clump of nerves that informed the head what was going on at the distant hind end.

TYRANNOSAURUS, THE TYRANT LIZARD. Among the dinosaurs there were both flesh eaters and plant eaters. Carnivorous forms, like *Tyrannosaurus* (tie-RAN-uh-soar-us), preyed upon the herbivorous creatures. Tyrannosaurus attained a length of forty feet and towered twenty feet on powerful hind legs. Like some gigantic kangaroo, he bal-

anced himself with a long tail. With short, grasping forelegs and enormous jaws lined with huge teeth, he was well equipped to hunt.

PTEROSAURS, FLYING REPTILES. During the 140 million years of the Age of Reptiles, new forms developed. Near the middle of the period, the flying reptiles, or *pterosaurs* (TER-uh-soarz), appeared.

Although they had no feathers, the structural plan of these reptiles was essentially birdlike. The wings were large, leathery sails, attached to both pairs of limbs. They had thin, hollow bones to give them lightness. Their brains were highly developed in comparison with other reptiles.

Fossils found in Germany and England indicate that there were many species of flying reptiles. Some were no larger than sparrows. Others, like the giant *Pteranodon*, had a wing spread of twenty-two feet.

ICHTHYOSAURS: DINOSAURS THAT RETURNED TO THE SEA. The name *ichthyosaur* (ICK-thee-uh-soar) means "fish lizard." These were the dinosaurs that returned to the sea. Fish were abundant in the seas so that food was plentiful. Externally, the ichthyosaurs resembled large porpoises. Their

29–2 Marine Reptiles. Among the ancient reptiles that invaded the sea were the porpoiselike ichthyosaurus and the long-necked plesiosaurus. Both forms had lungs, hatched eggs within their bodies, and were probably descended from land animals.

bodies were streamlined. Their limbs consisted of fins and paddles. The resemblance to oversized porpoises was emphasized by their long beaks.

Remains of the ichthyosaurs have been found on every continent. Since the reptilian egg is adapted for survival on land, one question puzzled biologists. How could the ichthyosaurs reproduce? The discovery of some fossils that contained tiny young within them provided the answer: they bore living young.

THE DINOSAURS DISAPPEAR. About sixty million years ago, the dinosaurs perished with geological suddenness throughout the world. Mystery continues to surround their disappearance.

Some scientists argue that a period of volcanic activity caused their extinction. But this supposition does not explain why those in nonvolcanic regions also perished. Others believe that the climate became too warm for them. Fossil plants of the period do not indicate that the temperature rise was extreme. A theory has also been advanced that dinosaur eggs were eaten by increasing numbers of mammals. But even the ichthyosaurs, whose eggs could not be attacked, perished.

Many things probably contributed to the downfall of the dinosaurs. It is probable that they may have become so specialized that they could no longer adapt themselves to even slight changes in their environment. A drying earth produced new types of plants that the vegetarians could not digest. As the plant eaters died, the flesh eaters had no food, and also perished.

Characteristics of Modern Reptiles

Today's reptiles are the remnants of a once vast population. Of the sixteen orders that flourished in a bygone age, only four remain. The turtles and tortoises comprise one order; the lizards and snakes another; the crocodiles and alligators a third. The fourth order has but one living representative, the *tuatara* of New Zealand, a "living fossil" believed to be a direct link with the past. Modern reptiles have certain fundamental characteristics:

1. A scaly skin, sometimes with bony plates.
2. Usually two pairs of limbs with claws.
3. Respiration is by lungs only.
4. Ventricle of heart imperfectly divided into two halves.
5. Eggs fertilized internally; development within shell.

TUATARA: A LINK WITH THE PAST. This is the most primitive living reptile and is found only in New Zealand. Fossils have been unearthed that are almost identical with this modern, lizard-like animal. When the first European settlers brought their farm animals to New Zealand, the pigs killed most of the sluggish, dark green tuataras. The government quickly intervened to save these "living fossils" by establishing conservation measures on certain offshore islands.

FREEDOM FROM THE WATER. What structural advances enabled the reptiles to live successfully on the dry land? Comparing them with the amphibians, we observe three distinct advances:

1. *Better limbs and stronger skeleton.* The limbs of reptiles are generally well developed. The skeleton is also stronger so that the body can be more easily supported. The exception is the group of snakes where limbs are entirely lacking.
2. *Dry, scaly skin.* Reptiles do not depend upon a moist skin for absorbing oxygen as do the amphibians. They obtain oxygen through their lungs alone. Contrary to common belief, the skin of reptiles is not slimy. Dry, horny scales cover the body.

29–3 Tuatara of New Zealand

3. *Eggs with shells.* The reptilian egg contains a large amount of yolk and is encased in a shell, much like a hen's egg. Unlike the unprotected amphibian egg, which must develop in water, the shell of the reptilian egg prevents drying while the young develop on land.

Equipped with strong limbs, a dry skin to conserve body moisture, lungs that could supply all of the oxygen required, a reproductive cycle that was free from water, the reptiles have survived on the land.

COLD- VERSUS WARM-BLOODED ANIMALS. Like fishes and amphibians, reptiles are cold-blooded animals. Zoologists use this term to describe an animal whose body temperature changes with the temperature of its surroundings. Some reptiles, for example, may undergo body temperature changes of fifty degrees between day and night. Birds and mammals are warm-blooded. They maintain a constant body temperature even though the temperature around them may change considerably.

A regulated body temperature is an important adaptation for living on land where temperature changes may be sudden and great. When it is too hot, cold-blooded animals must find shade. When it is too cold, they must find protection or they may freeze to death. This is probably the reason most reptiles live in the tropics. Only a few live in the temperate regions, and none are found in the polar regions.

Turtles and Tortoises

The body of these animals is encased in bony plates that are in turn covered by tough, horny plates. A dorsal, crowned section, the *carapace,* covers the back. A flat, ventral plate, the *plastron,* covers the belly. The carapace is a modification of the backbone and ribs. The plastron is a modified breastbone.

The shell has great survival value to a slow-moving animal. Although the head, legs, and tail project from between the two plates, they can be withdrawn when danger threatens. The familiar box turtle has a plastron with a cross hinge behind the forelegs. This permits the animal to close its shell completely by drawing up the front of the plastron over the head like a trap door.

GIANT MARINE TURTLES. The limbs of the sea turtles are modified into paddles or flippers. Perhaps because of the buoyancy of water, the marine turtles become quite large. The Green Turtle, may attain a weight of four hundred pounds, and may be four feet across. The Hawksbill Turtle is slightly smaller and gets its name from its peculiar head shape. The Loggerhead Turtle is larger than either of the others, sometimes tipping the scales at five hundred pounds. But the giant of them all is the Leathery Turtle. It reaches a length of nine feet and weighs as much as fifteen hundred pounds. Essentially land dwellers in structure, marine turtles must come to the surface to breathe air. They also come ashore to lay their eggs in burrows in the sand. They then return to the sea, leaving the eggs to be incubated by the sun. Instinct directs the young back to the sea as soon as they have hatched.

GIANT TORTOISES. These huge land turtles are confined to two island groups: the Galapagos, near the coast of South America, and Aldabra, an island near Madagascar off the east coast of Africa. At one time they were scattered among the islands of the Indian Ocean, but early mariners found them such a good source of food that they have almost become extinct.

Lizards

Lizards have a scaly body and four limbs. A movable tongue distinguishes them from the crocodiles. Most of the lizards are tropical. Some crawl rather slowly, but most are fast runners. Some have no legs and thus resemble snakes. These can be distinguished from the snakes, however, by the presence of ears and eyelids. Perhaps the most interesting lizard is the "glass snake." When pursued by an enemy, its tail drops off and continues

29–4   Box Turtle

to wriggle. While the pursuer stops to eat the tail, the lizard escapes.

IGUANAS. The iguanas of Central and South America are dragon-like creatures that grow to a length of six feet. They have powerful claws and teeth. The tail is long with numerous spines, which make it a formidable weapon. They have a grotesque appearance because of their spines and crests. Actually, they are usually quiet vegetarians that live on the abundant fruits of the tropical forests.

CHAMELEONS AND HORNED TOADS. Probably the best-known lizard is the chameleon. This is a small animal that has the ability to change its color to match its background. Pigment cells in the skin can change the animal's color from green to brown in a matter of seconds. The chameleon is a useful lizard for it feeds on insects. The tongue, several inches long, pops out of the mouth and returns with the insect stuck to it. True chameleons found in Asia and Africa have other, surprising characteristics. They are able to twine their short tails about the stems of trees and have eyes that can be moved independently of each other.

29–5   Komodo Dragon of Indonesia

The horned toad is a lizard that lives in the dry, southwestern states. A small reptile, about five inches long, it gets its name from the fact that it resembles a toad with horns. Actually it is a distant relative of the iguana and is not related to the toads at all. Horned toads can survive for many weeks without water.

29–6   Gila Monster

POISONOUS LIZARDS. Only two species of lizard are known to be poisonous. Both species are closely related and live in the southwestern states and in Mexico. They have scales that are shaped like beads and are sometimes called "beaded lizards." The American species is called the *Gila* (HEE-luh) *monster*.

Fortunately, the Gila monster is a very conspicuous reptile. It is one to two feet in length and its black body is marked with bright pink and orange spots. Grooved teeth, which allow the venom to flow into the wound, are found on the lower jaw. The poison is fatal to small animals and dangerous to man.

Snakes

The absence of limbs makes it easy to identify snakes. In addition, snakes have no movable eyelids and no ears. The absence of eyelids causes a snake to fix its prey with a glassy stare, a fact that has led to stories about its hypnotic powers. The body is covered with scales, showing their close kinship with the lizards. Some of the scales are important in locomotion. These are the *scutes,* large scales attached to the ribs. The scutes grip the ground so that the snake can slither forward.

The outer layer of the skin is shed several times a year. It is peeled back from the head to the tail as you would turn the finger of a glove inside out. Even the transparent covering of the eye is shed. A snake that is about to molt, therefore, can be identified by the whitish cast over its eyes. During this period the animal is partially blind.

Most species of snakes are quite harmless. Many species are useful to man and help to keep down the population of rodents. Of the several thousand species of snakes, less than a fifth are known to be poisonous.

Some of the most interesting snake adaptations are those associated with feeding. Snakes swallow their food whole. The teeth are curved toward the back of the mouth so that the victim cannot easily escape. But the problem of swallowing an animal larger than itself requires structural changes to make the mouth larger. An adaption of the lower jaw permits it to widen. Furthermore, the upper and lower jaw are not firmly joined. They are connected by several narrow bones permitting the mouth to open wider.

CONSTRICTORS. The largest constrictors are the boas, anacondas, and pythons. Opinion varies as to which is the largest. One report indicates that the regal python of India attains a length of thirty-three feet.

These giant snakes all use the same method for capturing prey. They coil themselves about the victim and squeeze until the lungs and heart cannot function. The

29–7 Python Digesting a Pig

victim is swallowed whole, usually head first. Once fed, the large snakes can sometimes go without food for several months.

SNAKE VENOM. Poisonous snakes produce a modified saliva, called venom, that kills their victims. Snake venom is a protein material. Its rate of action varies with the species. The Indian cobra's bite is fatal to humans within six hours.

Venom is injected by fangs, specially modified teeth attached to the upper jaw. In some species they are grooved. In other species, the fangs are hollow and connected with the poison glands on the sides of the head. The hollow fangs act like hypodermic needles, injecting the venom into the opening they make in the skin of the victim. In the six-foot African Gaboon viper these formidable teeth are an inch and a half long. Occasionally the fangs are broken off, but the snake grows new ones rapidly.

Snake venoms are of two types. The first, a *hemotoxin,* attacks and destroys the red corpuscles of the blood. The second, a

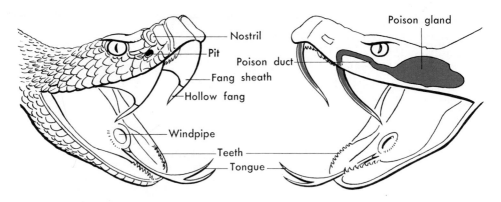

Nostril
Pit
Poison duct
Fang sheath
Hollow fang
Windpipe
Teeth
Tongue
Poison gland

29–8 Rattlesnake. The pits on each side of the head between the eyes and nostrils are very sensitive to warmth and can detect a warm-blooded animal up to several feet away.

neurotoxin, interferes with the proper operation of the nervous system, frequently causing suffocation as it attacks the centers of respiration. The venom of the rattler attacks the blood. The deadly cobra of India, however, injects a neurotoxin that quickly paralyzes its victims.

Venoms cause the blood to make counter poisons, *antivenins,* if only small amounts are introduced at a time. By gradually increasing the amount of venom injected into a horse, for example, a specific antivenin is made that is very effective in offsetting the effect of the poison. Promptly administered, antivenin is a most effective way to counteract the action of any snake venom.

POISONOUS SNAKES. There are generally two main kinds of poisonous snakes: (1) vipers, adders and rattlesnakes; (2) cobras and their allies. The former have long fangs that can be folded against the roof of the mouth and lowered into a vertical position for striking.

The cobra and related species have much shorter fangs, but they are much more venomous. They hold fast to their victim after the strike has been made, rarely letting go. One of the most interesting members of this group is the African spitting cobra, which spits its venom at the eyes of its victims.

There are four kinds of poisonous snakes in the United States. *Rattlers, water moccasins,* and *copperheads* belong to the viperine group. The *coral snake* is a relative of the cobra. Although most of them live in the arid Southwest, they are found in practically every state.

Rattlesnakes, water moccasins, and copperheads are known as *pit vipers* because of the presence of a small pit on each side of the head between the eye and nostril. The pit is believed to be a heat-sensitive organ that enables the snake to detect the presence of a warm-blooded animal several feet away.

SNAKE REPRODUCTION. Snakes either lay eggs or the eggs hatch within the body of the mother. The eggs that are laid are encased in a soft, leathery shell. They are originally soft and elongated, but soon become round and hard. The leathery covering permits moisture to be absorbed for the development of the young. The eggs of a snake may increase more than one-third their size during the period of incubation.

If you have explored the fields for snakes, you may have had the experience of uncovering a brood of young garter snakes. The mother will bear as many as thirty or more offspring at one time. The garter snake is an

example of a snake that is said to be *ovoviviparous;* that is, the eggs incubate within the mother's body and the young emerge as they hatch. *Viviparous* animals, such as mammals, also produce living young. In mammals, however, the developing young are not incubated, but are nourished within the body of the mother through her blood stream.

Alligators and Crocodiles

These are the largest reptiles (some reach a length of thirty feet) bearing limbs. Closely related to the crocodilians are the *caimans* of Latin America and the *gavial* of India, the latter having an extremely pointed snout. Generally they are tropical species that live in the swamps of India, China, Africa, the Malay peninsula, Central and South America, and in Florida. Alligators can be distinguished from crocodiles by their broad, rounded snout. The head of the crocodile is more triangular and the snout usually comes to a rather sharp point.

The hide is comprised, not of overlapping scales, but of plates attached to dermal bones. This results in a very protective armor. All of the crocodilians are strong swimmers. The eyes and nostrils on the top of the head enable them to see and breathe while almost totally submerged. All of them are carnivorous, feeding on fishes and small land animals. The jaws are lined with huge teeth, which are replaced continuously as they are lost.

The heart of these reptiles shows one striking advance over all other cold-blooded animals: it has four chambers. Other reptiles have only three. The four chambers allow for an efficient separation of oxygenated from nonoxygenated blood in the heart. The four-chambered heart is characteristic of birds and mammals, but the only reptiles exhibiting a heart constructed in this fashion are the crocodilians.

29–9 POISONOUS SNAKES
Timber Rattlesnake
Northern Copperhead
Water Moccasin
Coral Snake

Birds

The most outstanding feature of birds is their ability to fly. How did flying originate? One theory is that animals with limbs that were modified for gliding had a survival advantage in their ability to leap long distances from one tree to another. Another possibility is that modified forelimbs enabled them to run faster by taking some of the weight off the body.

The advantages of flight are obvious. Escape from nonflying enemies is easy. Hunting for food is less difficult. Finding uncrowded homesites is less of a problem. Birds can live on rocky crags far above the sea where most other animals would find life impossible. With the changing seasons some birds find it practical to journey thousands of miles to new homes.

29–10 Archaeopteryx, with its reptile characteristics, had feathers and was probably intermediate between reptiles and birds.

PREHISTORIC BIRDS. In 1861, a fossil of a bird about the size of a crow was discovered in a slate quarry in Bavaria. Had it not been for the presence of feathers the fossil might have been considered a reptile. The jaws had teeth. The head was covered with scales. There was no true beak that modern birds possess. The tail was long and bony. The breastbone was rather small. Even the wings were small and bore three fingers on their tips. In almost every way this first bird, named Archaeopteryx, was a reptile, yet it had feathers.

Except for the feathers, characteristics of modern birds are not present in Archaeopteryx. But we have to begin somewhere if we are to distinguish between reptiles and birds. We could call Archaeopteryx a feathered reptile, or we might call it a reptilelike bird.

In 1877, a similar fossil was discovered in Germany. Some slight differences in structure have led biologists to call this specimen *Archaeornis*. Essentially, it is the same as Archaeopteryx. Each is believed to be about 140 million years old.

Although it would seem natural to expect there to be a close link between the flying reptiles, the pterosaurs, and the first of the feathered forms, no such link has as yet been discovered.

MODERN BIRDS. Birds are commonly identified as feathered vertebrates whose forelimbs are modified in the form of wings. They have other important characteristics as listed below:

1. They are warm-blooded.
2. The heart is four-chambered.
3. They have a horny beak with no teeth.
4. Respiration is by lungs that are aided by air sacs located among the internal organs.
5. They are egg-layers. The eggs are covered by a limy shell and contain a large amount of yolk.

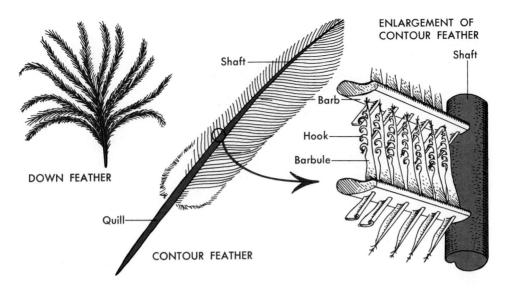

DOWN FEATHER

CONTOUR FEATHER

Shaft

Quill

ENLARGEMENT OF
CONTOUR FEATHER

Shaft

Barb

Hook

Barbule

29–11 Types of Feathers. Contour, or flight feathers, are stiff. Their barbules are interlocked by hooks. Feathers are molted at least once each year and replaced by new ones.

The Mechanics of Flight

Many of the early designs for flying machines were based upon the idea that birds flew by simply flapping their wings. These machines were all failures. Modern research reveals that flying is a much more complicated process. Birds do not pull themselves through the air in the manner of a swimmer in water. Slow-motion camera studies indicate that the wings move forward on the downstroke.

Just as in an airplane, there are two important factors that contribute to successful flight: (1) the wings must be shaped in such a way that they will experience an upward *lift* when air moves rapidly over them, and (2) the design of the entire structure must reduce the structure's total weight so that the lift will be effective.

FEATHERS AND WINGS. Feathers are peculiar to birds alone and are found in no other animals. They are believed to be similar to the scales of the reptiles, beginning as small outgrowths of the skin.

The largest feathers consist typically of a basal portion called the *quill* and a flat part called the *vane*. The quill and its extension, the *shaft*, make up the supporting axis. Extending sidewise from the shaft are many *barbs* that make up the main body of the vane. The barbs, in turn, branch into *barbules*. These are interlocked by tiny hooks so that all the barbules form a firm structure despite their lightness.

Feathers are generally of three types. *Contour feathers*, the ones we have just described, provide the main outline of the body. Those found on the wing and tail are the largest and strongest. Others are much smaller and more fragile; they lack a prominent quill and have no shaft at all. They are much softer. These are called *down feathers* and were once widely used for stuffing pillows. They insulate the bird's body, and, in many species, are found under the contour feathers. Down feathers are typical of young birds. They prevent the rapid loss of body heat. The third kind of feather is the so-called "hair" or *pin feather*.

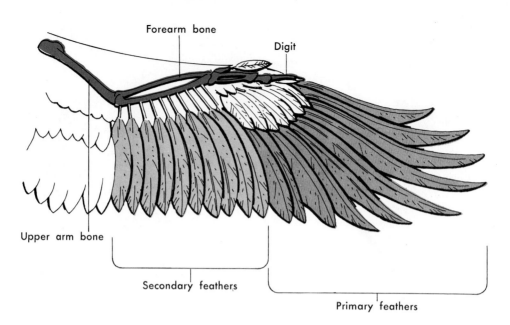

Forearm bone

Digit

Upper arm bone

Secondary feathers

Primary feathers

29–12 Wing Structure. The forelimbs of birds are developed as wings. In some cases, the wings are not used for flight but rather as paddles for swimming (penguin).

In flying birds, the large feathers attached to the wings increase the surface area. Those that are attached to what would correspond to our hand are called *primaries*. Those farther back in the forearm region are called *secondaries*. Although the tail of a bird is small, large tail feathers make it an effective organ for maneuvering. They help to steer the bird in flight and to slow it down as it lands.

The movement of the wings requires enormous chest muscles. The breastbone is extended in the form of a *keel*, providing for the attachment of these thick muscles. The powerful pectoral muscles that move the wings of a bird constitute what is commonly called the breast. In a bird like the pigeon, for example, these huge muscles may account for as much as one-half the total body weight.

How the Wing Works. From the standpoint of operation, the wing of a bird can be divided into two parts. Each part performs a separate function. The inner part, corresponding to our arm from the shoulder to the wrist, acts like the wing of an airplane. It is held almost rigid. In cross section it exhibits the typical curved upper surface of an airplane wing. Movement of air over this portion of the wing produces the lift. The reason for this is that the air flows more rapidly above the wing than below it. Greater pressure below the wing tends to push it upward.

The wrist and hand portion of the wing is covered by the primary feathers. Oscillating in a complicated way as the wing is moved up and down, they provide the air movement that is needed to move the bird forward and upward.

The chief obstacle to successful flight is excess weight. To achieve lightness, the bones must be light and at the same time strong enough to support the body. Lightness is obtained in airplanes by using light metals and tubular construction. A tube of metal is stronger in proportion to its weight than a solid rod of the same metal. The long bones of birds are thin, hollow tubes, yet they are remarkably strong.

Organ Systems

Flight requires energy. Most bird foods are high-energy materials. Seeds, a favorite bird food, contain starch, oil, and protein in high concentration. Fruits also contain a readily available supply of glucose.

DIGESTION. Birds digest their foods rapidly. Although they have no teeth, grinding takes place in the muscular portion of the stomach called the *gizzard*. Small bits of gravel in the gizzard act as substitute teeth. The entire process of food intake, digestion, absorption, and elimination takes about one hour. A young cedar waxwing was observed to pass fruit through its digestive tract in 27 minutes. Studies of young birds indicate that they are able to convert about one third of their food into body weight. Young mammals convert only about one tenth.

CIRCULATION. Birds have a high metabolic rate. Their body temperature indicates this clearly. Whereas we maintain a body temperature of 98.6 degrees Fahrenheit, some birds have a temperature as high as 113° F. This higher temperature indicates that the

FLIGHT SPEED OF COMMON BIRDS

Bird	Speed
	(miles per hour)
Barn swallow	20–45
Crow	25–60
Canada goose	20–60
Duck hawk	60–180
Great blue heron	18–35
Mallard	30–60
Osprey	20–80
Pheasant	40–60
Sharp-shinned hawk	15–60

body fuels are being consumed at a faster rate.

There are two related systems that supply oxygen to the body cells—the circulatory system and the respiratory system. Higher-metabolic rates require more oxygen. The oxygen must be taken in quickly in large amounts and circulated rapidly to the muscles.

The bird's heart is four-chambered. It consists of two atria and two ventricles, an arrangement that separates blood rich in oxygen from blood that is low in oxygen.

29–13 DIGESTIVE SYSTEM OF BIRD

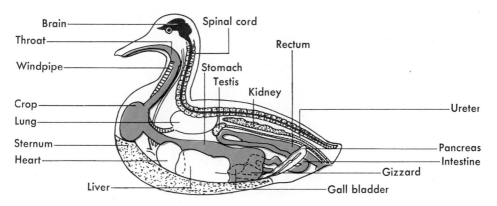

The size of the heart is significantly greater than that of other animals. In man the heart is slightly less than 0.5 per cent of the total body weight. In the pigeon it is about 1.7 per cent. In the hummingbird it is almost 2.4 per cent. The number of beats per minute is also far greater. The canary averages over 500 beats per minute compared to man's rate of 72.

One important difference in the blood of birds is the concentration of glucose. It reaches a level about twice as high as that found in man. The higher sugar concentration is easily understood in terms of greater energy output.

RESPIRATION. The respiratory system of birds is equipped with *air sacs*. The air sacs are auxiliary breathing spaces scattered among the organs of the body. These are in addition to the two large lungs. Whereas the respiratory system of man occupies about 1/20 of the body volume, in birds it is about 1/5. Most of this increased volume is taken up by the air sacs, found in the neck, chest, and abdomen. There are also branches leading to the upper wing bones.

The air sacs assist the lungs by bringing the air directly into the body where the oxygen can be used. They also serve to reduce the body temperature by bringing in cool air rapidly. Birds have no sweat glands. Sweat would hamper the action of the feathers and add to body weight. One scientist estimates that three-quarters of the air taken in by birds is used to cool the body and only one-fourth for supplying oxygen.

The Variety of Birds

Birds are found wherever man lives. They are also found in isolated places that man finds uninhabitable. Their brilliant plumage is seen in tropical forests and in the open meadows. Wings have made practically every place on earth accessible.

PERCHING BIRDS. About half of all the known species of birds are perching birds. Most of them are the familiar songbirds—

29-14   RESPIRATORY SYSTEM OF BIRD

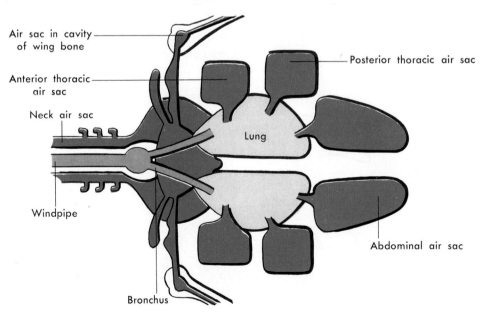

Air sac in cavity of wing bone

Anterior thoracic air sac

Neck air sac

Windpipe

Bronchus

Posterior thoracic air sac

Lung

Abdominal air sac

29–15 THREE KINDS OF BIRDS
Pheasant
Penguin
Toucan

the thrushes, warblers, larks, mocking birds, sparrows, tanagers, finches, and even the crows. Nearly all are small birds.

The feet of these birds are adapted for perching. There are three toes in front and one strong hind toe. Also, the tendons of the leg and toes are so arranged that they lock the toes around a branch when the body weight is supported. This permits the canary, for example, to sleep while resting its weight on one foot.

BIRDS OF PREY. These are the spectacular hunters of the bird world. Armed with powerful legs and curved, sharp claws, or talons, they seize their prey and tear it apart with their sharp beaks. The hawks and eagles are the swiftest of all birds. The duck hawk is reputed to be the fastest flying bird. It dives upon its prey at speeds of up to 180 miles per hour.

The diet of most birds of prey consists of other birds, fish, and small mammals, especially rats and mice. The destruction of rodents makes them especially useful to man.

FOWL. Many of the birds that are used the world over for food are in this group. The chicken is perhaps the most common representative. It is believed to be the first bird domesticated by man and is a descendant of the red jungle fowl of India. The American turkey is a relative of the wild varieties that roamed the American continent when our ancestors arrived. The pheasants are Asiatic species that have been introduced into this country.

UNUSUAL BIRDS. Some birds are so unusual that they deserve special comment. One such bird is the toucan, which has an enormous beak. Like the bones of the body, the bill is very porous and not heavy at all. Living in the treetops of Central and South America, toucans feed upon fruits, seeds, insects, and small reptiles.

The various species of woodpecker are relatives of the toucan. Although their beak is not large, it is very strong and pointed.

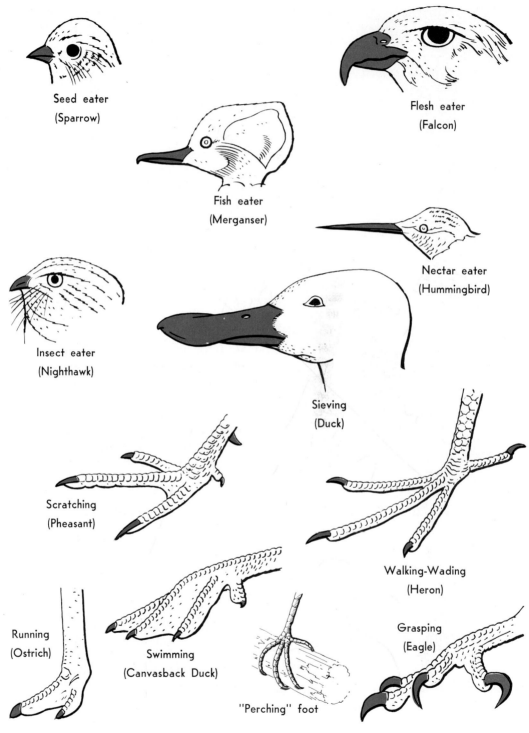

Seed eater
(Sparrow)

Fish eater
(Merganser)

Flesh eater
(Falcon)

Nectar eater
(Hummingbird)

Insect eater
(Nighthawk)

Sieving
(Duck)

Scratching
(Pheasant)

Walking-Wading
(Heron)

Running
(Ostrich)

Swimming
(Canvasback Duck)

"Perching" foot

Grasping
(Eagle)

29–16 ADAPTATIONS OF BIRD FEET AND BILLS

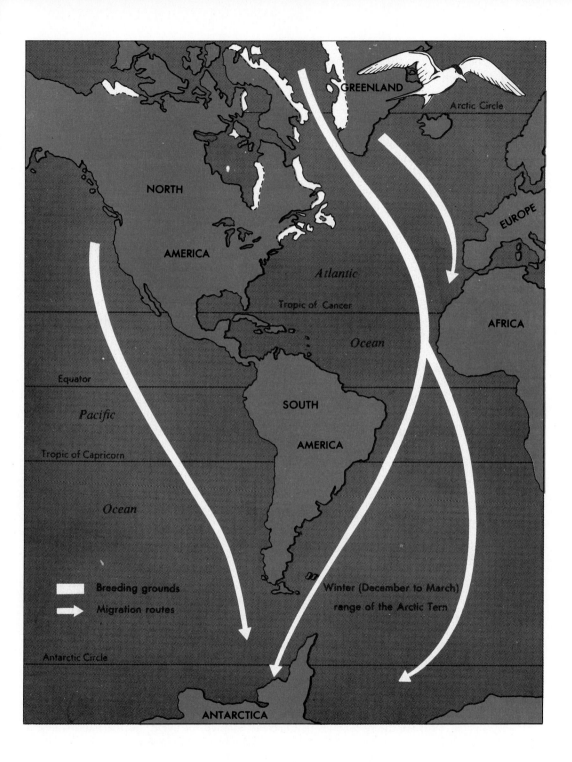

29–17 ARCTIC TERN MIGRATION

They feed upon woodboring insects. The bill is so strong that it is used to chisel out a cavity in which the bird lays its eggs. The long tongue can be extended far beyond the bill to draw in insects burrowing in wood.

Penguins look like upright ducks dressed in tuxedos. They cannot fly, but their stubby wings are used as flippers for swimming. Their underwater speed has been estimated to be as high as 30 miles per hour. Feeding upon fish and crustaceans, they store so much fat that they can survive a fast of 40 days. They are largely found in Antarctica, but some reach the Galapagos islands.

Bird Migration

The migratory habits of birds have been studied rather intensively. By placing lightweight tags on their legs it is possible to trace the course of their travels. One variety of golden plover departs from Alaska over the open waters of the Pacific. Its destination is Hawaii and it flies nonstop. Some birds follow coastal routes. Others follow routes that are entirely over the open sea. The champion migrant is the Arctic tern, which breeds within the Arctic Circle, but spends the northern winter in Antarctica. Its migration covers 11,000 miles each way.

The ability of birds to navigate over long distances has puzzled scientists for many years. Apparently their routes are not learned. Young plovers, for instance, do not depart with their parents. Instead, they wait for about a month after the older birds have left. Then they set off on their long ocean journey, seemingly with no guides. Investigations of migration suggest that birds may use a sort of celestial navigation. During the day they fly by the sun. At night they fly by the stars. Exactly how they find directions is not known.

Even more puzzling is the ability of migratory birds to locate the same nest that was used the previous year. European warblers migrate from Scandinavia to South Africa, yet the following spring they return to the exact point of their departure.

IMPORTANT POINTS

- For more than 100 million years, during the Age of Reptiles, dinosaurs were the dominant vertebrates. Among them were the largest animals that ever roamed the earth. All of the dinosaurs disappeared about 60 million years ago.

- Today there are only four orders of reptiles. One order consists of a single member, the tuatara of New Zealand. The others include the turtles, lizards and snakes, and the crocodiles and alligators. Most live in the warmer parts of the world.

- Reptiles are cold-blooded land animals whose bodies are covered with dry scales. Reptiles were the first vertebrates to free themselves completely from the water to live their entire life span on land. One of the reasons for their success was the production of eggs that could develop and hatch out of water.

- Aside from the poisonous snakes, most reptiles are harmless. The fear that many people have of the entire group is not well founded. Snakes, for example, benefit the farmer in keeping down the rodent population.

- Birds are the vertebrates that became adapted for flying. Feathers and wings, a skeleton which is especially light, and powerful chest muscles are all characteristics that contribute to the mastery of flight. The combination of external features and internal organ systems made flight possible.

- There are many orders of birds. The largest is the group of perching birds to which the songbirds belong.
- Scientists have not successfully explained the migrations of birds. Birds seem to use a navigational system that depends upon the sun and stars.

REVIEW QUESTIONS

1. What three advantages make the reptiles better fitted than the amphibians to live on land?
2. What is the main distinction between warm- and cold-blooded animals?
3. Give two reasons why marine turtles might be considered to be land dwellers.
4. How do the two kinds of snake venom differ in their action?
5. Why are the fossilized records of birds rather incomplete?
6. How were the flying reptiles of prehistoric times different from birds?
7. How do barbules achieve strength in spite of their light weight?
8. The high body temperature of birds indicates what about their metabolic rate?
9. Compare the feet and legs of perching birds and birds of prey.
10. Why are more reptiles likely to be found in tropical countries than in temperate countries?
11. Give the common name of one example in each of the four reptile orders.
12. How does the heart of the crocodile differ from that of other reptiles?

CHECK YOUR UNDERSTANDING

13. How does the disappearance of the dinosaurs show that conditions on the planet have changed?
14. Why might it be foolish to attempt to destroy all the snakes in the world?
15. What two reasons might have led biologists to consider Archaeopteryx a reptile rather than a bird?
16. List four characteristics of birds.
17. Describe two ways in which the bird's body achieves lightness.
18. How do the circulatory and respiratory systems of birds contribute to successful flight?
19. The metabolic rate of the hummingbird is about 100 times greater than that of the elephant. Can you explain?
20. Why do bird migrations offer a puzzling challenge to biologists?
21. Explain why a higher concentration of sugar is to be expected in the blood of birds.

RESEARCH PROJECTS AND REPORTS

1. Obtain information from your school or public library and prepare a report on one of the following topics:

Poisonous Snakes	**The Migration of Birds**
Giant Dinosaurs	**Birds of Prey**

2. *Care and Feeding of Small Reptiles:* Many of the common reptiles found in your locality, or purchased from a pet shop, may be maintained in your home or classroom. Generally, boxes or cages are unsuitable for this purpose. A large glass-enclosed terrarium, with an opening at the top is the best place to keep them. Patience and a knowledge of the animal's diet are also required.

SNAKES. Ground snakes, blue racers, and garter snakes do quite well in a woodland terrarium. Snakes need sunlight for warmth and a shady place to hide. Rocks and sticks can provide such a place. For best results temperatures should vary between 80 and 85 degrees. Provide a dish of water and sprinkle the terrarium at frequent intervals. Snakes will consume a variety of living animals, such as tadpoles, frogs, small lizards, earthworms, insects, and fish.

TURTLES. The box turtle, found in moist woodlands, will do well in the classroom. The terrarium should be well planted and provided with a shallow pan of water. Feeding is seldom a problem for these animals since they will accept mushrooms, apples, bananas, insects, snails, slugs, earthworms, and bits of meat.

LIZARDS. Try keeping the Anolis or American "chameleon." This is a bit more difficult than maintaining other reptiles and may offer a challenge. The terrarium in this case should have sturdy plants or sticks on which the animal can climb. Sprinkle once a day since these animals normally get their water by drinking drops from the leaves of plants. Feeding is the most difficult problem because they eat only living insects. Fruit flies, house flies, and other flying insects should be provided in the beginning. Mealworms, small earthworms, roaches, and grasshopper nymphs may be tried later.

3. *Bird Observations:* These can take two common forms: direct observation and photographic observation. The latter is accurate, but not always possible. If there is a bird-watching group in your community, joining it is the best way to get first-hand information and instruction. Accurate records of your observations should be kept. Include the date, time, place, and the birds seen.

4. *Bird Houses and Feeding Stations:* Build a bird house or set up a winter feeding station. Articles dealing with these projects appear in such publications as the Audubon magazine, published by the National Audubon Society, 1000 Fifth Avenue, New York, New York.

FURTHER READING

The Age of Reptiles. Edwin H. Colbert. W. W. Norton and Co., Inc., New York, N.Y. Author discusses the extinct reptiles and their great age of supremacy.

Handbook of Snakes. Albert H. Wright and Anna A. Wright. Comstock Publishing Associates, Ithaca, N.Y. Lists and identifies all of the species of snakes found in North America.

The Reptiles. Archie Carr and the Editors of LIFE. Time, Inc., New York, N.Y. Well illustrated account of ancient and modern reptiles.

"The Navigation of the Green Turtle." Archie Carr. *Scientific American,* May, 1965, page 79. Studies of this animal indicate that it navigates well enough to reach islands after 1400 miles at sea.

The Bird Biographies of John James Audubon. Alice Ford (ed.). Macmillan Company, New York, N.Y. Many of the original paintings by Audubon are included in this collection of his descriptions of native birds.

The Birds. Roger Tory Peterson and the Editors of LIFE. Time, Inc., New York, N.Y. A fine overview of all phases of bird life. Illustrated.

On the Trail of Vanishing Birds. Robert P. Allen. McGraw-Hill Book Company, Inc., New York, N.Y. Tells the story of how we are trying to save some American birds from extinction.

"**The Navigation of Penguins.**" John T. Emlen and Richard L. Penney. *Scientific American,* October, 1966, page 105. How do penguins travel hundreds of miles to their breeding grounds over a terrain that apparently has no landmarks? Experiments suggest navigation by the sun.

30

Mammals
Foremost Vertebrates

MAMMALS are the most highly developed of all the vertebrates. These are the animals with fur. They are generally intelligent animals, a trait that makes them especially valuable to man. All are descended from small animals about the size of a mole or shrew.

Fossils of reptiles with mammalian characteristics have been found in rocks in South Africa. These rocks are almost 225 million years old, an age that places them before the dinosaurs. Important changes that link these early reptiles with the mammals had already occurred in the skull, teeth, and jaws. Yet the fossils do not reveal whether these animals were warm-blooded or whether they nursed their young.

What happened to these reptile-mammals during the millions of years when the dinosaurs dominated the earth? They seem to have disappeared, crowded out by the dinosaurs. But smaller, mammal-like forms followed that did survive the dinosaurs. They left only a few fossils consisting mostly of teeth and jaws. These fossils indicate, however, that these small mammals were like moles or shrews. They had to hide by day for they could not compete with the flesh-eating reptiles that surrounded them.

The Rise of Mammals

What enabled the mammals to inherit the earth? Although mammal-like reptiles appeared upon the earth before the large dinosaurs, only a few survived. These apparently evolved into the very small mammals in existence during the period of dinosaurs. At that time their numbers were few. But when the dinosaurs disappeared from the earth, the mammals increased in numbers.

Perhaps the most important factor in the rise of the mammals was the disappearance of the dinosaurs. Other factors helped too. Mammals are warm-blooded and can withstand changes in climate very well. They have the ability to adapt themselves quickly to a changing environment.

The mammal-like reptiles seem to have been the ancestors of the three types of mammals living today. The first of these mammalian types are primitive egg-laying forms. The second type bear young that are very poorly developed at birth and are kept in a pouch in the mother's body. Such mammals are called *marsupials.* The third type bear well-developed young. These are the *placental mammals.* The development of young placental mammals occurs inside the body of the mother where they receive nourishment directly through a structure called the *placenta.*

The descendants of the first mammals are a very diverse group. Some of the earlier forms, the mammoth, the giant sloth, the saber-toothed tiger, are now extinct. Some living mammals are giants, larger than any dinosaur. The great blue whale, for example, is over 100 feet in length and weighs 125 tons.

CHARACTERISTICS OF MAMMALS. All mammals are warm-blooded. Nearly all bear living young, although a few lay eggs. At birth the young are nourished by milk secreted by the *mammary glands.* These glands give the mammals their name. Just as the feathers of a bird are its identifying feature, so the hair or fur of mammals identifies them. Fur insulates the body against heat loss. Some comparatively hairless forms, like man and the whale, have hair as embryos, but it is lost before birth. In some, like the pangolin, a lizardlike mammal from Africa, the hair is modified into horny overlapping plates. The average mammal produces fewer offspring than do other vertebrates. The young, however, are not left to fend for themselves.

The teeth of mammals are specialized for eating different kinds of food. Some are used for cutting. Others are used for tearing. Still others are used for grinding. Unlike reptiles, whose lost teeth are continuously restored, mammals have only two sets of teeth: a temporary set that is lost early in life and a permanent set that replaces the temporary set.

Although the metabolic rate in mammals is not as high as in birds, it is higher than that of the other vertebrates. To assist the lungs there is a muscular partition, the *diaphragm,* stretched across the bottom of the chest cavity. Its rhythmic movement draws air into the lungs and then forces it out of them.

Of all the special traits peculiar to the mammals, perhaps their most outstanding one is intelligence. In no other vertebrate group is this quality more pronounced. The cerebrum of mammals is large and well developed. This portion of the brain seems to account for their higher mental qualities.

DEVELOPMENT OF THE HORSE. One of the most baffling questions the biologist continually asks is: How did the present forms of life develop? Biologists have tried to piece the story together bit by bit. In some cases the evidence presented to show the relations of animals is very weak. The problem is somewhat like trying to put a jigsaw puzzle together with many of the parts missing. But in at least one case biologists feel sure of themselves. This is the story of how the modern horse developed.

MAMMALIAN CHARACTERISTICS

- They bear living young (except the platypus and the spiny anteater).
- Their young are nourished by milk from mammary glands.
- Their bodies are covered with hair or fur.
- They are warm-blooded and have a four-chambered heart.
- They have two sets of teeth.
- They have high intelligence and a well-developed nervous system.
- They breathe by lungs assisted by a muscular diaphragm.

About 50 million years ago *Eohippus*, the "dawn horse," roamed the western plains of the United States. Slightly larger than a cat or small terrier, it was about eleven inches tall. Its forelegs had four toes; its hindlegs had three. Its neck was short. Its head was not elongated like that of modern horses. Careful examination of the fossils indicates that they were unmistakably horses despite their smallness. A complete set of 44 small teeth seems to indicate that these "dawn horses" were forest dwellers that ate leaves.

Later fossils, perhaps 40 million years old, indicate that the descendants of Eohippus had become larger. This later form, called *Mesohippus*, was about the size of a large collie. It was about two feet tall. Its forelegs had changed, for now there were three toes and a splint, or bony extension, in place of the fifth toe. Its hindlegs, however, still had three toes. All three toes of Mesohippus touched the ground, but the middle toe was the largest. The middle toes supported most of the weight of the body. The teeth had also become larger. The neck had lengthened slightly and the head was longer.

In another ten million years further changes are evident. *Merychippus* is still larger, about 40 inches tall. Both the forelegs and hindlegs bear three toes, but the development of the middle toe is more

30–1 The fossil record of the evolution of the modern horse (Equus) from the cat-sized Eohippus is remarkably complete. The chart below and on the next page shows reconstructions of four stages with details of skulls and feet. Comparable series have been reconstructed from bones and teeth for other animals, including elephants, camels and monkeys.

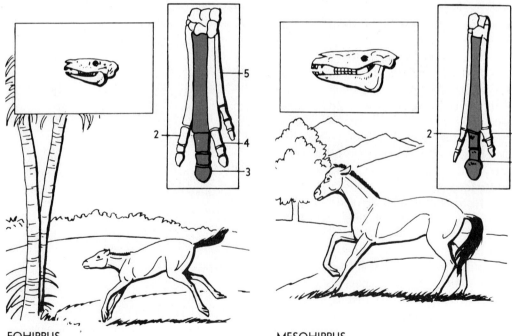

EOHIPPUS
Height: 11 inches
Forefeet: 4 toes (splint of first)
Teeth: short, rooted, no cement

MESOHIPPUS
Height: 24 inches
Forefeet: 3 toes (splint of fifth)
Teeth: longer than Eohippus, rooted, no cement

pronounced. Only the middle toe now reaches the ground, the other toes having become short and slender. The elongation of the neck and head had continued. The teeth had now become longer and more adapted for grinding the grasses on which the animal fed.

Pliohippus was the last step prior to the development of the modern horse. About the size of a pony, it had one-toed feet. The remains of the other toes are seen as reduced splints. The teeth are similar to those of the modern horse, but are not so elaborately ridged for grinding food. Pliohippus, dating back about 20 million years, is like a modern horse in almost every way.

The modern horse, *Equus* (EEH-kwus), is larger than any of its fossil ancestors, being about five feet tall. Each of its legs has only one toe, and the nail on each toe has become modified into the hoof. The reduction in the number of toes seems to have given this animal an advantage in running over the hard surface of the plains upon which it lived.

Mystery surrounds the final chapters of the story of the development of the horse. Shortly after the retreat of the glaciers that covered North America during the Ice Age, the horse disappeared from the North American continent. No one has been able to explain why. One idea is that some parasite may have killed them off. The horses of the western plains of the United States are descendants of animals that escaped from the early Spanish explorers who brought them to the new world shortly after the voyages of Columbus. The first domesticated horses were tamed by tribes living in southern Russia.

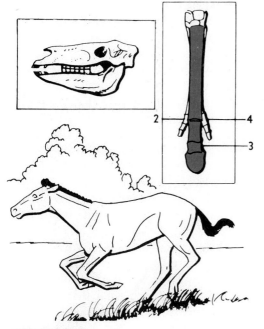

MERYCHIPPUS
Height: 40 inches
Forefeet: 3 toes (reduced second and fourth)
Teeth: long, short-rooted, cement

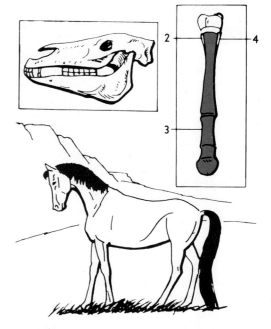

EQUUS
Height: 60 inches
Forefeet: 1 toe (splints of second and fourth)
Teeth: long, rootless, cement

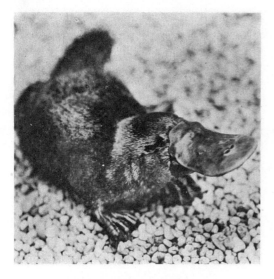

30–2　Duckbilled Platypus

30–3　Spiny Anteater

Mammalian Reproduction

One of the chief distinctions between the reptiles and the mammals is that the reptiles are egg layers. As a rule mammals do not lay eggs. There are, however, two prominent exceptions. One exception is the spiny anteater; the other is the duckbilled *platypus*. Both of these mammals are native to Australia. Unlike all other mammals, they reproduce by laying eggs.

THE EGG LAYERS. The platypus is a very strange animal that resembles a small beaver with a duck's bill for a snout. So odd is its appearance that when the first preserved specimen arrived in London in 1798 many naturalists declared it to be a hoax. However, living specimens in many zoos prove the platypus is no hoax. It is simply a curious link with a distant age.

Like a reptile, the female platypus lays large, leathery eggs. Then, like a bird, she incubates them with the heat of her body. Finally, like true mammals, the young obtain milk from the tiny mammary glands embedded in the mother's skin.

The *echidna*, or spiny anteater, resembles a small porcupine in that it has very sharp quills on its body. It lays a single leathery egg and rears its young in a small pouch on the abdomen. Its long beak is used to seek out ants, its favorite food.

Both the platypus and the echidna are animals that have survived through millions of years without significant changes in their body plan. Some biologists regard them as "living fossils" that mark one of the earliest branches from the reptiles. If this is so, they probably have a family tree that has been unbranched for 200 million years.

THE POUCHED MAMMALS. One of the most interesting sections of the world from the standpoint of the history of animal development is the continent of Australia. At one time Australia was part of the mainland of Asia. However, about 120 million years ago, it was separated from that continent by the invading ocean. It was just about this time that the relatives of the kangaroo and opossum, the pouched mammals, first appeared. Some of these early marsupials were in Australia when the land bridge with

Asia was broken. And since that time no other kind of land mammal (except the egg-layers) has been found there except those introduced by man.

Like other pouched animals, the kangaroo has young that are poorly developed. The mother may weigh over 200 pounds, yet her young weigh only a few ounces. They may be as small as a peanut. The mother carries her tiny young in her pouch. There they attach themselves to her mammary glands and receive nourishment. In the following months they grow large enough to be self-sufficient. At this time they hop in and out of the pouch at will.

The marsupials flourished in Australia and nearby islands, producing many animals quite different from the kangaroo. One, the Tasmanian wolf, looks like the wolves of other continents. Others resemble mice, moles, badgers, and squirrels. But all carry their young in a pouch. The familiar Koala (kuh-WALL-uh), or Australian "teddy bear," is another example of a marsupial.

In North and South America the only marsupial that has managed to survive is

30–5 Kangaroo

the opossum. In appearance it is somewhat like a large rat. It is even more primitive than the kangaroo. Its young are born 13 days after fertilization. Less than one-half inch long, they weigh about as much as a bee! Their only recognizable features are the clawed forefeet with which they climb into the mother's pouch. Within two months the young are well developed.

30–4 Millions of years ago, Australia was connected to the mainland of Asia.

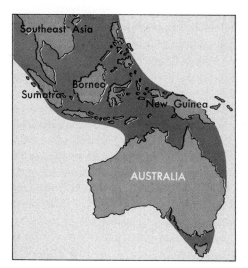

30–6 Koala

30–7 The opossum is North America's only marsupial. At birth the toes of the forelimbs have well-developed claws, which hold the young for two months in the mother's pouch.

At a time when the dinosaurs were beginning to disappear from the earth, the first marsupials made their appearance. Many of them were scattered all over the earth. Generally they were like the opossum, but much smaller. Yet, only in Australia where there was no competition from placental mammals were marsupials able to flourish until the present.

How then did the opossum, living in another part of the world, manage to escape extinction? Several of its adaptations may explain this. Like the ancient mammals, it forages for food only at night. Its most peculiar adaptation, however, is its habit of pretending to be dead when confronted with danger. As soon as an enemy approaches, it becomes completely motionless, only to come to life again when the enemy leaves.

PLACENTAL MAMMALS. By far the largest number of mammals are placental mammals, which bear living young that are well developed at birth. Unlike the opossum and kangaroo, they do not have a pouch in which the young develop. In order to understand the major difference between these two types of mammals, we will have to learn more about their reproductive system.

The female mammal has two ovaries, organs in which eggs are produced. These are connected by oviducts to the *uterus*. The uterus is an enlarged tube or sac in which the young develop. The *vagina,* or birth canal, leads from the uterus to the outside of the body. The eggs, which are produced in the ovaries, pass down the oviduct. If mating has occurred, the sperm cells fertilize the eggs in the oviduct. The fertile eggs begin to undergo cleavage while they continue their passage into the uterus. Once there, the membranes that have begun to form about the embryo press against the wall of the uterus. They anchor the embryo to the wall by means of the placenta. Through the placenta, the embryo now obtains oxygen and food from the blood vessels of the uterus. The placenta also permits the developing embryo, or *fetus,* to return carbon dioxide and other wastes to the mother's blood stream. Mammalian eggs contain practically no yolk. Development of the young depends upon obtaining nourishment from the blood of the mother. The placenta solves the problem.

With the food problem solved, the fetus undergoes growth until it is ready for birth. The time required varies in different species. This period, from fertilization to birth, is called the period of *gestation.* In the mouse the average period of gestation is only 20 days. In the African elephant, it is 640 days. In man it is 266 days.

At the time of birth, contractions of the uterus force the young along the birth canal to the outside. The *umbilical cord,* which connects the fetus to the placenta, is now severed, and the newborn animal is on its own. It will receive nourishment from the mother's mammary glands until it becomes entirely self-sufficient.

The young of mammals vary a great deal at birth. Some are practically helpless. Kittens have their eyes closed, as do puppies. Both can just about crawl. Human babies usually learn to walk the first year. A colt can follow its mother about within a few hours after birth. A jack rabbit is practically able to care for itself when born. But all mammals see to it that their young are cared for until such time as they can provide for themselves. This is one reason why they have been successful animals.

Orders of Mammals

There are 16 *orders* of living placental mammals. Zoologists classify them according to their teeth, claws, hoofs, and other specialized structures. We shall list and discuss some of the more interesting forms.

INSECT EATERS. Moles, shrews, and hedgehogs belong to the modern group of mammals that are most closely related to the earliest placental mammals. They belong to the order *Insectivora,* which means "insect eating."

Moles are small burrowing animals with enormously developed shovel-like forefeet. They spend most of their life underground. Their eyes, which are useless, are reduced to the size of pinheads. They feed upon grubs and worms, which they locate with their sensitive snouts. A single mole consumes about 40,000 insects and worms in a year. You may have seen the ridged mounds they leave near the surface of the ground as they burrow beneath it.

Most shrews are so tiny they can sit comfortably in a tablespoon. Their metabolic rate is high. They eat several times their weight in food daily. Their sharp, pointed jaws contain needlelike teeth. At least one species has poison glands in the mouth for killing its prey. They are hunters that work continuously night and day. It is from the remote ancestors of shrews that all the modern placental mammals have sprung.

30–8 Shrews are the smallest mammals. They eat several times their weight each day.

Toothless Mammals. The anteaters, sloths, and armadillos belong to the order *Edentata*. This name means "without teeth." Actually, some members of this order have poorly developed teeth but they are not found on the front of the jaw.

The giant anteater of South America is the largest edentate. It attains a length of five feet. Equipped with powerful forelegs that bear long claws, it tears open termite nests. Then its long sticky tongue laps up the termites by the hundreds.

Sloths are native to tropical America. They hang suspended upside down from the branches of trees. At the end of the limbs are large curved claws that permit them to hang in this manner for long periods of time. Even their fur grows forward, thus shedding the rain! Out of the trees a sloth is helpless. He flounders on the ground as though his skeleton were made of rubber.

Armadillos are well known for their bony armor. They remind us of armored tanks used in warfare. Some of the ancient relatives of the armadillo, the *glyptodons,* grew to a length of 16 feet. When threatened by

30–10 Sloths hang upside down as they travel through trees eating leaves and fruit.

an enemy, the armadillo rolls itself into a ball. This is a simple but effective defensive measure. During the last century the American nine-banded armadillo has stead-

30–9 The anteater's elongated snout houses a sticky tongue that can be extended as far as 20 inches when pursuing ants and termites.

30–11 Armadillo Quadruplets. They are believed to result from the splitting of a single egg during cleavage.

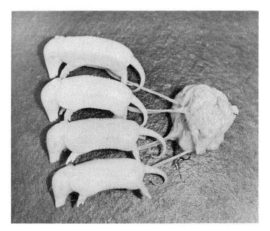

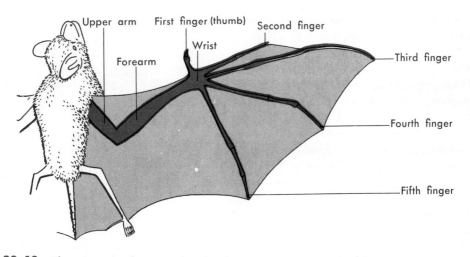

Upper arm   First finger (thumb)   Second finger

Forearm   Wrist

Third finger

Fourth finger

Fifth finger

30–12 The wing of a bat is a thin, leathery membrane stretched between four finger bones, the hind legs, and sometimes the tail. Most bats eat insects and are helpful to man.

ily increased its numbers. Spreading from southern Texas it has reached all parts of that state and crossed into Louisiana, Oklahoma, and New Mexico. It can even swim successfully by taking air into its digestive tract to make it lighter. Another curious fact about this animal is that it usually gives birth to quadruplets of the same sex. This suggests that its offspring result from a single fertilized egg that splits into four separate parts during cleavage.

FLYING MAMMALS. The order *Chiroptera* includes bats, the only mammals capable of flying. Because they can fly, bats are the most widely distributed mammals. The wing consists of a thin, leathery membrane that stretches between the fingers of the forelimb and extends backward to the hindlegs. This type of wing construction is like the wing of the ancient flying reptiles.

Bats are nocturnal hunters, catching insects on the wing. Their skill in flying in to-

30–13 Bats have poor eyesight but easily locate flying insects by a kind of "radar." They emit a high-pitched sound that echoes from the insect back to their very sensitive ears.

tal darkness has posed some interesting questions. How do they "see"? Investigations have shown that they utter high-pitched sounds, which range between 25,000 and 50,000 cycles per second. Like radar, the sound waves are reflected by obstacles and are then picked up by stalklike folds of skin in the bat's outer ear. The wavelength of the emitted sound is just about the size of the insects the bat feeds upon. Using this sort of echo location system, bats not only avoid obstacles, but locate their prey in total darkness.

The largest bats feed upon fruit. In these, the eyes are large and bat "radar" is not used. One of them, the "flying fox" of Indonesia, has a wingspread of five feet.

Other mammalian "fliers" cannot be compared with bats. The "flying lemur" of Asia, for example, cannot manage true flight. Belonging to the order *Dermoptera*, it has skin folds stretching between its fore and hindlegs that enable it to skim from tree to tree when it extends its limbs and leaps. It glides through the air like a flying squirrel.

OCEAN DWELLERS: THE CETACEA AND SIRENIA. Although we think of the mammals as being land dwellers, some have returned to the sea. There is an interesting similarity here between the reptiles and mammals. You will recall that some of the

30–14 Porpoises are placental mammals and are among the most intelligent animals.

reptiles, the ichthyosaurs, returned to the sea after the conquest of the land had been completed.

The whales, porpoises, and dolphins constitute the order *Cetacea*. All of these mammals are well adapted to the aquatic life. Their bodies are streamlined. The forelimbs are modified into flippers, but the hindlimbs are missing. The tail is used for propelling the body in the water.

Whales are the largest mammals. There are two types of whales: those that have teeth and those that have horny plates of whalebone in place of teeth. The sperm whale, porpoises, and dolphins are all toothed whales. Although the sperm whale is one of the largest, the toothed whales

30–15 The blue whale is the largest of all animals, living or extinct. Note the size of the elephant compared to that of the blue whale.

are generally smaller than the toothless. The porpoises and dolphins are the smallest species, being about five to eight feet long. You may have seen them frolicking in the surf at the seashore. The toothed whales feed upon the fishes and squids, swallowing them whole. The whalebone, or toothless, whales strain huge mouthfuls of sea water to obtain the small animals, shrimp and mollusks, that they eat.

The larger whales have been hunted by man for centuries. Oil and other valuable products are obtained from them. The sperm whale, which grows 60 feet long, has a head of enormous size. In it are stored immense quantities of sperm oil, as much as a ton. It is known to hunt the giant squids that live in the depths of the ocean, but it also feeds upon fish like the cod. *Ambergris*, an intestinal product obtained from the sperm whale, is used in the manufacture of expensive perfumes. It is a gray, soapy material that may sometimes be found floating in the sea. It is literally worth its weight in gold.

Sea cows, or manatees, are cousins of whales and belong to a different order, *Sirenia*. Like whales they have no hindlimbs. The tail operates in a horizontal plane, and the forelimbs are fashioned into flippers. Their heavier bones enable them to remain on shallow bottoms where they feed on water plants. Although they are hairless and quite ugly, they are believed to be the basis for fables about mermaids and sirens.

FLESH-EATING MAMMALS. Early in the history of the development of the placental mammals a few, perhaps with better teeth and more aggressive habits, became hunters. They preyed upon the plant eaters. They became more cunning and swift. Numerous flesh-eating animals are grouped together in the order *Carnivora*. The familiar land forms include the lion, bear, wolf, raccoon, dog, and cat. There are also aquatic carnivores, seals, sea lions, and walruses.

30–16 Manatees, or sea cows, are mammals found in tropical waters of America and Western Africa. They feed on freshwater weeds and roots, which they grasp with the two halves of their upper lip. Sea cows may grow eight to ten feet long and weigh as much as two thousand pounds.

All have large canine teeth. Frequently the other teeth are adapted for cutting flesh also. The toes of the land forms are equipped with claws. The limbs of the aquatic forms are paddle-like.

30–17 The jaws and the teeth of carnivores are well adapted for tearing flesh.

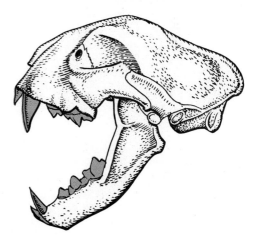

30–18 North American Grey Wolf

1. *The cats.* The domestic cat is related to the giant killers of the jungle. It is, like all the members of the cat family, marvelously adapted for preying upon other animals. The giant cats—the lion,

30–19 Alaskan Brown Bear

the tiger, the leopard—all creep close to their victims on silent, padded feet. Then, in a sudden burst of speed, they pounce upon them, slashing with teeth and claws to bring them down. The African cheetah, or hunting leopard, can catch the swiftest antelope. It attains a speed of 70 miles per hour over short distances.

2. *The dogs.* Dogs, wolves, foxes, and jackals form another large group of carnivores. Unlike the cats, they are adapted for running long distances in pursuit of their prey. Generally they hunt in packs. The wolf is the largest and most dangerous member of the group. The North American gray wolf is fast approaching extinction because man has hunted and trapped it relentlessly. Wolf packs have been very destructive to sheep, cattle, and other domestic animals. All of the many varieties of dogs, from St. Bernard to Chihuahua, are related to the original wolflike animals that man first tamed.

3. *The bears.* Although the bears are classed with the flesh eaters, many are vegetarians. Large and heavy, they are related to the dog family, but the tail is very short. The teeth are much less specialized than in other members of the order. They are the largest of the carnivores. The Alaskan brown bear may be nine feet long and weigh 1600 pounds. The polar bear is an expert swimmer and preys upon seals. His white color aids him in creeping stealthily upon his victim. His teeth are also better adapted for tearing flesh than in most of the other bears.

4. *Weasels.* Some of the finest furs of commerce are produced by such small members of the weasel family as the otter, mink, skunk, badger, and sable. Mink and sable are especially valuable pelts. Ermine is the white, winter pelt

of the brown weasel. Individual pelts of the sea otter have sold for as much as $1400.

5. *Raccoons.* The regular pattern of dark fur around the eyes of raccoons gives them the appearance of wearing a mask. Their habit of washing everything they eat has led Europeans to call them "wash bears." Even a freshly captured frog is dunked in the water before it is eaten. In addition to frogs, raccoons eat birds, small mammals, and many kinds of fruit. They are not completely carnivorous. Raccoons make good pets if they are trained when young. The pandas from China and Tibet are sometimes classified with the raccoon family. They are bearlike in appearance, one type resembling a black and white teddy bear.

6. *Seals and walruses.* Seals and walruses live in the sea, where they feed upon fish and crustaceans. Expert swimmers, they use their flippers to propel them in the water. They are believed to be related to the dog family. Their head structure and raucous barking at feeding time show some resemblance to canine characteristics. Seals that have external ears are called sea lions. The small California sea lion is common in the coastal waters of that state. It is intelligent and becomes a skilled performer when properly trained. These are the species that perform stunts in the circus. The fur seal breeds on the Pribilof Islands in the Bering Sea and is hunted for its valuable pelt.

Walruses are much larger than seals. Their enormous tusks are used to dig up oysters and clams. Even the stoutest mollusk shells are crushed by their strong teeth.

HOOFED MAMMALS. Certain types of mammals eat plants. We call them *herbivores* to contrast them with the carnivores. A common feature in most of the herbivores is the presence of hoofs. Hence, they are generally called ungulates, or hoofed animals. The ungulates are equipped with large, flat, grinding teeth. The long legs and hoofs

30–20   The jaws of hoofed mammals, such as the horse, have ridged teeth that grind plants.

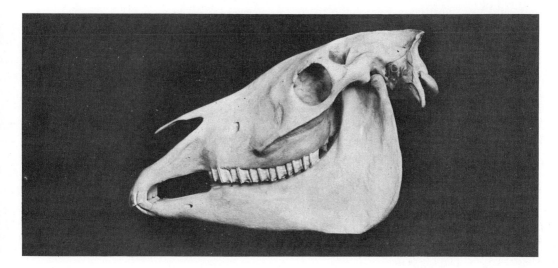

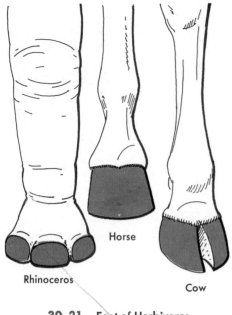

30–21   Feet of Herbivores

(ROO-muh-nants). The camels, deer, giraffes, cows, sheep, goats, and antelopes have complicated stomachs for digesting food. In the cow, for example, the food is stored in the first section of the stomach. It is later returned to the mouth as a "cud" for further chewing at a more leisurely pace. It is then swallowed again. This time the food passes on through the first section and then into the second, third, and fourth sections of the stomach. Such a four-chambered stomach makes it possible for the ruminants to digest the great amount of plant food they consume each day.

GNAWING MAMMALS. The gnawers or rodents, outnumber all of the other mammals. Of the more than 5000 species of mammals, over 2000 are rodents. Some, like the mouse, are tiny. Others, like the capybara of South

of the ungulates are adaptations enabling them to run swiftly when escaping from their enemies.

The hoofed animals have been extremely useful to man for centuries. Horses, oxen, and camels have been used as beasts of burden. Cattle, sheep, pigs, and goats are common barnyard animals. Meat, leather, milk, and wool are but a few of the many products derived from them.

Hoofed mammals developed from ancestors with five toes. Today they are conveniently divided into two groups: those that have an odd number of toes and those that are even-toed. The horse, tapir, and rhinoceros are odd-toed. Horses and zebras have but one hoof, whereas the rhinoceros has three toes on each foot. The tapir, closely related to the ancestors of the horse, has four toes on its forelegs, but only three on its hindlegs.

Most of the ungulates belong to the even-toed group. Except for the pig and hippopotamus families, all of them are *ruminants*

30–22 The stomach of a ruminant contains four separate sections. Cropped food is swallowed rapidly and enters the rumen, where it is stored temporarily. The food is later regurgitated as a cud, which is rechewed and swallowed into the second section, the reticulum. Water is absorbed in the omasum, or third section. Digestion begins in the true stomach, the fourth section.

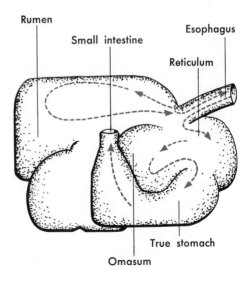

America, may weigh more than 100 pounds. Most rodents are scattered all over the earth as small animals that make their homes in burrows. Some, however, like the squirrels, live in trees. A few, such as the muskrat and beaver, have become adapted to the water. Rats, guinea pigs, and porcupines are also members of this large order, which is called *Rodentia*.

All rodents have two pairs of large, chisel-like teeth, called *incisors*, in the front of the mouth. The upper and lower pairs work together like shears to gnaw their food. Although their cutting edges are gradually worn away in the process, the incisors keep on growing throughout the life of the animal. Similarly, if the incisors are not used enough, they may actually grow in a circle and interfere with chewing, in which case the animal may starve.

The beaver and porcupine are among the most interesting rodents. The beaver builds its own swimming pool by constructing dams across small streams. Small trees are felled by gnawing through the trunk. These are placed across the stream, and spaces are filled in with mud. Porcupines are covered with sharp quills that bear barbed tips. They cannot shoot them at their enemies as is sometimes supposed. However, they are readily embedded in the nose of a foolhardy dog that risks attacking this bristly animal.

Rabbits and hares are like rodents in certain ways, but there are important differences. Although they have large incisors, there are two extra ones on the upper jaw. Their other teeth are not like those of true rodents. Their ears are much too big. Their hind legs are adapted for hopping. These are some of the reasons why some biologists place rabbits and hares in a separate group, the order *Lagamorpha*.

TRUNK-BEARING MAMMALS. Elephants are the largest of the mammals that live on land. Some may weigh more than seven

30–23 Woolly Mammoth

tons. The large trunk (proboscis) is the elephant's most prominent characteristic. With it he can pick up a tiny peanut or heavy log, bring water to his mouth, and dust himself after bathing. The elephant's trunk is really a modified nose. It gives the order of elephants its name, *Proboscidea*. The large tusks are very long incisor teeth. Two kinds of elephants are found on the earth today. One is the smaller species found in India; the other is the larger African species.

Huge as they are, the elephants do not quite match the size of their prehistoric ancestors, the mammoths. These woolly-coated animals inhabited nearly all of the northern hemisphere. Their bones have been discovered in practically all of the northern countries. But in 1901, in the frozen soil of the Siberian tundra, the greatest find of all was made. A practically intact mammoth, complete with woolly, shaggy coat, was found. Its stomach still contained the remains of its last meal. It had been in a deep freeze for 25,000 years! In fact, so well preserved was the animal that the dogs of the expedition were fed chunks of meat from its legs and trunk.

The Primates

In the entire drama of life there is probably no scene more interesting to view than that which leads to man. We seek our origins and speculate about our beginnings. What steps and processes led to man? Who were his immediate predecessors?

As we grope for answers to these questions, we come to the class Mammalia. We find that man has obvious mammalian characteristics. Then we study the animals within this class and seek out those that most closely resemble man. We find this resemblance among the *primates*. The lemurs, tarsiers, monkeys, and apes are similar to man in many ways.

1. The eyes are close together in the front of the head. Depth perception is improved.
2. The four limbs are modified for grasping. In many species the thumb or big toe can extend to the little finger, mak-

ing an ideal grasping organ. In the higher forms there is a great tendency toward hand specialization.
3. Most primates tend to walk upright, but only man is truly erect.
4. The brain is exceptionally well developed. Intelligence is an outstanding characteristic. The cranium is larger to accommodate the larger brain.
5. Primates usually bear only one offspring at a time, then provide it with prolonged care.

Most of the primates live in trees. Many use their limbs to swing from branch to branch. Except for man, they are largely tropical animals. Unfortunately they have not left a complete fossil record such as exists for the horse.

LEMURS AND TARSIERS. These are the most primitive of the primates. The lemurs resemble tree-dwelling foxes, having long snouts and bushy tails. Most species live on Madagascar.

30–24 PROBABLE DEVELOPMENT OF PRIMATES

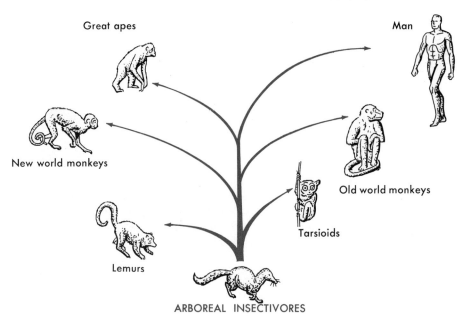

Great apes

Man

New world monkeys

Old world monkeys

Tarsioids

Lemurs

ARBOREAL INSECTIVORES

The oddest primate is the tiny tarsier, a native of the East Indies and Philippines. This small animal, about the size of a rat, has exceptionally large eyes that almost meet in the midline of the face. It sleeps during the day and forages for insects at night. On its fingers are adhesive pads, an adaptation that keeps it from falling out of the trees.

MONKEYS. The intelligence and antics of the monkeys make them top attractions in any zoo. The more than 500 species are divided into two major subdivisions: Old World and New World monkeys. The former have nostrils that are placed close together as in man. The New World monkeys are rather flat-nosed with the nostrils far apart. They also have *prehensile tails*, long enough to curl about a tree branch and grasp it firmly. The Old World monkeys cannot do this for their tails are straight. Generally, they are larger and heavier. Many have cheek pouches in which to stuff food. The baboons are the largest and best known of the Old World forms. These are powerful animals with doglike faces. Some species have vividly colored faces.

The small capuchin monkey of South America is the best known New World form. It is friendly, easily tamed, and often sold in pet shops. One of the most unusual New World species is the spider monkey. It has long, powerful arms and swings from branch to branch. This method of travel is common in apes, but rare in monkeys.

APES. These are the most manlike of all the primates. They are larger than the monkeys and have no tail. Of the four types, the gibbon and orangutan live in southeast Asia, while the chimpanzee and gorilla are native to Africa.

Both the gibbon and orangutan are tree dwellers with long hairy arms that are used for swinging from one branch to another. The gibbon is smaller, seldom three feet tall. The orangutan is considerably larger, fre-

30–25 Tarsier

quently approaching five feet. It is covered with a red fur. The name orangutan means "man of the woods" in the language of Malaya. It is much more intelligent than the gibbon, with a brain capacity that is far greater.

Neither the chimpanzee nor the gorilla is as much at home in the trees as the gibbon and orangutan. Gorillas are ground apes that take to the trees only at night. The chimpanzee is the smaller of the two. It thrives in captivity and is easily tamed. You can probably recall many of the tricks you have seen them do: riding a bicycle, skating, eating at a table. Not so the massive gorillas. These are powerful beasts that may be six feet tall and weigh as much as 500 pounds.

Both the chimpanzee and gorilla are very intelligent, but they have no language. There has been recent evidence that some apes will modify natural objects into crude tools. They have not, however, mastered the art of making tools. The skull and jaw proportions are not those of modern man. They do not walk erect. Perhaps at some future time we shall find more information about the ancestors of man. It seems certain that there are too many differences to link man closely to the apes.

THE AGE OF MAN. The most recent primate to make his appearance on our planet is man himself. In the last million years several species of man have left fossil records of their existence. All are now extinct except the single species to which we belong, *Homo sapiens,* which means "thinking man." Although man is the most recent arrival, he has, in a relatively short time, dominated all the other animals on the planet.

IMPORTANT POINTS

• Mammals are warm-blooded animals covered with hair or fur. They bear living young that are nourished with milk from the mammary glands of the mother.

• The ancestry of the mammals goes back to the early reptiles. During the reign of the dinosaurs, small shrewlike mammals survived. It is from these animals that modern mammals are believed to have descended.

• A few primitive mammals, such as the platypus, lay eggs. Marsupials, such as the kangaroo, bear poorly developed young that are then nourished in a pouch. By far the greatest number of mammals bear living young that develop within the mother's body. These young are well formed at birth. They are called placental mammals because they are attached to the uterus of the mother by a placenta, which permits them to obtain nourishment from her bloodstream before birth.

• There are 5000 species of living mammals, divided into a number of different orders. Among them are the flying specialists, the bats; various marine forms, the whales and porpoises; the flesh eaters, the lion and wolf; the hoofed animals, the horse and cow; the rodents; the elephants. Finally, there are the primates, the most intelligent of all. In this order are the lemurs, monkeys, apes, and man.

• Although the likenesses between the other primates and man are rather clear, many differences indicate the great gap between the apes and man.

REVIEW QUESTIONS

1. What is the chief difference between a marsupial and a placental mammal?
2. List four characteristics of mammals.
3. How are kangaroo young protected by the mother?
4. Compare the periods of gestation of the mouse, man, and elephant.
5. How do bats locate their prey in total darkness?
6. How are the teeth and limbs of carnivores adapted for their way of life?
7. Describe the two main kinds of hoofed mammals.
8. What is the main characteristic of the gnawing mammals?
9. List two main differences between monkeys and apes.

CHECK YOUR UNDERSTANDING

10. List three factors that may account for the rise of the mammals.
11. Trace the development of the horse's hoof from Eohippus to Equus.
12. What may account for the success of pouched mammals in Australia?
13. Why do the eggs of most mammals contain little yolk?
14. Why is the "flying squirrel" not considered to be a flying mammal?
15. Compare the methods used by the cat and dog families to catch prey.
16. Why must rodents continue to gnaw all their lives?
17. List four characteristics that set primates apart from other mammals.
18. What explanation might there be for the fact that fossils of mammals that lived during the Age of Reptiles are very scarce?
19. If Australia had not become separated from the mainland of Asia millions of years ago, what types of mammals do you think we would find there today?
20. Can you explain why the primates are successful mammals although most of them produce but one offspring at a time?

RESEARCH PROJECTS AND REPORTS

1. Obtain information from your school or public library and prepare a report on one of the following topics:

Whales and Whaling	**Mammals of Australia and Tasmania**
Bats	**Intelligence of Apes**

2. *Making a Mammal Book:* Visit the zoo and photograph various mammals. Mount the photographs in a notebook and write a short account of each animal on the opposite page. Include such data as classification by Order, Family, Genus, and Species. Note also the animal's size, habitat, diet, natural enemies, number of young produced, length of life, and value to man.

FURTHER READING

The Story of Horses. Pat Johnson. Random House, New York, N.Y. A brief history of the development of the horse from Eohippus to the present form. Told in a clear and interesting style.

How to Know the American Mammals. Ivan T. Sanderson. New American Library, New York, N.Y. Interesting and useful guide to our continent's mammals.

Furred Animals of Australia. E. Troughton. Charles Scribner's Sons, New York, N.Y. An excellent account of the mammals of Australia and the nearby islands and how they differ from the mammals inhabiting the rest of the world.

"New Discoveries Among Africa's Chimpanzees." Jane van Lawick-Goodall. *National Geographic*, December, 1965, page 802. A fascinating account of the author's one-year study of these animals in their natural surroundings.

"The Earliest Apes." Elwyn L. Simons. *Scientific American*, December, 1967, page 28. Fossil discoveries in the Fayum region of Egypt take us back 28 million years to study the ancestors of modern apes.

The Biology of Man

Man is the most interesting animal in the world. Each of us inhabits a world bounded by the limits of our body. We feel each moment the sensations of our life processes—the beating of our heart, the breathing of our lungs, the taste of our food, the feeling of pleasure or pain. It is natural, therefore, for us to want to know more about ourselves and the origins of the human species.

The study of the human body by dissection and experiment is comparatively recent in the history of biology. Prior to the Renaissance the two great medical authorities were the Greek Aristotle, born in 384 B.C., and the Roman Galen, born in 131. Aristotle did very little human dissection. Galen worked exclusively with animals. It is hard to believe that two men—with such little experience in human dissection—could have dominated the thinking of medical men for over a thousand years.

Not until the Belgian anatomist Vesalius dared to defy the authority of Aristotle and Galen in the 16th century do we find the beginning of modern anatomy and physiology. In the 17th century, William Harvey and Marcello Malpighi investigated the nature of the blood and circulation. The optical microscope was invented and improved. In this early period of the Renaissance, man's ideas about the structure and function of the body were changing. New instruments and techniques were devised. New theories and new disciplines sprang up. Invention and change were the order of the day.

Today, the instruments of science are directed toward gathering information about the human body. Surgeons perform apparent miracles. Repairs and transplants of the heart, and operations upon the brain have become almost routine. Chemical analysis has identified blood compounds that are the fundamental defense against disease. Electronic devices measure electrical pulses in the heart, in the brain, and even in the cell. The gross anatomy of the body has been reduced to the anatomy of cells and cell components.

We do not know how far backward man's ancestry stretches. We do know that man's beginnings are documented by fossils more than a million years old. The most ancient fossils that can be considered human are more ape-like than manlike. In this distinction between man and ape lies the germ of a controversy that has raged since the discovery of the first fossilized "men." Many scientists believe that such human traits as the use of fire and tools and the development of speech occurred more than one million years ago.

Man is the product of millions of years of biological change. Like every other living thing, he has survived only as he became better adapted to the conditions of a changing world. Man's ability to think and to communicate his ideas to his fellow man by a spoken and written language have made him the most successful animal on earth.

31

The Human Pattern Emerges

MAN is a recent arrival upon the earth. We can search the ancient beds of the dinosaurs in vain for his remains. Fossil remains of man are not found with the fossils of the earliest mammals. Only in a fairly recent geological time do we discover his ancient camp sites. Evidences of any remains that can be even remotely associated with man take us back two million years. Two million years is but a tick of the geological clock that has been running billions of years.

Man is different from the other primates. He is more creative, more curious, more intelligent by far. His intelligence has enabled him to control his environment. He learned long ago to make tools and to use fire. He tamed animals and grew plants. He lived in small groups and developed a spoken language. He has conquered the hostile climates. Having probed every corner of the world, he now explores space.

The development of a spoken language is perhaps man's greatest advantage. With language, ideas can be exchanged. The information of many people becomes available to all. With the development of a written language some 6000 years ago, another great advantage was achieved. Since then, each new generation has benefited from the recorded experiences of the past. The growing store of information that is preserved by the written language is the basis upon which a civilization is built.

Because man is so different, we are inclined to overlook his kinship with other animals. Structurally, he is a mammal related to the higher apes. Physiologically, his reactions and processes are so similar to other mammals that we can substitute them for him in our laboratories. We can use mice and monkeys to study nutrition and disease. We can study animal behavior to derive clues about human behavior. But there are certain peculiarly human characteristics. The human pattern is a unique design in the animal kingdom.

Homo Sapiens—Thinking Man

Have you ever seen the celebrated statue, *The Thinker*? The distinguished French sculptor Rodin modeled a man with his head supported by his hand as he gazes forward lost in thought. The same idea must have been present in the minds of scientists who first assigned man his scientific name. They called him ***Homo sapiens*** (SAPE-eeenz), which means "thinking man." Let us look at the complete classification of man.

KINGDOM:	Animal
PHYLUM	Chordata
SUBPHYLUM:	Vertebrata
CLASS:	Mammalia
ORDER:	Primates
FAMILY:	Hominidae
GENUS:	Homo
SPECIES:	sapiens

There are many animals in each of these subdivisions until we arrive at the family *Hominidae*. Man is the only living member of this group. "Thinking man" is unique.

HUMAN INTELLIGENCE. The cranium is the part of the skull that encloses the brain. Modern man has a cranium that is about three times the size of the average ape's. In the gorilla its volume is about 500 cubic centimeters. In man it is almost 1500 cubic centimeters. Most of the difference in size is in the frontal lobes of the cerebrum, the center of intelligence. The larger cranium gives a distinctly human shape to the entire head that is most noticeable above the eyes. Here the brow is more upright, not sloped backward as in the apes.

The bones of the human face are significantly different from those of apes. In humans the jaws are smaller, the chin line more pointed. The teeth, too, are smaller and more crowded together. Human facial bones are generally thinner and lighter than in the apes. Thus, human intelligence and the size and shape of the cranium seem to be closely related.

WALKING ERECT. Have you ever stopped to consider why man walks in an upright

31–1 Gorillas normally assume four-footed posture when walking. The erect posture of man is largely a result of differences in the size and shape of his hip and leg bones.

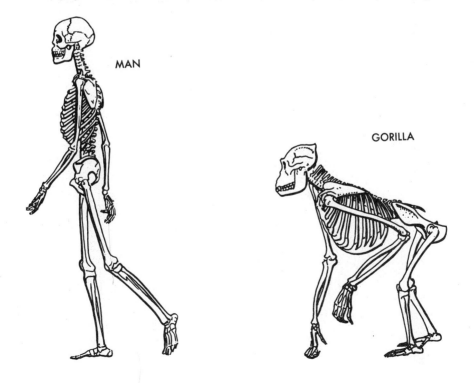

MAN

GORILLA

position instead of on all fours? The human infant takes a year or more to accomplish this feat. Even when he acquires the skill, he is not secure. He is always in danger of falling. Anthropologists are scientists who study the structure, origins, and races of men. One of them said, "Man stands alone because he alone stands." Even the apes that can stand erect walk and run in this position only with great difficulty. Normally they move on all fours. Only man walks with a truly erect posture.

Walking erect is possible because of the way our legs and feet are constructed. Our thigh bones are much longer in proportion to our body size than in the ape. The muscles of our legs are more powerful. The large heel, the arch, and the sole provide support and flexibility. An ape's foot is more like a hand, designed for grasping, not walking. The toes are long, and the big toe is like an outstretched thumb. Apes have practically no heel.

THE HUMAN HAND. Certain refinements make the hands of man more versatile than those of the apes. Man's fingers are slightly shorter, and the thumb is considerably longer. Try bending your thumb completely across your palm to the heel of the little finger. You can do it with ease. Yet this is an exclusive human accomplishment. It cannot be imitated by apes.

Some anthropologists believe that man's hands have contributed at least as much to his civilization as his intelligence. Hands make man an expert at fashioning and using tools. The human hand is a masterpiece of tiny muscles and bones that make small, precise movements possible. Moreover, walking erect has released the hand for work.

Remote Ancestors of Man

A century or two ago man was believed to have always had his present form. But the discovery of fossil animals raised some disturbing thoughts. Might not man, too, have developed from some previous form? The likeness between man and ape suggested that there might be an intermediate form. Much time was spent searching for this "missing link," an animal midway between the modern ape and man.

From what we know today the search for a "missing link" was doomed to failure from the start. A missing link between man and some present-day ape does not exist and probably never did. The relationship between man and the modern ape is like that of distant cousins. Both may have had a common ancestor several million years ago.

The search, however, produced some interesting results. Fossils provided evidence that manlike primates lived upon the earth about two million years ago. All of the evidence has come from the Old World—Asia, Africa, and Europe. No evidence has come from the New World. This is the distribution of apes in the world today. No apes exist in the New World.

PROCONSUL: AN EARLY PRIMATE. Many biologists believe that the ancestor of both ape and man was an ancient primate. Like branches from the trunk of a tree, the human line may have emerged as a separate and distinct branch that was paralleled by an equally distinct branch leading to the modern apes. Some evidence in support of this theory has come from fossils discovered in East Africa. There, a fossil primate, named *Proconsul,* was unearthed. Proconsul is thought to be 30,000,000 years old.

The importance of Proconsul is that he may be the trunk ancestor from which the two branches, ape and human, emerged. Proconsul was not a specialized primate in the sense that the modern apes are specialized. Although he could swing in the trees, his arms were not well adapted for that purpose. Although he could run on all fours, it is believed he often walked partially erect.

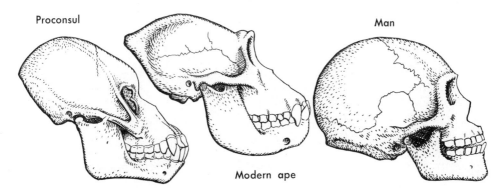

Proconsul

Man

Modern ape

31–2 Modern apes and man may represent divergent lines of development from some remote ancestral form, such as Proconsul. Note smooth forehead in Proconsul and in man.

Small and slight, the structure of Proconsul has caused some biologists to think that this ancient primate was more closely related to man than to the modern ape.

Was proconsul the ancestor of both man and ape, the "missing link" for which biologists have been searching? At the present stage of discovery no one can say with any certainty.

THE MANLIKE APES OF SOUTH AFRICA. In 1924, the discovery of large fossil deposits in limestone caves in the western Transvaal of South Africa added to our knowledge about the origins of man. Two South African anthropologists, Raymond Dart and Robert Broom, unearthed remains that appeared to be above the level of apes. The bones of the hip and leg seemed to indicate that the animals walked erect. The teeth had human characteristics. The brow ridges were not as prominent as those of modern apes. There were also nonhuman characteristics. The cranium was small, about 700 cubic centimeters, much more apelike than human. The forehead was low. The jaw was heavy and jutting.

The name *Australopithecus* (aus-tray-loh-PITH-ih-cuss) was given to these *hominoid* remains. Australopithecus means "southern ape" and indicates that the fos-

sils were considered more apelike than human. Was Australopithecus an ancestor of man? The experts were divided. Some contended that he was. Others contended that he was a side development of the modern apes.

ZINJANTHROPUS AND HOMO HABILIS. The number of prehuman fossils that have been found in Africa has led many anthropologists to argue that Africa may be the cradle of mankind. This line of reasoning supposes that a primitive species of man arose on that continent and migrated over the centuries to Europe and Asia where their more recent fossils were found. Scientists who hold this view include Dr. and Mrs. Louis Leakey, who have spent many years hunting primate fossils in East Africa.

In 1959, the Leakeys discovered several teeth and skull fragments in their excavations in Olduvai Gorge in Tanzania. Placing emphasis on certain human qualities of their fossils, they named their discovery *Zinjanthropus*, or East Africa man. Primitive pebble tools were found nearby. Stone flakes and a hammer stone seemed to indicate that the tools were made by manlike apes living at the site. Apparently, Zinjanthropus was not an expert hunter and preyed upon small animals.

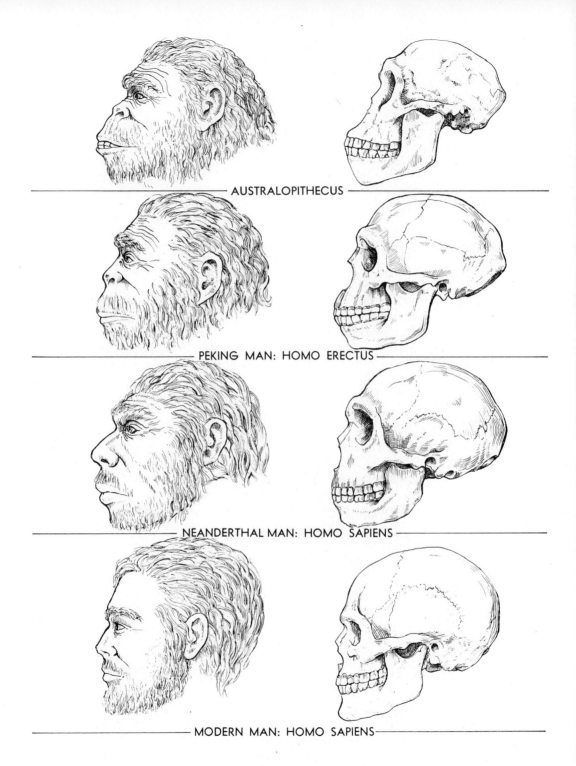

AUSTRALOPITHECUS

PEKING MAN: HOMO ERECTUS

NEANDERTHAL MAN: HOMO SAPIENS

MODERN MAN: HOMO SAPIENS

31–3 Examples indicating skull and facial development from manlike ape to modern man.

Leakey estimated the fossils to be about 600,000 years old. Later, rock samples in which the fossils were found were examined by geologists. By using the *potassium-argon* method of radioactive dating, they were able to estimate that the fossils were 1,750,000 years old.

The Leakeys first believed that Zinjanthropus was a primitive human who should be considered among man's earliest ancestors. Today, however, they are in general agreement with other anthropologists that Zinjanthropus is a variety of Australopithecus, the "pre-men" of South Africa.

In 1964, Leakey discovered another hominoid form in the lowest and oldest part of Olduvai Gorge. This hominoid walked erect, had a slightly larger cranial capacity than Australopithecus, and more manlike teeth. Was this another variety of manlike ape? Or was he a true man, perhaps the earliest human known?

Leakey named him *Homo habilis,* or "skillful man." By assigning him to the genus Homo, he gave him the status of man and placed him in the line of descent that leads to modern man. This classification has not been accepted by some scientists and has led to more controversy among anthropologists who seek to work out our origins.

More Recent Ancestors of Man

Biological change requires thousands of years. Slight changes gradually enable some animals to become better adapted to their environment than others. Through the reproductive process these slight changes gradually accumulate and change the nature of an animal. But when does a manlike ape become an apelike man? When shall we say that the borderline between ape and man has been passed?

JAVA APE MAN. In 1891, Eugene Dubois, a Dutch anatomist, found a few teeth and the top part of a skull in the mud of a river bed in the interior of Java. When reconstructed, the skull was too small for a modern man, but larger than that of any known ape. It had a brain volume of 900 cubic centimeters—between man and ape.

Several teeth and a thigh bone were found nearby. To Dubois, a trained anatomist, the size and shape of the thigh bone indicated that the individual had walked erect. The age of the fossils was carefully determined. After several years Dubois announced his conclusions. The remains were those of an apeman, about five to five and one-half feet tall. He walked erect, but his head hung forward. He had human characteristics. He probably had the ability to speak. And he lived about a half million years ago. Dubois named him *Pithecanthropus erectus,* which means "erect ape-man."

The claim that a fossil primate could be an early type of man was unheard of at the end of the 19th century. A storm of controversy greeted the announcement of the discovery. One group of scientists insisted the bones were those of an ape, possibly a giant gibbon. Still another group believed the skull and thigh bone were not from the same individual and that Dubois' findings were too confusing to have any importance.

With the passage of time Dubois gathered allies. Fossils of similar early men have since been discovered in many other parts of the world. Other expeditions have unearthed more skulls near the site that Dubois had originally explored. These skulls seemed to confirm the fact that Pithecanthropus was a member of the human family, Hominidae.

PEKING MAN. Before the controversy over Java man ended, another primitive man was discovered in China. A group of limestone caves in the hills southwest of Peking yielded the remains of forty individuals. These were collected over a ten-year period. Besides skulls, there were bones of the upper arm and thigh. There were also crude scraping tools made from *chert,* a flint-like stone.

A fairly complete picture of Peking man has been reconstructed from the remains. He was about five feet tall. Like modern man, he walked erect. His brain was somewhat larger than that of Java man—about 1000 to 1100 cubic centimeters. This is noticeably smaller than the brain of modern man.

We can even picture some of the activities of Peking man. He was a fire maker, as evidenced by the blackened areas in the caves, which locate the positions of his prehistoric hearths. He used primitive tools made of stone. Furthermore, these indicate that he was right-handed. Other evidence indicates that he was cannibalistic.

The discoverers of Peking man, Davidson Black and Frank Weidenreich, named him *Sinanthropus pekinensis.* This means China man from Peking.

HOMO ERECTUS. Today, anthropologists think that a number of different fossil men are all variations of a single form. Early comparisons of Java and Peking man revealed so many structural similarities that they appeared to be closely related. Differences in size and brain capacity may have resulted from the geographic isolation of two populations that stemmed from the same source. Although scientists continued to use their original names for a time, both men are now believed to belong to the same genus and species, and both are now classified as *Homo erectus.*

Certain fossil men found in other parts of the world—South Africa, Algeria, Germany, and Hungary—have shown the same characteristics. Although each find was given a separate name by its discoverers, it was noted that they had important traits in common. Their brain sizes were about midway between the gorilla and modern man, they were five to five and a half feet tall, and they lived 500,000 to a million years ago.

All of these fossil men are now classified as *Homo erectus.* The variations that existed among these men are now recognized as subspecies.

NEANDERTHAL MAN. The best known fossils of early man have been found throughout Europe. Called Neanderthal man after the Neander Valley in western Germany where his skull was first discovered, he represents a major step in the direction of modern man. Numerous finds in France, Italy, the Middle East, and northern Africa indicate his wide distribution. He probably survived in Europe until as recently as 35,000 years ago.

There is some controversy among scientists as to how to classify this ancient man. Some anthropologists designate him as *Homo neanderthalensis* and place him between *Homo erectus* and modern man. Others think he is an early variety of *Homo sapiens* (modern man). The controversy stems from the fact that two types of Neanderthal man have been identified.

Numerous fossils found in Europe, and more recently in Shanidar cave in Iraq, indicate that one type was very different from us in appearance. The "classic" Neanderthal had a long, sloping, thick skull with heavy brow ridges over the eyes. His head tilted forward. His arms, shoulders, and chest were powerfully muscled. He stood with slightly bent knees and was about five feet tall.

Another type of Neanderthal, more modern in appearance, has also been found. In 1932, in the Skuhl caves near Jerusalem, both "classic" and "modern" Neanderthal fossils have been unearthed. The discovery of both types at the same site indicates the great variation that existed in the Neanderthal people.

The massive head of Neanderthal man housed a brain slightly larger than that of the average man today. Its volume was about 1500 cubic centimeters. This does not necessarily mean he was more intelligent. The frontal area of the brain was not as well developed. Yet he survived during very difficult times, fashioned stone tools of fine quality, and probably invented sewing. Furthermore, he buried tools with his dead, indicating that he had some system of ritual.

NEANDERTHAL MAN AND THE ICE AGE. The years that witness the rise of modern man are the years that mark a period the geologists call the Ice Age. Beginning nearly a million years ago, large glaciers drifted southward from the polar ice caps. They brought cold weather. Eventually, large masses of ice blanketed most of Europe and parts of Asia. The North American continent was covered as far south as Ohio. The icy invasion lasted for thousands of years and caused the extinction of many plants and animals adapted to warmer climates. Then, as mysteriously as they descended, the huge rivers of ice receded. No one seems to know exactly why this happened.

The ebb and flow of ice occurred at four different times. Recent geological time is reckoned by these events. The Ice Age is divided into *glacial* and *interglacial periods*. Each glacial period lasted about 100,000 years and was followed by a longer, warm period. Then the ice returned. Today we are living in the fourth of the interglacial periods; it began about 25,000 years ago.

Neanderthal man lived in Europe from 150,000 years ago to about 35,000 years ago. This is the time of the fourth glacial period. He must have endured the rigors of this last great age of ice. It is easy to understand why he was a cave dweller. His cave protected him from enemies and was also a haven from the icy weather. During this time many of his kind migrated to the warmer climate of the south. Neanderthal men in northern Africa and western Asia were able to live untouched by the northern glaciers.

Earlier Neanderthal man lived in the warmth of the third interglacial period. He gathered edible roots, seeds, fruits, and nuts. Occasionally he ate meat. As the weather became colder, he became a skillful

31–4 The glaciers that exist today are only remnants of the vast ice sheets that covered much of the Northern Hemisphere in recent geological times. The advancing ice carved out the Great Lakes and blanketed northern United States with rock debris.

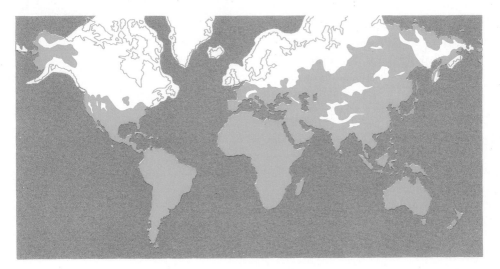

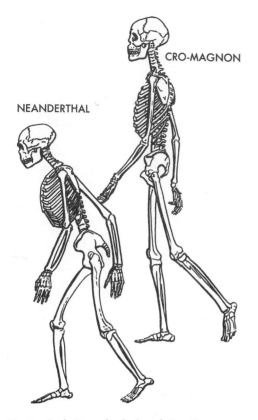

CRO-MAGNON

NEANDERTHAL

31–5 Both Neanderthal and Cro-Magnon are classified as human (Homo), but most scientists believe that structural differences mark them as separate species.

hunter. He hunted the large beasts that roamed Europe at that time, the mammoth and the woolly rhinoceros. To capture these animals required the organization of groups of hunters. Some men chased and confused the quarry. Others stood ready with flint-tipped wooden spears for the kill. Hunters among today's primitive tribes are no better equipped. Their spears are no improvement over the designs used by Neanderthal men thousands of years ago.

Suddenly, toward the end of the last glacial period, all record of Neanderthal man ceases. Like the disappearance of the dinosaurs, he presents us with another mystery.

Here was a man who had learned to use tools and to make fire. He was strong and intelligent. What caused his disappearance?

We know that modern men appeared in Europe long before Neanderthal man disappeared. Did Neanderthal man succumb to the rigors of the last glacial period leaving later men to inherit the earth? Or did he interbreed with these later men and become absorbed? The interbreeding of the two types of men might explain the fact that some Neanderthal fossils are less stocky and more modern in appearance.

The Rise of Modern Man

Evidence of the beginnings of modern man comes from a number of sources. In 1947, the French explorer Germaine Henri-Martin discovered two skulls in a cave at Fontechevade, France. The age of the remains placed them during the third interglacial period, about 150,000 years ago. Small fragments of a modern skull had been previously found at Swanscombe, England. These, too, had come from the same interglacial period.

Reconstructions show that these men had high, almost vertical foreheads. The heavy brow ridges of the Neanderthal men were absent. The cranium was more rounded, giving the head a higher appearance. There was no resemblance to the heavy facial features of Neanderthal man. The thickened jaws and heavy skull bones were not present. The other bones were thinner, more human in appearance.

Did the separate branches or races of modern man originate in different parts of the world at the time of his beginning? Or did they arise when he migrated in search of food during the Ice Age? Some anthropologists believe different varieties of man existed from the time of his earliest appearance. These varieties eventually gave rise to the present-day races of mankind. Others contend that races developed later.

CRO-MAGNON MAN. One type of early Homo sapiens that was probably a prehistoric race deserves special mention. Throughout Europe, in France, Italy, Poland, and Czechoslovakia, the remains of Cro-Magnon men have been discovered. Over a hundred fossils help us reconstruct a composite man looking something like the following. He was about six feet tall. He had a high forehead and his cranium was about 1600 cubic centimeters in volume. He made fine stone tools as well as delicate implements from bone and ivory. Some historians credit him with the invention of the bow and arrow. He was also an artist of considerable ability.

On the walls of the caves in which Cro-Magnon remains have been found are the paintings for which he is famous. Using only red earth and black animal charcoal from charred bones, he achieved remarkable results. The subjects of his paintings were the animals that he hunted—bears, mammoths, horses, and bison.

The appearance of Cro-Magnon man was a fairly recent event. Most estimates date his entrance into Europe about 30,000 to 40,000 years ago. This is near the end of the last great age of ice. Perhaps he migrated from Asia as the ice retreated. Along the Mediterranean fringe of North Africa, other prehistoric men very similar to Cro-Magnon have been found. It may be that Cro-Magnon people were widespread before their entry into Europe. Some scientists believe that Cro-Magnon characteristics may still be found among the tall Basque people of northern Spain.

MODERN RACES OF MAN. An interesting characteristic of modern man is his variety. There are differences in size, skin color, hair texture, and body build. In Africa we find four-foot pygmies and also seven-foot Watusi giants. In Asia we find Chinese with yellow skin and natives of New Guinea with black skin. The variations in body pro-

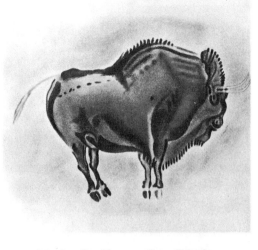

31–6 Cro-Magnon Cave Drawing

portions and weight are also striking when we compare different peoples.

Anthropologists generally recognize three basic human stocks, or *races*, believed to have originated in three major regions of the world. These are the *Caucasoid* (European), *Mongoloid* (Asiatic), and *Negroid* (African) races. It is important to note that all the races are classified in the same species, *Homo sapiens*. A criterion that is often used in determining the unity of a species is whether its members can interbreed. In the case of *Homo sapiens,* this fact has been clearly established. The colonizing of Asia and Africa by Europeans resulted in the intermarriage of many Europeans with the local population. Except in isolated regions it is likely that there is no such thing as a "pure" race because of mingling in the past.

Caucasoids, generally described as white, show considerable variation in skin color. Northern Europeans tend to be lighter. Mediterranean people tend to be darker. Caucasoids in the Near East and India are darker still. Hair and eye color also vary from light to dark. Caucasoids with light hair and eyes are a definite minority. Hair texture is straight or wavy, seldom kinky.

31–7 Modern man has developed variations in skin coloring, hair type, and facial characteristics; but these are insignificant differences, and all living men are the same species.

Mongoloids vary from yellow to tan. Generally they are shorter than the other two racial stocks. The presence of fat padding in the corner of the eyes gives the eyes a "slant." High cheek bones are a distinguishing feature.

Negroids have dark skins and hair that is often woolly. The nose may be flattened and characterized by broad nostrils. Generally, they are the tallest of the three races.

THE ORIGIN OF RACIAL CHARACTERISTICS. Anthropologists explain racial differences as adaptations to climate and geography. Skin color is an example of one of these adaptations. All human skin contains a varying amount of a pigment called *melanin*. Darker peoples have more melanin, lighter peoples have less.

In Negroid stocks (African), the large amount of melanin serves to screen out the excessive ultraviolet light of the tropical sun. Too much ultraviolet radiation is harmful. Caucasoids (European), having less melanin, can better tolerate the cloudier climates of the north. Overexposure to sunlight has been known to produce skin cancer and premature aging in light-skinned persons. Since a darker skin offers a protective advantage in tropical Africa, it may have become predominant in this region through natural selection. Thus, a racial character could have arisen as a survival mechanism.

Body build is also related to climate. Negroid peoples in hot regions tend to be tall and thin. This type of build is efficient for the release of excess body heat. Mongoloid peoples in cold regions (Eskimos) tend to be stocky, a build that conserves body heat. Over the years individuals having a body frame best adapted to the regional climate tended to survive. Poorly adapted individuals died earlier and left fewer offspring than did the better adapted individuals.

Facial types can be similarly explained. Anthropologists point out that the Mongoloid facial structure is well adapted to the bitter climate of northern Asia. Persons who survived best in this region had skulls with higher cheek bones, reduced brow ridges, and eye sockets that could accommodate a padding of fat about the eyes. These features served to protect the delicate sinuses. Hence, the flattened, "slant"-eyed face of the typical Mongoloid probably appeared as an aid to survival.

PHYSIOLOGY AND MODERN RACES. Dividing men into racial stocks is just a convenient way of describing some of their outstanding physical differences. It is important to note, however, that there are no fundamental differences in the physiology of people, no matter what the color of their skin, eyes, or hair.

The composition of blood is an example of a physiological characteristic that is identical in all races. Blood is probably the most fundamental of the body fluids. If we expect to find any significant racial differences, we should certainly find them here. But quite the opposite is true. As long as a compatible blood type is selected for a transfusion, it does not matter what race supplies it, nor what race receives it. In the matter of the most fundamental fluid in the body, no racial differences exist.

It is true, however, that certain national or regional groups show a greater percentage of one blood type over another. Almost all South American Indians, for example, have type O blood. Among North American Indians, about one in ten have type A and most of the rest have type O. Among Polynesian people, on the other hand, about six out of ten have type A blood.

MAN AND CIVILIZATION. Early man's life was incredibly harsh and dangerous. His life span was short. His control over his immediate surroundings was very slight. Today man's life is much improved. His average life span is constantly increasing. In many places he even controls the internal climate of his living. He can heat his home in winter and cool it in summer. The extent to which man exercises control over his surroundings is a measure of his civilization.

Man's development can be traced by examining the tools he developed. As early as a half million years ago, in a time called the Paleolithic Age, he made wide use of crude stone implements. This period is, therefore, more commonly called the Old Stone Age. Axes, knives, scrapers, and spears were fashioned out of stone by chipping and flaking. Yet it took time to master this difficult art. The stone implements of Peking man were very crude. The tools of Neanderthal and Cro-Magnon man were skillfully made.

31—8   Chopping tools and weapons, such as these, mark the beginning of technology.

Modern man entered into the Neolithic Age, or New Stone Age, about 10,000 years ago. Superior tools were now made by grinding and polishing. During this period man discovered the advantages of domesticating animals. Man also began to acquire such arts as weaving, sewing, and making pottery from clay. Later, he grew plants for his own use rather than depending upon wild varieties. The development of agriculture changed his nomadic habits. He settled in one place and formed communities. The communication of ideas was easier when man lived in groups.

The New Stone Age was of short duration. It ended some 5000 to 6000 years ago with the discovery of metals. The earliest metallic implements were of copper. Copper was easily extracted from its ore and shaped into useful forms. Later, tin was mined. Both metals had the disadvantage of being soft. But in a short time early man learned to combine them to make bronze. Bronze was much harder and so superior to anything that had been used before it that this period is sometimes called the Bronze Age. A more recent period in the history of metals began about 3000 years ago with the introduction of iron from the Near East. Steel, a form of iron, is now our most useful metal. We might, therefore, call our present civilization the *Iron Age*.

The development of a written language, which began about 6000 years ago, was probably the greatest step forward in the history of civilization. Each new generation added its knowledge to the knowledge of the past. Printing developed a means of bringing information to many people.

Due to this snowballing of knowledge, the advances of the last few centuries have been spectacular, greater than those of all the previous years put together. Man is beginning to realize, however, that his great steps forward are accompanied by responsibilities of a nature previously foreign to him. No longer can man grab whatever he wants from his environment without considering as well how he will replace it. Perhaps this will become the true measure of man's ability to achieve civilization—his willingness to accept the duties inherent in his freedoms.

IMPORTANT POINTS

● Man is superior to other primates because of his intelligence, his ability to walk erect, and his versatile hands. Man's brain is very large. His hind limbs are adapted for an erect posture. His fingers and thumb are adapted for fine manipulation.

● Man's remote ancestry may go back to an early primate, such as Proconsul. The manlike fossil apes found in South Africa walked erect, had teeth with human characteristics, but had small brains.

● *Homo erectus* had characteristics indicating that he was quite primitive. Although his brain volume was intermediate between ape and man, he was a maker and user of tools.

● Neanderthal man lived in Europe before and during the last Ice Age. His disappearance toward the end of the Ice Age may have been due to his interbreeding with more modern men.

● Man is classified into three basic racial stocks: Caucasoid, Mongoloid, and Negroid. The distinctions among the races are largely those of size, skin color, and facial features. These differences probably arose as adaptations to climate and geographical distribution during the last 20,000 years. No physiological differences are known to exist among races.

● Man passed through several stages of civilization. In the Paleolithic Age he was a maker of chipped stone implements. In the Neolithic Age he ground and polished stone, domesticated animals, and began to farm. About 6000 years ago he discovered metals and invented written language. In the last several centuries he has changed his environment more than he did during the first two million years.

REVIEW QUESTIONS

1. What three physical characteristics set man apart from the other primates?
2. Compare the brain volume of man and the gorilla.
3. How did the human hand contribute to the development of man's civilization?
4. How may Proconsul be considered a "missing link"?
5. List two human and two nonhuman traits of Australopithecus.
6. What characteristics of Java man convinced Eugene Dubois that he had found a primitive species of man?
7. In what two ways was Neanderthal man more advanced than *Homo erectus*?
8. In what ways did the Ice Age affect the activities of early man?
9. What are the three major races and where are they thought to have originated?
10. How is the structure of man's foot related to the tool-using function of his hands?

CHECK YOUR UNDERSTANDING

11. What evidence do we have that Neanderthal man displayed a high order of intelligence?
12. How might the disappearance of Neanderthal man be explained?

13. In what two ways might an anthropologist distinguish a fossil skull of *Homo sapiens* from that of an earlier species of man?
14. Give one example of how a racial character may have developed as an adaptation to climate and geography.
15. Trace the progress of the Age of Metals from the end of the New Stone Age to the present time.
16. Which of man's inventions marked the greatest step forward in the history of civilization?
17. There are many gaps in our knowledge of early man because his fossils are not very numerous. Can you suggest possible reasons for this?
18. Some scientists believe that huge glaciers will descend from the north in 50,000 to 100,000 years and cover many of man's cities. Why is this a logical theory?
19. Why might it be considered that an Eskimo is more "typically" Mongoloid than is a Japanese?
20. The human population remained small until a few thousand years ago, then it began to grow and today outnumbers that of all other mammals. Suggest reasons for this.

RESEARCH PROJECTS AND REPORTS

1. Obtain information from your school or public library and prepare a report on one of the following topics:

   Neanderthal Man   **The Cave Art of Cro-Magnon Man**

   Homo erectus   **The Ice Age**

2. *Man's Family Album:* Your community may have a museum that displays skulls or plaster reconstructions of prehistoric men. Photograph the exhibits of each type or make drawings of them. Mount the photographs (or drawings) on separate pages of an albumlike folder. Under each entry write the common and scientific name of the man, when and where he lived, and the types of tools he used. Indicate, also, the physical characteristics that serve to identify and differentiate the skulls displaying them.

3. *A Poster of Stone Age Implements:* Visit a museum that displays implements used by Stone Age men. Make drawings of ten or twelve of these implements, indicating the varying shapes and sizes from both the Old and New Stone Age. Mount your drawings on a large poster and under each picture write the approximate age of the implement, the men that used it, and the purpose for which it was employed.

4. *Variations in Modern Races:* Cut pictures from magazines or newspapers of members of the three races—Negroid, Mongoloid, and Caucasoid. Select six photos for each race. Vary the individuals within each group by age, sex, and country. Mount pictures in three rows according to race on a poster and carefully study the facial features. What types of variation, if any, do you find among different members of a single racial stock? Is this variation greater or less than that found between "average" members of two different races?

FURTHER READING

History of the Primates. W. E. LeGros Clark. University of Chicago Press, Chicago, Ill. Ranges from tree shrew to fossil man and covers a period of seventy million years.

Early Man. F. Clark Howell and the Editors of LIFE. Time Inc., New York, N.Y. Well illustrated and authoritative account of man's road from the earliest prehumans to modern man.

The Great White Mantle. David O. Woodbury. Viking Press, New York, N.Y. The story of the ice ages and the coming of man.

"Homo Erectus." William W. Howells. *Scientific American,* November, 1966, page 28. An anthropologist discusses the variety of fossil men that are now classified as *Homo erectus,* the immediate predecessor of modern man.

"Stone Tools and Human Behavior." Sally R. Binford and Lewis R. Binford. *Scientific American,* April, 1969, page 70. By analyzing the jobs performed by his different stone tools, anthropologists determine how Paleolithic man's life was organized.

32

Bones and Muscles

THE BASIC PLAN of the body may be seen in the more than 200 bones that make up the skeleton. Like the framework of a building, the skeleton limits the overall dimensions and sets off compartments where special functions are performed. If man were to disappear from the earth, some future species might well reconstruct his appearance and habits by examining his skeletal remains. In just this way, information about prehistoric man has been derived.

The length of the bones indicates an animal's dimensions. The thickness of bones indicates the bulk of the animal they supported. Comparison of the limbs indicates whether walking required two limbs or four. The skull reveals the shape of the brain. The jaws and teeth suggest the type of food the animal ate. All of these facts can be determined from an examination of the skeleton because its structure is closely related to its functions.

More than 600 muscles are attached to the bones. They range in size from very tiny ones that bend the fingers to the massive muscles that move the trunk and thighs. Muscles change chemical energy into body movement. Covering the bones, they provide the final outline of the body's form.

Other muscles work among the internal organs. These are not under our conscious control. Yet, they keep the body operating smoothly. The most important muscle is the heart. Another is the diaphragm, the large muscle that controls breathing. These and others regulate many internal processes.

The Body Framework

The skeleton has been compared with the beams of a skyscraper. In a sense this comparison is correct, for the large bones of the adult are the main structures that support the entire body. Yet the growth of the skeleton is far more complicated than the design of a building. The final form of the body has not been achieved at birth. There are structural changes that occur throughout the life of the individual—changes in length, changes in form, and even changes in chemical composition of the materials used.

FUNCTIONS OF THE SKELETON. The human skeleton does more than provide the basic framework of the body. The bones are the points of attachment for the muscles of the body as well. Many of the bones are adapted by means of extensions to anchor the muscles securely to them. By means of

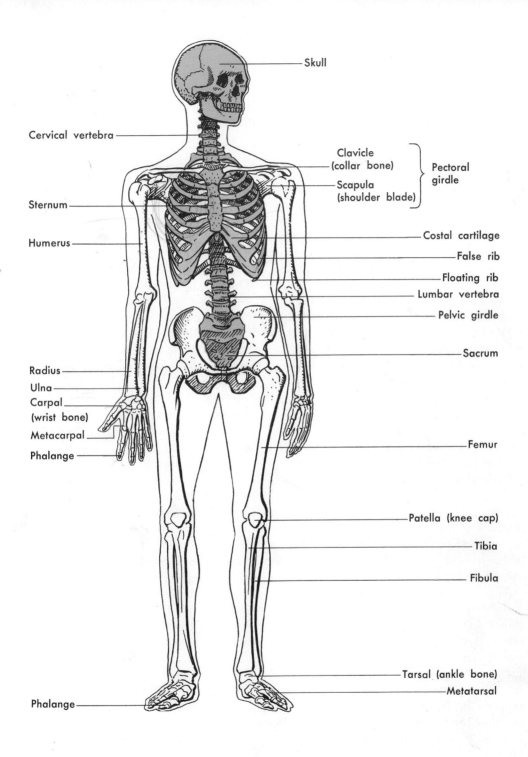

Skull

Cervical vertebra

Clavicle
(collar bone)

Scapula
(shoulder blade)

Pectoral
girdle

Sternum

Costal cartilage

False rib

Floating rib

Humerus

Lumbar vertebra

Pelvic girdle

Sacrum

Radius

Ulna

Carpal
(wrist bone)

Metacarpal

Femur

Phalange

Patella (knee cap)

Tibia

Fibula

Tarsal (ankle bone)

Metatarsal

Phalange

32–1   THE HUMAN SKELETON

these points of attachment the contraction of the muscles moves the body framework. The rib cage and the skull perform a third function of the skeleton—the protection of internal organs. The ribs protect the lungs and heart. The skull protects the brain. Another example of the way bones protect organs is seen in the structure of the brow, cheek, and nose, as these bones form the socket for the eye. A fourth function of the skeleton is to manufacture blood cells. Both red and white cells are made in the marrow of the bones. Finally, bones store calcium and phosphorus in the form of minerals that can be withdrawn when the supply of these minerals in the diet is insufficient.

CARTILAGE AND BONE. At birth the human skeleton is composed almost entirely of *cartilage*. Cartilage is an extremely flexible material that withstands the falls of early childhood. Similar falls by an adult could result in severe fractures.

Under the microscope, cartilage appears as a clear material with scattered cells embedded in it. When the clear material (the matrix) does not contain fibers, it is called *hyaline cartilage.* Hyaline cartilage is found at the end of the nose. It also covers the ends of long bones. Greater toughness is provided in some forms of cartilage by the addition of fibers. The pads of cartilage between the segments of the backbone are of this type. These pads of *fibro-cartilage* are able to resist shocks to the spinal column.

TEMPORARY AND PERMANENT CARTILAGE. As a result of the changes that occur in growth, we might classify all cartilage as either temporary or permanent. The ear and the end of the nose contain cartilage that does not change its form throughout life. Once formed it remains cartilage. It retains its highly flexible quality. Most of the cartilage in the body, on the other hand, is converted into bone as the infant grows. It becomes stronger and more brittle, losing much of its flexibility.

OSSIFICATION. Bones are produced by cells called *osteoblasts*. The most important charactertistic of these cells is that they form intercellular material of great strength. As a bone grows in length and width the osteoblasts gradually grow into the cartilage. The flexible cartilage matrix is replaced by strong, inflexible bone. The process is somewhat like building a tunnel. The bone cells advance into the cartilage and deposit calcium phosphate and calcium carbonate. The cartilage cells grow away from the area where this change is occurring. This results in growth in length. The ends of the bones are the last parts to be converted into bone. The change from cartilage to bone is called *ossification.*

BONE STRUCTURE. The tunneling operation we have described is rather complicated. Imagine building the tunnel walls of bricks and mortar. Living bone cells are spaced like bricks along the wall at regular intervals. Between the cells are ample amounts of intercellular material corresponding to the mortar. The "mortar" consists of calcium phosphate and calcium carbonate. Flexible reinforcing rods, made of a protein material called *collagen,* also lie between the cells.

Now let us imagine thousands of such tunnels being built side by side. Each tunnel is a *Haversian canal.* In cross section, bone is seen to be made of many such canals, each surrounded by several rings of bone cells. The cells are separated from each other by the intercellular material. We see, then, that bone is a porous material in spite of its great strength. The outer, denser bone contains thousands of such Haversian canals. In the center of each canal are blood vessels that bring the materials necessary for bone construction.

BONE MARROW. All of the large bones of the body consist of a very dense outer portion surrounding a central cavity. Within the cavity is a soft, fatty material called bone marrow. The marrow consists of a network of fibers and blood vessels in which there are large numbers of cells that produce blood cells. Almost 250 billion new blood cells are produced within the marrow each day to replace those that are worn out. The new blood cells are released into the general circulation by blood vessels that pass through the Haversian canals.

THE AXIAL SKELETON. The bones in the human skeleton are generally grouped into two classes: (1) those that compose the *axial skeleton,* or the main axis of the body, and (2) those that form the *appendicular skeleton,* or the limbs.

The backbone, composed of 33 vertebrae, is both strong and flexible. Seven *cervical vertebrae* of the neck support the head. Twelve *thoracic vertebrae* are the bases to which ribs are attached. Five *lumbar vertebrae* are the main supporting bones just above the hip. All of the cervical, thoracic, and lumbar vertebrae are separated from each other by discs of cartilage. The remaining vertebrae at the base of the spinal column are fused into two sections, the *sacrum* and the *coccyx.* The sacrum consists of five fused vertebrae. The coccyx, formed by the fusion of four vertebrae, is believed to correspond to the tail of other vertebrates.

The thorax, or chest, is the rib cage section of the body. It is formed by the twelve pairs of ribs. Each pair of ribs is attached dorsally to one of the thoracic vertebrae. The upper seven pairs of ribs are attached to the *sternum,* or breastbone, in the front of the body by means of *costal cartilages.* The next three pairs are attached to the ribs above them. The remaining two lowest pairs of ribs have no attachment in front and are called *floating ribs.*

Individual vertebrae are shaped differently and are adapted to the functions they perform. Generally, however, there is a thick, circular basal portion, the *centrum,* which provides strength. Above the centrum

is the *neural canal,* a ring of bone through which the spinal cord runs. Extensions of the vertebrae provide for the attachment of muscles and bones. Each vertebra is provided with a slight upward bulge that fits into the recesses of the vertebra above. This arrangement permits slight movements of one vertebra upon another. It also provides the flexibility to bend and twist the trunk.

The first two vertebrae are highly specialized to support the skull. They are called the *atlas* and *axis.* Perhaps you remember the mythological giant Atlas, who was so strong he could support the earth on his back. The broad vertebra called the atlas supports the weight of the head. The axis permits rotation of the head.

The skull, perched atop the long column of vertebrae, consists of two parts, the face and the cranium. Included among the facial bones are those of the cheek, the nose, and the upper and lower jaws. The cranium is the bony case that encloses and protects the brain. In the infant the eight plates that eventually grow closer to form the cranium are separate. At this time, the plates themselves are still soft and flexible. The margins along which the plates interlock are called *sutures.* During birth the plates may even overlap, slightly reducing the volume of the head.

The so-called "soft spot" on the top of the infant's head is a place where the cranial bones are widely separated. The blood can be seen gently pulsating here. Perhaps because of this, the area is called a *fontanelle,* or little fountain. With continued growth the cranial bones finally form an exceedingly hard, almost spherical cavity. At maturity the cranium has a surprising ability to resist shock.

The largest opening in the cranium is the *foramen magnum,* where the spinal cord enters. Smaller openings permit the entry of the auditory nerves, the olfactory nerves, and the optic nerves.

THE APPENDICULAR SKELETON: THE LIMBS.
Attached to the column of vertebrae are the two sets of bones that support the arms and legs. The *pectoral girdle* consists of two collar bones, *clavicles,* and two shoulder bones, *scapulas.* The *pelvic girdle* is formed by six bones that make a bowl-like container to support the internal organs. The arms are attached to the pectoral girdle, and the legs are attached to the pelvic girdle.

The bones of the arm and leg are remarkably alike. Yet when we compare them they reveal interesting changes that have occurred, resulting in man's erect posture. The leg bones, used for support, are heavier and thicker than the arm bones. The upper part of each consists of a single bone—the *humerus* of the arm, the *femur* of the leg. From the elbow to the wrist there are two bones—the *radius* and the *ulna.* From the knee to the ankle there arc also two bones—the heavy shin bone, or *tibia,* and the smaller *fibula* that lies just behind it. The

32–2   The femur of the leg is joined to the pelvic girdle by powerful ligaments.

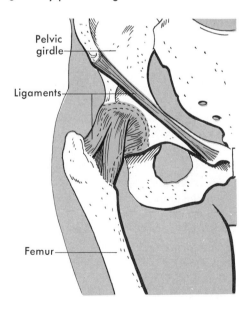

Pelvic
girdle

Ligaments

Femur

wristbones, *carpals,* have their counterparts in the ankle bones, or *tarsals.* The palm of the hand consists of *metacarpals.* The arch of the foot consists of *metatarsals.* The fingers correspond to the toes. Both fingers and toes are called *phalanges* (fuh-LAN-jez).

LIGAMENTS AND JOINTS. The bones are joined to each other by very strong bands of connective tissue called *ligaments.* In the developing human embryo, the temporary cartilage that forms the bones is surrounded by a covering that is continuous from one bone to the next. This sheath becomes the *periosteum,* the layer of tough tissue that surrounds the bone. The ligaments are actually extensions of the periosteum where joints occur.

Joints arise as separations within the solid cartilage that is formed in the embryo. The arm, for instance, develops as a rod that is separated into parts by the development of joints at the shoulder, the elbow, the wrist, and the fingers.

The joints that develop are of several types permitting different kinds of movement. At the hip and shoulder great freedom of action is permitted by the ball and socket joint. The knee is a hinge joint that operates in only one plane. Some joints permit a twisting action; hence, they are called pivotal joints. A good illustration of this is the turning of the head by means of the special construction of the second vertebra, the axis. Although other vertebrae permit only a slight twisting, the axis allows the head to be turned from one side to the other in a wide arc. Immovable joints, like the sutures of the cranium that we have previously mentioned, permit practically no movement. Finally, in gliding joints, bones slip over each other to attain flexibility.

ARTHRITIS AND BURSITIS. Joints must be well lubricated. A fluid somewhat like the white of egg is secreted by the cartilage at the end of a bone. Like oil placed on a bearing, this *synovial fluid* reduces friction in the

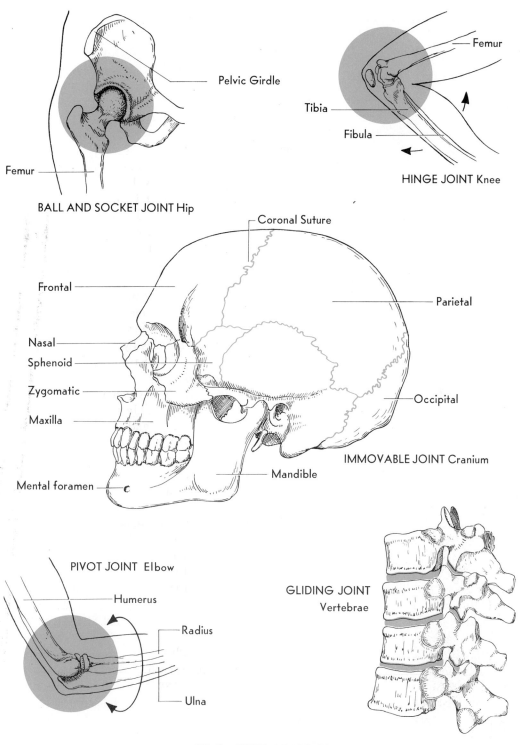

BALL AND SOCKET JOINT Hip

Pelvic Girdle

Femur

HINGE JOINT Knee

Femur

Tibia

Fibula

Coronal Suture

Frontal

Nasal

Sphenoid

Zygomatic

Maxilla

Mental foramen

Parietal

Occipital

Mandible

IMMOVABLE JOINT Cranium

PIVOT JOINT Elbow

Humerus

Radius

Ulna

GLIDING JOINT
Vertebrae

32–3   TYPES OF JOINTS

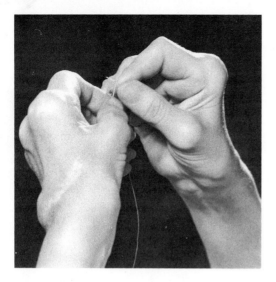

32-4 Arthritis attacks the joints, especially the finger joints. As the disease progresses, the hands become deformed.

joint. Any condition that interferes with the smooth movement of the bones at the joint results in inflammation and pain. The amount of synovial fluid may be too small. The cartilage cap at the end of the bone may start to build irregular calcium deposits. Whatever the reason, inflammation of the joint occurs. When it does, we call this condition *arthritis*.

Small sacs located around many joints are somewhat like air cushions that protect the joint against shock. Each small sac is called a *bursa*. When the joint is irritated, the bursa may become filled with an overabundance of mucus. This produces a swelling that makes the joint painful. You may have heard of "water on the knee." It is a condition often developed by workmen who spend too much time kneeling. *Bursitis* is inflammation of the bursa of a joint.

SPRAINS AND FRACTURES. We sometimes subject the body to greater stresses than it can withstand. Such is the case when a person sprains his ankle. The foot is twisted and the ligaments joining the tarsals are stretched and torn. The ankle swells and becomes discolored. Unless the ligaments have been very badly torn, however, there is no dislocation of the bones and, with rest, the injury soon heals.

When bones are severely injured, they may break, or *fracture*. X-ray photographs are taken to determine the kind of injury. The extent of the fracture may vary from a fine split, or fissure, to a severe *compound* fracture. In a compound fracture, the bone fragments pierce the skin, providing an open channel of infection into the wound.

The healing of a fracture illustrates the body's ability to repair itself. After the physician has carefully set the bone fragments in position and placed a cast about them, connective tissue begins to fill the break. At first the repair is made with very soft material. Later, the normal bone salts are deposited in this soft material, making it as hard as the original bone.

Muscles of the Body

Attached to the bony skeleton, giving the body its final form, are the muscles. Muscle tissue is the only tissue that is able to contract. And because it can contract, it flexes the joints and extends them, causing the body to move. Muscles are the real energy converters of our body. They change chemical energy into the mechanical energy of movement. This is an extremely complicated process, and physiologists are not certain exactly how it happens.

THE KINDS OF MUSCLE. Muscles not only move the skeleton, they perform other functions as well. The muscles of the digestive tract, for example, contract rhythmically, forcing food along the tract. The heart muscle pumps blood through the body. Some muscles regulate the amount of light that enters the eye. Others make us blush or become pale with anger.

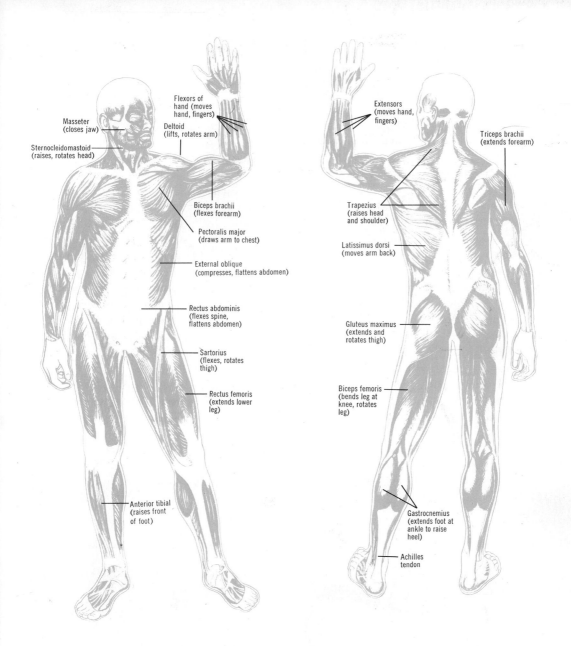

Flexors of
hand (moves
hand, fingers)

Masseter
(closes jaw)

Deltoid
(lifts, rotates arm)

Sternocleidomastoid
(raises, rotates head)

Biceps brachii
(flexes forearm)

Pectoralis major
(draws arm to chest)

External oblique
(compresses, flattens abdomen)

Rectus abdominis
(flexes spine,
flattens abdomen)

Sartorius
(flexes, rotates
thigh)

Rectus femoris
(extends lower
leg)

Anterior tibial
(raises front
of foot)

Extensors
(moves hand,
fingers)

Triceps brachii
(extends forearm)

Trapezius
(raises head
and shoulder)

Latissimus dorsi
(moves arm back)

Gluteus maximus
(extends and
rotates thigh)

Biceps femoris
(bends leg at
knee, rotates
leg)

Gastrocnemius
(extends foot at
ankle to raise
heel)

Achilles
tendon

32–5   THE HUMAN MUSCULAR SYSTEM.   The voluntary (or skeletal) muscles are attached to and move the bones. The muscles indicated here are some of the major voluntary
muscles whose contours can be seen under the skin. Muscle names are not as difficult as
may first appear, being derived from their: (1) points of attachment (the sternocleidomastoid is attached to the sternum, clavicle, and mastoid), (2) shape or size (maximus means
largest), (3) fiber direction (rectus means straight), (4) location (brachii means in the arm
region), and (5) action (flexors bend and extensors lengthen the angle at a joint).

One way in which we can classify muscles is by the control we exert over them. When we run or jump we use *voluntary* muscles. The muscles of the arms, legs, and trunk are all voluntary. These muscles come directly under our conscious control. Some muscles, however, operate even though we never give them a thought. The heart is an example. It continues beating year after year without any control on our part. Muscles that cannot be controlled by our will are called *involuntary* muscles. The muscles of the stomach and intestines as well as the heart are involuntary.

Another way of classifying muscles is by the differences in structure seen under the microscope. Microscopically, muscles can be grouped into three types: *striated, smooth,* and *cardiac.*

STRIATED MUSCLE. Each of the more than six hundred muscles attached to the skeleton is a complicated structure containing several million very long muscle fibers, or cells. Within each fiber lie several hundred contractile fibers, or *fibrils,* each of which is cross striped. Since the fibrils are arranged in an orderly fashion, their stripes give the fiber, and the entire tissue, a striped, or striated, appearance.

All the skeletal muscles are striated muscles. They are also voluntary muscles. Because voluntary muscles are striated, the terms are sometimes used interchangeably.

SMOOTH MUSCLE. If we prepare a piece of muscle from the stomach and examine it with the microscope, we observe that it is unstriped. Muscle tissue that lacks striation is called smooth muscle. Smooth muscles contain individual fibers that are tapered to a point at both ends. Sometimes they are described as spindle shaped. Smooth muscle cells are much shorter than striated muscle cells. All of the muscles of the internal organs, with the exception of the heart, consist of smooth muscles. The control of the internal organs is completely involuntary. For this reason, smooth muscle is also called involuntary muscle. Generally, smooth muscle is thought to be simpler and more primitive than striated muscle.

Smooth muscle tissue surrounds the stomach and intestine. Its contraction moves food along the food tube in an orderly, rhythmic motion. The blood vessels, the bladder, and the birth canal also have smooth muscles that control their actions. The contraction of smooth muscles is much slower than that of striated muscles.

32–6 Striated Muscle 32–7 Smooth Muscle 32–8 Cardiac Muscle

TYPES OF MUSCLE

Type	Appearance	Control	Examples
Striated	Striped, long fibers	Voluntary	Legs, arms, trunk
Smooth	Not striped, spindle shaped	Involuntary	Stomach, intestine, blood vessels
Cardiac	Striped, network	Involuntary	Heart

CARDIAC MUSCLE. The *cardiac muscle* tissue that makes up the heart looks like striated muscle, but the striations are not as clear. The fibers are arranged to form a network. The heart is involuntary even though its striped fibers resemble voluntary muscles. The heart, which is the hardest-working muscle of the body, beats between two and three billion times during a lifetime. It gets no rest except during the slight pauses between beats.

TENDONS AND MUSCLES. Muscles are bound into masses by thin sheets of connective tissue. At each end of the muscle this connective tissue is joined into a tough extension that is attached to the bones. The tough bands of connective tissue that connect muscles to bone are called *tendons*.

Muscles are closely associated with the movement of the joints. One end of a muscle is attached to a part of the skeleton that is comparatively fixed. This end is called the *origin*. The other end is attached to a bone that can move freely. This end is the *insertion*. Consider the biceps muscle of the upper arm as an example. Its origin is high on the shoulder blade, the scapula. Its insertion is on the radius, one of the two bones of the forearm. When the biceps contracts, it pulls the lower part of the arm upward. A muscle like the biceps that bends or flexes a joint is called a *flexor*.

Muscles are generally arranged in pairs that work in opposition to each other. In the case of the biceps, the opposing muscle is the triceps on the back of the humerus. The origin of the triceps is divided into two parts. One is on the lower part of the scapula while the other is high on the humerus. The insertion of the triceps is on the ulna, on the back of the forearm. When the tri-

32–9 The biceps and triceps are opposing muscles that flex and extend the arm.

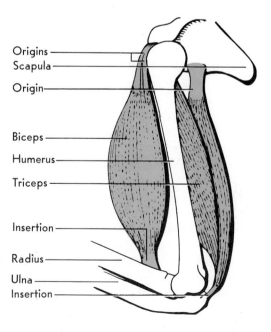

Origins
Scapula
Origin
Biceps
Humerus
Triceps
Insertion
Radius
Ulna
Insertion

ceps contracts, it extends the forearm; hence it is called an *extensor*.

Work your elbow back and forth, first bending it and then extending it. Note that as you bend the arm, the biceps becomes a small knot of muscle. If you feel the triceps at this time, it seems relaxed. As you extend the arm, the biceps knot disappears, and you can feel the triceps becoming hard as it contracts.

MUSCLE CONTRACTION. Attached to the muscle fibers are nerve endings that stimulate the fibers and cause them to contract. Each muscle may contain a million or more fibers. When a muscle contracts, not all of the fibers contract at once. Few or many of them contract, depending upon the need of the moment. For greater exertion more fibers are used simultaneously. For continued exertion over a period of time, the fibers work in relays. The number of fibers involved determines the extent of the pull the muscle exerts.

Measurements of the resting muscle indicate that there is a potential, or voltage, difference of about one-tenth of a volt between the inside and the outside of the muscle cells. The inside is negative with respect to the outside. When the nerve impulse arrives at the muscle fibers it reduces the voltage difference to zero, and the fibers contract. The potential difference is almost immediately restored, however, and the fiber is ready to contract again.

THE STRUCTURE OF MUSCLE FIBERS. Electron microscope studies of the skeletal muscles have enabled biologists to learn more about their fine structure. Within the tiny fibrils that make up the muscle fibers are smaller filaments. The filaments are believed to be the ultimate structures that cause muscles to shorten and thus contract.

Each fibril contains two kinds of filaments, one thick, the other thin. Chemical analysis has shown that the thick filaments are made of the protein *myosin*. The thin filaments are composed mainly of the protein *actin*. Cross bridges between the two kinds of filaments have also been observed. The orderly arrangement of these filaments is responsible for the striped appearance of voluntary muscles.

Each stripe on a muscle fiber has a finer structure when examined under high magnification. The stripes have been resolved into a close array of light and dark bands. The width of the light and dark bands changes as the muscle fiber contracts. The changes in the dimensions of the bands are due to the relative movement of the filaments of actin and myosin. It seems, therefore, that the basic cause of muscle contraction is to be found in the relation between those thick and thin filaments in the fibrils.

THE CHEMISTRY OF MUSCLE ACTION. The Hungarian biologist Albert Szent-Györgyi (sent-JOR-gee) discovered that the muscle proteins, actin and myosin, formed artificial fibers that could contract. To make them contract, he immersed them in a solution of adenosine triphosphate (ATP). ATP is the energy-rich compound found in all cells as part of their energy distribution system.

The three compounds that make the contraction of muscle possible, then, are actin, myosin, and ATP. The filaments of the fibrils contain the actin and myosin, but where does the ATP come from? The energy of ATP is derived from glucose brought to the muscle cells by the blood. As we learned in Chapter 7, the glucose is first converted to lactic acid. Later the lactic acid is oxidized to form carbon dioxide and water. Energy derived from the series of changes that converts glucose into its end products is stored in ATP. ATP is formed from the simpler compound adenosine diphosphate (ADP).

When muscles are being actively used, as in violent exercise, a critical shortage of oxygen may develop. Oxygen is not needed in the first stage that converts glucose to lac-

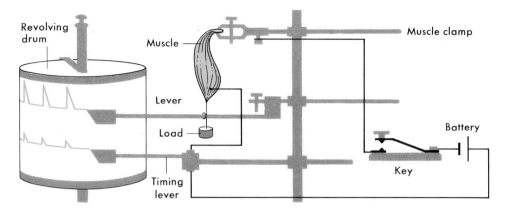

32–10 A kymograph is used to study the effects of stimulating a skeletal muscle. When the muscle contracts, it moves the muscle lever, which leaves a mark on revolving drum.

tic acid. Oxygen is needed to change lactic acid to carbon dioxide and water. A shortage of oxygen, therefore, permits lactic acid to accumulate. This deficiency of oxygen is known as oxygen debt. It causes the increased rate and depth of breathing associated with exercise. The accumulation of lactic acid in the muscles is the principal cause of fatigue. When there is sufficient oxygen the lactic acid does not accumulate, but is converted into carbon dioxide and water, which are removed by the blood.

TETANUS AND TONUS. Biologists have learned a great deal about how muscles contract by using an apparatus like that shown in Figure 32–10. A muscle such as the gastrocnemius from the shank of the frog's leg is suspended in such a way that one end is fixed. The other end is attached to a lever. The end of the lever, in turn, presses against a smoked revolving drum. The contraction of the muscle is recorded by a rising line on the drum. Another scribe can also be attached to the drum so that accurate timing can be made.

When an electric stimulus is applied to the muscle, it contracts. Then it relaxes. The entire cycle requires one-tenth of a second. But what happens if we stimulate the mus-

cle again before it has had a chance to relax completely? Suppose we apply the stimulus at intervals of one-tenth of a second for several seconds. It then has no opportunity to relax but remains in a state of contraction during the entire period. This continuous state of contraction is called *tetanus*.

It is this sort of continuous contraction over a short period of time that is characteristic of muscular effort. Flexing the biceps to bend the elbow in lifting a weight requires continuous effort. Once the weight is lifted, lengthening of the muscle occurs.

In certain body disorders, particularly those associated with low calcium content in the blood, the muscles have a marked tendency to remain contracted, a condition known as *tetany*.

Even when not in use, every muscle has a small number of fibers in a state of contraction. It is as though the muscle were taut and ready to work when called upon. This state of partial contraction is called *tonus*. Healthy tonus produces preparedness in the muscle similar to the tense condition of the sprinter who awaits the starter's gun. Fatigue produces a diminished tonus. It can be seen in the stooped shoulders, the shuffling walk, and tired appearance of the fatigued individual. Relaxation and sleep, on the other hand, produce the opposite effect. The individual looks alert and refreshed. The step is springier. The head is higher. The body is more erect. These are signs of increased muscle tonus.

ACTIVITY AND REST. Did you ever notice how refreshing it is to do something completely different in the way of physical activity? Let's suppose you have been reading for an hour or two. You have been sitting in one position for quite some time. Your muscles have become tired. You are drowsy. You decide to take a brisk walk or play ball. Immediately, your fatigue seems to disappear. How can we explain this?

The answer is that an entirely new set of muscles is now employed. The ones that were in almost constant use do not now have the difficult job of holding your head in position for reading. Other muscles are now active. Furthermore, your circulation is now more rapid. The products of fatigue are being rapidly removed. Take time out for some exercise or diversion, and you can go back to work with renewed drive.

IMPORTANT POINTS

- The bones of the body are its main supporting structures. They provide for the attachment of muscles, protect certain internal organs, manufacture red and white blood cells, and store calcium and phosphorus.

- At birth most of the skeleton is cartilage. Much of the cartilage is changed to bone as a result of growth. Some cartilage remains as permanent cartilage.

- Bone tissue is composed of bone cells arranged in a circle around a hollow Haversian canal. Among the bone cells are large amounts of intercellular material consisting of calcium carbonate, calcium phosphate, and collagen.

- The soft material within the central cavity of all the large bones is the bone marrow. Special cells in the marrow produce a total of almost 250 billion red blood cells each day, replacing an equal number of the body's worn out cells.

- The axial skeleton consists of the skull and vertebrae. The appendicular skeleton consists of the pectoral girdle, the arm bones, the pelvic girdle, and the leg bones.

- The joints are of several types and provide for different kinds of body movement. Joints are lubricated by the synovial fluid. Painful joints may be caused by arthritis or bursitis.

- Contraction of muscles causes body movement. Striated, or voluntary, muscles are attached to the skeleton and can be controlled at will. Smooth muscles are involuntary and control the internal organs. Cardiac muscle appears striped but is involuntary.

- Muscles flex and extend the limbs by means of tendons which are attached to the bones.

- Muscle contraction is begun by the receipt of a nerve impulse that reduces the voltage difference in the muscle. Actin and myosin filaments in the muscle fibrils are acted upon by ATP, the energy-rich compound found in cells. ATP obtains its energy from the oxidation of glucose.

- Tetanus occurs when a muscle is held in a state of contraction by the reception of closely spaced nerve impulses. Tonus is the state of partial contraction.

REVIEW QUESTIONS

1. What is the difference between temporary and permanent cartilage?
2. Describe the way in which bone is formed.
3. What three substances compose intercellular material in bone?
4. How is bone marrow related to the blood?
5. List the principal parts of the axial and appendicular skeletons.
6. How are the joints lubricated?
7. List the three kinds of muscle tissue and give the function of each.
8. What electrical event occurs to begin muscle contraction?
9. List the two muscle proteins that form the thick and thin filaments.

CHECK YOUR UNDERSTANDING

10. List four functions of the bones of the body.
11. What is the advantage of a skeleton made of cartilage at birth?
12. How does the backbone protect the spinal cord?
13. What difference is there in the shape of striated and smooth muscle fibers?
14. Why are the skeletal muscles arranged in opposition to each other?
15. What fundamental structures has the electron microscope revealed in muscle fibrils?
16. Explain how glucose provides energy for muscle contraction.
17. Under what conditions does lactic acid accumulate in muscles?
18. How is muscle tonus maintained?
19. Can you think of any reasons why it is advantageous to have blood cells made in the bone marrow?
20. Why might you expect the chemistry of motion in the cilia of a protozoan to be the same as the chemistry of contraction in a human muscle cell?
21. How might you explain the fact that it is very difficult to cause fatigue in a dissected frog muscle that is subjected to repeated stimulation?

RESEARCH PROJECTS AND REPORTS

1. Obtain information from your school or public library and prepare a report on one of the following topics:

   Albert Szent-Györgyi   **Muscular Dystrophy**

   How Muscles Move   **Tetany**

2. *Removing the Calcium Salts from Bone:* Place the humerus of a chicken or turkey in a 300 cc beaker about half-full of dilute hydrochloric acid. If it is left in the solution long enough, the calcium salts will be removed by the acid. The remaining bone is very soft and flexible.

3. *Removing the Organic Matter from Bone:* Try heating a chicken femur in a Bunsen flame for five to ten minutes. Examine the bone carefully after it has cooled. Is there any evidence of a change in its appearance and properties?

4. **Muscle Contraction:** Dissect the entire gastrocnemius muscle from a frog and attach the tendon of Achilles by means of a short, sturdy thread to a burette clamp on an iron stand. Attach the other end of the muscle loosely by another thread to a second burette clamp. Stimulate the muscle by applying the leads from several dry cells arranged in series (plus to minus). The muscle will have to be kept moist with a one per cent salt solution if contraction is to occur for any length of time.

FURTHER READING

Animal Physiology. Knut Schmidt-Nielsen. Prentice-Hall, Inc., Englewood Cliffs, N.J. An excellent discussion of the electrical events that occur in muscle contraction appears on pages 68 to 77.

Man in Structure and Function. Fritz Kahn. Alfred A. Knopf, Inc., New York, N.Y. Why do we get "gooseflesh"? Why are some people left handed? What is the "second wind" of the athlete? Can muscles be trained? These and other questions are discussed in "The Musculature," Part III of Volume I, pages 123–165.

The Body. Alan E. Nourse and the Editors of LIFE. Time-Life Books, New York, N.Y. Chapter 3, *The Team of Bone and Muscle,* is especially good in illustrating the close relationship that exists between bone and muscle in providing body movement.

"How Cells Move." Teru Hyashi. *Scientific American,* September, 1961, page 184. All of the processes that bring about the movement of cells appear to have a striking similarity whether in plants, single-celled organisms, or muscles.

"The Sarcoplasmic Reticulum." Keith R. Porter and Clara Franzini-Armstrong. *Scientific American,* March, 1965, page 73. A very advanced discussion of the structure of the muscle as revealed by electron microscopy.

CHAPTER

33

Food and Nutrition

THE ENERGY we need to live is provided by the food we consume. The chemical energy of food is converted into the life-giving energy that enables us to walk, to breathe, to laugh, to run.

What is the source of food energy? Where does it come from? Green plants make food molecules from water and carbon dioxide. They do this by using the energy of sunlight, which is then stored in the food molecules. Thus, the sun is the original source of the energy required for all living things. When food is oxidized in the body, heat is given off. Body warmth is almost as sure an indication of life as the beating heart.

The human body uses foods not only for energy, but also for the growth and repair of tissues. Growth means the construction of many billions of new cells. These are made from the materials supplied by the foods we eat. The body is continuously repairing and replacing cells. Almost two million blood cells are formed every second. These, too, are made from digested foods.

Thus, it is important to know the specific foods required by the body—what function or functions each performs, what quantity of each is necessary, and what we can do to ensure getting these necessary amounts.

How the Body is Nourished

The study of foods and their use in the body is called *nutrition*. Although we eat many kinds of food, only six basic kinds are generally recognized:

1. *Carbohydrates* (starches, sugars) are energy producers.
2. *Fats* and *oils* are also producers of energy.
3. *Proteins* are tissue builders.
4. *Water* is the principal body fluid and makes up about 70 per cent of the body's weight.
5. *Minerals* are important in the construction of bone, teeth, and muscle.
6. *Vitamins* are regulators of body growth and function.

Carbohydrates, fats, and proteins are generally referred to as the organic nutrients. They are made of very large molecules containing carbon. Carbohydrates and fats are especially rich sources of energy. Proteins supply most of the material for body growth.

MEASURING THE ENERGY OF FOODS. To measure the amount of heat given off by a fuel like alcohol, a carefully measured amount can be burned and its heat can be collected in a measured amount of water. Thus, a gram of ethyl alcohol releases an amount of heat that raises the temperature of 1000 grams (approximately 1 quart) of water seven degrees Centigrade. Similarly, when one gram of the sugar glucose is burned, its heat raises the temperature of 1000 grams of water only four degrees Centigrade. The heat energy content of alcohol and glucose are thus compared.

The unit used in making the comparison is the *Calorie.* A Calorie is defined as the amount of heat necessary to raise the temperature of 1000 grams of water one degree Centigrade. In the preceding illustrations, ethyl alcohol released seven Calories of heat per gram; glucose released almost four Calories per gram. The Calorie that defines the heat energy content of foods is always spelled with a capital C. This Calorie, or kilogram calorie, is 1,000 times as large as the calorie used by chemists and physicists.

Chemists have measured the caloric value of practically all of the common foods by

33–1   A calorimeter burns a known amount of food. The heat absorbed by the surrounding water is recorded by a thermometer and is a measure of the food's energy value.

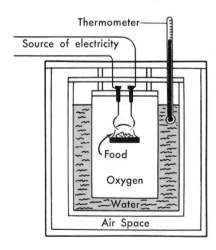

Thermometer
Source of electricity
Food
Oxygen
Water
Air Space

using a device called a *calorimeter.* From these measurements, we know the varying ability of foods to supply us with energy. Thus, a teaspoon of table sugar weighing four grams yields 16 Calories of heat energy when burned in a calorimeter. The same amount of sugar yields the same quantity of energy when oxidized in the body.

OUR ENERGY REQUIREMENTS. Each of us requires a certain amount of energy daily. The amount required depends upon many factors—weight, age, sex, and, of course, the amount of activity we engage in. According to the Food and Nutrition Board of the National Research Council, the average high school girl requires about 2500 Calories daily. A man working at hard manual labor requires considerably more, perhaps as many as 5000 Calories. A formula sometimes used for a boy in his teens is to multiply the weight in pounds by a value between 23 and 33, depending upon daily activities. Using the maximum figure for a 160-pound football player would give us an energy requirement higher than that for the working man. The teen-age girl would use a factor between 20 and 27 in the same type of calculation. It certainly seems sensible to say that more Calories are needed for playing football than for studying.

Our daily intake of food is largely controlled by our appetite. But appetite alone is not always a reliable guide. It may result in the intake of too many high-energy foods that build up a surplus of Calories. The body then stores the surplus as fat. Careful attention to the body's needs without excessive eating is the key to proper weight control.

Organic Nutrients

Foods may be broadly classified in two categories: those that produce energy, and those that do not. Each of the three kinds of organic nutrients (the carbohydrates, fats,

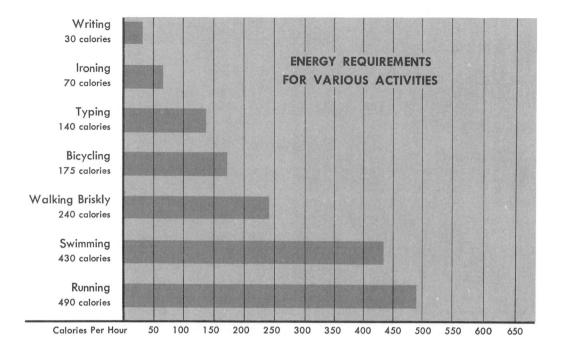

Activity														
Writing 30 calories														
Ironing 70 calories														
Typing 140 calories														
Bicycling 175 calories														
Walking Briskly 240 calories														
Swimming 430 calories														
Running 490 calories														

ENERGY REQUIREMENTS FOR VARIOUS ACTIVITIES

Calories Per Hour 50 100 150 200 250 300 350 400 450 500 550 600 650

and proteins) yields energy when oxidized in the cells of the body. The organic nutrients are all compounds of carbon that derive their energy from the sun.

CARBOHYDRATES. The carbohydrates (the starches and the sugars) supply us with most of our energy and make up over half of the food we eat. Such important carbohydrate foods as wheat, rice, corn, barley, oats, and rye are grown in almost every land. These cereal grains are the principal source of the flour that is made into such foods as bread, pastries, noodles, and spaghetti. Plants are thus the basic source of the carbohydrates. Many fruits are rich sources of carbohydrate. The potato, a common staple in Europe and America, is still another rich source of carbohydrate.

One of the simplest carbohydrate molecules is *glucose,* a sugar that has the formula $C_6H_{12}O_6$. Chemists call glucose a *monosaccharide.* This distinguishes it from other sugars that are made of chains of simple sugars. Thus, the next more complicated

sugar would be a *disaccharide,* such as *sucrose,* or table sugar, which is formed by joining two simple sugars. *Lactose,* milk sugar, is another example of a disaccharide. When large numbers of simple sugar molecules are joined together the result is a *polysaccharide.* The starch molecule is of this type. There are other polysaccharides, among them *cellulose,* which we cannot digest. Cellulose is the rigid material of plant cell walls. Herbivores, such as cows and horses, are able to digest cellulose regularly and extract its energy.

Starch is by far the most important of the carbohydrates. However, before it is used by the cells of the body, it is changed chemically into the simple sugars that make up its chainlike molecule. This results in the establishment of glucose in the blood. In the case of hospital patients who are unable to be fed by mouth, the glucose level in the body can be maintained by injecting it directly into the blood. This is known as intravenous feeding.

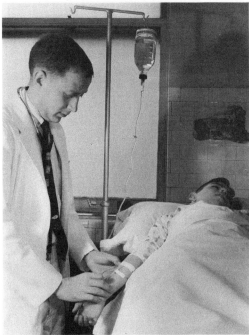

more than twice as much. Most of the fats and oils we eat are animal products. Milk, butter, cheese, meats, and fish are among the principal sources. Some oils and fats derived from plants include those from nuts and seeds. These nuts and seeds are used in making cooking oils, salad oils, and shortening used in baking.

The high energy content of fats is explained by the structure of their molecules. Fats are compounds formed by the union of *glycerol* and *fatty acids*. They contain the same elements as the carbohydrates—carbon, hydrogen, and oxygen. But the proportions are different. Fats contain much less oxygen than starches or sugars. In sugars the ratio of oxygen atoms to hydrogen atoms is one to two. But in fats this ratio is much lower. For example, the formula for the fat olein is $C_{57}H_{104}O_6$. In it there are more than

33–2 Intravenous Feeding. Patients who cannot eat or drink can be fed by injections of a glucose solution into a vein of the forearm. The solution may consist of water and sugar (glucose) or a combination of glucose, amino acids, vitamins, and salts.

When the amount of glucose in the blood exceeds a certain level, the body withdraws it. The surplus is stored in the form of *glycogen* in the liver. When the blood sugar level drops below a minimum level, the liver converts the stored glycogen back into soluble glucose. The liver is therefore a storage area for our carbohydrate needs. Not only can carbohydrates be changed into glycogen, they can also be converted into fat. This fact is important to individuals who have difficulty controlling their weight.

FATS AND OILS. Fats contain more energy than other organic nutrients. Whereas a gram of starch or of protein yields about 4 Calories, a gram of fat yields 9 Calories,

DAILY CALORIC REQUIREMENTS

Group	Calories
Boys	
13–15 years (108 lbs.)	3100
16–19 years (139 lbs.)	3600
Girls	
13–15 years (108 lbs.)	2600
16–19 years (120 lbs.)	2400
Men (154 lbs.)	
Sedentary	2400
Physically Active	3000
Doing Heavy Work	4500
Women (123 lbs.)	
Sedentary	2000
Moderately Active	2400
Very Active	3000

seventeen times as many hydrogen atoms as oxygen. An "oxygen poor" compound of this type uses more oxygen for oxidation than do the carbohydrates. Hence, it releases more energy by "burning" longer.

Ideally from 25 per cent to 35 per cent of our caloric intake should be made up of fats. The average for the United States is believed to be considerably higher than that and is still rising. Too high a daily consumption of fats leads to overweight. Surplus fats are stored, and they encourage the conversion of surplus carbohydrates to fats as well. Surplus fats also increase the blood level of the fatty chemical *cholesterol*. Cholesterol is associated with heart disease and other circulatory ailments. Thus, excess weight not only imposes an extra burden upon the circulatory system, but also impairs the functioning of the system.

PROTEINS. Proteins are the most complex foods we eat. Their energy value is about the same as that of the carbohydrates—four Calories per gram. But proteins generally are not used for the production of energy when fats and carbohydrates are available. Normally they are used for building tissues. Fats, starches, and sugars can substitute for each other in producing body energy, but they cannot take the place of proteins. Proteins are essential for the growth and repair of body tissues.

Protein molecules consist of huge intertwined chains of fundamental links, the amino acids. This is just like the construction of the polysaccharide glycogen from chains of glucose molecules. One of the simplest of the amino acids is glycine (CH_2NH_2COOH). Note that it contains the element nitrogen in addition to carbon, oxygen, and hydrogen. The distinguishing feature of the proteins is that they are nitrogen foods.

Just as the letters of the alphabet can be assembled in many ways to form the words of a language, so amino acids can combine to form an almost infinite variety of pro-

teins. It is not uncommon for several thousand amino acids to form a single protein molecule. About 30 per cent of our proteins are found in muscles. Another 20 per cent helps form bone. Still another 10 per cent becomes part of the skin. The remaining 40 per cent makes up the body fluids and internal organs. Some idea of the complexity of a protein molecule can be obtained from the formula of *hemoglobin*, an important part of the red blood cell:

$$C_{3032} H_{4816} O_{872} N_{780} S_8 Fe_4$$

Not all of the proteins we eat supply us with the complete set of amino acids needed. Nor do they supply these building blocks in the right amounts. Animal proteins found in milk, eggs, fish, and meat are generally the most satisfactory. Plant proteins found in grains, nuts, and beans are less satisfactory. A balanced diet includes both types.

Unlike the other organic nutrients, excess proteins are not stored by the body. Surplus amino acids are broken down by a complex chemical process called *deamination*. This results in the release of energy and the formation of ammonia and urea. Ammonia and urea, both nitrogen compounds, are excreted by the kidneys.

Inorganic Nutrients

Carbohydrates, fats, and proteins are all carbon compounds, that is, organic compounds. Water and mineral salts do not contain atoms of carbon, hence are inorganic. They are not sources of energy, but are important in proper growth.

WATER. The human body is composed of about 70 per cent water. Water is the medium in which all of the chemical reactions of the body take place. You might live for over a month without food, but you could not live without water for more than a few days. In hot, dry climates a single day without water can result in dehydration and death.

Water is released from the body in urine, in perspiration through the sweat glands of the skin, and in the form of water vapor from the lungs. Breathing may release as much as two pints of water daily under normal conditions. The loss of body water through sweating varies with the amount of body activity. A football player, for example, may lose as many as five quarts of body water in a single game. Many foods have a high water content, which helps replace lost water. Fluids, like milk, cocoa, and soups, may contain over 90 per cent water. Vegetables and fruits often contain surprisingly high amounts of water. An apple or raw carrot contains about 85 per cent; a tomato or cantaloupe 95 per cent.

The body's need for water is signalled by a thirst mechanism, which is not well understood. Experiments have indicated that the thirst center is located in an area of the brain called the *hypothalamus*. Laboratory rats with their hypothalamus destroyed show no thirst symptoms. They die for lack of water even when it is available.

MINERAL SALTS. Salt is a vital nutrient. More than a century ago farmers noticed that cattle whose diet did not include salt became sickly. Today, we recognize the need for small amounts of compounds called mineral salts. Mineral salts contain such elements as sodium, potassium, calcium, phosphorus, iron, chlorine, iodine, sulfur, magnesium, and copper. The absence of some of these elements from the diet often has serious effects. *Goiter,* a swelling of the thyroid gland in the throat, is caused by lack of iodine in the diet.

The mineral salts found in foods are derived originally from the soil. The salts in the soil are absorbed by plants in soil water. Uncooked fruits and vegetables supply us with many of the minerals we need. Cooking, however, generally removes many of the salts since they dissolve in water. This is why a baked potato tastes different from a boiled one. Many animal foods, like milk, also contain abundant minerals. The animals obtain the minerals from the plants they eat.

The amount of any particular mineral that we require varies a great deal. A teenage boy needs about 1.4 grams of calcium and phosphorus each day. The same boy needs about 1/10,000 of that amount of iodine. And the iodine is in many ways just as important, even in that tiny amount.

CALCIUM AND PHOSPHORUS. These two elements are commonly associated with each other in the tissues of the body. Together they give hardness to our bones and teeth. During bone formation they are deposited in about equal amounts. Calcium and phosphorus make up about 3 per cent of the adult's total body weight.

Although practically all of the calcium and most of the phosphorus are found in bone, these elements have important uses in other parts of the body. Calcium is necessary to form blood clots. It also regulates the rhythm of the heartbeat. Both calcium and phosphorus are essential for muscles and nerves. Phosphorus is especially important in the energy reactions of the body, for it is part of adenosine triphosphate (ATP). This is the compound that is the key to all energy release in the body.

Milk is probably the best source of calcium and phosphorus. In addition to being a source, milk contains *lactose*, a sugar that seems to aid the absorption of calcium and phosphorus. Many fruits, vegetables, cereal grains, meat, and fish are also good sources of these elements.

SODIUM AND POTASSIUM. The fluid that surrounds the cells of the body contains relatively large amounts of sodium and little potassium. Within the cells this concentration is reversed. The sodium content is low; the potassium content is relatively high. The varying amounts of sodium and potassium control the passage of water into and out of the body cells.

The concentration of sodium in the fluid surrounding the cells is probably the main reason why we become thirsty. Suppose we eat some salty (sodium chloride) food. It raises the sodium level in the blood. A higher level of sodium in the blood and tissue fluid causes water to move out of the body cells. The movement of water out of the cells is interpreted by the thirst center as a need for more water. When we drink more water, the concentration of sodium is reduced, and water flows back into the cells.

The sodium-potassium balance affects every cell in the body. The first cells to react to an imbalance are the muscle and nerve cells. Actual damage to the heart and brain may occur as a result. Some biologists believe that some of the diseases associated with age may be due to the failure of the body to maintain the balance between these two elements.

Both sodium and potassium are widely distributed in most of the foods we eat. There is, therefore, little chance that we will not obtain enough of them in our diet. The amount of sodium ingested by certain people is regulated when they show a tendency to develop high blood pressure. You have probably heard of a "salt-free diet." Perhaps you can suggest why a low salt diet might reduce blood pressure.

MAGNESIUM, IRON, AND TRACE ELEMENTS. Most of the magnesium found in the human body is in the bones. It is also widely distributed in the muscles and blood cells. In very small amounts magnesium acts as a catalyst for many of the chemical reactions of the body. Experimental animals fed on a diet deficient in magnesium become nervous and irritable. A magnesium-deficient diet in humans, however, is rare since the small amounts we need of this element are present in most ordinary foods.

Elements that are important in nutrition in very small amounts are called trace elements. We have already mentioned the significance of iodine in the thyroid gland. Iron is also an important trace element. It is an essential part of hemoglobin, the oxygen-carrying protein of red blood cells. If there is insufficient iron available in the diet, hemoglobin cannot be formed in proper amounts. A condition known as *anemia* results. Liver, oysters, and dried fruits are foods rich in iron.

Trace elements such as cobalt, zinc, and copper, are important parts of *enzymes*. Enzymes are complicated proteins that regulate many of the fundamental life processes. Fluorine has been linked with the ability of teeth to resist decay. As a result many communities have added fluorine compounds to their drinking water. Fluoridation is discussed in Chapter 34.

Vitamins

Today the word vitamin is a household term. Vitamin pills can be purchased in drugstores and supermarkets. Bread wrappers, cereal boxes, and milk cartons list the vitamins these foods contain. Yet some sixty years ago no one even knew that vitamins existed.

The discovery of vitamins is a dramatic chapter in the story of man's growing knowledge of nutrition. A little more than sixty years ago, growth experiments with laboratory animals often ended in failure even though the animals were fed what appeared to be a balanced diet. Something was obviously missing, for the animals sickened and died. The missing "something" turned out to be vitamins.

Unlike the mineral salts, the chemical composition of the vitamins is complicated. At first their chemical nature was not understood. As a result they were named by letters: A, B, C, and so on. Later, when their chemical composition was discovered they were given chemical names. The vitamins belong to different classes of organic compounds. Some vitamins are alcohols, some are organic acids, and some are amines. Most vitamins assist specific enzymes in catalyzing the chemical reactions of the body. The vitamins that assist enzymes are called *co-enzymes*. The list of known vitamins is constantly increasing as more refined chemical techniques identify them.

The absence of vitamins from the diet produces what are known as *deficiency diseases*. Each disease is associated with a specific vitamin deficiency.

VITAMIN A. This vitamin increases our resistance to colds and other common respiratory infections. Prolonged deficiency of vitamin A in the diet results in a condition known as *xerophthalmia* (zear-auf-THAL-me-ah). The eyes become very dry and susceptible to infection. Lack of this vitamin may also impair vision and a condition known as night-blindness develops. This is the inability to see clearly in dim light.

Proper tooth development also depends upon vitamin A.

Milk, butter, eggs, and cheese are good sources of vitamin A. Plants do not produce it. However, the pigment *carotene,* found in many plants, can be converted into vitamin A by the body. Carrots, therefore, are often listed as a source. Substances like carotene that can be converted into vitamins by the body are called *provitamins*. They are just about as important in the diet as the vitamin itself.

THE B VITAMINS. Beriberi is a nerve disease that has long been a problem in the Orient. There, many people live on polished rice—rice that has had the outer shell, or husk, removed. Characterized by a gradual paralysis, beriberi leads to total paralysis and death.

In 1897, the Dutch physician Christian Eijkman was studying beriberi in a military hospital in Java. He noticed a strange thing about the chickens he was using for his experiments. When he left them free to forage for their own food, they remained in good health. But when they were confined and fed table scraps, mostly polished rice, they

33–3   Vitamin A Deficiency in Rats. Rat at right was fed a diet lacking in vitamin A.

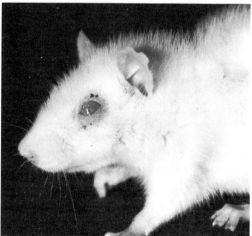

33-4 Vitamin B Deficiency in Chicks. Chick at right was fed a diet lacking in vitamin B.

developed paralysis. Their heads drooped. They had difficulty standing. He wondered if they had caught beriberi from his hospital patients. Perhaps some infectious organism was spreading the disease from the patients to the fowls.

Later, Eijkman fed the chickens with rice that had not had the outer husk removed. In a short time his sick chickens recovered. Apparently something in the husk of the rice was needed to maintain their health. Eijkman reasoned that rice starch was a nerve poison and that the hull contained an antidote for it. But another Dutch physician, G. Grijns, came closer to the truth. In 1901, he stated that the husk of rice grains contained an essential food substance that prevented beriberi.

Since that time chemists have sought to extract vitamins from foods. One of the earliest successes was that of Casimir Funk. In 1912, he was able to obtain an extract from rice husks that cured beriberi in fowl.

Funk believed that his extract was a member of a class of compounds known as *amines*. These are derivatives of ammonia in which replacement of one or more of the hydrogen atoms occurs. As a result, Funk called his extract a "vitamine." The name vitamin has persisted even though it has been shown that not all of these substances are amines.

Later research proved that vitamin B, as the anti-beriberi compound had been named, was really a mixture of many compounds. It has since been renamed the vitamin-B complex. The compound that cures beriberi is now called vitamin B_1. Its chemical name is *thiamine*. Other members of the B complex include *riboflavin* (B_2) and *niacin*. There are at least nine others that have been prepared in pure form. Both folic acid and B_{12} are important agents in the prevention of anemia. The B-complex vitamins are found in many foods. Milk, leafy vegetables, eggs, liver, and yeast are

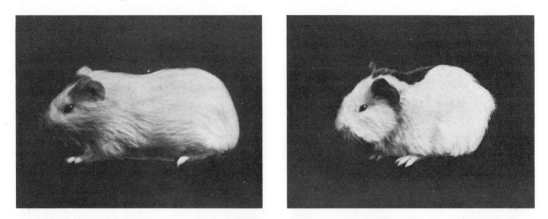

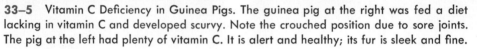

33–5 Vitamin C Deficiency in Guinea Pigs. The guinea pig at the right was fed a diet lacking in vitamin C and developed scurvy. Note the crouched position due to sore joints. The pig at the left had plenty of vitamin C. It is alert and healthy; its fur is sleek and fine.

especially rich sources. Lack of the B-complex vitamins is a serious cause of malnutrition in many parts of the world.

VITAMIN C AND SCURVY. Scurvy is a disease that was a special problem among the sailors who manned the early sailing ships. Sometimes the ship would be at sea for as long as several months. No fresh foods could be kept aboard. The crew ate hard biscuits and salted meat. As the voyage progressed, many of the crew would fall victims of the disease. Their skins roughened, their gums bled, and their teeth fell out. If the voyage included stops where fresh foods, particularly citrus fruits, could be obtained, fewer cases of scurvy appeared. In 1795, the British Navy adopted the practice of provisioning its ships with lemons and limes. This innovation sharply reduced the problem of scurvy. The term "limey" for a British sailor comes from this innovation.

Vitamin C was finally isolated in pure form from lemon juice in 1932 by two University of Pittsburgh chemists. Named *ascorbic acid,* to link it with its role in the prevention of scurvy, vitamin C can now be purchased in pill form. Thus, the modern explorer need only provide himself with a sup-

ply of pills to prevent the disease that was once the curse of sailing men. The conquest of scurvy has been called one of the ten greatest advances in medical science.

VITAMIN D: THE SUNSHINE VITAMIN. Sunlight does not contain vitamins. But the ultraviolet portion of the sun's rays can convert the cholesterol in our skin into vitamin D. That is why D is called the sunshine vitamin. The growth of infants and small children is greatly influenced by vitamin D. Sometimes the bones become soft and deformed from lack of it. This is a condition known as *rickets.* Curvature of the spine and bowed legs are two of the more serious symptoms of rickets. Vitamin D is linked with ossification, or bone formation.

Scientists were long puzzled by the fact that rickets was found mostly in the temperate regions. Few cases were reported in tropic or arctic countries. Two reasons were discovered for this. Exposure to sunlight increased the amount of cholesterol converted to vitamin D in the tropics. And in the far north, diets rich in fish oil supplied the need. Fish liver oil is one of the richest sources of vitamin D.

Few other foods contain very much vitamin D. We can help build up our supply by

VITAMINS ESSENTIAL FOR GROWTH AND HEALTH

Vitamin	Source	Function	Deficiency Symptoms
A	Milk, egg yolk, beef liver, fish oils	Helps keep skin, hair, eyes, and lining of nose and throat in good condition; prevents "dry eyes" and night blindness	Dry, rough skin; lowered resistance to respiratory infections; poor vision in twilight
Niacin (B-complex)	Liver, meat, whole wheat, milk	Protects skin and nerves; aids digestion; prevents pellagra	Pellagra, mental depression, digestive disturbances
B_1 Thiamine (B-complex)	Milk, pork, egg yolk, cereal, vegetables, fruit	Protects health of nervous system; aids appetite and digestion; prevents beriberi	Beriberi, fatigue, listlessness, loss of appetite
B_2 Riboflavin (B-complex)	Milk, pork, liver, eggs, vegetables, fruit	Increases general body resistance; prevents harmful changes to eyes	Eye fatigue, lessened vitality, inflammation of tongue and lips
C Ascorbic Acid	Tomatoes, most citrus fruits	Helps form bones and teeth; helps strengthen walls of capillaries; prevents scurvy	Scurvy, sore joints, tender gums, poorly formed bones and teeth
D	Fish liver oils, irradiated milk, sunlight	Prevents rickets; utilizes calcium and phosphorus to build bones and teeth	Rickets, poorly formed bones and teeth
E	Vegetable oils, cereal products, eggs	Believed to play important role in reproduction	In humans not definitely known; may cause muscular dystrophy in laboratory animals
K	Green leafy vegetables, soy beans, rice, bran	Aids in coagulation of blood	Hemorrhage

soaking up some sunshine out of doors. A method scientists have devised to supplement our diet with vitamin D is to *irradiate* milk with ultraviolet light. This greatly increases its vitamin D content. A fatty substance, *ergosterol,* found in milk is changed into vitamin D in the process.

33–6 The child in the photograph is suffering from rickets, a disease in which the bones do not harden properly. The weakened bones bend into abnormal shapes. Vitamin D prevents rickets because it enables the bone cells to use calcium and phosphorus in building the hard part of the bones.

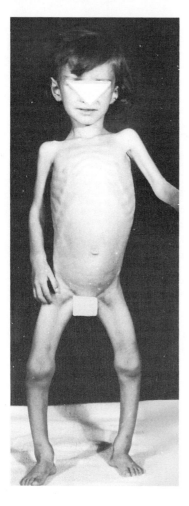

VITAMIN K. The formation of a blood clot involves a number of complicated chemical reactions. The Danish biologist Carl Henrik Dam was able to extract a fat-soluble vitamin from alfalfa leaves that plays an important role in this process. He named it the Koagulations-vitamin, now referred to as vitamin K. A strange fact about this vitamin is that much of our supply of it is made by bacteria living in our intestines. Deficiencies in vitamin K usually occur only when digestive disorders have reduced the number of these bacteria.

Surgeons sometimes administer vitamin K to patients before operating to prevent excessive bleeding. This reduces the time required for coagulation. It is also given to newborn babies to reduce the possibility of hemorrhage. Infants have no reserve of the vitamin, since their intestinal bacteria have not begun to manufacture it.

VITAMIN CLASSIFICATION. Vitamins can be classified in a variety of ways. One that suggests itself immediately is the use of the letter for the vitamin itself. This, however, describes none of the properties of the vitamins. Another method is to classify vitamins on the basis of solubility. Vitamins B and C are soluble in water. Vitamins A, D, E, and K are soluble in ether, a common liquid that dissolves fats. Hence, they are fat-soluble vitamins.

The distinction between fat-soluble and water-soluble vitamins has an important significance. Water-soluble vitamins are easily removed from foods by cooking, especially when large amounts of water are used. This is why it is better to cook vegetables, for instance, in a relatively small amount of water, allowing the steam to aid in cooking the uncovered portions. In addition, water-soluble vitamins cannot be stored by the body but are excreted through the kidneys. Fat-soluble vitamins can be stored. Thus, the average daily requirement for these vitamins is not as high as for the water-soluble vitamins.

MULTIPLE VITAMIN CAPSULES

Each capsule contains:

		MDR[1]
Vitamin A Palmitate	5000 U.S.P. units	125
Vitamin D (Calciferol)	500 U.S.P. units	125
Thiamine Mononitrate (B1)	3 mg.	300
Riboflavin (B2)	3 mg.	250
Pyridoxine HCl (B6)	1 mg.	
Vitamin B12 as Cobalamin Concentrate	2 mcg.	
Niacinamide	20 mg.	200
Ascorbic Acid (C)	50 mg.	167
Calcium Pantothenate[2]	5 mg.	

1 Percent minimum daily requirement
2 Need in human nutrition not established

To help prevent vitamin deficiencies.
Dose: 1 capsule daily or more as recommended.

Control: 2L81035

Keep in a cool place
Protect from direct sunlight

33–7 A vitamin bottle label lists the names and amounts of vitamins in each capsule. When buying vitamins, remember that differences in price should reflect only the differences in capsule quantities. All vitamin capsules must be of equal quality to meet government standards.

Foods and Health

In the midst of abundance it is possible to suffer from malnutrition. To supply the nutrients our body requires we must eat a variety of foods that contain proper amounts of all the basic foods.

Studies indicate that one American family in ten does not provide a balanced diet for its children. This does not mean that insufficient calories are supplied. These are usually overabundant. But often too many of the calories are derived from fats. Protein content in the diet is sometimes lower than desirable, especially in low-income families. This complicates a difficult situation because protein foods generally supply vitamins and minerals in good quantity. Other dietary necessities that were deficient in poor-diet families were: calcium, iron, vitamin A, vitamin B complex, and vitamin C.

FOUR BASIC FOOD GROUPS. A general guide to good nutrition is provided by the chart prepared by the Council on Foods and Nutrition of the American Medical Association. It recommends certain amounts from four basic food groups—dairy foods, meats, vegetables and fruits, breads and cereals (see table on following page). Carefully followed, its suggestions for good eating should provide all the things we need for healthy living and growth.

VITAMIN PILLS. Eating a balanced diet, which includes enriched milk and fresh foods properly prepared, is the best way to get all the vitamins you need. Vitamin preparations should then be unnecessary. In certain circumstances, vitamin pills are of value in supplementing normal intake. In most cases, however, proper eating makes them a needless expense.

33–8 These healthy children are enjoying the benefits of a balanced diet.

FOUR BASIC FOOD GROUPS
With Daily Requirements

Food Group	Foods in Group	Daily Requirement
Milk Group	Milk, butter cheese, ice cream	4 glasses or their equivalent
Meat Group	Meats, poultry, eggs, peas, dry beans, nuts	2 or more servings
Vegetable-Fruit Group	Dark green and yellow vegetables, citrus fruits, tomatoes	4 or more servings
Bread-Cereal Group	Bread, cereals, crackers, spaghetti	4 or more servings

IMPORTANT POINTS

• Foods are required for energy, for tissue building, and for the overall promotion of good health. Foods consist of six classes of essential substances called nutrients. These are carbohydrates, fats, proteins, water, minerals, and vitamins.

• Carbohydrates and fats yield energy. Weight for weight, fats are over twice as energy-rich as carbohydrates. Food energy is measured in heat units called Calories. Greater activity means more Calories are needed per pound of body weight.

• Proteins are tissue builders that are essential for growth. They also furnish Calories because they can be oxidized to release energy. This occurs when carbohydrates and fats are not present in necessary amounts.

• Water makes up a substantial part of all body fluids and accounts for 70 per cent of our body weight. It is found in almost all foods.

• Small amounts of minerals are present in all foods. Calcium and phosphorus are essential for bone building. Sodium and potassium are needed for normal cell activity. Iron is required for the formation of hemoglobin. Trace elements—manganese, iodine, copper, cobalt, and fluorine—also influence our body functions.

• Vitamins regulate many body processes. Their absence from the diet results in deficiency diseases. Vitamin A increases resistance to infection and preserves good vision. The B complex vitamins prevent many nerve and skin disorders. Vitamin C prevents scurvy; vitamin D, rickets. Vitamin K influences blood-clotting.

• Good health depends on good nutrition. Good nutrition is best achieved through a balanced diet. Foods from the four basic food groups should be eaten daily.

REVIEW QUESTIONS

1. List the six groups of nutrients and explain the role of each in human nutrition.
2. Define a Calorie. Why does the daily caloric requirement vary among different persons?
3. List five foods rich in carbohydrates, in fats, in proteins.
4. Why may carbohydrates and fats generally not be substituted for proteins in the diet?
5. What happens to excess proteins in the diet?
6. In what three ways does the body release water?
7. What is the chief danger of an iron-deficient diet?
8. What are two ways of getting adequate amounts of vitamin D?
9. List three sources of the B-complex vitamins.
10. What four food groups provide the basis for a balanced diet?

CHECK YOUR UNDERSTANDING

11. Explain how a starch is related to the simple sugars.
12. What is the technique of intravenous feeding and when is it used?
13. How does the liver regulate the glucose level of the blood?
14. What is the chemical difference between carbohydrates and fats?
15. Why are fats more than twice as energy-rich as carbohydrates?
16. What are the roles of calcium and phosphorus in body growth? Name several good sources of these elements.
17. List three trace elements and explain their importance in nutrition.
18. Describe Eijkman's experiments with beriberi.
19. Why is vitamin K sometimes administered prior to surgery?
20. Why would a diet consisting of bread, potatoes, pastries, and confections be undesirable although it would supply the daily caloric requirements?
21. Why do some dietitians advise that the water in which vegetables are cooked should be served with them?

RESEARCH PROJECTS AND REPORTS

1. Obtain information from your school or public library and prepare a report on one of the following topics:

   Christian Eijkman   **Dietetics as a Career**

   Reducing Diets   **Interview with the School Dietitian**

2. *Food Tests:* The presence of organic nutrients, starch, simple sugars, protein, and fat may be determined with a minimum of apparatus and materials.

   Testing for Starch. A dilute solution of iodine turns starches to a blue-black color in a few minutes. Place a few drops of iodine solution on bread or a raw potato and notice the results. If a pinch of flour is heated with water in a test tube, the reaction is almost instantaneous.

Testing for Simple Sugars. Benedict's or Fehling's solution A and B will indicate the presence of simple sugars (glucose, fructose, but not table sugar, which is a disaccharide). These indicators may be purchased from a biological supply house.

Place a few drops of corn syrup in a test tube with a little water. Add Fehling's solution A and B (or Benedict's solution) and heat gently in a Bunsen flame. Liquid will go through a series of color changes from green to red or orange. Repeat, using table sugar. What are your results? Repeat, using various fruit juices.

Testing for Fats. Rub a freshly opened Brazil nut vigorously on brown, unglazed wrapping paper. Sprinkle paper with water and allow to dry. Water spots disappear but fats and oils leave a translucent area.

Mix various foods with ether or carbon tetrachloride in a test tube. Pour off liquid in an evaporating dish. If the food contained fat, fat droplets will remain in the dish after the solvent evaporates.

Testing for Proteins. Place a bit of hard boiled egg white in a test tube. Add concentrated nitric acid. Shake gently until egg white turns yellow. Pour off acid and add a few drops of ammonium hydroxide. The yellow will now change to deep orange. Repeat test with other foods. Which foods contain protein? **Caution: Do not get nitric acid on your skin. Even a small amount will cause a yellow-orange discoloration.** Why?

The protein test can be performed with such fibers as silk, nylon, cotton, and wool. Which fiber gives a positive reaction? Why?

FURTHER READING

Food Values of Portions Commonly Used. Anna dePlanter Bowes and C. Church. College Offset Press, Philadelphia, Pa. Authoritative tables of food values of practically everything we eat.

Great Experiments in Biology. Mordecai L. Gabriel and Seymour Fogel, Editors. Prentice-Hall, Englewood Cliffs, N.J. In pages 74–77, Christian Eijkman describes his investigations that led to the discovery that beriberi was a deficiency disease and not caused by a germ.

Foods and You. Edmund S. Nasset. Barnes and Noble, Inc., New York, N.Y. A well-written book that contains much sound information on human nutrition.

The Teen Age Diet Book. R. West. Julian Messner, New York, N.Y. Good nutrition is especially important to the rapidly growing teenager. Contains many excellent pointers on health and attractiveness through diet.

The Great Nutrition Puzzle. Dorothy Callahan and Alma S. Payne. Charles Scribner's Sons, New York, N.Y. Where our food goes and how it nourishes our bodies. Discusses function of saliva and gastric juices and the role of minerals and vitamins in our diet.

34

Digestion
A Chemical Process

WE KNOW that foods give us energy and help build our bodies, but how does this come about? What actually happens to the foods we eat?

The research that has led us to at least a partial answer to this question began as a result of a strange event. William Beaumont, an Army surgeon serving in the Michigan Territory in 1822, was called upon to treat Alexis St. Martin, a Canadian Indian, who had suffered a severe gunshot wound in the abdomen. Following Beaumont's surgery, St. Martin recovered. But his wound left an opening through his abdominal wall directly into his stomach. Such an opening is called a *fistula*. Thus, Beaumont was able to observe first-hand the digestion of foods in his patient's stomach. He noticed, for instance, that meat was dissolved after a period of about two hours. St. Martin became a living laboratory, one of those rare accidents that provide opportunities for scientific investigation.

From Beaumont's time until the present our knowledge of digestion has steadily increased. Advances in chemistry have played the major role in helping us understand what happens to foods when they are consumed. Stated in chemical terms, *digestion* is the process by which large food molecules are changed into simpler molecules. The simpler, smaller molecules can then diffuse into the blood stream and enter the cells. Inside the cells, the food molecules provide energy and the raw materials for building other cells.

The Work of Enzymes

Digestive enzymes are substances that speed up the digestion of foods. Chemists call such substances catalysts. Catalysts are substances that hasten chemical reactions without being used up in the process. Even in tiny amounts catalysts can promote chemical change because they are used over and over again.

Some enzymes are concerned with body building, bringing the materials within the cell together so that new tissue is made. Others, like the digestive enzymes, split complex molecules into simpler ones. The large starch chain is split into simpler glucose molecules. The enormous protein molecules are split into smaller amino acids. Fat molecules are changed into fatty acids and glycerin. Thus, enzymes separate foods into their component, useful parts.

How do the digestive enzymes split molecules? Biochemists do not really know. But they can supply us with a picture that will help us understand the process.

Suppose we think of food molecules as special chains made of links that are held together in certain places with padlocks. These locks require different keys to open them. If we unlock the links at one point, two shorter lengths will result. If the shorter lengths are similarly unlocked, still shorter lengths are obtained. The digestive enzymes can be thought of as the different keys that open the locks that hold the links together. Note, also, that the keys are not destroyed in the process. They can be used over and over again.

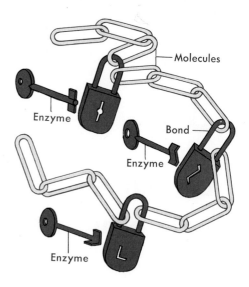

34–1   Enzymes may be thought of as keys that open locks, or the bonds between molecules.

34–2   A diagrammatic representation of the hydrolysis of maltose is shown below. First, the enzyme maltase combines with maltose. Apparently the maltose fits into a portion of the surface of the maltase molecule. The oxygen bond (—O—) between the glucose molecules is broken on one side by hydrolysis. This oxygen then combines with the hydrogen (H) from the water to form a hydroxyl (OH) group. The OH from the water combines with the other side of the molecule. This results in two molecules of glucose. The enzyme maltase is not altered in any way.

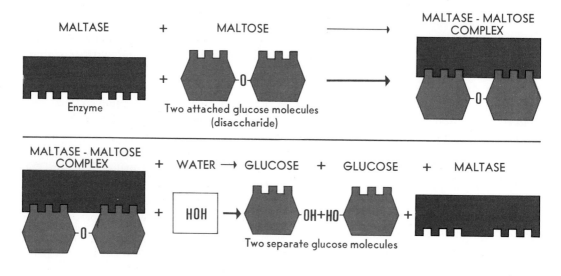

One further thing about our imaginary keys—they fit only one kind of lock. Enzymes unlock only certain kinds of molecules. The enzyme *amylase* found in saliva splits starch into smaller *maltose* molecules. Maltose is a sugar somewhat like cane sugar. The maltose molecules are split further by *maltase,* an enzyme that acts only upon maltose sugar and no other. It changes maltose into glucose molecules.

Being highly specific in their action, enzymes that split proteins do not affect fats. Those that act upon starch do not act upon sugars. Each type of food is changed into simpler molecules, and specific enzymes control the changes. Thus, the three main food types may be acted upon by a dozen or more enzymes during digestion.

WATER AND ENZYMES. Water plays an essential part throughout the digestive process. Enzymes perform only in its presence. A general equation represents the entire digestive process:

Large food molecules + water

$$\xrightarrow{\text{enzymes}} \text{smaller molecules}$$

Since water is used, chemists call this process *hydrolysis.* It is evident from the formulas that *smaller* molecules are produced as a result of digestion. In the case of maltose we can write the following:

$$C_{12}H_{22}O_{11} + H_2O \xrightarrow{\text{maltase}} 2C_6H_{12}O_6$$

maltose   water   glucose

34–3 ENZYME ACTION IN DIGESTION

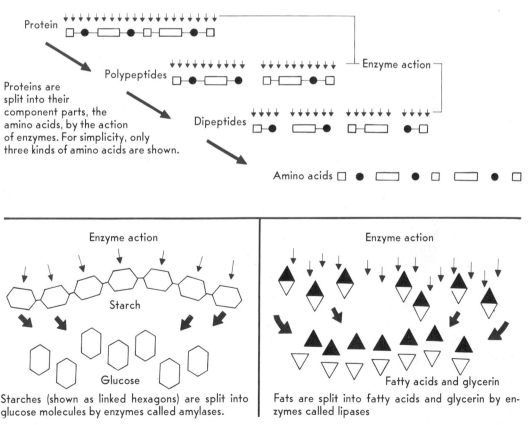

Proteins are split into their component parts, the amino acids, by the action of enzymes. For simplicity, only three kinds of amino acids are shown.

Starches (shown as linked hexagons) are split into glucose molecules by enzymes called amylases.

Fats are split into fatty acids and glycerin by enzymes called lipases

Proteins are the largest of all the molecules. As you might expect, they are split into smaller molecules in a series of steps. Several of these are shown below:

Whole protein + Water $\xrightarrow{\text{enzyme 1}}$ Polypeptides

Polypeptides + Water $\xrightarrow{\text{enzyme 2}}$ Dipeptides

Dipeptides + Water $\xrightarrow{\text{enzyme 3}}$ Amino acids

As the large molecules are split into smaller ones they become more soluble in water. Then they can be transported easily by the blood.

The Mouth and Teeth

Digestion begins in the mouth where food is chewed into a soft mass before it is swallowed. Associated with the mouth and teeth are numerous glands that supply water and enzymes. These enzymes begin the digestion of the food, which will be completed in other parts of the food tube.

34-4 Salivary Glands

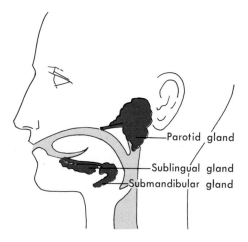

Parotid gland

Sublingual gland

Submandibular gland

THE CHEMICAL ACTION OF SALIVA. The aroma of a delicious roast in the oven causes the mouth to "water." In a sense, this is a good description of what actually happens, for saliva is mostly water. But it is much more than water. It also contains the enzymes that convert starch into sugars.

To try an experiment, chew a cracker for about a minute. Don't swallow it. Just let the saliva act upon it. Soon the cracker begins to taste sweet.

Most starchy foods must be cooked before they can be acted upon by saliva. Cooking breaks down the cellulose and allows salivary enzymes to come into contact with the starch. It is the enzyme amylase that splits the starch of the cracker into maltose, a sugar. Fats and proteins are not affected by saliva.

THE SALIVARY GLANDS. Saliva is secreted from three pairs of glands into the mouth by means of *salivary ducts.* One pair of salivary glands, the *sublinguals,* is located just beneath the tongue. Another pair lies farther back in the mouth along the margin of the lower jaw. These are the *submandibulars.* The third pair is located near the hinge of the jaw just beneath the ears. These are the *parotids,* glands that become very noticeably swollen when you get the mumps.

Under normal conditions the salivary glands pour more than a quart of saliva into the mouth each day. Because most of it is water, it assures that this compound will be available for the hydrolysis of foods. Dry foods, like crackers, stimulate a greater flow than do watery foods. Some animals, including the fishes, don't have salivary glands. Birds that eat dry seeds have enormously developed ones.

The sight or smell of food tends to stimulate the glands to greater secretion. The mouth waters. This is an automatic response that prepares us for eating. The sight or smell of unpleasant things has quite the

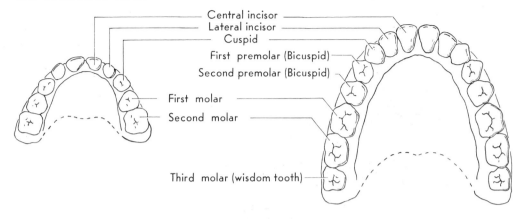

Central incisor
Lateral incisor
Cuspid
First premolar (Bicuspid)
Second premolar (Bicuspid)
First molar
Second molar

Third molar (wisdom tooth)

34–5   The Deciduous and Permanent Teeth

opposite effect. Then the mouth becomes dry and we are in no mood for eating.

THE TONGUE AND TASTE. Scattered over the surface of the tongue are *taste buds.* Four kinds of taste buds have been identified—sweet, sour, bitter, and salt. These are the only sensations the tongue can distinguish. Much of what we call "taste" is actually a combination of taste and smell. When we have a head cold, or if we pinch our nostrils together, our food loses its "taste." Foods that are very sweet, very sour, very bitter, or very salty are likely to be rejected.

The tongue also plays an important part in preparing foods for further digestion. Its surface is rough, owing to numerous projections all over it. As the food is chewed, the tongue rubs and kneads it into small particles. In this way the saliva is mixed thoroughly with the food. Breaking the food into smaller pieces permits enzymes to act upon it more easily.

THE TEETH. Chemical reactions occur much more rapidly when the reacting substances are finely divided. Did you ever try to burn a piece of aluminum foil? It may melt, but it won't burn. But a pinch of pul-verized aluminum blown through a long glass tube into a Bunsen burner flame burns with an almost explosive violence.

Since digestion is a chemical process, it proceeds more rapidly when foods are finely divided. The teeth are the principal agents that pulverize food. The surface area exposed to the action of enzymes increases a great deal when foods are ground into small particles. Hence, the chemical reaction is faster.

The human adult has 32 teeth, 16 in each jaw. Each is held firmly in its socket in the jawbone. The larger teeth have as many as three tapering roots. The types of teeth are related to the special functions they perform.

We can enumerate the types of teeth by dividing the upper and lower jaws down the midline. This gives us four similar quadrants, each with eight teeth. From the midline back we have two *incisors* (with cutting edges for biting), three *cuspids* (with points for biting and tearing), and three *molars* (with flat surfaces for grinding). The first cuspid has one point, the other two have two points, hence their special name, *bicuspids.* The third molars are

AGE OF ERUPTION AND SHEDDING OF TEETH

Names of Temporary Teeth	Age When Shed	Names of Permanent Teeth	Age at Eruption
Central Incisors	6 to 7 yrs.	First Molars (6 yr. molars)	5½ to 6 yrs.
		Central Incisors	6 to 7 yrs.
Lateral Incisors	7 to 8 yrs.	Lateral Incisors	7 to 8 yrs.
First Molars	9 to 11 yrs.	First Bicuspids	10 to 11 yrs.
Second Molars	9 to 11 yrs.	Cuspids	10 to 11 yrs.
Cuspids	11 to 12 yrs.	Second Bicuspids	11 to 12 yrs.
		Second Molars	12 to 13 yrs.
		Third Molars (wisdom teeth)	16 to 21 yrs.

commonly called the "wisdom" teeth because they do not erupt until the late teens or early twenties. In some individuals they never appear at all.

As do all mammals, we have two sets of teeth—*deciduous teeth* that are lost and *permanent teeth* that replace them. There are twenty deciduous teeth. These are formed deep in the jawbones long before birth and begin to erupt between six and eight

34–6 Vertical Section of a Molar

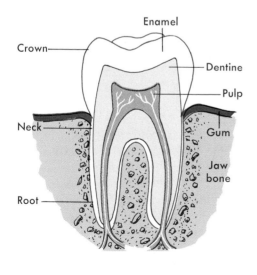

months after birth. The first to appear are the central incisors. These are gradually followed by the others. By the time the average child is two and a half, all twenty are in place.

Between the ages of six and thirteen, the deciduous teeth are lost and replaced by the permanent ones. In addition, twelve more permanent teeth erupt at various ages. Four molars appear at age six, and four more at age twelve. The last four molars to erupt are the "wisdom" teeth.

Deciduous teeth require as much care as the permanent teeth. It is normal for them to become loose and fall out as they make way for the second teeth. If they are prematurely lost, the permanent teeth may grow in crooked.

Covering each tooth from the gumline upward is the extremely hard *enamel*. It is composed of thousands of microscopic rods arranged at right angles to the surface. Each rod is shaped like a six-sided lead pencil, fitting snugly against its neighbor to form the hardest substance of the body.

The bulk of the tooth is made of *dentine*, a material like hard bone. Within it is the *pulp cavity* that contains the blood vessels and nerves. These enter the pulp cavity through openings at the base of the root.

TOOTH DECAY. Almost everyone has been troubled by tooth decay. It is estimated that Americans spend over a billion and a half dollars each year for the repair of their teeth. Yet the causes of tooth decay are not thoroughly understood.

One factor in tooth decay seems to be the presence of certain bacteria in the mouth. These bacteria apparently thrive better when large amounts of sugars and starches are eaten. Laboratory hamsters that were fed carbohydrates through a tube that by-passed the mouth and led directly into the stomach developed no cavities. Certain trace elements, especially fluorine, found in food and water are important in preventing tooth decay. Heredity is also a factor. Studies indicate that tooth decay is more prevalent in some families than in others. Slight differences in the saliva and the way the teeth are ridged may account for this.

Proper care of the teeth involves brushing them several times daily, especially after meals. Careful attention to diet is important. If you see your dentist regularly and follow his advice, you will do as well as can be done under the present state of our knowledge.

FLUORINE AND TOOTH DECAY. As early as 1916, dental researchers reported that people living in certain regions of the United States had an above average number of mottled or discolored teeth. By 1931, chemists traced the cause of their mottled tooth enamel to small amounts of *fluorides*, salts of the element fluorine, that were present in their drinking water. Analysis also showed that the fluorides in these regions varied from two to five parts per million parts of water.

An even more important discovery soon followed. The mottled teeth were less subject to decay than normal teeth. This discovery about "man's most common ailment"

was considered so significant that the United States Public Health Service began to study the matter. They examined the teeth of 12- to 14-year-old children from fluoride regions, then compared them with young people of the same age who lived in non-fluoride regions. The study resulted in two important findings:

1. The individuals from fluoride areas had 60 per cent fewer decayed teeth than individuals of the same age who lived in fluoride-free regions.
2. In regions where fluorides make up less than 1.5 parts per million parts of water, no tooth discoloration was found.

Apparently, then, the presence of fluorides in drinking water helps to reduce dental decay. However, the way in which they work is not definitely known. Experiments using radioactive fluorine have since shown that the element enters the tooth enamel. One possibility, then, is that flourine helps to produce a harder enamel, one that is less easily eroded by mouth acids or bacterial activity.

Following the Public Health Service findings, a number of communities whose water is not naturally fluoridated sought ways to add fluorides artificially in order to improve the dental health of their citizens. One part fluoride per million parts of water was selected as a practical solution. This amount does not produce discoloration. It is also considered safe because it is well below the amounts of fluoride normally found in many foods. Furthermore, excess fluorides are excreted through the kidneys.

In 1945, several cities, including Grand Rapids, Michigan; Newburgh, New York; and Brantford, Ontario, began the artificial *fluoridation* of their drinking water. Other communities followed. Today thousands of communities have adopted this practice. It is now estimated that more than a third of

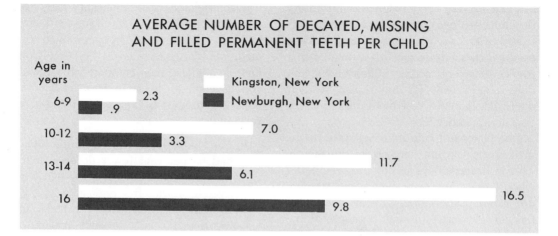

AVERAGE NUMBER OF DECAYED, MISSING
AND FILLED PERMANENT TEETH PER CHILD

Age in years

☐ Kingston, New York
■ Newburgh, New York

6-9 2.3 .9

10-12 7.0 3.3

13-14 11.7 6.1

16 16.5 9.8

34–7 Fluoridation of Water. The results of a controlled study in fluoridated Newburgh, N.Y., and nearby fluorine-free Kingston. Later studies have shown similar results.

the population of the United States lives in communities with water supplies containing enough natural or added fluorides to protect their teeth. Many communities have conducted studies in an effort to learn just how effective fluoridation is against tooth decay. In these studies, yearly dental examinations of school children were compared with results obtained from communities in which fluorides were neither added to nor sufficiently natural to the water supply. Such studies established the value of fluoridation.

One such study is often cited. In each of the fifteen years after adding fluorides, tooth decay figures for pupils in fluoridated Newburgh were compared with figures for equivalent-age pupils in nearby fluorine-free Kingston. The results showed that in Newburgh:

1. Seventeen-year-olds had 30 per cent fewer cavities.
2. Six- to ten-year-olds had 60 per cent fewer cavities.
3. Almost four times as many deciduous teeth of children under six were decay free.

Studies in other fluoridated communities generally show the same results. Public Health officials interpret these figures to mean that flourides are most beneficial to young children whose teeth are still forming, less beneficial to teenagers, least beneficial to adults. There is general agreement, however, that there is some benefit at any age.

Although there is much evidence that fluorides in the water supply serve to reduce tooth decay, many persons oppose artificial fluoridation. Some object on the ground that adding flourides is a form of "compulsory medication." Others believe it to be unsafe. Longer studies, they say, may reveal that fluoridation can damage other parts of the body, particularly the bones. Examination of individuals from naturally high fluoride regions, however, shows no damage to their skeletons.

The Digestive Tube

Essentially, the digestive system is a long, coiled tube with large related glands. As the food passes through the tube the chemical reactions of digestion occur. As mentioned in the previous section, digestion of food begins in the mouth. The food then passes through the esophagus and into the stomach. After it has been thoroughly mixed in the stomach, it is passed into the small intestine. This long, coiled tube fills most of the abdominal cavity. After the food has passed through the small intestine, digestion is complete. By this time the originally large food molecules have been split into smaller ones. These, in turn, have been absorbed into the blood. Food residues that have not been digested now pass into the large intestine, or *colon*. It is a shorter, yet wider, part of the food tube. Here the food wastes accumulate for a time. Then they are voided through the anus.

Assisting in the digestion of food are various glands. Some of these glands line the tube itself. Others are located some distance from the tube but send their secretions into it by means of ducts. Among the latter are the salivary glands, the pancreas, and the liver. The liver is the largest gland in the body. Certain areas of the digestive tract are specialized for digesting particular foods. Fats, for example, are digested only in the small intestine.

THE ACT OF SWALLOWING. At the back of the mouth is the enlarged area that marks the entrance to the trachea (windpipe) and to the food tube, the esophagus. This enlarged upper section of the throat is called the pharynx. When food is swallowed, it is pushed into the pharynx, then into the esophagus. If it falls into the trachea, it causes choking.

As food is forced into the pharynx two things happen. First, the *soft palate,* the arched back of the roof of the mouth, moves upward and prevents food from entering the nose. Next, the *epiglottis,* a small flap of muscle at the back of the tongue, jerks downward and covers the entrance to the trachea.

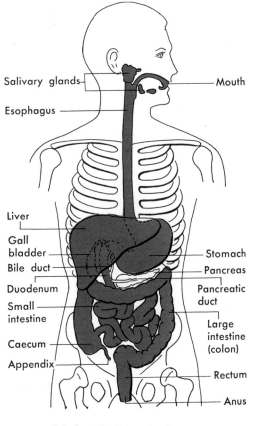

34–8 The Digestive System

THE ESOPHAGUS AND PERISTALSIS. As the food enters the esophagus it is held like a link of sausage in a section of the tube. The muscle layers of the tube control the movement of the food in a slow, orderly passage. The muscles ahead of the food relax while the muscles in back of it contract and gradually force it along. It is this controlled movement that enables a performer to drink water in an upside-down position. The wavelike movement along the food tube is called *peristalsis.* It occurs not only in the esophagus, but along the entire digestive tract.

THE STOMACH. This organ is the largest reservoir for food in the body. It has a capacity of about two pints and can be stretched. Situated at the base of the esophagus, it receives and stores food temporarily. The end connected to the esophagus is the *cardiac portion*. The opposite end is the *pyloric portion*.

The walls of the stomach consist of thick layers of muscle, which churn and mix the food. Circular muscles at the cardiac entrance and at the pyloric exit regulate the entry and exit of food. Internally, this muscular pouch is lined with a thick layer of mucous membrane. Viewed under the microscope, the inner wall is seen to be deeply indented. Lining these indented portions are millions of tiny glands that make several kinds of secretions. One of these is watery mucus. Another is the substance that will produce the enzyme *pepsin*. This substance is called *pepsinogen*. Hydrochloric acid is also secreted by some of these gastric glands.

The gastric juice, then, consists of a watery acid solution that contains pepsinogen. What effect does this juice have upon our food? The acid acts as an activator. It changes pepsinogen into the enzyme pepsin. This enzyme is a specific key for opening the links of the huge protein chain of amino acids. Thus, protein digestion begins in the stomach. But it is not completed there. Protein molecules are made of huge chains of 50 to 10,000 amino acids. The very long chains are first broken into smaller chains by pepsin. Two of the more important protein fragments are peptones and polypeptides. They will be split still further in the small intestine.

Starch continues to be digested by amylase from the mouth until it enters the stomach. Then the acid of the stomach mixes with the amylase and prevents its further action. Fats are not acted upon to any great extent in the stomach.

The length of time that food remains in the stomach depends upon the amount and kind of food eaten. Fats seem to be especially important in determining the time required for food to move through the stomach. This is not because they are digested there; but fats surround other food particles with a thin film making it difficult for the enzymes to act upon them.

When the food has been mixed thoroughly by the contractions of the stomach walls, it passes into the small intestine by way of the opening at the pyloric end. Controlling this opening is a circular muscle called the pyloric valve. The pyloric valve acts as a filter, permitting only finely divided food to pass through. The mixture of digested food and digestive juices is *chyme*.

PEPTIC ULCERS. The stomach wall, which is essentially a protein structure, is not digested by pepsin. A mucous membrane lining protects the inner wall effectively. In spite of this protection, however, damage does occur in some people. Excessive acid is secreted and ulcers develop. The reasons for the beginning of this condition are not well known. Some causes may be nervous tension and anxiety. Conditions producing emotional stress may cause the stomach to produce more acid than usual. Ulcers are apt to make the patient more irritable and disturbed, and the situation becomes still worse.

Ulcers are usually treated by having the patient eat very bland foods. Antacid medicines, or alkalizers, are also helpful. In some cases the penetration of the stomach wall by an ulcer may be complete. These perforated ulcers can be fatal unless they are corrected by surgery.

THE SMALL INTESTINE. As the food leaves the stomach it enters the small intestine, a narrow tube only one inch in diameter. The first part, the duodenum (due-uh-DEE-num), is about a foot long. It is the loop that curves beneath the stomach. The next section, the jejunum, is seven feet long. It is followed by the extensive *ileum* that runs

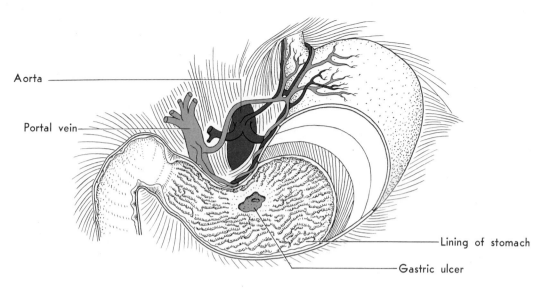

Aorta

Portal vein

Lining of stomach

Gastric ulcer

34–9 The stomach and duodenum partially open to show ulcer.

some fifteen feet to connect finally to the large intestine.

As do the other parts of the digestive tube, the small intestine has a muscular wall. Longitudinal and circular muscles continue the movement of food by means of peristalsis. The inner surface is covered by mucous membranes. Indentations along the inner wall are the site of millions of glands that make the intestinal juices. But certainly as important as the intestinal juices are the secretions that pour into the duodenum from the liver and the pancreas.

THE LIVER AND BILE. The liver, weighing about three pounds, is the largest gland in the body. The liver converts surplus glucose into an insoluble starch, *glycogen*. It stores fat-soluble vitamins and manufactures vitamin A from carotene. It destroys certain kinds of bacteria. It also destroys the older red cells of the blood. But, most important from the standpoint of digestion, the liver makes a fluid called *bile*.

Bile is a yellow liquid that contains organic salts, mineral salts, and water. The pigments that give bile its color are largely obtained from the destruction of red blood cells. The liver produces bile at a steady rate and stores it in a small sac, the *gall bladder*. About a quart of bile is produced daily. It is released periodically by the gall bladder. Then it flows down the bile duct and empties into the duodenum.

Before fats can be acted upon by enzymes, they must be broken up into small droplets. This process is called *emulsification*. When you shake a mixture of oil and water, you can see some evidence of emulsification. If you add an emulsifying agent, the droplets do not settle out quickly. This is what bile does. It breaks up fats into tiny droplets so that they can be digested easily.

The gall bladder is a frequent source of of trouble in older people. Gall stones form in the bladder. If they are large enough they may even block the flow of bile through the bile duct. Then the person cannot digest fats. Sometimes gall stones are very painful, but in many cases they are not. Doctors estimate that one person in ten may have gall stones by the age of 50.

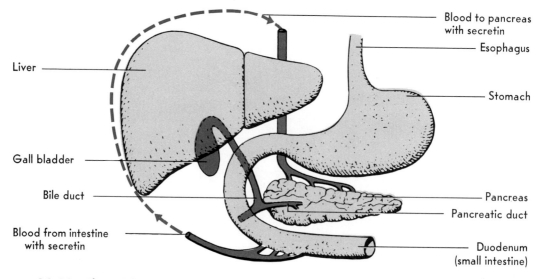

Liver

Gall bladder

Bile duct

Blood from intestine
with secretin

Blood to pancreas
with secretin

Esophagus

Stomach

Pancreas

Pancreatic duct

Duodenum
(small intestine)

34–10 Flow of digestive juices from the liver and pancreas into the small intestine. Secretin, a hormone, is produced in the small intestine, absorbed by the blood, and carried to the pancreas where it stimulates the production of pancreatic enzymes.

If the bile duct is blocked so that bile cannot flow, bile accumulates in the liver and is absorbed into the blood. This gives the eyes and skin a characteristic yellow color, a condition known as *jaundice.*

THE PANCREAS. Just behind and slightly below the stomach lies a small gland called the *pancreas.* The pancreas makes enzymes that act upon each of the three main types of food. It is the only digestive gland that does so. The secretion of the pancreas enters the duodenum through the pancreatic duct. The pancreatic duct and the bile duct unite as a single duct just before their entry into the intestine. There is no structure equivalent to the gall bladder to store pancreatic fluid. The secretion from the pancreas contains three enzymes: (1) *trypsin,* which acts upon proteins, (2) *lipase,* which acts upon fats, and (3) *amylase,* which acts upon starches.

The production of both bile and pancreatic fluid is controlled by an interesting mechanism. The entry of acidic chyme from the stomach into the duodenum stimulates the lining cells there. These lining cells make a hormone called *secretin,* which is immediately carried by the blood to the liver and the pancreas. The secretin triggers them to activity. Within only two minutes, pancreatic juice and bile are received in the intestine.

CHEMICAL ACTION IN THE INTESTINE. The small intestine is the most active digestive area in the body. Here the final digestive products are made. As the food moves through the duodenum, it is bathed in the secretions of the liver and pancreas. Later, the food is further digested by the intestinal juices formed in the millions of glands that line the intestinal walls.

Starches that enter the small intestine are acted upon by amylase, one of the secretions from the pancreas. Additional amylase is produced by the intestinal glands. This double supply insures that practically all starch in the small intestine will be digested. These intestinal glands also make enzymes that act upon sugars. *Sucrase* splits sucrose into simple sugars. *Lactase* acts similarly upon milk sugar, lactose.

Fats are emulsified by bile as they enter the duodenum. Then the enzyme *lipase* from the pancreas splits the fats into the smaller fatty acids and glycerin. Once again, additional lipase is produced by the intestinal glands.

Proteins, or protein-derived compounds, are acted upon by trypsin. Trypsin is an active enzyme formed in the small intestine from the inactive enzyme trypsinogen. The trypsinogen from the pancreas is changed into trypsin by another enzyme, called *enterokinase,* found in the small intestine. Additional protein-splitting enzymes are produced in the intestine. Among these are *erepsin* and *dipeptidase.* The last is the final enzyme to act upon these complicated foods. It splits a dipeptide, or two amino acids linked together, into single amino acids.

Absorption and Elimination

Viewed from the outside, the intestine is seen to be compressed into numerous folds, somewhat like the pleats of an accordion. The food is retained within these pleats while it is being mixed and acted upon by the intestinal juices. Then it is moved along by peristalsis. Movement of the food is thus slowed down so that digestion can be completed and absorption begun.

Internally, the intestinal wall not only presents a folded appearance, but also has a further adaptation to improve absorption. Scattered all over the surface are millions of tiny tufts, like the nap of fine velvet. The tufts consist of microscopic fingers, or *villi,* that absorb the digested foods.

A villus is not much thicker than a hair. Fifty, placed side by side, would make an inch. Within this tiny structure are two sets of vessels, capillaries and *lacteals.* The capillaries absorb glucose and amino acids

PRINCIPAL DIGESTIVE ENZYMES

Enzyme	Food Acted Upon	Source	Product
Salivary amylase	Starch	Saliva	Maltose
Pepsin	Protein	Gastric Juice	Polypeptides
Amylases	Starches		Maltoses
Lipases	Lipids	Pancreatic Juice	Glycerin and Fatty Acids
Trypsin	Proteins		Peptides
Dipeptidase	Peptides		Amino Acids
Sucrase	Sucrose		Simple Sugars
Maltase	Maltose	Intestinal Juice	Simple Sugars
Lactase	Lactose		Simple Sugars
Lipase	Lipids		Glycerin and Fatty Acids
Erepsin	Peptides		Amino Acids

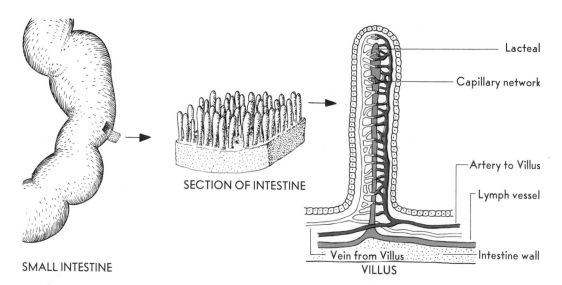

SMALL INTESTINE

SECTION OF INTESTINE

Lacteal

Capillary network

Artery to Villus

Lymph vessel

Vein from Villus

Intestine wall

VILLUS

34–11 Section through small intestine showing structure of villus. Simple sugars and amino acids are absorbed by capillaries. Fatty acids and glycerin are absorbed by the lacteals and enter the blood by way of the thoracic duct.

directly into the blood. The lacteals absorb fatty acids and glycerin as well as some undigested fat.

The process by which the digested foods are taken into the capillaries and lacteals is called *absorption*. It is not a simple process of diffusion. Since the digested foods are concentrated in the intestine, it would seem that they would tend to spread into the blood and lymph where they are less concentrated. This probably happens at the beginning of the exchange, but later when the concentration of digested food reaches a low level it could not occur. It is therefore believed that some means of active transport for the digested foods must exist.

GLYCOGEN STORAGE IN THE LIVER. The veins that receive digested food from the intestine are gathered together, like the roots of a tree, to unite into a common trunk. This trunk is the *portal vein* which leads into the liver. There the vein divides into a maze of capillary nets that reach every liver cell. The final composition of

blood is affected by what happens in the liver.

The liver controls the amount of glucose that enters the blood. The liver also removes excess glucose and changes it into insoluble glycogen. Glycogen is then stored in liver cells. When the glucose content of the blood is low, the liver cells reverse the process. They change stored glycogen into soluble glucose and release it into the blood.

Another function performed by the liver is the regulation of the blood's amino acid content. Although the liver does not store amino acids in the same way as it stores glycogen, some of them can be made there to fill the body's needs. The liver also produces most of the special proteins that are found in blood plasma. The albumins, the globulins, and other proteins are formed from the amino acids so abundant in the portal circulation.

FATS AND THE LYMPHATIC SYSTEM. The lacteals, the special fat-absorbing branches of the lymphatic system, require additional mention. Just why fats are absorbed by the lacteals is not clearly known. It is interesting to note, however, the way in which the fatty acids and glycerin finally get into the blood. The branches of the lymphatic system in the intestine unite to form a common tube, the *thoracic duct*. The thoracic duct runs upward alongside the esophagus into the region of the left shoulder. Here it empties into the left subclavian vein. In this roundabout way the end products of fat digestion finally make their way into the blood.

THE COLON AND ELIMINATION. The end of the small intestine is marked by its entry into the *colon*, or large intestine. The colon is about two to three inches wide and about five feet long. Here the waste material that cannot be digested accumulates. It is mainly cellulose from a variety of plant sources—woody parts of stems, shells of seeds, skins of fruits. There are also connective tissues and meat fibers that have not been reduced by enzyme action.

At the junction of the colon and the small intestine there is a small pouch, the *caecum*. Extending from it is the *appendix*, a blind tube about the length of a finger. The appendix has nothing to do with digestion. Occasionally it becomes infected, a condition known as *appendicitis*.

From the caecum the colon extends upward and across the abdomen like an inverted **U**. The right branch carries the food upward as the ascending colon. Then there is a transverse colon followed by a descending colon on the left side. The descending colon leads to the *rectum* and *anus*. Accumulated food wastes are voided through these last two structures.

Several processes are associated with the passage of undigested wastes through the

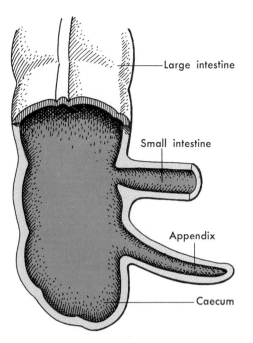

34–12 The Human Appendix. The appendix, which projects into the abdominal cavity, is hollow. Substances from the caecum easily enter it. Certain substances may infect the inner walls and result in appendicitis. Symptoms are abdominal pains, nausea, vomiting, and tenderness over the lower right abdomen.

colon. Much of the water that had been mixed with food as it passed along the digestive tube is recovered in the colon. This water is absorbed into the blood capillaries. Some dissolved minerals are recovered in the same way. The fluid waste material that enters the colon is thus changed into semi-solid *feces*. Millions of bacteria inhabiting the colon attack the cellulose and bring about the formation of certain vitamins. Vitamin K and possibly others are supplied by this means.

IMPORTANT POINTS

- Digestion is a chemical process. Enzymes in the mouth, stomach, and small intestine split large food molecules into smaller ones. The small molecules are then absorbed into the blood and distributed to the cells of the body.

- Digestion begins in the mouth where food is mixed with saliva. Saliva contains enzymes that digest starches. The teeth grind food into small particles. This makes the work of enzymes more effective.

- Human beings have two sets of teeth: deciduous and permanent. The 20 deciduous teeth erupt during childhood and are lost by age thirteen. These are replaced by 32 permanent teeth. The shape and size of the teeth are related to the foods we eat.

- Tooth decay may be due to bacteria, poor diet, heredity, or lack of dental care. Recent evidence indicates that fluorides in drinking water reduce tooth decay.

- Protein digestion begins in the stomach. Starch digestion begins in the mouth. Fat digestion begins in the duodenum. Bile from the liver emulsifies fats before they are acted upon by lipase, a fat-splitting enzyme made in the pancreas and intestinal glands. Further digestion of starches, sugars, and proteins occurs in the small intestine.

- The movement of food in the digestive tract is brought about by peristaltic contractions of the muscle layers. By this means, the undigested wastes eventually reach the colon. Here the removal of water concentrates unusable materials into feces.

- Digested foods are brought into close contact with the villi of the small intestine as they pass through it. Amino acids and glucose are absorbed into the capillaries of the villi, while fatty acids and glycerin are absorbed into the lacteals. The lacteals are special branches of the lymphatic system in the intestine. Digested fats are emptied into the blood by way of the thoracic duct.

REVIEW QUESTIONS

1. What is the function of a digestive enzyme?
2. Compare the action of amylase with that of maltase.
3. How do the teeth assist in the digestive process?
4. Compare deciduous and permanent teeth as to number and type.
5. Describe the process of peristalsis.
6. How do stomach ulcers develop?
7. What is the function of bile?
8. How are the liver and pancreas triggered to activity?
9. How does the small intestine absorb digested foods?
10. List two functions of the liver.

CHECK YOUR UNDERSTANDING

11. Write one equation to illustrate hydrolysis.
12. Why are several enzymes required to change proteins to amino acids?

13. What two arguments are advanced by opponents of water fluoridation?
14. What is the role of hydrochloric acid in the stomach?
15. How do excess fats slow down the digestion of other foods?
16. In what two ways may physicians treat stomach ulcers?
17. How is the length and pleating of the small intestine related to its role in absorption?
18. List the mechanical and chemical processes that act upon a protein from the time it is eaten until it is absorbed.
19. Why can small amounts of digestive enzymes act on large amounts of foods?
20. How is it possible for persons who have had their entire stomach removed to continue eating the same foods as before?
21. Why do the glucose and amino acids absorbed in the small intestine go to the liver before they enter the general circulation?

RESEARCH PROJECTS AND REPORTS

1. Obtain information from your school or public library and prepare a report on one of the following topics:

William Beaumont	**The Pancreas**
Stomach Ulcers	**The Fluoridation of Drinking Water**

2. *Digestion of Starch:* Collect some saliva in a test tube. In a second tube, place a pinch of starch, add water, and shake into a suspension. Add a drop of dilute iodine to the starch suspension. Now add saliva from the first test tube and observe color changes. Warming the tube with the hands will increase rate of change. What happened to the starch? Now test contents of the second tube for simple sugars with Benedict's or Fehling's solution. Can you explain the action of saliva?

3. *Digestion of Proteins:* Place a few bits of hard-boiled egg white in each of two tubes. Add some dissolved commercial meat tenderizer containing the protein-splitting enzyme papain to one tube and observe the effect on the pieces of egg white. Now boil some of the tenderizer solution and add it to the second tube. Does the tenderizer now have the same effect on the egg white that it had when it wasn't boiled? Can you explain your observations?

4. *Emulsification and Digestion of Fats:* Add a few drops of olive oil to an inch of water in a test tube. Shake thoroughly until an emulsion forms. Let the tube stand and observe what happens. Now add a few drops of a 5 per cent solution of sodium taurocholate (bile salt) and shake again. Does the emulsion last longer when allowed to stand?

    Add a pinch of pancreatin to an inch of water in a test tube and allow it to dissolve. Pancreatin, which contains lipase, is a commercial preparation that is made from the pancreas glands of hogs. Now add the pancreatin solution to the emulsion of olive oil in water. Warm the test tube for half an hour in a beaker of water that has been heated to approximate body temperature. Test the contents of the tube with litmus paper. Note: The end products of fat digestion include fatty acids.

FURTHER READING

Experiments and Observations on the Gastric Juice and the Physiology of Digestion. William Beaumont, M.D. Dover Publications, New York, N.Y. Dr. Beaumont reports his experiments in digestion carried out on a human subject, Alexis St. Martin, more than a century ago.

Understanding Food: The Chemistry of Nutrition. Beulah Tannenbaum and Myra Stillman. McGraw-Hill Book Co., Inc., New York, N.Y. How foods are assimilated and used by the body to give energy and rebuild tissues.

The Body. Alan E. Nourse and the Editors of LIFE. Time-Life Books, New York, N.Y. Chapter 5, Fueling the Body's Machinery, is a good summary of digestion.

"Protein Digesting Enzymes." Hans Neurath. *Scientific American,* December, 1964, page 68. For the advanced student who wants to learn more about the action of protein-splitting enzymes.

35

Circulation and the Heart

Howshall we know when life begins or when it ends? A common sign is the beating of the heart. Continued pulsations are an indication that all is well. The significance of the heartbeat was not clearly understood before the time of William Harvey, a 17th century English physician. Before his day no one knew just what the blood did. Since the time of Aristotle, it was believed that blood carried a "vital spirit." The heart was considered the organ that supplied the vital spirit to the blood.

Harvey proposed that the heart is like a pump. He made calculations showing that the blood must be pumped from the heart into the blood vessels and then returned to the heart by other blood vessels. Harvey did not know how this circulation was accomplished, but he believed that it must be so. Later experimenters, among them the Italian Marcello Malpighi, showed that Harvey's conclusions were correct.

Blood: The Life Fluid

Almost 70 per cent of the total weight of the body is made up of water. Most of the water is inside body cells. About 15 per cent of the water surrounds and bathes the

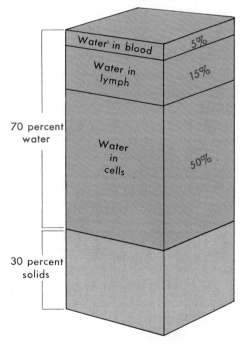

TOTAL BODY WEIGHT

Water in blood 5%

Water in lymph 15%

Water in cells 50%

70 percent water

30 percent solids

35–1 Water accounts for about 70 per cent of the body's weight. The diagram above indicates the percentage distribution of water in blood, lymph, and cells.

cells. About 5 per cent makes up much of the blood. The average person has between five and six quarts of blood. About half of this volume is water.

The functioning of the body depends upon maintaining the blood volume at a proper level. If an injury results in extreme loss of blood, the blood must be replenished quickly or death results. Transfusions of whole blood, or of the liquid portion of it, must be made. With this treatment the lives of many persons have been saved.

How can we determine the amount of blood in the body? One method uses a part of blood called serum albumin "tagged" with radioactive iodine. This is injected into a vein in the arm in a carefully measured amount. About fifteen minutes later when the blood has diluted the "tagged" material, a measured amount of blood is withdrawn from the opposite arm. A Geiger counter is used to count the activity of the radioactive albumin before injection and after dilution by the blood. From these figures the blood volume can be calculated. For example: five cubic centimeters of radioactive material is injected. If the count ratio before and after is determined to be 1000/1, then the blood volume must be 1000 times greater than the five cc injected, or 5000 cc.

Blood and Lymph. Blood is confined to the blood vessels of the body in a completely closed system. However, the liquid portion of the blood can diffuse through the thin walls of the smallest blood vessels and flow about the tissue cells. This liquid is sometimes called *tissue fluid*. It surrounds the cells of the body and brings to them vital substances for growth and repair. The tissue fluid also removes wastes from the cells. When the tissue fluid is collected into vessels, or tubes, it is called *lymph*. The volume of lymph is about three times that of blood. The lymph vessels of the body compose the lymphatic system.

The Functions of the Blood. Blood circulates about all the cells. It brings the chemical products of the cells into contact with each other, no matter how remote the cells may be. Blood transports oxygen from the lungs to the cells in the fingertip. The waste products of the metabolism of muscle cells in the legs are transported by the blood to the kidneys and lungs where the wastes are eliminated. The chemical products of certain glands are carried to other parts of the body where they may regulate growth or control emotional states. Some of the important functions of blood are listed below:

1. Transports digested foods to all cells.
2. Removes metabolic wastes from cells and carries wastes to the kidneys.
3. Carries oxygen to the cells, receives carbon dioxide from the cells, and returns carbon dioxide to the lungs.
4. Protects the body against disease.
5. Heals wounds by clotting reaction.
6. Transports the secretions of ductless glands throughout the body.

Blood Plasma. The fluid portion of the blood is the *plasma*. Blood plasma is about 90 per cent water. It contains many dissolved and suspended materials. Among these are glucose, proteins, many kinds of salts in very small concentrations, products from the glands of internal secretion, digested foods, waste products from the cells, and chemical agents to fight disease.

An interesting fact about plasma is that the mineral salts dissolved in it have about the same concentration as in sea water. Some biologists see this as a confirmation of the fact that life originated in the sea. The chief salt in plasma is ordinary table salt, sodium chloride. Other salts include phosphates, carbonates, and sulfates. The concentration of these salts in the plasma is a major factor regulating the flow of materials into and out of the cells.

SUBSTANCES FOUND IN BLOOD PLASMA

Substance	Use
Water	Solvent for all other materials.
Plasma Proteins albumin, globulin, fibrinogen	Insure the proper exchange of tissue fluids between tissues and capillaries. Antibodies. Blood types. Clotting.
Digestive End Products amino acids, glucose, fats, cholesterol	Materials used by cells for energy and for tissue building or special product formation.
Metabolic Wastes Urea, uric acid, ammonia salts, and carbon dioxide	Formed by oxidation of proteins, fats, and carbohydrates.
Mineral Salts sodium, potassium, calcium, magnesium, and iron compounds	Tiny concentrations are necessary for making many important compounds in the body, such as calcium in blood clotting.
Hormones secretions of the ductless glands	Regulate fundamental body processes.

PLASMA PROTEINS. Huge protein molecules make up about eight per cent of the plasma. The high concentration of proteins increases the thickness, or viscosity of blood. The commonest protein in the plasma is *serum albumin,* a substance that is somewhat like egg white. It makes up more than 65 per cent of the protein material. Another 28 per cent is composed of proteins called *globulins.* Globulins are especially important in the production of *antibodies,* substances that resist infection. They also account for blood type differences. Another protein, *fibrinogen,* makes up about four per cent of the plasma protein and is the active agent in forming blood clots. Other plasma proteins are enzymes that regulate specific body processes. An-

other protein, *prothrombin,* is among the principal "clotting factors" necessary to heal wounds.

The presence of huge protein molecules is especially important in regulating the movement of tissue fluid in and out of the blood vessels. Any condition that causes a drastic lowering of plasma proteins results in a greater movement of water into the tissue fluid. This produces a local swelling that may further interfere with proper circulation. When blood pressure is low, as it is after losing large amounts of blood, the tissue fluid moves into the blood vessels to increase blood volume. But the walls of the smallest blood vessels act like selective membranes through which the largest protein molecules move out with difficulty. Tissue fluid contains practically all of the plasma proteins in reduced concentrations.

RED CORPUSCLES. Blood cells, or corpuscles, are formed within the marrow of bones. Both the red and the white corpuscles are formed from irregularly shaped marrow cells that contain large nuclei. Certain of these marrow cells become red corpuscles while others become white ones.

When a thin film of blood is examined under a microscope, it is found to contain a large number of red corpuscles, or *erythrocytes* (eh-RITH-ruh-sites). In a cubic millimeter, there are about 5,000,000 red corpuscles. A red corpuscle has no nucleus. The nucleus is lost as the corpuscle matures from the marrow cell. The shape of the corpuscle is strikingly regular. Red corpuscles are circular discs with concave surfaces.

Red corpuscles transport oxygen from the lungs to all parts of the body. This is possible because of the presence of *hemoglobin*, a compound of *hematin* and *globin*. In oxygen-rich surroundings hemoglobin unites with oxygen to form a compound called *oxyhemoglobin*. In surroundings low in oxygen, oxyhemoglobin gives up its oxygen readily. Hemoglobin carries oxygen from the lungs to all the body cells.

35–2 Red Corpuscles

Carolina Biological Supply Company

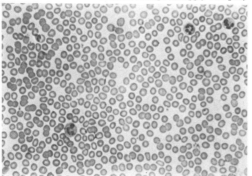

The fact that red corpuscles are being continuously produced in the marrow means that they are also being destroyed. Otherwise we would continuously increase their number. Estimates made by the use of radioactive atoms indicate that about 2,900,000 red corpuscles are produced each second. This means that in approximately 140 days we have a completely new set of red corpuscles.

ANEMIA. Let us suppose now that something happens to the orderly processes of red corpuscle formation. Gradually the total number drops. Instead of 5,000,000 per cubic millimeter, the count may go down to 3,000,000 or less. As the number decreases certain effects are observed. The person with a low red corpuscle count is not getting enough oxygen in all parts of the body. He feels fatigued and breathless even with slight exertion. Often he feels faint or dizzy. If the condition is severe, he may have to remain in bed. *Anemia* is the term used to describe this disorder in which the red corpuscle count is low.

What causes anemia? Generally, there is an adequate supply of iron in the diet. Without iron, hemoglobin cannot be made. Yet in some patients, the red corpuscles are produced in smaller numbers even though there is no lack of hemoglobin.

In 1927, George R. Minot, a Boston physician, discovered that a material extracted from liver was necessary to make red corpuscles in sufficient number. In 1948, biochemists identified the material as vitamin B_{12}. Today, small amounts of vitamin B_{12} are injected into the blood stream of anemic individuals to help keep their red corpuscle count at a normal level. Prior to Minot's discovery many victims of this type of anemia died. The condition was known as pernicious anemia because no cure was known. Modern treatment with vitamin B_{12} enables many anemic people to live normal lives.

Lack of vitamin B_{12} is not the only cause of anemia, however. Any condition that destroys red blood cells or interferes with their production may cause anemia. Sometimes the bone marrow is destroyed by certain chemicals, such as benzene or lead. The contact of industrial workers with these two chemicals must be carefully controlled to avoid the incidence of anemia. In some cases, anemia is hereditary, as in sickling of the red cells. (See page 160.) In still other cases, anemia is due to lack of iron in the diet, which is needed in the production of hemoglobin.

WHITE CORPUSCLES. There are far fewer white blood corpuscles, or *leucocytes,* than red corpuscles. In a cubic millimeter of blood there are about 9000 white corpuscles compared to 5,000,000 red. But the white corpuscle count varies much more than the red count. The white count is usually quite high when infection strikes the body. A high white corpuscle count may be used as an indication of infection when other symptoms are absent.

The leucocytes, or white corpuscles, are one of the body's defenses against disease. Some leucocytes are able to surround and ingest bacteria. When bacteria invade tissues, the bone marrow produces greater quantities of white corpuscles. The white corpuscles accumulate in large numbers where the bacteria are present.

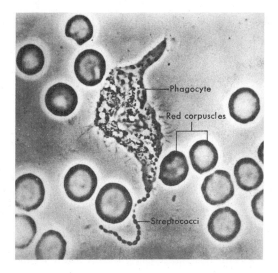

35–3 Certain white corpuscles, called phagocytes, surround and destroy bacteria.

Although red and white blood corpuscles originate from the same kind of marrow cell, they are quite different when they mature. The white corpuscles are irregular in shape and do not contain hemoglobin. Also they are much larger than the red corpuscles and contain nuclei. Unlike the red corpuscles, which are uniform, there are five distinct kinds of white corpuscles. One of these, the *lymphocyte,* is not made in the marrow. It originates in the lymph glands found all over the body.

The life span of the white blood corpuscles is considerably less than the red corpuscles' 140 days. Estimates range from three days to two weeks.

LEUKEMIA. The white corpuscles, like the red corpuscles, are produced in a series of stages that depend upon orderly chemical processes. Sometimes the processes become disordered, resulting in excessive numbers of white corpuscles. This condition is known as *leukemia.* A variety of harmful symptoms are associated with the disease. Leukemia may be chronic, returning from time to time, or acute.

PRINCIPAL BLOOD FRACTIONS

	Per Cent of Volume
Plasma	55.0
Red Cells	44.4
Platelets	.4
White Cells	.2

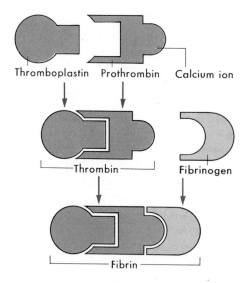

35–4 Template Construction of a Fibrin Molecule. Some of the factors that produce fibrin are shown as interlocking pieces.

Leukemia of fowls and cats has been shown to be caused by a virus. One might, therefore, expect that a virus causes human leukemia. Researchers have directed their attention to this problem. In the summer of 1969, scientists at the National Cancer Institute in Bethesda, Maryland, discovered that the feline leukemia virus is indeed able, in tissue culture and under laboratory conditions, to infect human cells. However, there is still no evidence that the feline leukemia virus is the agent that causes the disease in man.

It seems likely that some chemical agent that regulates the way in which white corpuscles mature is either absent or destroyed. A few research biologists believe that an RNA virus may be the cause of leukemia, as it is in the cat. However, the specific RNA virus that may cause human leukemia has not been found.

Medical research continues to seek effective ways to treat leukemia. X rays and radioactive phosphorus have been used for

a number of years. More recently, two chemical compounds have been isolated from the periwinkle plant that have proved to be very effective. Treatments such as these can retard the symptoms and prolong the patient's life for many years. Another chemical, the enzyme asparaginase, has even given hope that leukemia may finally be controlled.

PLATELETS AND CLOTTING. The smallest formed elements in the blood are *platelets.* They resemble red corpuscles but are only about one-third as large. Unlike the red corpuscles, platelets contain no hemoglobin and are colorless. They are not as numerous as the red corpuscles, which outnumber platelets about 25 to 1. In a cubic millimeter of blood there are about 200,000 platelets. The chief role of these fragile cells is associated with blood clotting.

The reduction of blood volume by even small amounts produces unconsciousness in many people. The loss of a large amount of blood may cause death. For this reason the flow of blood from a wound must be quickly stemmed by applying pressure to the arteries. The body has an automatic way of reducing the flow of blood by means of *coagulation,* or clotting. There is no general agreement as to the exact way in which coagulation occurs. One of the most widely accepted theories is presented here.

The blood plasma contains the materials that produce a clot. One of these materials is fibrinogen, a soluble protein. From this material, *fibrin* threads are formed that make an interlaced patch across a wound. To change soluble fibrinogen to insoluble fibrin, *thrombin* is necessary. At least ten "clotting factors" form thrombin. Three of these factors are *prothrombin, calcium ions,* and *thromboplastin.* Thromboplastin is found in the platelets and in tissue cells.

We can summarize the sequence that produces a clot. First, the injury damages tissue cells or platelets, which release thromboplastin. The thromboplastin then reacts with prothrombin and calcium ions to form thrombin. Finally, the thrombin reacts with fibrinogen to form threads of fibrin. The threads act as a flexible mesh that stops the flow of blood. The fibrin threads trap blood corpuscles and connective cells. The connective cells form the scar that develops as the wound heals.

BLOOD GROUPS AND TRANSFUSIONS. When a person is injured, it may be necessary to transfuse whole blood from a donor into his veins. However, using any person as a donor might be disastrous because there are several different blood types. Some types are compatible with each other; others are not. When blood types are incompatible, the donor's red corpuscles clump together.

Four major blood groups are recognized: A, B, AB, and O. The differences between them are principally associated with two conditions: (1) the presence of two chemical compounds, called *antigen A or B*, on the surface of the red blood corpuscles, and (2) the presence of two globulins in the blood plasma, called *antibody A or B*.

The blood type assigned to an individual indicates the type of antigen on the surface of his red corpuscles: Type A blood contains type A antigens. Type B blood contains type B antigens. Type AB has both type A and type B antigens. Type O blood has neither antigen. The blood plasma of a type A person, on the other hand, contains antibody B. The blood plasma of a type B person contains antibody A. The blood plasma of a type AB individual contains neither antibody. The plasma of a type O person contains both antibody A and B.

To illustrate how incompatibility occurs, let us imagine that type A red corpuscles have four V-shaped notches on the surface. The notches represent type A antigens. Now let us imagine that type B blood plasma contains diamond-shaped antibodies that exactly fit these notches. When type A blood is transfused into a type B patient, the antibodies in the type B plasma join many of the type A red blood corpuscles together, causing them to clump, or *agglutinate*. The clumping of the donor's blood is dangerous to the recipient and may cause death.

In a similar way we can imagine that type B red corpuscles have antigens in the form of round notches, and that type A plasma contains antibodies that fit those notches. Hence, type B red corpuscles cannot be transfused into type A plasma because clumping occurs in this case also.

Type AB red blood corpuscles contain both type A and type B antigens. For this reason, type AB blood cannot be transfused

35–5 Types of red corpuscles are shown with differently shaped notches to represent antigens. Antibodies in the plasma of each blood type are shown as particles that do not fit the corpuscular notches. When antibodies fit donated antigens, clumping results.

BLOOD TYPES

Type	Red corpuscles	Plasma antibodies
A	Type A antigen	B antibodies
B	Type B antigen	A antibodies
AB	Type B antigen / Type A antigen	No antibodies
O	No antigens	A and B antibodies

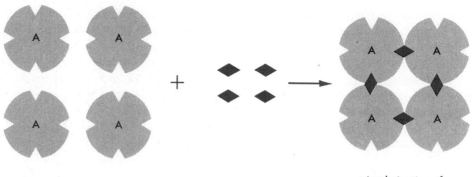

Type A blood   Type B plasma   Agglutination of red corpuscles

35–6 When type A blood is transfused into a patient with type B plasma, the antibodies of the plasma link with the antigens of the blood and cause the donated corpuscles to agglutinate.

into a patient with either type A or type B blood since agglutination would result. Type O red corpuscles contain neither type A nor type B antigens and thus cannot be clumped by any kind of plasma. Therefore, type O blood can be given to people of any type blood. You can think of the corpuscles as not being notched, hence there are no plasma antibodies that fit them. People with type O blood are said to be universal donors.

The most important point to note in establishing compatibility is whether the donor's red corpuscles are clumped by the plasma of the recipient. The effect of the donor's plasma is of no great importance since it is diluted by the recipient's plasma. Suppose a person with type AB blood requires a transfusion. There are no type A or type B antibodies in type AB plasma; hence it will not clump any type of blood. Because he can safely receive blood from any group, a person with AB blood is called a universal recipient.

While whole blood must be used in some transfusions, it has been found in many cases that the use of blood plasma is very effective. During World War II dried plasma was shipped overseas where base hospitals added distilled water to it. The restored plasma saved thousands of lives. The use of blood plasma has one great advantage. Blood matching is not necessary since there are no red corpuscles to agglutinate in the donor's plasma.

THE RH FACTOR. *Rh-positive* individuals have Rh antigens identical with those of the Rhesus monkey. About 85 per cent of the human population is of this type. The remaining 15 per cent is Rh-negative. Rh-negative individuals do not have plasma antibodies that clump Rh-positive corpuscles, but are able to make such antibodies.

The Rh factor is especially important in childbirth. If the unborn child is Rh positive and the mother is Rh negative, the mother's blood may be stimulated to produce Rh antibodies. Carried in the tissue fluid, the antibodies may reach the child's circulation and begin the destruction of its red corpuscles. Severe anemia or death may result. Generally, the first child is not seriously affected, since insufficient antibodies are produced by the mother. However, the danger increases greatly with each successive birth.

Milestones in Biology

Charles Richard Drew
(1904–1950)

ALTHOUGH MAN has studied blood for centuries, only recently has he found ways of preserving it in blood banks. Without blood banks, major surgery is an extreme risk. The techniques for preserving and storing human blood were largely the work of Dr. Charles Drew. Charles Drew had little thought of studying blood when he graduated from Amherst College in 1926. After two years of teaching at Morgan College in Baltimore, he was admitted to McGill Medical School in Montreal, Canada. At McGill, Charles Drew met Dr. John Bettie, a friendly instructor who changed his life. When Bettie lectured about the nature and structure of blood, Drew's mind was aroused. In 1933, Charles Drew was awarded his doctor's degree from McGill.

In 1938, at Presbyterian Hospital in New York City, Dr. Drew met Dr. John Scudder, whose main interest was blood transfusion. Working with Scudder, Drew and his assistants devised ways of separating and refrigerating whole blood. A blood bank was established, and Dr. Drew became its medical director. A technique for separating and drying plasma was developed.

In 1940, Dr. Drew became the medical supervisor of the Plasma Project for Great Britain. In February of 1941, Drew became the director of the American Red Cross Plasma Bank. In May of 1941, the Blood Transfusion Association and the Red Cross combined forces to create a national blood bank with Dr. Drew as the medical director of the combined program.

A controversy arose over the segregation of the blood of Caucasian and Negro donors. When asked to comment on this, Dr. Drew said, "The fact is that test by race does not stand up in the laboratory." Dr. Drew quietly "resigned" because of his conviction and returned to his post as professor of surgery at Howard University. He died in an automobile accident in April, 1950.

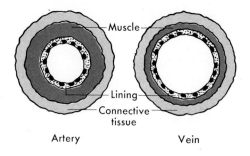

35–7 Cross Sections of Artery and Vein. Note thickness of muscle layer in artery. (Also see Figure 5–11.)

The Blood Vessels

The blood is carried to all parts of the body by a system of branching tubes. The largest of these tubes are those that enter and leave the heart. The smallest are the capillary nets that are microscopic in diameter. Although the *arteries, veins,* and *capillaries* are the principal blood vessels, there are other tubes that carry lymph. These are called lymphatics, or lymph vessels.

ARTERIES. The blood vessels that carry blood away from the heart are arteries. Since the heart acts as a pump and pushes the fluid through the arteries, it exerts pressure upon them. The arteries must retain their flexibility. Otherwise they break, and blood is released into the tissues.

In cross section, an artery wall is seen to consist of three distinct layers. The outside layer consists of tough connective tissues containing many elastic fibers. Beneath this is a layer of smooth muscle cells. These can be contracted to reduce the size of the artery and regulate blood flow. The inside artery layer consists of flat covering cells.

As the main arteries leave the region of the heart, they subdivide into smaller arteries. With each subdivision their diameter becomes smaller. When their diameter begins to approach the width of a hair, they are called *arterioles.*

CAPILLARY NETS. If we inject a liquid rubber solution into the circulatory system of an animal, such as a frog, we can follow the route of the blood very clearly. Suppose we treat an injected organ, such as the kidney, with a chemical that will remove the tissues but will not affect the solidified rubber. When the tissue has been removed, the outlines of the blood vessels provide a definite outline of the organ. This is because the blood vessels completely penetrate every part of the organ.

The branching arteries and arterioles eventually form networks of microscopic blood vessels, the *capillaries.* Capillaries do not have any connective or muscle tissue. They consist only of very thin covering tissue. The plasma can ooze through them into the tissue fluid. Even white corpuscles are able to squeeze through. An occasional red corpuscle also gets through. Generally, the capillary walls are thick enough to keep

35–8 Capillary and Tissue Cells. The capillaries come into close contact with the tissues of the body. Surrounding the tissue cells is the tissue fluid, or lymph.

nearly all of the blood cells confined within them. But smaller chemical molecules penetrate them with ease. It is in the capillary networks that most of the exchange of chemicals between the cells, tissue fluid, and the blood takes place.

So great is the number of capillaries that branch from the arterioles that they greatly slow down the movement of blood. Blood reaching the capillaries is like a swift narrow stream that suddenly enters several hundred channels and slows down. This allows more time for the diffusion of materials to and from the capillary network. Oxygen from the lungs and digested foods from the intestine can pass into the tissue spaces. Carbon dioxide and other wastes can pass from the tissues through the thin capillary wall into the blood.

On the other side of a capillary net the tubes begin to unite to form small veins, the *venules.* Each successive union forms a tube of slightly larger diameter.

VEINS. The blood vessels that return the blood to the heart are called *veins.* They arise from the union of venules. Like the arteries, veins have three layers of tissue in their walls: connective tissue, smooth muscle, and a lining layer. However, the first two layers are much thinner in the vein than in the artery. Materials cannot diffuse through the walls of veins.

Another major difference between arteries and veins is the presence of valves in veins. Let us consider for a moment the flow of blood in the legs. In the arteries of the leg the blood flows downward. The force of gravity helps the downward flow. In the veins, however, the situation is reversed. Gravity pulls the blood downward, opposite to the way the blood flows. Along the walls of the veins there are flaps of connective tissue that are pressed against the vein when the blood flows in one direction. When the blood flows in the opposite direction, however, the flaps are extended,

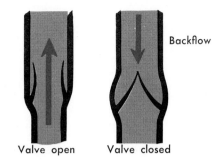

Backflow

Valve open   Valve closed

35–9 Cuplike valves in large veins prevent backflow, especially in the lower body.

acting as valves that do not permit downward flow.

These valves are subjected to the greatest pressure in the legs. Here the weight of the entire column of blood must be supported. For this reason swollen veins are more common in the legs than in other parts of the body. When the valves become inefficient the movement of blood is reduced. When veins become swollen and unsightly, they are sometimes removed by a surgeon.

HARDENING OF THE ARTERIES. All parts of the body undergo change as we grow older. Since the flow of blood in the body is so critical for correct body functioning, changes that occur in the circulatory system are especially important. With age the walls of the arteries become thicker. The increase in thickness results from an accumulation of materials on the inner wall. This narrows the inner diameter and impedes the flow of blood. This general condition is known as *arteriosclerosis.*

One of the commonest materials that accumulates on the inner wall of the arteries is cholesterol, a complex substance closely related to the fats. Frequently, other materials, calcium salts and some fibrous tissue, accumulate around the cholesterol. The result is an obstruction that reduces the volume of blood the artery can carry. A complete shutting off of blood flow in an artery

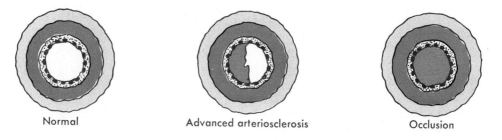

Normal   Advanced arteriosclerosis   Occlusion

35–10 Stages in the Development of Arteriosclerosis. The accumulation of materials on the inner wall of an artery may lead to occlusion, or complete restriction of blood flow.

may cause local swelling. It may cause a heart attack if the artery is one that supplies blood to the heart tissues. It may cause a stroke if the artery supplies part of the brain.

THE LYMPHATICS. Tissue fluid bathes the individual cells and acts as the intermediate fluid between the blood and the tissues. What means are provided for the circula-

35–11 Lymph returns to the blood where the thoracic duct enters a large vein near the heart.

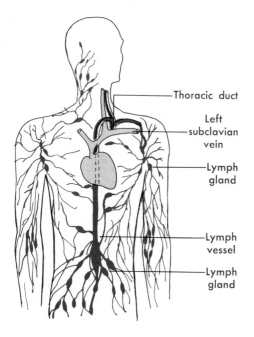

Thoracic duct

Left subclavian vein

Lymph gland

Lymph vessel

Lymph gland

tion of this fluid? What is its relation to the system of closed blood vessels?

Tissue fluid, which resembles blood plasma, originates from the diffusion of the components of plasma through capillary networks. The fluid is called lymph when it is gathered together in lymph capillaries. Eventually the lymph capillaries unite to form larger lymph vessels called lymphatics. Lymphatics are similar to veins, but generally have slightly thinner walls. The system of lymphatics is far more extensive than that of the arteries or veins. As the smaller lymph vessels join together they form larger vessels that transport lymph toward the heart. The largest of these is the thoracic duct. The thoracic duct empties into a large vein just before it enters the heart. The thoracic duct receives lymph from most of the internal organs as well as from the arms and head.

A thorough filtering of the lymph takes place in the numerous lymph glands scattered along the lymphatics. The lymph glands guard the body against the attack of bacteria. The tonsils and adenoids are lymph glands that protect the nose and throat. All lymph glands have the ability to accumulate white blood cells, which can ingest bacteria in large numbers. When infection strikes, one common symptom is swollen lymph glands. The glands are gorged with lymph and bacteria.

The Heart

Slightly larger than a man's fist, the heart has been a symbol of life since ancient times. Yet its function was not understood until Harvey explained its action in the 17th century.

The heart beats more frequently than once every second. A good average is 72 beats per minute. If you multiply this by 60, you have 4320 beats per hour. Now multiply this by 24 hours, then by 365 days. The result is that the heart beats about 38,000,000 times each year. With each beat the heart pumps about a tenth of a quart of blood, so that each day it pumps about 10,000 quarts.

Actually the heart is a dual pump, divided into two distinct halves by a partition, or *septum.* Each half, in turn, is divided into an *atrium,* the part that receives blood from the veins, and a *ventricle,* the part that pumps blood into the arteries. The human heart, then, consists of four chambers—the right and left atria, and the right and left ventricles.

PULMONARY AND SYSTEMIC CIRCULATION. Blood returning from the head, neck, and arms enters the right atrium through the *superior vena cava.* Blood returning from the legs and internal organs enters the right atrium through the *inferior vena cava.* This blood is called *systemic blood,* that is, blood from the entire body. It is a dark red color, rich in carbon dioxide and deficient in oxygen. The right ventricle pumps the systemic blood to the lungs through the *pulmonary artery* and its branches. Once in the lungs the systemic blood releases its carbon dioxide, receives a fresh supply of oxygen, and becomes bright red in color. Blood from the lungs returns to the left atrium through the *pulmonary veins.*

The part of the circulatory system from the heart to the lungs and back again is called the *pulmonary circulation.* When the left ventricle contracts, it forces blood out through the *aorta* (ay-OAR-tuh) to all parts of the body. Some reaches the head and arms, while the remainder goes to the internal organs and the legs. The blood vessels that supply the entire body make up the *systemic circulation.*

VALVES OF THE HEART. Within the heart are valves that control the direction of blood flow. In the right side, the *tricuspid valve* controls the flow from the right atrium into the right ventricle. A similar valve in the left side is called the *mitral valve.* These two sets of valves insure that blood will not be forced back into the atria as the ventricles beat. The valves are held securely in place by strong threads of connective tissue.

At the point where the pulmonary artery leaves the right ventricle there are *semilunar valves.* These valves prevent the blood from returning into the right ventricle after it has contracted and forced the blood into the pulmonary artery. A similar set of valves controls the flow of blood from the left ventricle into the aorta. Damage to any of these valves reduces the regular flow of blood and reduces the heart's efficiency.

If you listen to the beating heart with a stethoscope, you can recognize the characteristic lub-dub, lub-dub sound. The first sound is produced by the closing of the mitral and tricuspid valves and the opening of the semilunar valves in the aorta and pulmonary arteries. The second sound is produced by the closing of the semilunar valves and the opening of the mitral and tricuspid valves. The heart does not beat as a unit. Instead there is a definite sequence of events marked by the following steps:

1. Blood flows into the atria and the ventricles from the veins when the heart is relaxed.

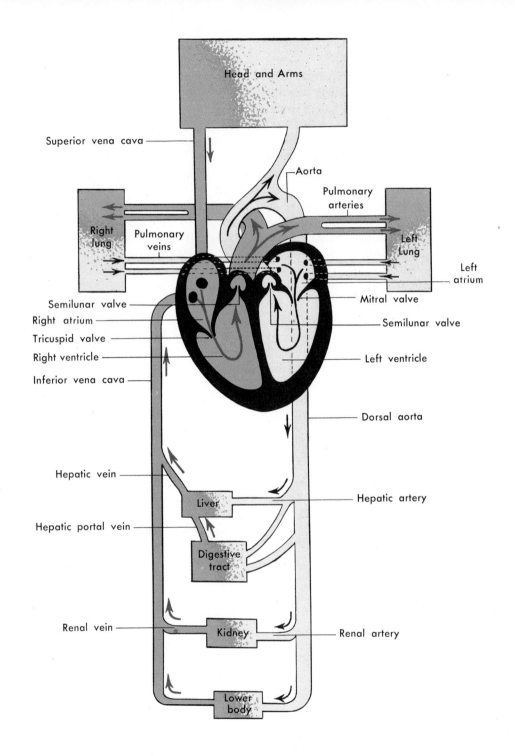

Head and Arms

Superior vena cava

Aorta

Pulmonary arteries

Right lung

Pulmonary veins

Left Lung

Left atrium

Semilunar valve

Mitral valve

Right atrium

Tricuspid valve

Semilunar valve

Right ventricle

Left ventricle

Inferior vena cava

Dorsal aorta

Hepatic vein

Hepatic artery

Liver

Hepatic portal vein

Digestive tract

Renal vein

Kidney

Renal artery

Lower body

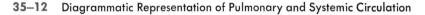

35–12   Diagrammatic Representation of Pulmonary and Systemic Circulation

2. The atria contract and pump more blood into the ventricles.
3. The mitral and tricuspid valves close and the ventricles contract, forcing the blood into the aorta and the pulmonary artery.
4. The semilunar valves close, preventing the blood from returning to the ventricles. The tricuspid and mitral valves open and admit blood to the ventricles.

What controls this orderly procedure that continues throughout life? Apparently, a special tissue, called the *pacemaker,* is responsible. The pacemaker is located in the right atrium where the veins enter. Other similar tissue in the atria and the ventricles is stimulated by the pacemaker to produce the rhythmic series of pulsations that constitute the heartbeat.

The alternate contraction and relaxation of the heart chambers is called *systole* and *diastole.* Since contraction (systole) forces blood forward in the blood vessels, the pressure is greatest at that time. This is called the *systolic blood pressure.* When the heart is relaxed (diastole), blood pressure is at its lowest. This is the *diastolic blood pressure.*

PULSE AND BLOOD PRESSURE. The heartbeat causes a rhythmic expansion of the arteries, seen as a pulsation if the artery is close to the surface of the body. The pulse in the radial artery of the wrist can be felt by placing the fingers along the underside behind the thumb. The pulse rate corresponds with the rate of the heartbeat.

Several factors determine the blood pressure in the arteries. One of these is the force with which the heart beats. Another is the amount of blood in the body. Finally, there is the width of the blood vessel. Extremely high or extremely low blood pressure is usually interpreted as a danger signal by a physician. For this reason, the

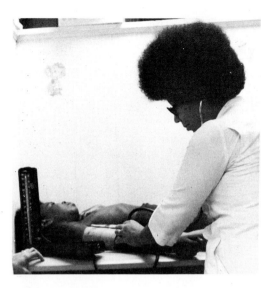

35–13 A doctor measures arterial blood pressure with a sphygmomanometer.

blood pressure determination is part of every general physical examination.

The device used to determine blood pressure is the *sphygmomanometer* (sfig-moe-muh-NAUM-uht-uhr). A hollow rubber cuff is wrapped around the upper arm. The cuff is inflated by air until the pressure it exerts upon the arm stops the flow of blood. This pressure is measured by a mercury column that is part of the apparatus.

CORONARY CIRCULATION. Like all the tissues of the body, the heart muscle must receive a constant supply of nutrients and oxygen. The heart's needs are especially critical. If the heart stops beating, the individual loses consciousness within seconds. Death may occur within minutes.

Two *coronary arteries* branch from the aorta and subdivide on the surface of the heart. The subdivisions enter the heart muscle where they divide again and again to form fine capillary networks. The capillaries deliver a continuous supply of oxygen and nutrients to the muscle cells of the heart. The capillaries remove wastes and

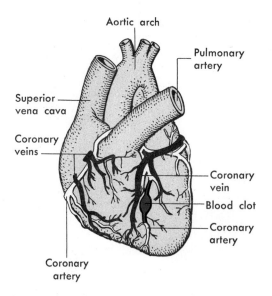

Aortic arch

Pulmonary artery

Superior vena cava

Coronary veins

Coronary vein

Blood clot

Coronary artery

Coronary artery

hardly dreamed of. How could a surgeon operate on the pump without shutting off the supply of life-giving blood? How could the correct oxygen level in the blood be maintained?

With the invention of a heart-lung machine, it became possible for the surgeon to release the heart from its normal activity for hours as the machine continued the work of the heart. The blood receives oxygen as it is rerouted through the machine. Meanwhile, repairs of the septa and valves of the heart can be accomplished.

Improved surgical techniques led to the first attempt to transplant the human heart from one person to another in December, 1967. The surgery was performed by Dr.

35–14 Coronary Heart Disease. When the coronary arteries, which carry nutrients and oxygen to the heart tissues, become blocked or otherwise impaired, the situation is extremely critical. The blood supply may be cut off because of the thickening walls of the coronary arteries, a condition known as coronary sclerosis. Coronary thrombosis occurs when a blood clot forms in a coronary artery. When the obstructing clot has moved to the coronary artery from another part of the body, it is called a coronary embolism.

35–15 Most unsuccessful transplants are due to the body's rejection of foreign matter. The more transplants a man undergoes, however, the less the danger of rejection.

carbon dioxide produced by the metabolism of the heart tissue. Three *coronary veins* are formed by the union of the venules arising from the capillaries. The veins return the blood from the coronary circulation to the right atrium.

The most common cause of heart failure is the closing of a part of the coronary circulation. Usually this occurs with advancing age. Severe chest pains may accompany a sharp reduction in the blood supply to the coronary arteries. This condition is called *angina pectoris*.

HEART SURGERY AND TRANSPLANTS. Not many years ago any attempt to correct structural defects of the heart by surgery was

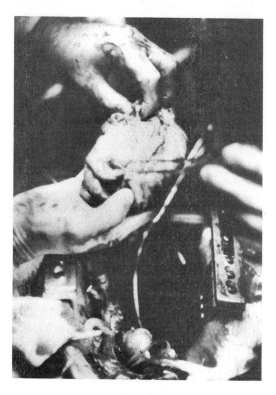

Christian Barnard in Cape Town, South Africa. This first heart transplant patient survived only eighteen days. Since that time, many other heart transplants have been performed in many countries of the world with varying degrees of success. Louis B. Russell received his heart on August 24, 1968, and in August of 1970 he was still teaching school and making five to ten speeches a week.

IMPORTANT POINTS

• Blood is pumped through a closed system of blood vessels by the heart. The principal parts of blood are the plasma and the corpuscles.

• The plasma contains water, mineral salts, digested foods, and proteins. The concentration of the salts is about the same as it is in sea water.

• Red corpuscles are circular discs that contain hemoglobin. Hemoglobin combines with oxygen in the lungs to form oxyhemoglobin. The oxygen is carried in this form to all the cells of the body.

• White corpuscles, which are fewer in number than red corpuscles, are irregular in shape. The principal function of white corpuscles is to ingest bacteria in the blood stream and thus prevent infection.

• A blood clot is formed by a series of chemical changes that finally result in the formation of threads of fibrin. The blood platelets release the chemical thromboplastin, which begins the clotting reaction.

• Blood types are identified by the kind of antigen associated with the red blood corpuscles. The reaction in the plasma between antigens and antibodies of differing blood types causes clumping of the corpuscles.

• The principal blood vessels are the arteries, capillaries, and veins. Arteries carry blood away from the heart. Veins return blood to the heart. Capillaries are minute tubes that connect the arteries to the veins. Lymphatics are vessels that carry lymph, a liquid derived from the tissue fluid that surrounds all cells.

• The heart maintains a continuous blood flow, pumping about 72 times per minute. Half the heart pumps blood to the lungs; half pumps blood to the rest of the body. The coronary circulation supplies blood to the heart muscle tissue; reduction of this blood flow is the commonest cause of heart failure.

REVIEW QUESTIONS

1. How much blood does the average person's body contain?
2. List four substances contained in plasma.
3. Where do the blood corpuscles originate?
4. Why is hemoglobin an important part of the red corpuscle?
5. How is vitamin B_{12} related to anemia?
6. Compare platelets with red corpuscles in size and number.
7. Which part of the blood is associated with antigens in blood typing?
8. List three kinds of blood vessels.
9. List the valves of the heart.
10. What invention has made open-heart surgery possible?

CHECK YOUR UNDERSTANDING

11. Describe a method for determining the blood volume.
12. Compare red corpuscles with white corpuscles in shape, number, and function.
13. List the main chemical steps in the clotting reaction.
14. Why is the effect of the donor's plasma of little importance in a blood transfusion?
15. What is the effect of the capillaries upon the rate of blood flow?
16. What changes occur in the walls of arteries as part of the aging process?
17. What is the relation between the heart sounds and the heart valves?
18. How is blood pressure determined?
19. The blood and tissue fluid have been called the "internal environment" of the body. How do you interpret this?
20. From your knowledge of chemistry, can you think of any reason why it might be appropriate to use geometric forms that fit each other to explain antigen-antibody clumping reactions?

RESEARCH PROJECTS AND REPORTS

1. Obtain information from your school or public library and prepare a report on one of the following topics:

   William Harvey   **Blood Banks**

   Marcello Malpighi   **Heart Transplants**

2. *Making a Red Cell Count:* If you wish to make a standard determination of the number of red corpuscles in a blood sample, you will need a special diluting pipette and a counting chamber. These can be purchased from biological supply houses.

   Sterilize a clean, bright needle by immersing it in 95 per cent alcohol for at least ten minutes before use. Swab the fingertip vigorously with absorbent cotton soaked in alcohol.

   A drop of blood is then obtained by piercing the skin of your finger tip with the sterile needle. The blood is drawn into the diluting pipette exactly to the 0.5 mark, then diluted by drawing in Hayem's solution to the 101 mark. (Hayem's solution is made by dissolving 5 grams sodium sulfate, 1 gram sodium chloride, and 0.5 gram mercuric chloride in 200 cc distilled water.) After shaking and discarding the material in the stem, the pipette is touched to the counting platform where the diluted blood is drawn into the counting chamber by capillarity.

   After several minutes the counting chamber is transferred to the microscope stage and the count is made. The number of red cells in 80 of the tiniest blocks is determined and the mean value per block is calculated. This represents 1/4000 of a cubic millimeter because of the way the counting chamber is made. Multiplying this number by 4000, then by 200 (the dilution factor) gives the number of red corpuscles per cubic millimeter of whole blood.

3. *Blood Typing:* If you want to try your hand at typing blood, you can obtain the necessary equipment from a biological supply house. They will supply you

with the blood plasma antibodies, anti–A and anti–B. If you obtain agglutination with anti–A, but not anti–B, then the sample being tested must be type A blood. Similarly, if anti–B alone causes agglutination, then the sample is type B. If both antibodies cause clumping, then it is type AB. If neither causes clumping, then it is type O.

FURTHER READING

"The Clotting of Fibrinogen." Koloman Laki. *Scientific American,* March, 1962, page 60. Discusses the complicated chemical processes that result in the formation of a blood clot.

"The Heart's Pacemaker." E. F. Adolph. *Scientific American,* March, 1967, page 32. Specialized cells within the heart set the rhythm of its beat. The heart acts largely as an independent organ.

"Surgery for Coronary Disease." Donald B. Effler. *Scientific American,* October, 1968, page 36. Students interested in heart surgery will marvel at the many kinds of heart operations described in this article.

"L-Asparagine and Leukemia." Lloyd Old, Edward Boyse, and H. A. Campbell. *Scientific American,* August, 1968, page 34. Discusses one of the latest means of attacking leukemia by means of an enzyme that destroys a critical amino acid.

The 1969 Britannica Yearbook of Science and the Future. See article on page 174 titled, "New Parts for Old: The Latest Medical Adventure," by John Bergan. Discusses the history of transplant surgery and the modern techniques used by the surgeons.

36

The Lungs, Kidneys, and Skin

THE HUMAN BODY derives its energy from foods, which are its fuels. After foods are digested and absorbed into the blood stream, they are transported to all of the cells by the blood and tissue fluids. Food by itself, however, is not enough. If the food is to be oxidized and to release its energy, it must have oxygen. Oxygen supply is a function of the lungs, which absorb free oxygen from the air to the blood stream. After entering the lungs, oxygen is carried by the blood to the cells.

The metabolic processes that occur in the cells produce many wastes that must be eliminated. These are gathered into the blood and transported to the organs that remove them from the circulation. The kidneys, the skin, and the lungs are organs for waste removal.

The Respiratory System

We know that the energy for life comes from the foods we eat. Nobel prize winner Hans Krebs explained the oxidation of foods as a complex series of chemical reactions. (See pages 114–116.) The Krebs cycle results in the formation of energy rich molecules of ATP (adenosine triphosphate).

These molecules store the energy obtained from foods. The Krebs cycle reactions occur in the mitochondria of the cells. *Respiration* is the release of the stored energy of foods. Each type of food transfers its energy to ATP molecules as the food is gradually changed into a simpler form in the cells of the body. Of fundamental importance to the process of respiration is the oxygen we breathe into our lungs. Man lives at the bottom of a vast ocean of air, the atmosphere that surrounds the earth. About four-fifths of the air is nitrogen and one-fifth is oxygen. Before oxygen can be transported to the cells it must be introduced into the blood stream. This is the function of the respiratory system. The parts of the respiratory system include the nose, the pharynx, the trachea, the bronchi, the lungs, and the diaphragm.

THE NOSE AND PHARYNX. The nose is a combination air-conditioner and heating unit for the air we breathe. The nasal passages are lined with mucous membranes that warm the air and raise its water content. The membranes are very moist and richly supplied with blood vessels. The warmth of the blood creates a steamy condition about the membranes over which the incoming air must pass. The incoming air is thus preheated.

Two other factors help in the air-conditioning process. One is the presence of numerous hairs at the entrance to the nostrils. These act as a crude sieve that strains out large particles of dust and dirt. The second factor is the millions of ciliated cells that make up the mucous membranes. The cilia of these cells beat with a greater force in one direction than the other, forcing dust particles toward the outside of the body. The ciliated cells extend along the entire respiratory tract. Warmed and clean, the air passes into the throat, or *pharynx* (FAHR-inks).

Millions of bacteria are brought into the body by the air we breathe. The moist mucous membranes trap most of these, preventing their entry into the lungs. On either side of the throat lie the lymph glands called the *tonsils*. If the tonsils become enlarged, they tend to block the throat passage to air and food. They protect the throat by consuming bacteria in vast numbers. Sometimes the tonsils become badly infected. In this case the physician usually recommends that they be removed.

TRACHEA AND EPIGLOTTIS. Two tubes run parallel to each other through the neck. One, the esophagus, carries food. The other, which carries air, is the trachea, or windpipe. The top of the trachea is covered by a broad flap of tissue that prevents food from falling into it. This is the epiglottis. As air is inhaled, the epiglottis rises and permits the air to enter the trachea. Sometimes we try to inhale at the same time that we are swallowing food. This leads to violent coughing as the food drops into the windpipe. Coughing is an automatic reaction that keeps the trachea clean.

The trachea must keep a supply of life-giving air coming into the lungs. Coughing removes foreign particles that would interfere with breathing. In the wall of the trachea are numerous rings of cartilage, which prevent it from collapsing. If you press your fingers gently against the top of the trachea in your throat, you can feel the rings of cartilage.

THE BRONCHI AND LUNGS. Located in the extreme upper part of the chest cavity are the lungs. Each is a large, spongy mass of delicate tissue on either side of the heart. Despite their size, each lung weighs little more than a pound. As the trachea leaves the neck and enters the chest it branches into two *bronchi,* one going to each lung. The bronchi in turn subdivide into smaller tubes, the *bronchioles.* The branching continues until the smallest bronchioles are slightly more than the width of a fine needle. Clustered at the end of each bronchiole are about twenty tiny sacs. It is as though each tube had expanded into a little bunch of microscopic grapes. Each sac is an *alveolus,* the functioning unit of the lung.

DIFFUSION IN THE ALVEOLUS. Surrounding each alveolus is a net of capillaries. The arterial end of each capillary is connected to the pulmonary artery. The venous end is connected to the pulmonary vein. Blood coming into the capillary net around the air sac is rich in carbon dioxide but poor in oxygen. As the blood leaves the alveolus the situation is reversed. During the second or two that is required for the blood to pass through the net, the exchange of gases between the blood and the air sac takes place.

The only partitions that separate the blood from the air are the thin wall of the aveolus and the equally thin wall of the capillary. The oxygen and carbon dioxide involved in the exchange consist of very small gas molecules. Furthermore, gas molecules travel at high speeds. For example, the oxygen molecules in the air sac move with a speed of about 950 miles per hour. In a small fraction of a second, millions of

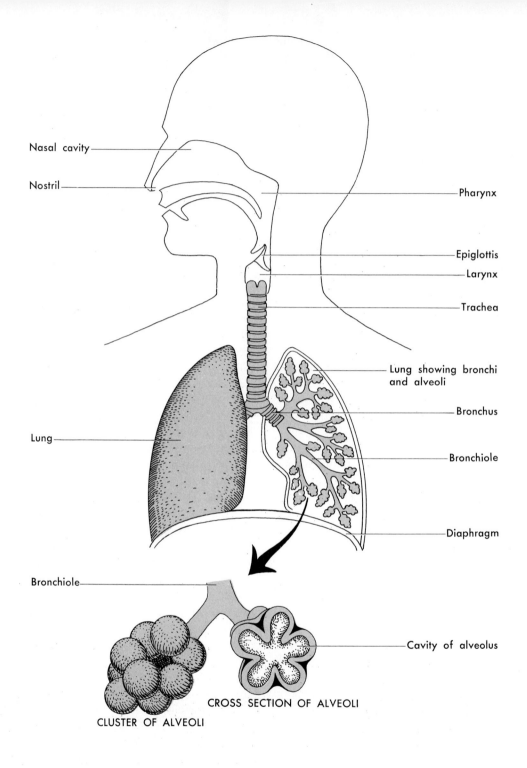

Nasal cavity

Nostril

Pharynx

Epiglottis

Larynx

Trachea

Lung showing bronchi and alveoli

Bronchus

Lung

Bronchiole

Diaphragm

Bronchiole

Cavity of alveolus

CROSS SECTION OF ALVEOLI

CLUSTER OF ALVEOLI

36–1   RESPIRATORY SYSTEM

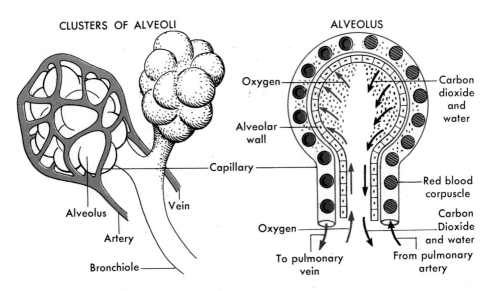

CLUSTERS OF ALVEOLI · ALVEOLUS

Oxygen · Carbon dioxide and water

Alveolar wall

Capillary

Alveolus · Red blood corpuscle

Vein · Carbon Dioxide and water

Artery · Oxygen

Bronchiole · To pulmonary vein · From pulmonary artery

36–2 At left is a bronchiole ending in air sacs. The diagram at the right shows the exchange of gases through the walls of an alveolus and capillary. Oxygen from the air diffuses into the blood, and carbon dioxide diffuses from the blood into the air.

oxygen molecules have darted through the membranes into the blood. There the oxygen combines with the hemoglobin in the red corpuscles to form *oxyhemoglobin*. Meanwhile the carbon dioxide molecules are leaving the plasma of the blood and moving into the air sac, where their concentration is much lower. With each breath the process is repeated. The total effect is to supply the blood with oxygen and to relieve it of carbon dioxide.

DIAPHRAGM, RIBS, AND PLEURA. The breathing movements that draw air into the lungs are brought about by coordination of the ribs and the *diaphragm*. The diaphragm is a muscular layer that extends across the body cavity just below the lungs. Each lung is surrounded by a thin protective membrane, the *pleura*, which keeps it moist and reduces friction between the lung and other internal organs.

As air is inhaled the rib cage is raised and the diaphragm is lowered. The total volume of the pleural cavity is increased.

This creates a low pressure in the pleural cavity area. Then atmospheric pressure forces air into the lungs.

During exhalation the opposite occurs. The diaphragm is raised, and the ribs return to their lower position. This reduces the volume of the lung cavity, increasing the pressure above that of the surrounding air. Then air from the lungs is forced out.

BREATHING CAPACITY AND RATE. If you record the number of times you inhale during a minute, you'll find it's about 16 to 20. This rate goes up if you exercise. Although the normal capacity of the lungs is about 3000 cubic centimeters (about three quarts), only about 500 cubic centimeters of air are taken in with each breath. With strenuous exercise the air taken in may greatly exceed this amount.

What causes the change in breathing rate when we exercise? Experiments show that if the amount of oxygen is gradually reduced while the carbon dioxide remains constant, there is no increase in the rate.

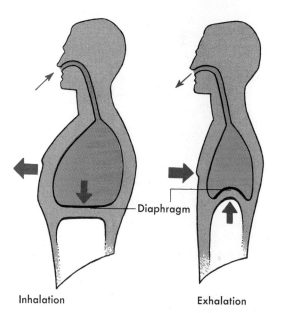

Inhalation   Exhalation

36–3 During inhalation, the diaphragm moves down and the chest cavity expands. This increases the volume of the chest cavity and lowers the air pressure in the lungs. In exhalation, the reverse occurs.

If, on the other hand, the amount of carbon dioxide increases while the oxygen remains constant, the rate goes up markedly. It is the amount of carbon dioxide remaining in the blood that affects the respiratory control center and speeds up breathing. More rapid breathing helps to make up any deficit in oxygen.

RESPIRATORY DISORDERS. The branches of the bronchioles that end in the alveoli are very fine tubes lined with delicate mucous membranes and surrounded with smooth muscle fibers. When irritating materials cause the mucous membranes to secrete mucus too abundantly, the bronchioles become clogged. Breathing becomes very difficult. The circular smooth muscles cut off the tubes almost completely, further complicating the problem. Sometimes an *allergy*, sensitivity to certain kinds of pollen or dust, causes the condition. The term *asthma* is used to describe the condition. The labored breathing of the asthmatic patient indicates the extreme difficulty the lungs are experiencing in obtaining oxygen.

The warm, moist membranes that line the respiratory tract are excellent sites for the growth of bacteria and viruses. Since these tissues are very accessible, respiratory diseases are common. Infections of the throat result in *pharyngitis*, and infections of the bronchi result in *bronchitis*. Both of these are common complaints in the winter. Deeper invasion of the alveoli by pneumococci or tubercle bacilli produce pneumonia and tuberculosis.

THE VOICE BOX OR LARYNX. At the extreme top of the trachea, just beneath the epiglottis, are thick pieces of cartilage that make up the framework of the *larynx*, or voice box. Another name for the larynx is the Adam's apple. Stretched across the top of the larynx at right angles to the direction of the trachea are the *vocal cords*. Varying the tension of these elastic cords changes the pitch of the sounds we utter.

All of the tonal range of the human voice is brought about by the vocal cords in combination with the resonant chambers of the throat and mouth. By raising and lowering the tongue, or opening the mouth wider, the quality of the voice is altered.

The Kidneys

Carbon dioxide is eliminated by the lungs. But what happens to the other waste products of respiration? Water, urea, and uric acid are excreted mainly by the kidneys.

FUNCTIONS OF THE KIDNEYS. The water that composes 70 per cent of the total body weight is derived from two sources: (1) from liquids or foods that we eat and (2) from the oxidation of foods. The main function of the kidneys is to regulate the amount of water in the body. Other organs, such as the skin, the lungs, and the intestine, may aid in water regulation; but the kidneys perform the major part of this function. That is why kidney failure is fatal.

While regulating the body's water content, the kidneys also control and stabilize the composition of blood. Small amounts of mineral salts are excreted that regulate the blood's acid-base balance. The most important of these salts are compounds of sodium and potassium.

Finally, the kidneys excrete the end products of protein metabolism. Urea is the principal dissolved material found in *urine*. Over 30 grams of urea are eliminated daily. Uric acid, creatinine, and ammonia are also excreted by the kidneys in smaller amounts. All are the final products formed by the breakdown of huge protein molecules.

THE KIDNEYS AND BLADDER. The kidneys are situated high on the dorsal wall of the abdomen on either side of the backbone. Each is shaped like a lima bean the size of a man's fist.

The blood supply of the kidneys is especially rich. Two branches from the dorsal aorta, the principal artery of the body, lead directly to the kidneys. Within the kidney the *renal arteries* subdivide into fine capillary nets; they then unite to form venules that are joined into larger *renal veins*. These empty into the vena cava.

The dissected kidney has two fundamental parts: an outer *cortex* and an inner *medulla*. Urine collects in tiny tubes that unite to form larger tubes in the medulla. The larger tubes finally empty into a central portion, or pelvis. A single duct extends from the pelvis of the kidney to the *bladder*. This duct is the *ureter*. The bladder stores the accumulated urine until it is voided through the *urethra*.

The functional units of the kidney are the *nephrons*. They filter water and wastes from the blood. There are about a million nephrons in each cortex. The nephron consists of an intertwined system of capillaries and urinary tubules. At the top of the urinary tubule is a cup, *Bowman's capsule*, which surrounds a capillary net, the *glomerulus*. The twisted tubule is also surrounded by a bed of capillaries before it leads into one of the collecting tubes that lead to the kidney pelvis.

EXTRACTING URINE FROM BLOOD. The glomerulus with its surrounding Bowman's capsule resembles the alveolus of the lung. Here again are a capillary net and a sac in intimate contact. Only thin, membranous walls separate them. It is here that the first filtration of the blood occurs. The filtered material amounts to about 173 quarts per day. Almost two and a half pounds of sodium chloride and about a pound of sodium bicarbonate are also extracted from the blood by the capsules daily. About twelve times each hour the entire blood volume passes through this elaborate blood filtration system.

36–4 Human Kidneys and Bladder

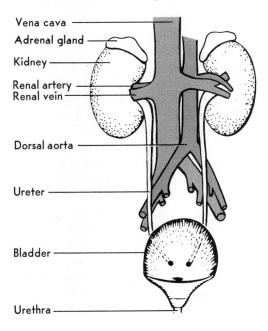

Vena cava
Adrenal gland
Kidney
Renal artery
Renal vein
Dorsal aorta
Ureter
Bladder
Urethra

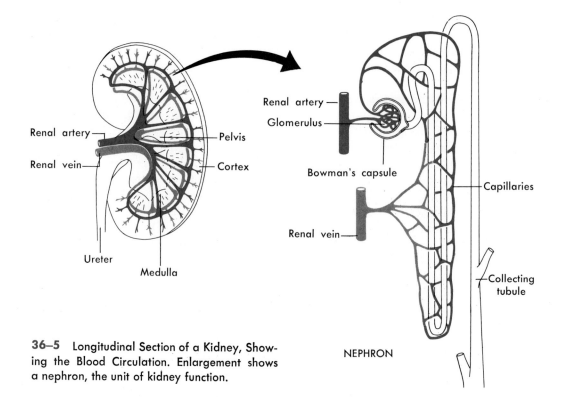

Renal artery
Renal vein
Pelvis
Cortex
Ureter
Medulla

Renal artery
Glomerulus
Bowman's capsule
Renal vein
Capillaries
Collecting tubule

NEPHRON

36–5 Longitudinal Section of a Kidney, Showing the Blood Circulation. Enlargement shows a nephron, the unit of kidney function.

You are probably wondering about the figures just quoted. They seem very high, but nearly all of these materials are reabsorbed as they move along the tubules. They pass out of the tubule and return to the blood in the capillary net that surrounds it. In this way about 171 of the 173 quarts of fluid are reabsorbed. Only one or two quarts remain to be excreted as urine. This is the daily average output.

In the same way, many other materials extracted by the capsules are reabsorbed from the urinary tubules. Less than a third of an ounce of sodium chloride is excreted of the two and one-half pounds originally extracted. Most of the glucose found in urine in the Bowman's capsule is returned to the blood. Only a trace is excreted. Of the pound of sodium bicarbonate that is absorbed daily into the capsule, practically none is retained in the urine. Even the waste product urea is reabsorbed. Less than 50 per cent of the urea originally extracted from the blood is finally excreted.

DIFFUSION AND THE NEPHRON. The normal processes of diffusion are not sufficient to explain the functioning of the kidney nephron. We know that the direction of diffusion is from the place where the molecules are more concentrated to the place where they are less concentrated. Quite the opposite of this occurs when certain substances are reabsorbed in the tubules. The molecules go from a place where they are less concentrated to a place where they are more concentrated. The movement of materials under these circumstances involves complex chemical changes. These changes, in turn, are brought about by enzymes operating in a way that produces an effect totally different from that of diffusion.

URINALYSIS AND KIDNEY FUNCTION. Because of the intimate relation between kidney function and the composition of blood, analysis of a urine sample is part of any complete health check-up. A routine check of the amount of glucose is made. A surplus of glucose may indicate a diabetic condition. Color, albumin, and specific gravity determinations are made and compared with normal samples. Further tests quickly follow if any abnormal constituents, such as blood or pus, are found. Finally, with the microscope, red and white blood cell counts are made and insoluble crystals are identified.

36–6 Diagram of Reabsorption. The filtrate of the glomerulus contains minerals, vitamins, and other substances of value to the body. These substances are recovered by reabsorption from the walls of the tubules into the blood of the surrounding capillaries.

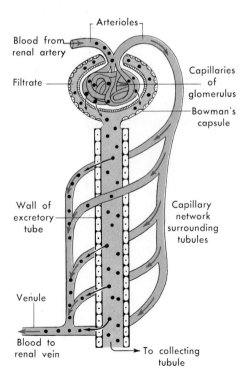

Arterioles

Blood from renal artery

Filtrate

Capillaries of glomerulus

Bowman's capsule

Wall of excretory tube

Capillary network surrounding tubules

Venule

Blood to renal vein

To collecting tubule

When there is some question about proper functioning of the kidneys, more exact quantitative tests can be performed. The rate at which the blood flows through the kidneys can be determined. The rate at which the glomerulus filters the blood can be calculated, using special substances like mannitol or inulin. These are almost completely filtered by the glomerulus and are not reabsorbed. A somewhat similar test provides information about reabsorption in the tubules. With the information thus gathered a more precise determination of kidney disorders can be made.

KIDNEY INJURY AND DISEASE. Injury to the kidneys poses a serious threat to life. Furthermore, the location of the kidneys makes them susceptible to mechanical injury. They are not well protected by bones. In professional boxing, punches in the small of the back, where the kidneys are located, are forbidden.

Disease germs readily find their way to the kidney because of its rich blood supply. If they lodge there they can cause serious damage. Sometimes the poisons, or toxins, formed by germs cause the kidney to function improperly. Diseases such as scarlet fever, diphtheria, and tonsillitis seem to be especially hazardous.

In old age, as a result of arteriosclerosis, the blood flow to the kidneys may be reduced. Impaired blood flow means that less urine is excreted because the filters do not receive enough blood from which to extract it. If the kidneys do not function properly, the blood's wastes are not eliminated. Accumulation of wastes interferes with the metabolism of cells and may cause death.

Some of the substances found in urine are not very soluble in water. Uric acid is one of them. If these substances do not dissolve, they remain as crystals. Small crystals do not cause any hardship. But if they accumulate into larger masses, or *kid-*

ney stones, they may block the kidney tubules, the ureter, or urethra. Then they cause extreme pain. Removal of the stones by surgery may then be necessary.

The Skin

The kidneys and the skin work together in controlling the amount of water retained in the body. Although the kidneys exercise primary control, the skin is an important auxiliary. Even on a day when temperatures are not high, the skin eliminates about a pint of water through perspiration. During very hot weather, the skin may eliminate three quarts of water daily.

Perspiration is not water alone. It is more like a very dilute urine with more than the usual amount of sodium chloride. You may have noticed the salty taste of perspiration. At times you can even see the salt crystals that form when the perspiration evaporates. Urea is also present, but in small amounts. Less than a tenth of the thirty-gram urea

output of the kidneys is eliminated by the skin each day. The skin is thus another organ that helps maintain the proper water, salt, and urea balance within the body. It is subordinate to the kidneys in this respect, however.

Even though the skin may release large quantities of water, it also saves water by providing a waterproof surface over most of the body. This same covering is effective in keeping bacteria, molds, and other infectious agents from entering the tissues. The skin also has hundreds of thousands of sense organs embedded in it. These make us sensitive to heat, cold, pressure, and pain. The skin also helps regulate body temperature by the evaporation of perspiration.

STRUCTURE OF THE SKIN. Human skin consists of two distinct layers, the outer *epidermis* and the inner *dermis*. The epidermis is about the thickness of tissue paper. The dermis is about as thick as cardboard. It is the epidermis that peels off after a severe sunburn.

36–7 Cross Section of the Skin

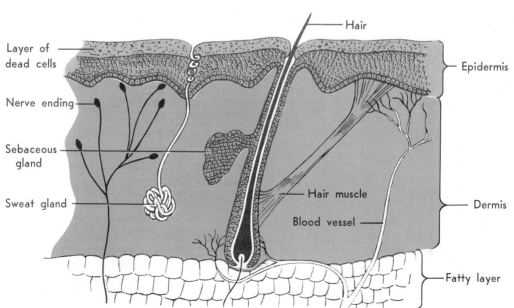

Layer of dead cells

Nerve ending

Sebaceous gland

Sweat gland

Hair

Epidermis

Hair muscle

Blood vessel

Dermis

Fatty layer

The top of the epidermis consists of dead cells that are continually being worn away. As they are removed from the body, other cells from a lower layer of the epidermis replace them.

The deeper layer of the skin, or dermis, contains many nerves and blood vessels. In it can also be found the sweat glands with their twisted ducts, or tubes, leading to the surface. The roots of the hair shafts, enclosed in the *hair follicles,* also lie in the dermis. Near the follicles are the *sebaceous glands.* The oily secretion of these glands keeps the hair and skin flexible. It also prevents excessive absorption or excretion of water over the surface of the body. At the base of the hair shafts are nerves and the muscles that cause the hairs to stand on end.

The skin weighs more than almost any internal organ. Its blood and nerve supply is richer than most other organs. Within its thin layers are more than 2,000,000 sweat glands, 200,000 hair shafts, and 300,000 sebaceous glands. Its sensory system for the detection of cold, heat, pressure, and pain is connected by 49 miles of nerve fibers. If sewed together in one continuous string, the blood vessels of the skin would stretch a distance of 12 miles.

SKIN HYGIENE. The sweat provides a means of losing body heat rapidly. After heavy exercise the skin releases large amounts of perspiration. Athletes often wrap themselves warmly after a contest to prevent this extremely rapid loss of body heat. The release of oil and sweat on the skin sometimes creates a problem. The sticky layer traps bacteria and other microorganisms. In one way this is desirable, for these secretions inhibit their growth. The acidic sweat stops bacterial reproduction. However, in many cases the microorganisms may get beneath the protective layer. The pores of the skin are excellent hiding places. Unless we can rid the skin of these germs, they multiply, and skin blemishes follow.

Washing with warm, soapy water is the best care for the skin. Not only does soap remove the oily layer along with the trapped bacteria, but it removes many of the outer epidermal cells, too. That is why we feel so refreshed after a hot bath or shower. The grimy layer has been removed. The sweat glands have been stimulated to activity and have cleaned themselves.

Care of the skin is particularly important during the teens. Changes in the internal organs, particularly in the glands of internal secretion, make the skin prone to blemishes. It is more important for a person to take care of his skin during his teens than at any other time in his life. He should set up a careful schedule to maintain skin cleanliness and stick to it.

IMPORTANT POINTS

- Respiration is a process in which energy is released within the cells of the body. The energy comes from the foods we eat. The process uses oxygen and results in the formation of energy-rich ATP (adenosine triphosphate).

- The oxygen required by the cells for respiration is transported to them by the blood. The lungs are the organs that introduce oxygen into the blood and remove carbon dioxide from it.

- The functional unit of the lung is the alveolus, or air sac. It is built like a subminiature hollow grape. The oxygen and carbon dioxide diffuse through the walls of the alveolus into and out of the capillary network that surrounds it. Oxyhemoglobin is formed when oxygen combines with hemoglobin in the blood. It is then carried in this form to the cells.

• Most of the products of respiration are removed from the blood by a filtration process in the kidneys. Another function performed by the kidneys is regulating the water content of the body. In so doing, the kidneys control the composition of the blood.

• The nephron is the structural and functional unit of the kidney. The filtrate of the glomeruli contains minerals, vitamins, and other substances of value to the body. These substances are recovered by reabsorption from the kidney tubules. Only one to two quarts are excreted as waste.

• The skin is an auxiliary organ of excretion. In addition to its protective and sensory functions, it excretes more than a pint of water each day under average conditions.

REVIEW QUESTIONS

1. How is the Krebs cycle related to ATP?
2. In what two ways is the air we breathe cleaned?
3. What physical characteristics of the alveolus permit the rapid exchange of gases between the blood and air?
4. How is the breathing rate regulated?
5. List three of the substances formed by the metabolism of proteins.
6. What are the two principal parts of a nephron?
7. Why is the operation of the nephron not considered to be an example of simple diffusion?
8. How are kidney stones formed?
9. List three chemical substances found in perspiration.
10. What two kinds of glands are found in the dermis?

CHECK YOUR UNDERSTANDING

11. List the six parts of the respiratory system.
12. Why may coughing be considered a defense mechanism for the respiratory system?
13. What are the three subdivisions of the trachea?
14. Describe how hemoglobin obtains oxygen in the alveolus.
15. How does the diaphragm regulate the movement of air in and out of the lungs?
16. What events produce the condition known as asthma?
17. Describe the processes of extraction and reabsorption of materials by the kidney nephron.
18. What functions does the skin perform in addition to assisting the kidneys?
19. Why are the kidneys sometimes referred to as the "regulators of our internal environment"?
20. What complications do you see in diffusion in the nephron as contrasted with diffusion in the alveolus?

RESEARCH PROJECTS AND REPORTS

1. Obtain information from your school or public library and prepare a report on one of the following topics:

   Respiration and ATP   **Asthma and Its Causes**

   Kidney Transplants   **Skin and Health**

2. *Lung or Kidney Dissection:* Obtain a pig's lung or kidney from a butcher shop. Locate the structures that are shown in the text. You may want to make some thin sections of the material to study cell structure under the microscope. If latex injecting material is available, you can try injecting the entire tissue mass with it, then eliminating the tissue with a corrosive material. What ideas do you have for accomplishing this?

3. *Ciliated Epithelium:* The beating of the cilia of the epithelial cells of the frog can be observed if a living animal is available. Anesthetize it and obtain scrapings from the roof of the mouth. The blunt end of a scalpel can be used for this purpose. The scrapings are placed in a drop of one per cent salt solution on a slide and gently teased apart. Search for evidence of motion, then switch to high power to view the cells more carefully.

FURTHER READING

Animal Physiology. Knut Schmidt-Neilsen. Prentice-Hall, Inc., Englewood Cliffs, N.J. Excellent accounts of the structure and function of the kidney, page 60, and the lung, page 17.

"The Artificial Kidney." John P. Merrill. *Scientific American,* July, 1961, page 56. Discusses the physiology of the kidney and the machine now used by physicians to treat patients with kidney failure.

"The Lung." Julius H. Comroe, Jr. *Scientific American,* February, 1966, page 57. Discusses the elaborate mechanisms for the control of breathing and regulation of the functioning of the lung.

"The Skin." William Montagna. *Scientific American,* February, 1965, page 56. The skin is really a huge organ that maintains the body temperature besides acting as a shield against attacks on the body.

The Body. Alan E. Nourse and the Editors of LIFE. Time-Life Books, New York, N.Y. Chapter 6 is an excellent account of the lungs and kidneys with pictorial coverage of kidney transplant operations.

37

Nervous Coordination

THE NORMAL ACTIVITY of the body requires the coordination of billions of cells. Throughout a lifetime, the nervous system plays an important role in making the parts of the body work together. Even such simple acts as walking or running require coordination of a high degree. Not only must the muscles work together, but the heartbeat and breathing rate must be adjusted also.

Two distinct phases of coordination can be recognized. The first is concerned with operating the internal organs. The lungs must operate twenty-four hours a day. The heart must beat without failure. The digestive tract must process food. The kidneys must regulate the composition of the blood by eliminating wastes. The second phase is concerned with receiving and interpreting information from outside the body. The eyes receive visual signals, which are then sent to the brain for interpretation. The ear receives sound waves. The sense organs of taste and smell send information about the chemical nature of foods we eat. The information that is received from the various sense organs determines how we react to various stimuli from the outside environment.

The nervous system thus performs two important functions. It regulates the internal environment of the body through its control of the internal organs. The nervous system also responds to the external environment by means of the sense organs and other receptors found on all the external surfaces of the body.

The Sense Organs

The sense organs provide man with a rich variety of information about his environment. The smell of food, the sight of snow-capped mountains, the feel of fine silk, the sound of music, the sharp stab of pain, the coolness of water are impressions obtained from our external environment. Each impression is the result of the ability of a sense organ, or receptor, to respond to certain stimuli. The eyes respond to light. The ears respond to sound. The tongue responds to chemical substances.

Each sense organ may originate what the biologist calls a nerve impulse. These are short bursts of electrochemical energy. The nerve impulses travel along nerve pathways to the brain. There they are interpreted. If the impulse is from the eye, we see. If the impulse is from the ear, we hear. If the pathways are interrupted so that the impulses do not reach the brain, we cannot see or hear. Damage to the optic nerve causes blindness even though the eye is intact.

NATURE OF THE NERVE IMPULSE. Nerve impulses originate as a result of electrical changes that occur within nerve cells. Careful measurements of the resting nerve cell have shown that the inside of the cell is negative with respect to the outside. The potential difference is about .07 volts. When a triggering action occurs at the end of a nerve cell in a sense organ, the potential difference is changed. The inside of the cell now becomes about .04 volts positive with respect to the outside. The action potential has now been reached, and the nerve impulse sweeps down the length of the nerve cell.

A nerve impulse travels from 100 to 450 feet per second in the human body, con-

siderably slower than electricity in a wire. Some biologists have compared the movement of the impulse with the burning of a fuse. As the impulse travels along the nerve cell, the permeability of the cell membrane changes locally. This change in permeability permits sodium ions to rush into the cell, thereby producing the positive pulse that constitutes the action potential. As soon as the impulse has passed, there is a rush of potassium ions outward and the former negative condition of the inside of the cell is restored.

Recordings have been made of nerve impulses to establish their duration. Each impulse is found to last between one- and two-thousandths of a second and is followed by others sometimes as closely as three-thousandths of a second later. When these recordings are changed into sound, the effect is that of an interrupted buzzer.

THE EYE AND VISION. The human eye is often compared to a camera. Light passes

37–1 The Nerve Impulse. As a nerve impulse moves along an axon, positive sodium ions (Na^+) move into the cell at that point. This changes its resting voltage of -70 millivolts to the action potential of $+40$ millivolts. The nerve impulse is really an electrochemical event caused by changes in the membrane's permeability to sodium ions.

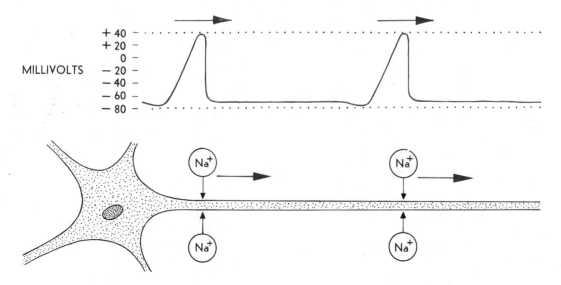

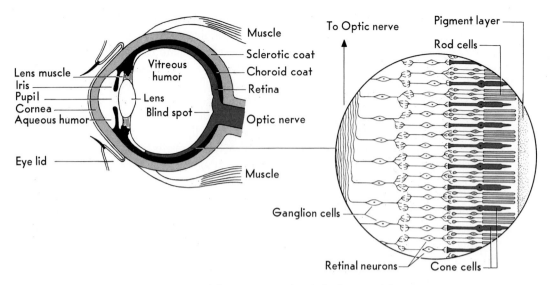

37–2 Structure of the Eye. Inset shows the layers of the retina.

through the *lens* and is focused by it on the sensitive area corresponding to the camera's film. In the eye this area is the *retina*. The opening that admits the light is the *pupil,* which is surrounded by the colored *iris.* The amount of light admitted is controlled by the opening and closing of the iris. The term iris is also used to describe the part of the camera that regulates the size of the lens opening.

The lens of the eye is regulated automatically so that it can focus light from distant objects as well as from close ones. This shift in focusing is accomplished by muscles that alter the thickness of the lens. The lens is flattened to focus distant objects and thickened to focus nearer ones.

Under conditions of bright light the human eye can perceive color. When light becomes dim, objects are seen only in black and white. The reasons for this appear to be associated with the specialized cells found in the retina. Color vision is due to the presence of *cone* cells. Fairly bright light is needed for them to send nerve impulses to the brain. As light be-

comes dimmer other elements in the retina, the *rod* cells, become active. Thus, under conditions of low light intensity, we can see only blacks, grays, and white.

The retina is the innermost of three layers of tissue that make up the eye. The outer white layer is tough connective tissue and is called the *sclerotic coat.* Within it is the dark *choroid coat.* The *cornea* is the transparent section of the sclerotic coat that covers and protects the pupil.

The nerve impulses from the rod and cone cells travel to the brain over the *optic nerve.* There are no rod or cone cells where the optic nerve originates in the eye. This is the blind spot. Around the blind spot there are numerous cone cells. The rod cells are more concentrated around the edge of the retina. That is why it is easier to distinguish objects in dim light by not looking directly at them.

How does the nerve impulse originate in the eye? At least four light-sensitive pigments seem to be responsible. *Rhodopsin,* a red pigment, is found in rod cells. When rhodopsin reacts with light, it is chemically changed and initiates nerve impulses to the brain. These impulses are interpreted as shades of black and white. Three additional pigments found in the cone cells are associated with color vision: one with red, a second with blue, and a third with green. Under ordinary light conditions, it appears that all four pigments send nerve impulses to the brain. There the impulses are interpreted as color. Although these facts seem to indicate that color vision is completely understood, this is not the case. The problem of explaining how a person perceives color still causes debate among biologists.

THE EAR AND HEARING. The ear is the specialized sense organ for responding to sound waves. As sound waves reach the ear, they travel down the *auditory canal* and strike the eardrum, or *tympanic membrane*, causing it to vibrate. The human ear responds to a range of frequencies varying from a low of about 20 cycles per second to a high of 20,000 cycles per second. In early childhood the upper range is high, but decreases with age.

Three tiny bones about the size of these printed letters connect the eardrum to the inner ear. The *malleus,* or hammer, is attached to the eardrum. The *stapes,* or stirrup, is attached to a membrane that forces fluid back and forth in the inner ear. Between the malleus and the stapes is the *incus,* or anvil. The effect of these three bones is to magnify the pressure on the eardrum twenty-two times. This makes it possible for us to hear even a faint whisper.

Within the inner ear is the *cochlea,* a snail-shaped structure, which makes two and one-half coiled turns of diminishing diameter. The cochlea contains a fluid that receives vibrations from the membrane to which the stapes is attached. These vibrations are transmitted to the *organ of Corti,* the hearing organ within the cochlea. Along the organ of Corti there are about 24,000 *hair cells.* The hair cells vary in

37-3 Structure of the Ear. Inset shows inner chambers and organ of Corti.

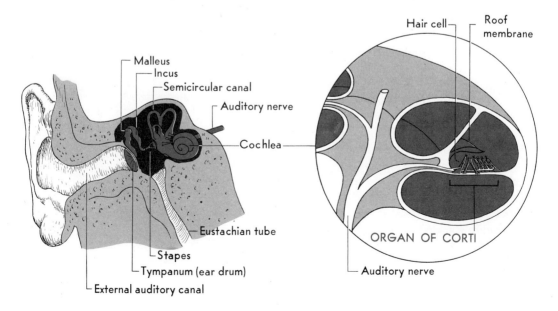

length, somewhat like the strings of a piano. The longest hair cells respond to the lowest pitched sound waves. The shortest hair cells respond to the highest sounds. This is like the piano, for the shortest strings produce the highest sounds. The hair cells near the base of the cochlea respond to the high sounds; when this part of the cochlea is injured the person is deaf to upper tones.

The fluid enclosed in the cochlea is somewhat like lymph. The membrane that closes the entrance to the cochlea is attached to the stirrup. As the stirrup vibrates, the fluid is agitated. The fluid in turn stimulates the hair cells, but only those hair cells of the proper frequency initiate nerve impulses. When these nerve impulses reach the brain, we hear the sound of that frequency.

THE SENSE OF BALANCE. Lying next to the cochlea within the inner ear are three *semicircular canals* and two small sacs which regulate the sense of balance. Special hair cells within the sacs send nerve impulses to the brain when they are stimulated by specks of calcium carbonate that float in the lymph within the sacs. The sacs tell us which way is up or down when our eyes are closed.

The three semicircular canals are tiny loops that also contain lymph. Each loop is arranged at right angles to the others, like the two walls and floor in the corner of a room. The loops also contain hair cells that are stimulated by the movements of the body. The peculiar feeling we experience when starting or stopping quickly in an elevator is due to the stimulation of these hair cells. The movements of a ship or aircraft overstimulate the semicircular canals and cause seasickness or airsickness.

TASTE AND SMELL. High in the upper part of the nose is an area about as big as a postage stamp where the sense organs of smell are located. They react to small groups of molecules borne into the nose by the air. On the tongue and in the back of the mouth are the *taste buds,* which react to small amounts of chemical substances dissolved in water or saliva. Both the *olfactory cells* for detecting odors and the taste buds are stimulated by chemicals. For this reason they are called the chemical senses. These two senses are closely related. What we describe as "taste" is nearly always a combination of odor and taste. When we eat an orange, for example, the odor of the fruit is a major factor in making it "taste" like an orange.

The olfactory cells detect chemicals that vaporize easily. While there seems to be a large variety of odors, certain main kinds can be identified. Among these are fragrant or flowery, burnt, fruity or spicy, and the odor of decay. The olfactory cells are shaped like tiny laboratory flasks. From the tops of the flasks little hairs emerge. When the molecules of an odor strike these hairs, the nerve impulse is dispatched to the brain over the olfactory nerve. The nose is sensitive to small quantities of vaporized substances. A bottle of perfume,

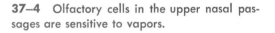

37–4 Olfactory cells in the upper nasal passages are sensitive to vapors.

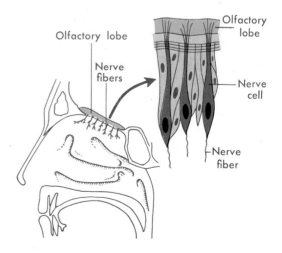

Olfactory lobe

Olfactory lobe

Nerve fibers

Nerve cell

Nerve fiber

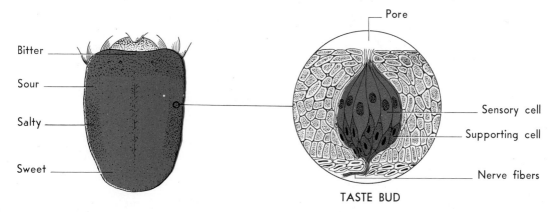

Bitter
Sour
Salty
Sweet

Pore
Sensory cell
Supporting cell
Nerve fibers

TASTE BUD

37–5 Taste buds are scattered all over the tongue, but groups of specialized taste buds are more numerous in certain regions. Inset shows individual taste bud.

for example, need only be opened for the odor to be detected.

The taste buds are found mainly toward the edge of the front, sides, and back of the tongue. Some taste buds are also located on the walls of the pharynx, epiglottis, and larynx. Although all taste buds appear to be the same, they distinguish four primary kinds of taste: sweet, salt, bitter, and sour. Sweetness is detected near the tip of the tongue, sourness and saltiness on each side of it. Bitterness is detected on the back of the tongue.

SENSE ORGANS OF THE SKIN. Embedded in the skin are at least five kinds of receptors. The sense of touch is associated with tiny structures of two main types. One of these is found in the upper layer of the skin and gives us our first impression of touching something. Another type is found in the deeper layer of the skin and responds only when the pressure upon the skin is greater. Each of these two receptors is a small group of cells attached to a nerve ending. Two kinds of receptors in the skin respond to heat and cold. The cold receptors outnumber the heat receptors about ten to one. Scattered throughout the skin are nerve endings that are not associated

with any structure. These are called free nerve endings and are believed to be associated with the experience of pain. The skin is not uniformly sensitive. The head and face, for example, are much more sensitive than the shoulders and back.

Operation of the Nervous System

The fundamental unit of the nervous system is the nerve cell, or *neuron*. Neurons conduct nerve impulses from the sense organs to the spinal cord and to the brain. Neurons also conduct nerve impulses from the brain and spinal cord to the muscles. *Sensory* neurons conduct the nerve impulse away from the sense organs to the spinal cord and brain. *Motor* neurons conduct the nerve impulse away from the spinal cord and brain to the muscles and glands. *Associative* neurons within the brain and spinal cord provide pathways between the sensory neurons and motor neurons.

STRUCTURE OF THE NEURON. The neuron consists of three fundamental parts: the dendrites, the axon, and the cell body. The *dendrites* are branching extensions of the cytoplasm, which carry impulses into the

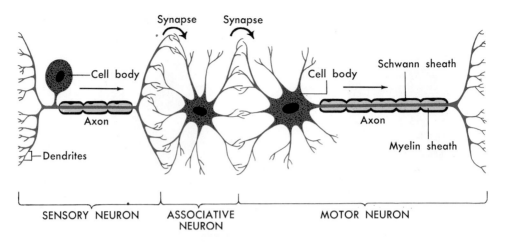

SENSORY NEURON   ASSOCIATIVE   MOTOR NEURON
                     NEURON

37-6 Three types of neurons carry nerve impulses from sensory organs to muscles or glands. Sensory neurons carry impulses to spinal cord or brain where associative neurons relay impulses to motor neurons. Motor neurons carry impulses to muscles or glands.

cell body. They begin the transmission of the nerve impulse along the neuron. The dendrites branch out in all directions. At the other end of the neuron is the *axon*, a long single extension of the neuron. The axon carries the nerve impulse away from the cell body. Located between the dendrites and the axon is the *cell body*. The cell body contains a nucleus and is the center of control of the neuron. It carries on the processes that keep the neuron alive. Despite the many variations in neuron structure, the direction of the nerve impulse is always the same: *from dendrite to axon*. Neurons, unlike wires, conduct in just one direction.

Many axons have a fatty protective sheath called the *myelin sheath*. This sheath acts somewhat like the insulation on a wire and is responsible for the greater speed with which some neurons transmit nerve impulses. Neurons that do not have a myelin sheath transmit the nerve impulse more slowly than those that do. A second coat, the *Schwann sheath,* envelops the myelin covering. All neurons have a

Schwann sheath even though the fatty sheath may be lacking.

NEURONS AND NERVES. The thousands of neurons that extend to and from the spinal cord are bound together like wires in a cable. Nerves are bundles of neurons surrounded and protected by a tough layer of connective tissue. If you dissect a frog, you can easily locate the nerves leading from the spinal cord. When a cross-sectional slice of such a nerve is examined under the microscope, it is seen to be composed of many neurons.

THE SYNAPSE. Nerve cells have no direct connection with one another. Actually a small gap exists between the axon of one neuron and the dendrites of the next one. This gap is called a *synapse*. How, then, does the nerve impulse cross the gap from one neuron to the next?

An older theory of learning assumed that a bridge was constructed across the synapse when we learned something. This led to the interesting conclusion that a learned act was easy to repeat since the synapse had been bridged. Since a pathway was assumed to have been built in the nervous system, it was easy to follow. Such bridges have not been observed, and the theory is not accepted today.

37–7 In diagram A, one nerve ending is releasing a chemical exciter called acetylcholine, but not in sufficient quantity to trigger a response. In diagram B, a second nerve ending is adding more acetylcholine, triggering an impulse. In diagram C, a third nerve ending is releasing an inhibitory chemical that blocks the transmission of the nerve impulse. The nature of this chemical is not yet known. As a rule, more than one exciting impulse is necessary for transmission to occur.

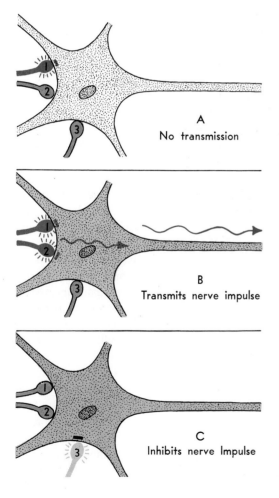

A
No transmission

B
Transmits nerve impulse

C
Inhibits nerve Impulse

The fact that the nerve impulse is not purely electrical, but chemical-electrical in nature, points to a different theory. Scientists have discovered that the ends of some motor nerves secrete a chemical, *acetylcholine*. This chemical crosses the synapse and transmits the nerve impulse. It is probable that a similar chemical event transmits nerve impulses across all synapses. Acetylcholine is formed in small sacs contained at the end of the axon. On the other hand, some motor nerves secrete a chemical that prevents the movement of the nerve impulse across the synapse. Just as the rate of the heartbeat is regulated by two opposing sets of nerve impulses, one accelerating, the other decelerating, so the synapse may be crossed or blocked by competing signals. The chemical that prevents the nerve impulse from crossing the synapse has not yet been identified.

THE REFLEX ARC. What happens when you stick your finger with a pin? Pain receptors in the finger send a nerve impulse along a sensory neuron to the spinal cord. In the spinal cord there are several pathways the impulse may follow. The simplest path is to motor neurons, which conduct the impulse to the muscles of the arm. When the impulse reaches the arm, the muscles contract and the finger is withdrawn. Although this is the simplest pathway the impulse can follow, it is not the usual one.

Generally, a sensory neuron transmits its impulse to an associative neuron, which transmits the impulse to a motor neuron. This route followed by a nerve impulse from receptor to effector is called a *reflex arc*. The smallest number of neurons in a reflex arc is two, a sensory neuron and a motor neuron, but in vertebrates the reflex arc nearly always includes an associative neuron as well. The reflex arc leads to a quick response. Because of its speed, a reflex action protects the body by reducing the possibility of extensive damage.

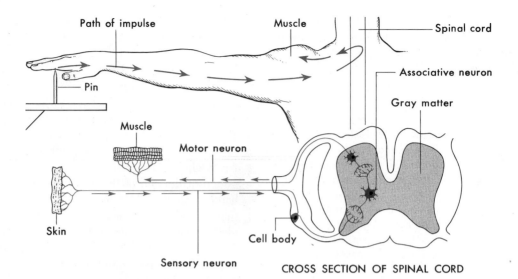

Path of impulse　　Muscle　　Spinal cord

Pin

Associative neuron

Gray matter

Muscle

Motor neuron

Skin

Cell body

Sensory neuron

CROSS SECTION OF SPINAL CORD

37–8 A reflex action, such as jerking the finger away from a pin, is an unlearned or inborn response. It takes place without thinking and does not involve the brain. The quickness of the response depends on a nerve pathway called a reflex arc.

If we return to the previous illustration, sticking your finger with a pin, another important aspect of the nervous system becomes clear. You stick your finger and immediately withdraw your hand. Only afterwards do you become conscious of pain. Not only did the nerve impulse stimulate withdrawal of your hand, but it also stimulated an impulse in a neuron leading to the brain. When this impulse arrived in the brain, you realized you were hurt. It is only when certain parts of the brain are stimulated by nerve impulses that we become conscious of an act.

Sometimes a person may even experience an injury without being aware of it. For instance, it is a common occurrence for an athlete to be cut or scratched during the heat of competition without realizing it until later, when he is away from the fray. A very plausible reason for this may be that so many impulses are reaching the brain at the same time that it does not recognize all of them individually.

The Central Nervous System

The human body has two nervous systems that are closely interrelated. One, the *central nervous system*, is mainly concerned with the conscious acts we perform. The other, the *autonomic nervous system*, controls activities that are not subject to the will. Such activities include the heartbeat, breathing, and the secretion of the glands. The central nervous system consists of the brain, the spinal cord, and the nerves that extend from them to the organs and tissues of the body. All of the "command" decisions are made by the central nervous system. It is the center of memory, will, and conscious thought.

THE SPINAL CORD. The spinal cord is the largest trunk of nerve fibers in the body. Running throughout the entire length of the spinal column, it performs a variety of functions. It is the center of many reflex actions. It relays nerve impulses to the nerve centers of the brain. It receives impulses from the brain and relays them to the muscles and glands. The spinal cord is also directly related to the functioning of the autonomic nerves. Much of the involuntary activity of the body is regulated by the spinal cord.

Along the sides of the spinal cord there are 31 pairs of *spinal nerves.* As each nerve enters the cord, it divides in two. One part enters the dorsal side of the cord; the other enters the ventral side. The dorsal branch of the nerve contains sensory neurons. The cell bodies of the sensory neurons form a clump of nerve tissue called the *spinal ganglion* at the point of entry. The ventral branch of a spinal nerve is composed of motor neurons. The cell bodies of the motor neurons are located within the spinal cord. Each spinal nerve is thus a mixed nerve, containing both sensory and motor neurons. The spinal nerves conduct nerve impulses into the spinal cord from the receptors and conduct nerve impulses away from the cord by means of the motor neurons.

A cross section of the spinal cord reveals a gray core surrounded by white material. The gray matter is shaped like a pair of butterfly wings, but the shape changes with the level at which the cross section is made. The gray color is due to the presence of millions of the cell bodies of neurons that are not covered by a fatty myelin sheath. The white area is made up of neuron fibers that are covered with a myelin sheath.

The nerve cells within the spinal cord are organized into definite tracts. Each tract leads to or from certain parts of the brain. One carries impulses from the pain and temperature receptors. Another carries the impulses of touch. At least two tracts lead downward to the muscles and cause them to contract. The location of the tracts within the cord was discovered by studying patients with spinal injuries.

Three membranes, or *meninges,* surround the spinal cord. The outermost membrane, the *dura mater,* is thick and tough. Closely

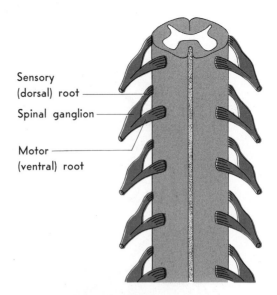

Sensory (dorsal) root

Spinal ganglion

Motor (ventral) root

37–9 A portion of the spinal cord showing the dorsal and ventral branches of several spinal nerves. Dorsal branches contain dendrites of sensory neurons. Ventral branches contain axons of motor neurons.

attached to the spinal cord is the *pia mater,* a delicate fibrous covering. Between the dura mater and the pia mater is the thin *arachnoid membrane.* The spinal fluid is contained between the arachnoid membrane and the pia mater. This fluid acts as a shock absorber and provides mechanical protection for the spinal cord.

THE MEDULLA OBLONGATA. The spinal cord is not uniform in width. It is narrowest at its lowest point and gradually widens as it approaches the brain. As it enters the cranium it widens to form the *medulla oblongata.* This part of the brain is a center for controlling some of the most vital body functions. The automatic regulation of the entire digestive tract is centered in the medulla. The control of breathing and the beating of the heart are also regulated by the medulla. It is responsible as well for the swallowing movements that are associated with eating and drinking.

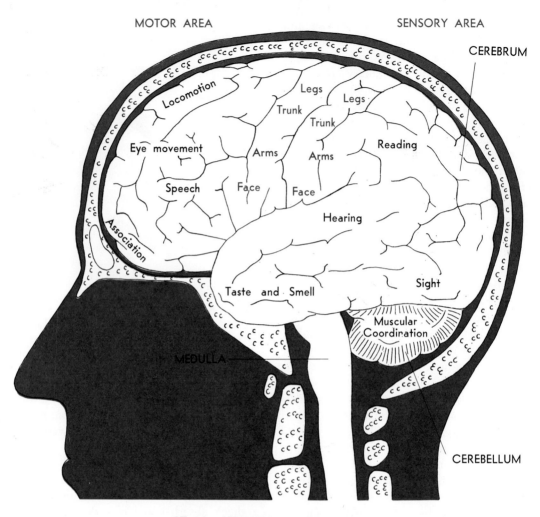

37–10   STRUCTURE OF THE BRAIN

THE CEREBELLUM. Directly above the medulla, where the brain stem enters the cranium, is the part of the brain called the *cerebellum.* Deep ridges cross the cerebellum from side to side. This is part of the brain that is concerned with coordinating muscle movement.

To the cerebellum come nerve impulses from the semicircular canals of the inner ear as well as impulses from the touch receptors. Receptors in the muscles also send impulses to the cerebellum. Impulses from the heat, cold, and pain receptors, from the eye, and from the ear are also sent here. All of the impulses received by the cerebellum are coordinated so that the muscles of the body function in harmony.

Consider what happens when a child is learning to catch a ball. His hand movements are not fast enough at first to intercept the ball. The eyes relay information about the moving ball, but his arm and hand muscles do not react quickly enough for the catch to be made. With practice, however, the necessary adjustments are made and catching becomes automatic. The cerebellum brings about the quick coordination that is necessary. Nerve impulses in the spinal tract leading to the cerebellum travel at high speed, about 450 feet per second. The cerebellum is like a computer routing incoming messages to the muscles so that they make just the right corrections in order to work together smoothly.

THE CEREBRUM. The largest part of the brain, occupying most of the cranium, is the *cerebrum*. Its surface is marked by deep ridges, or convolutions. The cerebrum consists of distinct right and left halves, the cerebral hemispheres are extensions of the bridge of nerve tissue in their centers. The cerebral hemispheres are extensions of the brain stem that have grown in a semicircle up and backward in the cranium, much like a ram's horn.

Like the spinal cord, the entire brain is encased by three protective membranes, the dura mater, the arachnoid membrane, and the pia mater. These membranes, or meninges, are continuous with those of the spinal cord. The cerebrospinal fluid, which circulates between the arachnoid membrane and the pia mater, is contained within the meninges in somewhat the same manner as water in a cellophane sac. The cerebrospinal fluid is similar to lymph and is secreted by cells located deep within the hollow areas of the cerebrum.

THE CEREBRAL CORTEX. The outer portion of the cerebrum, the *cortex*, consists of billions of neurons arranged in six distinct layers. The cortex receives sensory impulses relayed to it from a lower center in the brain stem. The parts of the cortex are interconnected by associative neurons. Motor impulses are also sent from the cortex to other parts of the body.

The cerebral cortex is believed to be the center of all perception, memory, and will. Thus, all of the so-called higher thought

processes come under its control. All voluntary muscle control is regulated by this part. of the brain. The cerebral cortex has enabled man to develop a written and spoken language, thus raising him above the level of other animals.

Specific functional areas of the cortex have been identified as a result of studying the case histories of patients who have suffered brain injury. One area is concerned with vision, another with hearing, and still another with the sense of smell. Most of these localized functions have been confirmed by direct stimulation during brain surgery.

Parts of the brain other than the cortex have been explored in a different manner. James Olds of the University of Michigan embedded slender probes of fine silver wire deep into the brain stem of rats. With these probes he was able to discover "pleasure centers" in the rat brains. Another scientist, Walter J. Freeman of the University of California, embedded as many as eighteen delicate probes in the brain of a cat without causing any apparent injury to the animal. Similar experiments done with monkeys have given biologists more information about the functions of the brain.

LEARNING AND MEMORY. When a child touches a hot stove he quickly withdraws his hand and experiences pain. In the future he will probably remember the experience and not touch the stove. In some way that scientists do not understand, experience can be stored in the cells of the cerebral cortex. This is memory.

Stored impressions are very closely associated with the areas of the cortex that receive the original impulses. Identification of objects we see is performed by areas of the cerebral cortex close to the visual area. Similar identification areas border the auditory area of the cortex. Yet the identification of an object may involve different types of sensations. Recognizing a rose, for example, means identifying its color, odor, thorns, and leaves. The memories stored in different parts of the cortex are somehow correlated.

Dr. Wilder Penfield of McGill University, Montreal, stimulated part of the cerebral cortex of 39 epileptic patients during brain surgery. He found that his patients recalled certain experiences during stimulation. He found, too, that what they recalled depended upon the area of the cortex that was stimulated.

BRAIN WAVES. The human brain is a center of electrochemical activity because of the great number of nerve impulses traveling through it. The first recordings of the electrical activity of the brain were made by Hans Berger, a German psychiatrist, in 1924. Instruments called *electroencephalographs* (ee-lek-tro-en-SEF-uh-lo-grafs) record the brain's electrical activity by picking up impulses from electrodes that are attached to a patient's head. On the recording, or electroencephalogram (EEG), the impulses appear as wavy lines; hence, they have been referred to as "brain waves." Most of the record is difficult to interpret because the significance of changes in brain wave patterns is not understood. However, with instruments such as the electroencephalograph, progress toward understanding the complex activities of the brain is being made.

Brain wave recordings have provided some interesting information. The wave patterns of an infant are not the same as those of an adult. Waking patterns are different from sleeping patterns. Different regions of the cortex provide different types of wave patterns. The patterns are different under stimulation, such as light, than when resting. But most important, the brain waves of persons suffering from certain brain disorders, such as epilepsy, are different from the brain waves of a normal person.

The Autonomic Nervous System

Most body functions do not come under the control of the will. We are not aware that the heart is beating unless we listen with a stethoscope or press our fingertips to the wrist to feel the pulse. The digestive tract continues its rhythmic contractions without conscious effort on our part. Yet numerous nerves carry nerve impulses to the internal organs to regulate their functions. The autonomic nervous system is composed of all of these nerves that keep the unconscious activities of the body operating. Autonomous means "self governing."

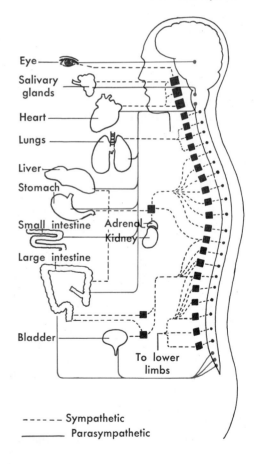

37–11   The Autonomic Nervous System

Eye
Salivary glands
Heart
Lungs
Liver
Stomach
Small intestine   Adrenal
Kidney
Large intestine

Bladder
To lower limbs

- - - - - Sympathetic
———— Parasympathetic

The internal organs govern themselves in the sense that they are not controlled by our will. The autonomic nervous system is subdivided into the *sympathetic* division and the *parasympathetic* division.

SYMPATHETIC NERVES. The origins of many of the nerves that send impulses to the internal organs are found in clumps of nerve tissue that lie on either side of the spinal column. These clumps are the *sympathetic ganglia.* They contain the cell bodies of the nerves that form the sympathetic division of the autonomic system. Twenty-six pairs of these ganglia extend from the base of the spine to the base of the skull. All the ganglia are connected by nerves that run lengthwise along the sides of the spinal column. The ganglia are also connected directly to the spinal cord by means of the spinal nerves.

Nerves leading from the ganglia carry impulses to the glands and internal organs. In the head the nerves extend to the muscles that control the thickness of the lens of the eye, to the tear glands, and to the salivary glands. Other sympathetic nerves lead to the epiglottis, lungs, heart, blood vessels, stomach, intestines, kidneys, bladder, and reproductive organs.

PARASYMPATHETIC NERVES. Some of the autonomic nerves are not connected to the sympathetic ganglia. Four of these *parasympathetic nerves* have their origins in the cranium. The most important member of this cranial group is the *vagus,* a nerve that supplies the heart and many other internal organs. The other cranial nerves of the autonomic system supply nerve impulses to the ciliary muscle of the eye, to the tear glands, and to the salivary glands. The remaining parasympathetic nerves are located in the pelvic region, where three of them fuse to form the *pelvic nerve.* Branches of the pelvic nerve extend to the lower colon, the bladder, and the reproductive organs.

Many of the internal organs receive nerve endings from both the sympathetic and parasympathetic divisions of the autonomic system. When this occurs, dual control over the organ is exercised by the two divisions. One division accelerates the action of the organ; the other division retards the action. This is somewhat like the accelerator and brake of an automobile.

CONTROL OF THE HEARTBEAT. Several nerves of the sympathetic division lead to the heart and accelerate the heartbeat. Three branches of the vagus nerve also lead to the heart, but they retard the heartbeat. The opposing sets of nerve impulses originate in a center within the medulla oblongata. When the impulses reach the heart, they affect the *pacemaker,* the special tissue that is the local center of control over the heart's rate.

Regulation of the heartbeat is also brought about by sensory nerve fibers in the vena cava, the principal vein, as well as the aorta and the carotid arteries. The sensory fibers act as flowmeters, sending the heartbeat center information about the rate of blood flow in these blood vessels. Impulses from the vena cava become acceleration pulses. Impulses from the arteries become braking pulses.

IMPORTANT POINTS

• The nervous system coordinates the activities of the internal organs and provides us with information about our environment. Sense organs originate nerve impulses that the brain interprets as sound, touch, or light depending upon the area of the brain that receives them.

- The eye sends nerve impulses to the brain as the result of the action of light upon light-sensitive pigments in the rod cells and cone cells.

- The ear responds to sound waves. Vibrations move the eardrum and are transmitted to the inner ear. The hair cells in the organ of Corti send nerve impulses to the brain. Semicircular canals in the inner ear also control the sense of balance.

- Taste and smell are the chemical senses. Chemicals stimulate the taste buds of the mouth and throat and the olfactory cells of the nose.

- Receptors in the skin identify pressure, temperature, and pain.

- The operation of the nervous system depends upon the transmission of nerve impulses by nerve cells. The reflex arc demonstrates a simple method of operation and consists of a sensory neuron, an associative neuron, and a motor neuron.

- The central nervous system consists of the brain and spinal cord, and the nerves that lead from these organs to other organs of the body.

- The spinal cord is a relay trunk of nerve tissue that brings nerve impulses to and from the higher nerve centers in the brain. It is also a center of reflex action. The medulla oblongata is the extension of the spinal cord into the brain and regulates internal body functions. The cerebellum is a small part of the brain that coordinates body movements.

- The cerebrum is the center of memory, conscious thought, and will. Special areas of the cerebral cortex have been identified with sight, hearing, and smell. Cerebral electrical activity has been studied by analyzing brain wave patterns.

- The autonomic nervous system regulates the involuntary activities of the internal organs. It consists of two divisions, the sympathetic and the parasympathetic. Nerves from these two divisions often supply the same organ and are antagonistic in their action, one accelerating an organ's action, the other retarding it.

REVIEW QUESTIONS

1. How are sense organs related to nerve impulses?
2. How is the human eye adapted for close and distant vision?
3. List the three bones that transmit sound waves to the inner ear.
4. How is the ear concerned with the sense of balance?
5. List the four primary kinds of taste sensation.
6. In what direction does a nerve impulse travel along a neuron?
7. Under what circumstance does a reflex act become conscious?
8. How have the functional areas of the cerebral cortex been identified?
9. What is the significance of studying brain waves?
10. Explain why the autonomic nervous system is so called.

CHECK YOUR UNDERSTANDING

11. Under what electrical condition is the action potential of a nerve cell reached?
12. Make a comparison of the eye and camera, labelling corresponding parts.
13. Describe the main kinds of receptors in the skin.
14. What are the three main parts of the reflex arc?

15. Describe the method of conduction of the nerve impulse across the synapse.
16. List the main parts of the central nervous system and describe the functions of each part.
17. Compare the functions of the central and autonomic nervous systems.
18. Describe the dual system of controls that regulates the heartbeat.
19. Why might the sense of smell be considered a more effective adaptation for protection than the sense of taste?
20. Many biologists believe that the autonomic nervous system evolved before the higher centers. What reasons might support this belief?
21. How might you explain the speed of the nerve impulses that supply the cerebellum as an adaptive advantage?

RESEARCH PROJECTS AND REPORTS

1. Obtain information from your school or public library and prepare a report on one of the following topics:

Meningitis	**Electroencephalograms**
Epilepsy and Its Treatment	**Brain Research**

2. *Nerve Stimulation:* Insert a thin copper wire into the tendon of Achilles of an anesthetized frog and run it to the positive terminal of several dry cells connected in series. Carefully dissect the sciatic nerve in the thigh by removing the skin and probing for it. When you have located it, touch the negative lead from the dry cells to it and note the result.

3. *Taste and Smell:* Prepare a series of chopped foods and juices to test your friends' sense of taste. One suggestion is chopped apple and pear; another, orange and tangerine juice. Blindfold a volunteer, then insert plugs of absorbent cotton in the nose. Explain that you want to try to discover whether we actually taste or smell foods to identify them. Now try the apple by giving just a small amount on the tongue. Next, sample the pear. In a similar way, test the orange juice, then the tangerine.

FURTHER READING

"The Functional Organization of the Brain." A. R. Luria. *Scientific American,* March, 1970, page 66. The study of brain injuries provides clues that lead biologists to understand how the normal brain functions.

"The Split Brain in Man." Michael S. Gazzaniga. *Scientific American,* August, 1967, page 24. Experiments indicate that the human brain can act as two separate brains, each cerebral hemisphere acting separately.

"The Nerve Axon." Peter F. Baker. *Scientific American,* March, 1966, page 74. Discusses experiments with the giant axon of the squid that help us understand the way in which nerves operate.

"Retinal Processing of Visual Images." Charles R. Michael. *Scientific American,* May, 1969, page 105. The complicated manner in which the brain operates is examined by considering the way the eye processes information it receives.

38

The Endocrine Glands and Human Behavior

THE CELLS of the human body live within the fluids that surround them. Like the Ameba, the body cells can survive only as long as the surrounding fluids are suitable for life and growth. Changing the composition of the fluids produces changes in the cells. For example, if we increase the concentration of salt in an ameba culture to a high enough level, all of the animals die. The introduction of small amounts of other chemicals produces other effects.

A delicate chemical balance in the body maintains normal coordination. The balance can be disturbed easily. Furthermore, the nervous system is affected in many ways by body fluids. Therein lies the key that may unlock the secrets of mental illness.

The Ductless Glands

When you studied the digestive system, you read about the liver and its secretion, bile. A duct, or tube, carries the bile to the small intestine where it acts upon fats. Similarly, the sweat glands in the skin have ducts that lead the sweat to the sur-

face of the body. There are certain glands, however, that do not have ducts. They are called *endocrine glands*.

HORMONES. The secretions of the endocrine glands are called *hormones*. Hormones are absorbed into the blood stream and are carried to all parts of the body. Thus, the endocrine glands are sometimes called the "glands of internal secretion."

Just as the nervous system coordinates activities of the body by means of nerve impulses, so the endocrine glands coordinate certain activities. The hormones are the agents that perform this function. Fright, for example, causes certain hormones to be released into the blood. The mouth feels dry, the face feels drained of blood, and the muscles tense. Each of these is a reaction similar to a nervous reaction.

THYROID GLAND. People vary in the "drive" with which they tackle a job. There may be many causes for such behavior. One cause is associated with the *thyroid gland,* located at the base of the voice box, or larynx. The secretions of the thyroid gland set the pace of the body's general rate of activity. When too much of its

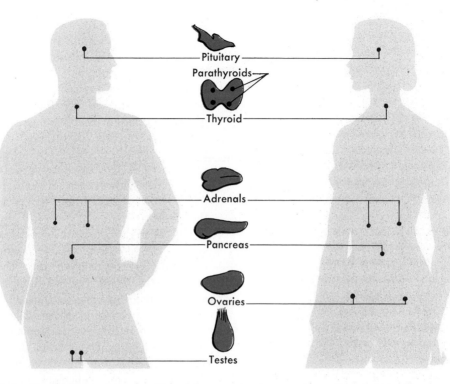

38–1 The Endocrine System. The endocrine glands are also called ductless glands or glands of internal secretion. The hormones they secrete diffuse directly into the blood.

secretion, *thyroxine,* is poured into the blood, the person becomes excitable and irritable. When too little is secreted, the person becomes dull and inactive. The production of thyroxine depends upon the presence of very small amounts of iodine in the diet. In the normal person the concentration of iodine in the blood is only about six parts in 100 million.

A swollen condition of the throat known as *goiter* results when the thyroid gland becomes enlarged. Fish and other sea foods are rich sources of iodine and prevent goiter. The addition of small amounts of potassium iodide to ordinary table salt has been very effective in reducing goiter. Scientists estimate that the average person needs only 15 billionths of an ounce of iodine in the diet each day.

The coordinating action of thyroxine is well shown in the condition known as *cretinism.* Cretinism results from too little thyroid activity in infancy. The infant does not grow normally. The teeth and bones do not form properly. Mental development is not normal, and permanent damage to the brain may result. A prompt dosage of thyroid extract is usually quite helpful.

Overactivity of the thyroid gland produces many symptoms that are the result of increased activity of the cells. The person feels warmer and is generally uncomfortable in a normally heated room. The appetite increases. There is less energy to perform usual work because energy is used up too quickly. The heart rate is higher. The person complains of being nervous and excitable all the time.

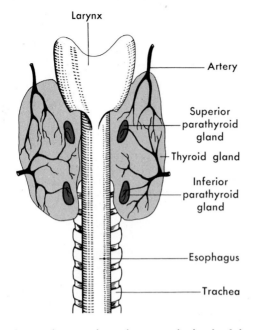

Larynx
Artery
Superior parathyroid gland
Thyroid gland
Inferior parathyroid gland
Esophagus
Trachea

38–2 The parathyroids are on the back of the thyroid, two on each lobe.

A special hormone from the pituitary is responsible for this action. It has been found that removal of the pituitary gland causes the thyroid to shrink.

PARATHYROID GLANDS. Attached to the back of the thyroid are four *parathyroid glands* no larger than pinheads. In the early days of thyroid surgery, the parathyroids were sometimes removed along with parts of the thyroid. Severe muscle spasms resulted. It was later shown that the spasms were caused by removal of the parathyroids.

The secretion of the parathyroids is known as *parathormone*. It is important in regulating the calcium and phosphorus levels in the blood. Both of these elements are essential for bone and muscle formation. The lowering of blood calcium produces severe muscle contraction and twitchings. The joints of the body flex in such a way that little control is possible. When there is a severe deficiency of parathormone, death results. The presence of an excessive amount of the hormone causes calcium to be withdrawn from the bones. This results in a weakening of the entire skeletal system.

What sets the pace at which the thyroid operates? At the base of the brain lies a small gland that exerts control over many body processes. This gland is called the *pituitary*. The pituitary regulates the thyroid.

38–3 Interspersed among the enzyme-secreting cells of the pancreas are areas of insulin-secreting cells called islets of Langerhans after the man who first described them.

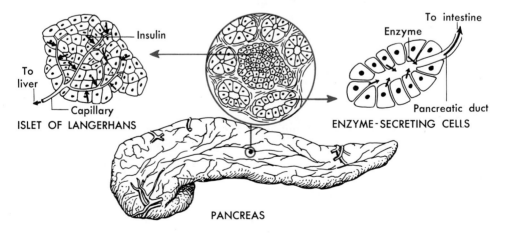

Insulin
To liver
Capillary
ISLET OF LANGERHANS

To intestine
Enzyme
Pancreatic duct
ENZYME-SECRETING CELLS

PANCREAS

THE PANCREAS. Some glands have an endocrine function in addition to their other function. Such a gland is the *pancreas*. Besides making digestive enzymes, the pancreas manufactures the hormone *insulin*. Scattered among the tissues of the pancreas are special areas called the *islets of Langerhans*. Insulin is produced by the cells of the islets of Langerhans.

Insulin is closely linked with the use of glucose by the cells of the body. The amount of sugar maintained in the blood is kept at a constant level in the normal person. When the level is lowered, the liver releases part of its store of glycogen. When the blood sugar is too high, excess glucose is changed back into glycogen and stored in the liver. Insulin regulates the entry of blood sugar into the cells. When insulin is lacking, the sugar has difficulty getting through the cell membrane into the cell where it is to be used. In some way the insulin molecule seems to provide a way for the sugar to enter.

Only one or two milligrams of insulin, about the size of the tiniest pinch of salt, are enough to keep the sugar metabolism normal each day. But, without it, the sugar content of the blood rises. The patient suffering insulin deficiency may become unconscious, and even death may result. This condition is known as *diabetes*.

In 1922, Frederick G. Banting and his associates at the University of Toronto succeeded in extracting material from the pancreas that was successful in treating diabetes. Since that time, the insulin molecule has been identified as a huge protein. Insulin is now extracted from the pancreas of many animals to treat diabetics. Cattle and sheep are the commonest sources. The extract must be injected directly into the blood stream. This led to the search for a drug that could be taken by mouth. One such drug is widely used to stimulate the production of insulin by the pancreas. Al-

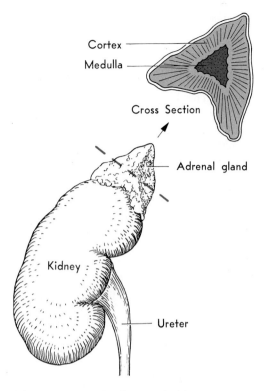

38-4 Sectioned Adrenal, Showing Cortex and Medulla. The adrenals are located on top of each kidney.

though the drug is not a substitute for that hormone, it has proved effective in many cases.

ADRENAL GLANDS. The *adrenal glands* are located at the upper end of each kidney. Like the kidney, each adrenal gland consists of an outer cortex and an inner medulla. The two zones of the gland produce different hormones.

The hormone of the medulla is called *adrenalin*, or epinephrine. It has sometimes been called the hormone of rage or anger. When adrenalin is released in large quantities, the effects of those emotions are experienced. The heart pounds furiously. The mouth and throat become dry. The stomach and intestinal tract seem as though tied in knots. The skin becomes pale. The muscles are tense. Actually, all of these developments are preparations the body is making for combat. The blood supply is withdrawn from the internal organs and skin and diverted to the large muscles. The blood sugar level rises and more fuel becomes available for muscle contraction.

Practically all of these effects can be achieved by general stimulation of the sympathetic nerves. The effect of adrenalin is perhaps the best illustration of the close relation that exists between the nervous organization of the body and the chemical coordinators.

Not until the 1920's was it known that the adrenal glands produced other hormones in the cortex. Great difficulty has been experienced in trying to isolate them and identify specific functions. One, *cortisone,* is effective in treating arthritis. Others seem to be related to the absorption and use of proteins. Still others seem to control the amount of potassium and sodium in the blood.

Another example of the interplay between the endocrine glands is the control exerted by the pituitary gland over the adrenal cortex. A secretion from the anterior lobe of the pituitary called ACTH stimulates the adrenal cortex. ACTH is shorthand for *adrenocorticotrophic hormone.* When ACTH is not secreted in sufficient amounts, the cortex of the adrenal gland shrinks in size and does not function properly.

THE GONADS. The hormones of the *gonads,* or sex glands, are responsible for the onset and development of the secondary sex characteristics.

Scattered among the tissues of the *testes,* or male sex glands, are specialized cells responsible for the formation of *testosterone* (tes-toss-tuh-rone), the principal male hormone. It is one of several male hormones called *androgens.* The increasing level of testosterone and other androgens in the blood as the boy approaches young manhood produces male characteristics. The voice deepens. The beard develops. The growth rate quickens and body muscles become tougher.

The corresponding hormones that produce the female characteristics are called *estrogens.* They are secreted by the ovaries. The higher voice and characteristic contours of a woman's body are associated with estrogens, as are the development of the breasts and the establishment of the menstrual cycle.

It is interesting to note that both male and female hormones are present in both sexes. The relative amounts of each determine sex differences. The varying degrees of "maleness" or "femaleness" displayed by different persons depend somewhat upon the relative ratios of the sex hormones. A more detailed discussion of sex hormones will be presented in Chapter 39.

THE PITUITARY GLAND. The pituitary gland is sometimes called the master gland because it controls the secretions of many of the other endocrines. We have already noted this in the case of the thyroid and the adrenal cortex. The pituitary gland also exerts control over the sex glands, the mammary glands, certain functions of the kidneys, the diameter of arterioles, and general body growth.

The pituitary is about the size of a bean. It is attached to a section of the brain called the *hypothalamus* at the base of the cerebrum. At this point in the body the nervous system and the endocrine glands have their closest contact. Some biologists believe that the hypothalamus secretes much of the material that is later modified by the posterior lobe of the pituitary. The functions of these two structures are very closely related.

The earliest recognition of the importance of the pituitary occurred when it

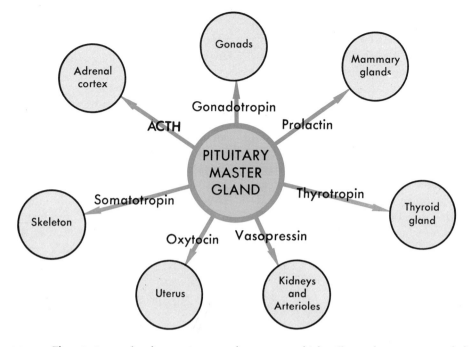

38–5 The pituitary gland secretes many hormones, which affect other organs and the ductless glands. For this reason it is often referred to as the "master gland."

was associated with abnormal growth. Case histories of giants and dwarfs have been linked with too much or too little secretion of a growth hormone from the anterior portion of the pituitary gland. The growth hormone regulates the length of the bones of the body during the normal growth period. The giants and dwarfs of the circus are usually the result of pituitary excess or deficiency. After maturity has been reached, the same hormone stimulates the bones to grow wider and thicker. Oversecretion of this growth hormone in adults produces very coarse-featured individuals. The condition is especially noticeable in the bones of the hands, cheeks, and jaw.

During adolescence the pituitary releases hormones that begin the process of sexual maturation. Before these *gonadotropins* (go-nad-uh-TROP-inz) are released, the testes do not produce sperm cells, nor do the ovaries produce egg cells. Without gonadotropins, the gonads do not produce the sex hormones that cause the development of secondary sex characteristics.

The pituitary produces two other hormones related to the reproductive process. At the time of birth, contractions of the uterus force the young along the birth canal. These contractions are begun by the release of a hormone, *oxytocin,* formed in the posterior lobe of the pituitary. Later, when the infant is nursed, milk production is started by the hormone *prolactin.* This is made by the anterior portion of the pituitary.

Several other functions are performed by hormones from the pituitary's posterior lobe. One of these is the control of the amount of urine excreted by the kidneys. Another function is the control of the diameter of the smallest arteries. The latter restricts the flow of blood to certain parts of the body.

HORMONE IMBALANCE. The failure of certain endocrine glands to function properly results in severe disturbances. The diabetic patient may lapse into unconsciousness when insulin is not available in the blood stream. Low amounts of thyroxine produce a dull individual. High amounts of the same hormone produce a high-strung, excitable person. Failure of the pituitary gland may affect body growth and interfere with the maturing of the sex organs and reproductive functions. The hormones are like pieces of a huge jigsaw puzzle. Trying to explain their interactions is like trying to put a puzzle together when you are not certain you have all the pieces.

Chemistry and Behavior

Why are some people so calm while others seem continually disturbed? Why are some people so enthusiastic while others rarely become enthusiastic about anything? What is wrong with the person who must be confined to a mental hospital?

The search for answers to such questions provides some of the most exciting episodes in man's attempt to understand himself. When dealing with many phases of the body's activity, we are dealing with complex chemical systems. The endocrine glands pointed the way, and research has provided some interesting facts.

HALLUCINATIONS AND LSD. One day in the year 1943, Albert Hofmann, a Swiss biochemist, had a most unusual experience. He was working with a chemical derived from a fungus that grows on rye. He sniffed the tiniest bit of it. Soon he was not himself. His hands began to feel as though they were floating away. He saw little brightly colored blobs. He was experiencing what psychologists call *hallucinations,* or sensations with no external cause. These are the kinds of sensations that some mentally disturbed patients describe. In Hof-

mann's case, however, there was a difference. He had produced the hallucinations with a substance called LSD, an abbreviation for *lysergic acid diethylamide.*

The use of certain substances to produce hallucinations was nothing new. The Mexican Indians have used a derivative of the cactus *Lophophora* for many years. This substance, *mescaline,* produces hallucinations of color and sound. Other people have used the deadly Amanita mushroom in very small amounts to produce somewhat the same results. But it was the size of the dosage in Hofmann's case that was most interesting. If such small amounts of chemicals could produce these effects, was it not possible that here was an insight into mental disturbances that should be investigated? The unusual chemical LSD has been tried on many normal people. With it, much information about the reactions of the mentally disturbed has been gathered.

DRUGS AND MENTAL ILLNESS. You have probably had the experience of trying to explain some disagreement to a relative or friend. The reactions that are common may be either indifference or strong objection. In either case you have a real problem. You cannot explain something to a person who refuses to talk with you. Nor can you explain anything if he talks so much that you are not heard.

Now imagine that this situation is made more intense. The person to whom you speak is either in a rage or says nothing by word or gesture. These extremes are two of the conditions observed in many mentally disturbed patients. Before anything can be done to help them, the doctor must try to communicate with them.

In India a tea has been made from the leaves of the snakeroot plant (Rauwolfia) for centuries. It was a household remedy used for many purposes. Biochemists have extracted a substance from the plant that has remarkable properties. Called *reserpine,* the extract was found to calm mentally disturbed patients. With reserpine, the patients were able to talk about their condition. Unfortunate victims of mental illness who had not been able to talk coherently for years were helped by the drug. They could now discuss their problems with trained specialists.

The discovery of reserpine led to investigations of its chemical structure. Might not other similar compounds have the same effect? Many other such tranquilizing drugs are now manufactured. These drugs are not cures, but they have helped us understand how a person's behavior is determined. Tiny amounts of chemical agents have a profound effect upon the nervous system. What, then, is the relation between these chemicals and the brain?

THE ACTIVATING CENTER. In the upper part of the brain stem is an area that seems critical in regulating consciousness. This part of the brain, about as big as your little finger, is called the activating center. Discovered in 1949 by H. W. Magoun and Giuseppe Moruzzi at Northwestern University, the activating center controls the activity of the cerebral cortex. These two biologists found that a cat could be aroused from sleep when an electric current was sent into the activating center through small electrodes implanted in the cat's brain stem. Recordings of the brain waves in the cortex of the cat showed the effect of stimulating the center. The waves changed from a pattern indicating sleep to one indicating wakefulness.

The effect of sleep-producing drugs upon the brain has been investigated. The drugs seem to block nerve impulses from the activating center to the brain, thus inducing sleep. The opposite effect is achieved when stimulants are administered. Then, the conduction of nerve impulses is increased. The effect of drugs upon the activating center has led biochemists to believe that this center may be the portion of the brain mainly concerned with mental health. One theory holds that mental disease is caused by faulty chemistry in the brain stem.

SEROTONIN. In 1946, a substance was discovered in the blood that has a powerful effect upon the blood and its circulation. *Serotonin* causes the contraction of certain smooth muscles. It has been found in lower animals such as the clam and octopus. Even the lowly jellyfish seems to be able to sting its prey with small amounts of serotonin injected from stinging capsules in the tentacles.

How does this chemical affect human behavior? Although biochemists are not sure, they think that it is related in some way to mental illness. Large amounts of it are found in the brain. Normal people have some means of releasing just the right amount of it so that their mental processes function well.

Chemists worked out the molecular structure of the serotonin molecule. Then it was made in the laboratory. Next, it was compared with other chemicals. The serotonin molecule proved to be closely related to the LSD that gave the Swiss chemist Hofmann his strange hallucinations. The next step was to compare the action of LSD and serotonin with each other. Did they perform the same functions, or were they opposite in effect?

BALANCE AND IMBALANCE. In practically all of the body's processes there is the problem of control or balance. The secretion of thyroxine is a good example of the problem of balance. A high thyroxine level in the blood makes the person nervous and excitable. A low level makes the person dull and withdrawn. May not the same reasoning apply to the chemistry of the brain? And may not mental illness, like many other illnesses, be due to a chemical imbalance in the nervous system?

The effect of serotonin is to slow down brain activity when small amounts are administered. The effect of LSD is quite the opposite. LSD stimulates brain activity. These discoveries hold the hope that some forms of mental illness may find a chemical solution.

The "medicines for the mind" can be broadly classified into two large groups. One group, like reserpine, tranquilizes the patient. The other group, like LSD, stimulates the patient. Physicians who have used such drugs have reported success in relieving extreme depression and excitability.

Behavior and Mental Health

The behavior of the infant is the starting point for all of the child's future reactions. Through the years of infancy and early childhood he learns many things. At birth, however, he already has certain abilities. He can cry, sneeze, and cough. He can kick his legs about and cling firmly to your finger. He can nurse from the breast of the mother. Many creatures learn many things, but none has the mental capacity of the human infant.

THE CONDITIONED REFLEX. In 1904, the Russian physiologist Ivan Pavlov conducted a series of experiments that have had a profound influence upon our understanding of how we learn. Pavlov knew that he could stimulate the flow of saliva in a dog's mouth by giving it food or even by showing it food. On the other hand, he also knew that ringing a bell did not make saliva flow. What would happen if he rang a bell each time he presented the food?

He set up an experiment to seek the answer. He had a special harness built for the dog. A careful bit of surgery was performed

38–6 Diagrammatic Representation of the Stages of Pavlov's Conditioning Experiment

Dog salivates at sight of food.

Dog does not salivate at sound of bell.

1.

2.

Dog salivates at sight of food.
Bell is rung.

After a number of trials, dog salivates at sound of bell alone.

3.

4.

Milestones in Biology

Ivan Pavlov
(1849–1936)

ONE of the most fundamental questions asked by the psychologist is, "How do we learn?" Scientists have no complete answer to this question. One important key to the learning process is thought to be the "conditioned reflex," a type of behavior discovered by Ivan Pavlov. In his famous experiment, Pavlov found that dogs presented with food while a bell was rung would eventually salivate at the sound of the bell alone. Thus a learned response (to a bell) was substituted for an inborn response (to food). This discovery marked a milestone in the study of psychology because learning could be seen as a physiological process.

The discoverer of the conditioned reflex was born in Ryazan, a small town in central Russia. As a young man he attended a religious seminary but soon found that he was more interested in science than in his other studies. He transferred to the University of Petersburg (now Leningrad) where he studied the life sciences. Later he attended the Military Medical Academy and was graduated a doctor in 1879.

The young Doctor Pavlov became a staff member of an important medical clinic, but he devoted more time to research than he did to medical practice. His main field of interest was digestion, especially the way in which digestive glands produced their secretions. In 1904, he was awarded a Nobel prize in physiology.

Acclaimed throughout the world as an outstanding scientist, and past fifty, Pavlov began a new field of investigation: the physiology of the nervous system. Most scientists consider this work even more important than his work in digestion. His discovery that learned behavior is built upon inborn responses encouraged many other scientists to study this important field in psychology.

upon the animal to connect a drainage tube to one of the salivary glands. The saliva could then be measured. The dog could not see the experimenters and be distracted by them. Furthermore, the work was done in a soundproof room. Each time the dog was presented with food, a bell was rung. After a number of trials the bell was rung without food being presented, and the saliva began to flow. Thus the ringing of a bell, seemingly in no way related to the flow of saliva, was able to produce it. The dog had been conditioned by the experimenter. Its salivation in response to the bell was called a *conditioned reflex.*

TRIAL AND ERROR. Perhaps the most basic of all the ways we learn is the method of trial and error. If you have watched a *Paramecium* ensnared by a mass of tangled cotton threads, you know what the method is. It bumps a thread, backs off, redirects itself, and tries again. This is repeated many times, but always in a new direction.

Isn't this a fundamental way of solving a problem? The child that does not want to eat a certain food may try a number of things. He may turn away, whimper, scream, kick, or stamp. Even at the highest levels of human activity the trial and error method is valuable.

MOTIVATION. What makes us do the things we do? Why do we seek certain things and avoid others? The most basic motives are those that aim to satisfy certain needs of the body. We need food and water to live. Civilized man also requires clothing and shelter. In a primitive society, hunting, fishing, preparing food, making clothing, and building shelters occupy most of the time.

Even among primitive tribes, social motives govern behavior. Children seek the approval of parents and relatives. Men and women seek the approval of the opposite sex that leads to courtship and marriage. Young adults conform to custom so that the elders approve.

In general, our behavior is the result of basic needs we seek to satisfy. One group of needs deals with our survival. A second group deals with our social relations, our

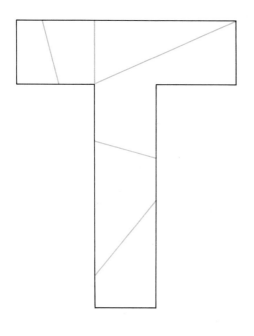

38–7 **Trial and Error Learning.** Prepare a number of pieces of cardboard that, when fitted together, form the letter T as shown. Place the pieces in an envelope. Give the envelope to a classmate and ask him to fit the pieces to form the letter T. He will make a number of trials before he succeeds in fitting the pieces together correctly. Note the number of trials and the time for each trial. Use a stop watch or a watch with sweep second hand. Repeat with other students. For each student construct a bar graph, plotting the number of trials and the time for each trial. Do your results provide evidence that learning has taken place?

38–8 Pavlov's experiments with conditioned reflexes focused attention on how behavior may be changed by combinations of stimuli. A hunting dog, for example, is "conditioned" to carry birds without harming them. In training, the dog carries an artificial bird containing pins. If he chews the bird, pain results. He eventually carries over this learned impression when retrieving real birds. This is known as learned (conditioned) behavior resulting from experience with painful stimuli.

need for the approval of our family, our friends, our community.

What happens when we seek the goals that will satisfy the needs we have just identified? In many cases we run into problems that result from competition with others.

Consider this situation. Joe is a candidate for the football team. He weighs about 180, but is only five feet eight and inclined to be fat, rather than muscular. He's a little slow, as well. Many of the other candidates are just as heavy, faster, and more muscular. Joe has problems, but he's strongly motivated and perhaps he'll make the team.

Mary likes the people the cheerleaders associate with. She wants to be a cheerleader. So do a lot of other girls. But Mary is an expert baton twirler. She is also popular and attractive. Her qualities present problems to her competitors, not to her.

Many things affect our getting what we want. Many of them are the physical and

38–9 Competition with others occurs not only in game situations but also in making the team.

mental qualities with which we are born. The boy who cannot run fast is not going to become a champion sprinter. Yet, he may have the rugged physical qualities of an excellent center on the football squad. As a sprinter, he's a failure. As a center, he's a success. You can think of many such illustrations. Much of our life is spent groping for those activities in which we can find some measure of success. To worry over insurmountable obstacles that we cannot change is to react unintelligently. We are helped or hindered by our physical makeup, depending upon our aims. Making the most of what we have is the only intelligent thing to do.

MENTAL HEALTH. Many people believe that sudden, unexpected problems are the causes of mental illness. While this may be true in some cases, it is not true in all. For instance, most soldiers return to their homes without any serious mental scars of battle. Most people are able to recover from even severe misfortune rather quickly. There is an elastic, resilient quality to the person in good mental health that enables him to cope with disaster. We are able to identify many of the characteristics of such a person. The following are some of them:

1. He understands his strengths and weaknesses. He has realistically evaluated his capacities.
2. He can recognize the limitations placed upon him by his surroundings and has decided to make the most of them.
3. He has set reasonable goals for himself and strives hard to attain them.
4. He enlists the assistance and cooperation of other people. He also aids them, in turn, to achieve their ambitions.
5. He works hard, but he also plays hard. He has developed hobbies that he enjoys.

6. He has a sense of humor. He can laugh when the joke's on him.

NEUROSES AND PSYCHOSES. A physician who is especially trained to treat mental illness is called a psychiatrist. Generally, the psychiatrist classifies his patients in two extremely broad categories. In the first category, he places those who suffer from relatively mild forms of mental disturbance. These patients are called *neurotics* (new-ROT-icks). Their illness is described as a *neurosis.* In the second group are those patients whose disturbance is very severe, the *psychotics* (sigh-COT-icks). Their condition is described as a *psychosis.*

The neurotic individual is much closer to normal than is the psychotic. He is easier to understand. He yields to treatment more readily. Yet, there are aspects of his behavior that are quite unusual and therefore puzzling. For instance, if you are called on to make a speech in front of the student assembly, your heart probably pounds and your mouth becomes dry. Your stomach tightens. But soon you gather your thoughts and begin to speak. The ordeal is over and you return to normal. Not so the neurotic! Indeed, cases have been known where loss of voice has occurred not for a moment, but for weeks.

The psychotic person is so far removed from normal behavior that he is not held legally responsible for his acts. There is no logic or reason in his actions. He has no sense of social responsibility. His imaginings are completely real to him, but have no connection with reality. He is God. He is a billionaire. He has a built-in radio set that enables him to hear the thoughts of anyone. He is surrounded by evil persons sent to kill him. He laughs or cries for no apparent reason. He sings in an unintelligible way. Often his speech is completely disorganized, a jumble of meaningless words.

Drugs, Alcohol, and Tobacco

What happens to the person who cannot find satisfaction in the ordinary activities of life? The answer is that he seeks substitutes in other ways. Estimates place the number of drug addicts in the United States above 100,000. The number of chronic alcoholics is over four million. Battered by a world that seems hostile to them, unable to solve the ordinary problems of living, these people have chosen drug addiction or alcoholism as their solution. It is not a good one.

DRUGS. Opium has been used in the Orient for centuries. It is smoked or chewed. Derived from the flower of the poppy, it has a long history of use in medicine, for it deadens pain and produces sleep. *Morphine* and *heroin* are two of the several other medicines that have been extracted from it. Opium and its products are habit forming. Furthermore, they must be taken in increasing amounts in order to produce the same effects. Each dose builds up within the body a craving for more. A stage is finally reached where the pleasant feeling the drug produced originally is no longer felt. If the addict attempts to stop at this point, severe digestive disorders follow, as well as excessive perspiration, chills, and fever.

Marihuana is a narcotic obtained from the flowers of the hemp plant, *Cannabis sativa*. Sometimes it is called loco weed or, in some countries, hashish. Marihuana is called "pot" by its users. In its early stages, the drug produces a feeling of confusion, a sense of being apart from oneself. In some cases, the drug produces a state of intense rage. Acts of violence are then common.

Some drugs have been used quite commonly in medicinal preparations for many years. Since some of them are habit forming, it is clear that protection should be provided

38–10   Marihuana Plant

for the consumer who is unaware of this fact. One of the duties of the Federal Food and Drug Administration is to enforce the provisions of the law that deal with prescription drugs. All of the habit-forming drugs are sold under carefully regulated conditions. Many may be prescribed only by a physician.

ALCOHOL. The use of fermented beverages is almost as ancient as man, going back to very primitive societies. Every nation has its alcoholic drink made from a variety of materials—grains, potatoes, crushed fruit, even the juice of the cactus plant. In each case, yeasts from the air act upon the sugars in the material and change them into alcohol.

Although it is not used for that purpose, alcohol is a food. It is oxidized in the body and provides energy. However, many other foods provide as much or more energy without the harmful effects alcohol produces.

Alcohol changes the normal activity of certain body organs. In small amounts it acts as a stimulant. The circulatory rate increases. The person apparently becomes more alert and talkative. In larger doses, however, the effect is depressing. Alcohol acts upon the brain and reduces its efficiency. Reactions are slower. Judgment is impaired. Even though there is a feeling of greater efficiency, tests show that quite the opposite is true. This can be especially dangerous in driving an automobile. It leads the driver to take chances at a time when he is poorly equipped to do so.

There is little direct evidence that alcohol alone has a harmful effect on the body organs when it is taken over a long period of time. The conditions popularly associated with the drinker are also found in non-drinkers and are due to causes other than alcohol. Alcohol does, however, irritate liver

tissue, often making it more susceptible to cirrhosis. Many conditions often linked with alcoholism seem to be due, not to the alcohol, but to the malnutrition associated with alcoholism. Still, through the years, the excessive use of alcohol indirectly manifests its damage. Mental function is reduced. Malnutrition leads to vitamin deficiencies and poor liver function. Resistance to disease declines and there is a shortened life span.

THE PROBLEM OF ALCOHOLISM. As long ago as 1778, Thomas Trotter, a student at the University of Edinburgh, described drunkenness as a disease. Since then the idea has grown that alcoholism, the continued excessive use of alcohol, is, in fact, a disease. A number of the states now pay sickness disability benefits to medically proved, compulsive drinkers who cannot work.

Studies have revealed that there are over four million alcoholics in this country. Investigations into the cause of alcoholism have centered about the possibility that there is some physiological defect that produces it. These have not been very successful so far. On the other hand, the idea persists that most heavy drinkers acquire that habit because alcohol helps to relieve their tensions and fears. But then the solution is worse than the problem, for it results in mental collapse and destruction of personality.

Because of the theory that alcoholism is caused by some fault in the metabolism of the alcoholic, both vitamins and hormones have been tried as treatments. They have not had much success, however. Various substances have been added to beverages that make those beverages unpleasant to take. At least one drug, called *Antabuse*, has been used with some success. Taken beforehand, the drug reacts with the alcohol and produces a feeling of nausea.

SMOKING AND HEALTH. Americans smoke cigarettes in alarmingly large numbers.

38–11 It has been estimated that more than three per cent of all American workers are alcoholics—over four million workers, with a ratio of about five men to one woman.

THE COSTS OF ALCOHOLISM

ACCIDENTS

MEDICAL & MENTAL HOSPITALS

WAGES LOST IN INDUSTRY

Accidents, Absences, and Turnover

Alcoholism

$1 BILLION

$½ BILLION

WELFARE COSTS

COURT & JAIL EXPENDITURES

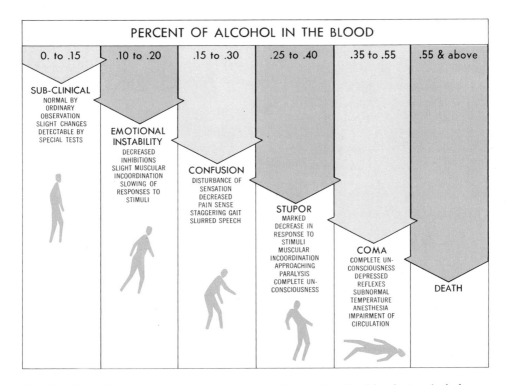

PERCENT OF ALCOHOL IN THE BLOOD

| 0. to .15 | .10 to .20 | .15 to .30 | .25 to .40 | .35 to .55 | .55 & above |

SUB-CLINICAL
NORMAL BY
ORDINARY
OBSERVATION
SLIGHT CHANGES
DETECTABLE BY
SPECIAL TESTS

EMOTIONAL
INSTABILITY
DECREASED
INHIBITIONS
SLIGHT MUSCULAR
INCOORDINATION
SLOWING OF
RESPONSES TO
STIMULI

CONFUSION
DISTURBANCE OF
SENSATION
DECREASED
PAIN SENSE
STAGGERING GAIT
SLURRED SPEECH

STUPOR
MARKED
DECREASE IN
RESPONSE TO
STIMULI
MUSCULAR
INCOORDINATION
APPROACHING
PARALYSIS
COMPLETE UN-
CONSCIOUSNESS

COMA
COMPLETE UN-
CONSCIOUSNESS
DEPRESSED
REFLEXES
SUBNORMAL
TEMPERATURE
ANESTHESIA
IMPAIRMENT OF
CIRCULATION

DEATH

38–12   The effect of increasing concentration of alcohol in the blood. An alcohol concentration of 100 milligrams of alcohol per 100 milliliters of blood is said to be a concentration of 0.1 per cent. Four bottles of beer may produce this result.

The per capita consumption of cigarettes is about 4300 per year. This figure is based on population age 18 and over. What makes the figure alarming is that cigarette tobacco contains a powerful poison, *nicotine*. Fortunately, not all of the nicotine is inhaled and absorbed into the blood; otherwise death would result.

Nicotine exerts a powerful effect upon the digestive tract. Some beginning smokers have discovered this, much to their sorrow. It causes a feeling of nausea and may produce vomiting. It may also produce intestinal cramps and diarrhea. Yet, after the smoking habit becomes established, tolerance to nicotine increases. These effects disappear, and smoking is said to be a relaxing habit.

Chemical analysis of tobacco smoke has shown that it contains many compounds besides nicotine in very small amounts. The number of compounds has been estimated to be as high as 300. Tobacco smoke is a mixture of gases and tiny droplets. As much as 50 per cent of the inhaled smoke may be retained in the lungs, the proportion vaying with the smoker. Cigarettes are smoked with deeper inhalation than pipes or cigars. About 16 of the compounds found in tobacco smoke have been proved to produce cancer in laboratory animals, such as rabbits and mice. Other compounds in tobacco smoke, among them ammonia and volatile acids, have a pronounced irritating effect upon the respiratory system.

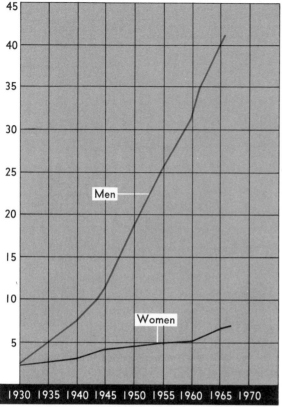

45

40

35

30

25

20

15

10

5

Men

Women

1930 1935 1940 1945 1950 1955 1960 1965 1970

1969 Cancer Facts (Am. Cancer Society)

38–13 Deaths Attributed to Lung Cancer per 100,000 Men and Women in the U.S. from 1930 to 1967. The figures are weighted to allow for the gradual aging of the population. Lung cancer is one of the few diseases with an increased death rate over the period shown on the chart.

Researchers have been able to show the effect of tobacco smoke upon test animals such as mice. When subjected to smoke as highly concentrated as that inhaled by the human smoker, many mice have convulsions and die. The remaining mice survive only a short time. However, where lower concentrations of tobacco smoke have been used on mice, it has been possible to study its effect upon their lungs.

The lining of the bronchial tubes of these mice undergoes changes similar to those that have been observed in the lining of the bronchial tubes of human cigarette smokers.

In the last few decades there has been a large increase in the incidence of lung cancer in men. (See Figure 38–13.) Between 1930 and 1969 alone, deaths from this cause have risen from 3000 to about 60,000 per year. Because of this increase, it has been assumed that human lungs have been exposed to some new cancer-causing agent. Among the agents suggested as causes are automobile exhaust gases, general air pollution, and cigarette smoke. The American Cancer Society states in *Shall I Smoke?* that "most scientists who have studied the evidence agree that cigarette smoking is a major cause of lung cancer."

In 1964, an advisory committee of medical scientists appointed by the Surgeon General of the U.S. Public Health Service analyzed approximately 8000 studies made in various parts of the world on the effects of smoking. With this information, the committee prepared a 387 page report titled *Smoking and Health.* "Cigarette Smoking," they concluded, "is a health hazard of sufficient importance in the United States to warrant appropriate remedial action. It contributes substantially to mortality from certain specific diseases and to the overall death rate." Furthermore, the committee found that the effects of cigarette smoking were in direct proportion to the number of cigarettes smoked and the number of years the habit had been maintained. Specifically, the report stated:

In comparison with nonsmokers, average male smokers of cigarettes have approximately a 9-to-10-fold risk of developing lung cancer and heavy smokers at least a 20-fold risk.

- Cigarette smoking is the most important cause of bronchitis in the United States and increases the risk of dying from chronic bronchitis.
- Heart disease death rates are markedly higher among heavy smokers than among nonsmokers.
- Associations exist between cigarettes and cancer of the esophagus, cancer of the bladder, emphysema (lowered efficiency of the lungs), and the death rate from pneumonia and influenza.

The 1964 Report was a landmark, warning Americans of the cause and effect relationship between cigarette smoking and cancer. Various federal agencies have become greatly concerned about the health hazard of cigarette smoking. The Federal Trade Commission recommended that packages and cartons of cigarettes carry a health warning. The Commerce Committee of the United States Senate has said, ". . . no disinterested medical or scientific body which has investigated the relationship between smoking and disease has failed to conclude that cigarette smoking is a serious health hazard." Responding to public opinion, Congress passed the Federal Cigarette Labeling and Advertising Act. The Act, which became effective January 1, 1966, required that cigarette containers bear the following warning, "*Caution: cigarette smoking may be hazardous to your health.*"

A second report titled *"The Health Consequences of Smoking"* was submitted to the Surgeon General in 1967. This report was similar to the 1964 report in noting the higher death rates of smokers as compared with nonsmokers from such causes as lung cancer, bronchitis, and coronary heart failure. The report also noted the relation between higher death rates and the number of cigarettes smoked daily. It also related the higher tar and nicotine con-

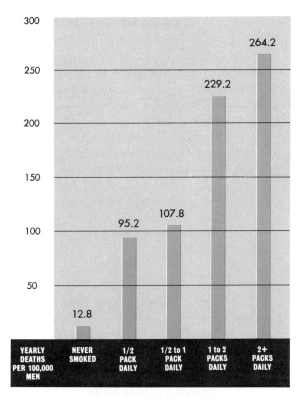

38–14 The risk of lung cancer appears to increase with the number of cigarettes smoked daily, according to the Hammond-Horn study. A person who smokes only ten cigarettes daily is eight times more likely to die of lung cancer than a nonsmoker. For a two-packs-a-day smoker, the risk is almost twenty times greater.

tent of cigarettes with the likelihood of harmful effects.

Dr. William H. Stewart, the Surgeon General of the United States Public Health Service, had no doubt about the harm of cigarette smoking. Speaking at the 1967 World Conference on Smoking and Health, Dr. Stewart said, "The proposition that cigarette smoking is hazardous to human health is no longer controversial." Furthermore, he felt that the nation's energies must be directed toward eliminating the hazard, or at least reducing it.

Shortly after the conference, Dr. Stewart appointed a Task Force on Smoking and Health. The purpose of the Task Force was to suggest means of encouraging young people not to start smoking and to suggest methods of obtaining less hazardous cigarettes. When the Task Force delivered its report in 1968, it had some sharp comments about cigarette advertising. "The Task Force is unable to see how, in the long run, a product involving the health hazards of cigarettes can continue to be advertised." The tobacco industry had increased its budget for cigarette advertising from $200 million in 1964 to $300 million in 1967.

Mounting public concern had its first visible effect in 1968 when, for the first time, per capita consumption declined 1.8 per cent. Although the percentage appears very slight, this represented a decline of 3.5 billion cigarettes consumed during the year. It is now estimated that there are 23 million former cigarette smokers in the nation. Among them are 100,000 physicians.

Young people are among the persons most likely to be influenced by cigarette advertising. Studies indicate that the smoking habit is formed most often in the teens. Once established, the habit is extremely hard to break. It has been estimated that each minute of smoking subtracts a minute from the life span of the heavy smoker. Don't start the habit! If you have started smoking, the best advice anyone can give you is to stop.

IMPORTANT POINTS

* Chemical coordination of the body results mainly from the secretions of the endocrine, or ductless, glands. These affect many of the fundamental processes of the body and are closely associated with human behavior and emotions.

* The thyroid gland, at the base of the larynx, regulates the general level of body activity. Imbedded in the thyroid are four parathyroid glands that regulate the amount of calcium and phosphorus in the blood.

* The pancreas produces insulin, which regulates the amount of sugar in the blood.

* The adrenal gland is concerned with the emotions of fear and anger. It also makes hormones that are useful in the treatment of arthritis.

* The reproductive glands produce hormones that regulate the secondary sex characteristics.

* The pituitary is the master gland. It is so called because it produces secretions that affect the thyroid, the adrenal, and the sex glands. It also regulates growth and other body activities.

* Small amounts of certain chemicals have a pronounced effect upon mental activity. One such chemical, LSD, produces hallucinations by stimulating brain activity.

* Human behavior begins as a result of the infant's attempt to satisfy certain needs. Psychologists believe that some of these needs are personal, while others are social.

* Neurotics suffer from the milder forms of mental illness. Psychotics are severely disturbed mental patients living in a completely unreal world.

- Drug addiction and alcoholism may be due to mental and emotional disturbances. The causes in either case are not very clear, but inability to adjust to the problems of life may be partly responsible.
- The smoking habit is believed to be one of the major causes of lung cancer. Cigarette smoking is also believed to contribute to the development of coronary heart disease.

REVIEW QUESTIONS

1. Contrast the effect of an overactive thyroid gland with an underactive one.
2. How was thyroid surgery related to the discovery of the parathyroid glands?
3. How does the pancreas illustrate the fact that a gland may have an endocrine function in addition to a digestive function?
4. What are some of the effects of adrenalin in the body?
5. How is the pituitary gland related to the development of sexual maturity?
6. What was the effect of LSD upon the Swiss biochemist who discovered it?
7. What evidence is there that trial and error is a basic method of learning?
8. What three social motives can be discovered in a group of people?
9. How would you compare the neurotic and the psychotic individual in terms of normal behavior?
10. What two effects are common in the early stages of drug addiction?
11. What are the two effects of alcohol that make the drunken driver a very dangerous person?
12. With what two major diseases has cigarette smoking been linked?

CHECK YOUR UNDERSTANDING

13. What two chemical substances in the body are regulated by the parathyroid gland?
14. Why are the adrenal glands sometimes called the "glands of combat"?
15. Give two examples that illustrate how the pituitary gland controls other glands.
16. How may an understanding of the chemistry of the nervous system eventually be used to treat mental illness?
17. What evidence does the diabetic coma offer of the relationship between the nervous system and blood chemistry?
18. Why might a biochemist have suspected that mental illness had a chemical basis even before some of the facts were discovered?
19. Describe Pavlov's experiment to produce a conditioned reflex.
20. Why must the assessment of our own limitations be considered an important part of sound mental health?
21. How are habit-forming drugs sold in order to protect the consumer?
22. What facts support the contention that alcoholism is a disease?
23. Explain the statement, "The successful man is one who has profited by his failures."
24. It has been said that cigarette smoking is a greater health problem than drug addiction. What is your explanation of this?

RESEARCH PROJECTS AND REPORTS

1. Obtain information from your school or public library and prepare a report on one of the following topics:

    Hallucinations   **Experimental Psychoses**

    Alcoholism   **Psychiatric Drugs**

2. *Conditioning:* Try a conditioning experiment on a pet dog or cat. Each time you feed your pet, rattle the food tray or pan so that it makes a noise. Do this just as you are presenting the food to the animal. After about twenty repetitions, try one trial where you make the noise while the pet is in an adjoining room. See if he comes without being called.

3. *Self-Evaluation:* One of the signs of growing up is our ability to analyze our strengths and weaknesses. Make a list of traits that you think are basic parts of personality. Some of your friends can help on this. Then make a personal evaluation of your skills and aptitudes on this list. If the list is not very long, consult a psychology text, or ask your guidance counselor if he can suggest where you might obtain a list.

4. *Thyroid Extract and Tadpole Development:* Isolate five tadpoles in each of two bowls of pond water. Add a small amount of thyroid extract to one bowl each time the water is changed, but do not add extract to the other. The extract may be obtained from a biological supply company. Feed the tadpoles small amounts of crumbled hard-boiled egg yolk once every two days just after you have changed the water. Observe any differences in growth rates of your two sets of tadpoles.

FURTHER READING

A Man Against Insanity. Paul de Kruif. Harcourt, Brace and Company, New York, N.Y. Discusses the use of tranquilizers in the treatment of mental illness.

Discovering Ourselves. Edward A. Strecker and Kenneth E. Appel. Macmillan Co., New York, N.Y. Discusses the causes of human behavior and why we do the things we do.

"The Biochemistry of Anxiety." Ferris N. Pitts, Jr. *Scientific American,* February, 1969, page 69. The amount of lactate in the blood appears to influence feelings of anxiety in people.

"LSD Spells Danger." *Life Magazine Educational Reprint #22.* Time-Life, Inc., March 25, 1966. A discussion of the dangers of experimenting with this powerful hallucinogenic drug.

"How Opiates Change Behavior." John R. Nichols. *Scientific American,* February, 1969, page 80. Experiments with rats suggest that human addiction may depend upon the circumstances of drug intake.

"Marihuana." Lester Grinspoon. *Scientific American,* December, 1969, page 17. A wide-ranging article that examines the effects of this widely discussed drug.

CHAPTER

39

Human Reproduction

Thus far your study of human biology has been concerned with life processes that maintain the individual. If the human race is to survive, however, the maintenance of the individual is not sufficient. The individuals of the race must reproduce. New individuals bring fresh vitality to the population, a vitality that further increases the ability of the race to survive. Among ancient people, fertility and birth were considered sacred. The Babylonians worshipped the birth goddess Ishtar, and the Egyptians worshipped Isis. Today, although much of the myth and superstition of ancient times has been dispelled by modern knowledge, the sense of wonder that reproduction and birth inspire still persists.

Like all placental mammals, man reproduces by a sexual process. Sexual reproduction is the most common type of reproduction throughout the animal kingdom. Why is sexual reproduction so common? From your study of genetics, you probably recall that this kind of reproduction produces great variation in the offspring. The union of the egg and sperm cells create many different combinations of genes, which produce many variations in the traits they express. These variations give the organism greater adaptability to its environment, a distinct biological advantage in its struggle for survival.

The Male Reproductive System

Although the sex organs begin to develop before birth, they do not become functional until the age of *puberty*. In young men, puberty occurs in the early teens. At this time, sex hormones called *gonadotropins* are secreted by the pituitary gland. These sex hormones stimulate the gonads of both sexes to become active. The activity of the male gonads, the *testes,* produces profound changes in the boy as he develops into early manhood. These changes are caused by the secretion of other hormones called *androgens*. Androgens, literally male-formers, are made by special cells in the testes. The androgens trigger rapid growth in body length, deepening of the tone of the voice, and growth of the beard. As these external evidences of sexual maturity appear, the testes are commencing their primary function. This is the manufacture of male sex cells, the *spermatozoa,* or simply sperm.

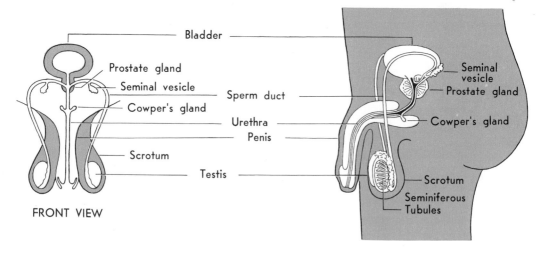

Prostate gland
Seminal vesicle
Cowper's gland
Sperm duct
Urethra
Penis
Scrotum
Testis
Seminal vesicle
Prostate gland
Cowper's gland
Scrotum
Seminiferous Tubules

FRONT VIEW

39–1   The Male Reproductive System

THE TESTES AND RELATED ORGANS. The testes are a pair of small glands suspended from the body in a pouch called the scrotum. The scrotum is an outgrowth of the abdominal wall. Prior to birth, the testes develop within the abdominal cavity. Before or shortly after birth, the testes descend into the scrotum. The suspension of the testes outside the abdominal cavity is characteristic of nearly all the mammals. In rare cases, the testes do not descend into the scrotum. In such cases, the sperm cells do not develop. The temperature inside the scrotum is slightly lower than inside the abdomen. This slight temperature difference appears to be critical for the formation of sperm in man. In a few mammals, such as the opossum, the testes remain inside the abdomen and are fully functional.

Attached behind each testis is a storage tube called the *epididymis* (ep-uh-DID-uh-miss). Sperm are stored in the epididymis before being expelled during sexual excitement. A sperm duct leads from the epididymis upward through the opening in the abdominal wall and loops around the bladder. Behind the bladder, each

sperm duct is joined by a *seminal vesicle*. The seminal vesicles produce a secretion that contains nutrients for the sperm. These nutrients increase the motility of sperm, which swim about in the fluid. Below the bladder, each sperm duct empties into the urethra. The urethra is the tube that conducts urine from the bladder to the outside. Lying at the junction of the two sperm ducts and the urethra is the prostate gland. The *prostate gland* secretes a fluid that is added to that of the seminal vesicles. Beyond the prostate is another pair of tiny glands. These *Cowper's glands* make small amounts of mucus. The secretions of the seminal vesicles, the prostate gland, and Cowper's glands, together with sperm make up the seminal fluid, or *semen*. During sexual excitement, the seminal fluid is forced by muscular contraction through the sperm duct into the urethra to the outside. During sexual union, the seminal fluid is introduced into the body of the female.

FORMATION OF SPERM CELLS. If we could examine a testis in cross section, we would discover that it is really a hollow organ. The wall of the testis is extended inward by thin partitions that divide the testis into more than 200 compartments. In each of these hollow compartments, there are about three tubules. Each tubule is coiled and twisted about itself like a clump of thread. Lining the wall of each tubule are the *spermatogonia.* Spermatogonia are the primary male sex cells from which the sperm cells are formed.

Before the secretion of gonadotropins by the pituitary, the spermatogonia divide by mitosis. However, after the gonadotropins reach the testes, the primary sex cells begin to divide by meiosis. Now primary and secondary *spermatocytes* develop inside the outer wall of each tubule. The meiotic divisions that occur in the spermatocytes reduce the number of chromosomes from the diploid number of 46 to the haploid number of 23. The immature *spermatids* formed by these meiotic divisions eventually develop into mature sperm cells.

The sperm cell is one of the smallest cells of the human body. Only one-hundred-thousandth the volume of the human egg, the sperm cell is about one-thousandth of an inch long. In appearance the sperm cell resembles a miniature tadpole, having a small, tapered head and a long flagellum for a tail. The small head, about one-tenth the length of the entire cell, contains genetic information packaged in the 23 chromosomes of the nucleus. A thickened neck joins the head to the tail, which propels the sperm cell. In movement and appearance, the sperm cells remind us of flagellated protists.

Sperm cells are produced continuously by the testes in enormous numbers. There are about 80 million sperm cells in one cubic centimeter of seminal fluid. Since about four or five cubic centimeters of seminal fluid are ejaculated during copulation, about 400 million sperm cells enter the female reproductive system. Although sperm cells are rather inactive while stored in the epididymis, the secretions of the seminal vesicles and prostate gland increase their activity. Their increased activity hastens the approach of the sperm to the ovum. Studies indicate that both the number of sperm and their activity are important factors in fertilization.

The Female Reproductive System

As in the male, the development of sexual maturity in the female is induced by the secretion of gonadotropins by the pituitary gland. The female gonads, the *ovaries,* become functional under the stimulus of these hormones. The ovaries, in turn, begin to secrete hormones that regulate the development of female characteristics. The breasts begin to develop, and the contours of the body become rounded. The beginning of puberty in the female is also marked by the first flow of blood and other fluids from the uterus, a process called *menstruation* (men-stroo-AY-shun). Closely related to menstruation is the primary function of the female system, the production of a mature *ovum,* or egg cell. Since the development and fertilization of the ovum occurs internally, the female reproductive system is adapted to care for the developing embryo before birth.

THE OVARIES, OVIDUCTS, AND UTERUS. The two ovaries are located low in the abdominal cavity on either side of the body. Each ovary is about the size of a large almond. The ovaries usually alternate in producing one mature ovum each month.

Partially surrounding the ovaries, like the fingers of a cupped hand, are the flared openings of the *oviducts.* The mature ovum passes into the funnel-shaped portion of the oviduct. The oviducts, sometimes called *Fallopian tubes,* are about five inches long and carry the ovum to the *uterus,* or womb. Lining the walls of the

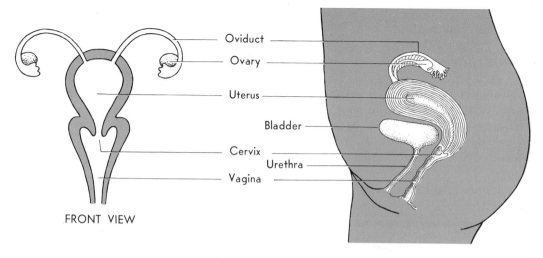

FRONT VIEW

39–2   The Female Reproductive System

oviducts are ciliated cells that cause fluid to flow toward the uterus. The uterus is a thick-walled, hollow chamber in which the fertilized egg develops prior to birth. Shaped somewhat like a pear, the uterus has a narrow portion called the *cervix*. The cervix leads into the *vagina,* or birth canal, which opens to the outside.

FORMATION OF EGG CELLS. The human ovum is the largest cell in the body. About one-hundredth of an inch in diameter, it is the only cell that can be seen with the naked eye. Long before birth, the immature ovary contains a fixed number of potential egg cells. Biologists estimate that each ovary may contain several hundred thousand potential eggs, of which about one out of a thousand will mature. In sharp contrast with the production of sperm cells, the ovaries produce only one mature egg each month. The mature egg, or ovum, is formed by meiotic divisions of the primary and secondary oocytes. These meiotic divisions reduce the chromosome count from the diploid number of 46 to the haploid number of 23. (See Oogenesis, page 124.) The chromosome-containing nucleus occu-

pies only a small part of the ovum. Most of its bulk consists of cytoplasm.

The ovary is a solid organ with the immature ova developing near the surface. At puberty, stimulated by gonadotropins, the immature egg begins the final stages of its development. The egg enlarges and becomes surrounded by other cells to form a *primary follicle.* The follicle becomes larger and is filled with a fluid. This fluid is rich in the female hormone *estrogen.* Finally, the mature follicle bursts through the surface of the ovary and releases the egg and fluid. *Ovulation* is the release of the mature egg from the follicle. The ovum is then drawn into the Fallopian tube and begins its passage down the oviduct.

After ovulation, the follicle begins to change in appearance. The cells lining the follicle take on a yellowish color. The changed follicle is now called the *corpus luteum,* a term that means yellow body. The stimulus for the conversion of the follicle into the corpus luteum is a second gonadotropin from the pituitary gland. The corpus luteum then produces the hormone *progesterone.*

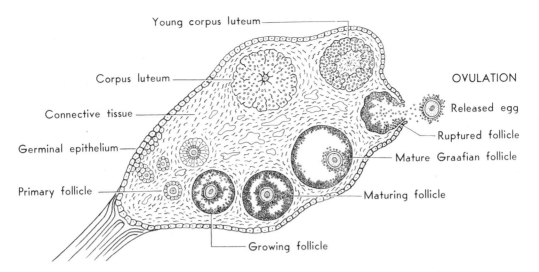

Young corpus luteum

OVULATION

Corpus luteum

Released egg

Connective tissue

Ruptured follicle

Germinal epithelium

Mature Graafian follicle

Primary follicle

Maturing follicle

Growing follicle

39-3 Schematic cross section of ovary, showing development of a single ovum, its release from the follicle at ovulation, and the resulting corpus luteum. The corpus luteum produces progesterone, called the pregnancy hormone due to its continued secretion if the ovum is fertilized. If it is not, secretion of progesterone ceases and menstruation follows.

Reproductive Hormones

All of the preparations for reproduction and birth are controlled by hormones made in the pituitary and reproductive glands. As we have already stated, gonadotropins from the pituitary trigger the onset of sexual maturity. Two gonadotropins have been identified: FSH and LH. *FSH* means *follicle stimulating hormone. LH* means *luteinizing hormone.* In the male, FSH induces the testes to begin the process of sperm formation. LH induces special cells in the testes near the sperm tubules to produce the hormone *testosterone.* In the female, FSH begins the formation of the egg follicle, while LH triggers ovulation and the development of the corpus luteum. Puberty, the age at which sexual maturity begins, is reached by young women at about the age of thirteen. For young men, puberty usually occurs about a year or two later. In both sexes, the formation of mature sex cells causes the production of

hormones that profoundly affect the reproductive system.

OVULATION AND MENSTRUATION. A complicated interaction of hormones regulates the cycle of events occurring between successive periods of ovulation. This cycle lasts about twenty-eight days, although there may be considerable variation in individual cases. The cycle is begun by the release of FSH, which triggers the formation of the ovarian follicle. The follicle in turn produces estrogen. Estrogen affects the uterus, causing the uterine lining to thicken. Feedback of estrogen to the pituitary gland lowers the production of FSH and increases the production of LH. As more estrogen is produced by the follicle, its increased concentration stops the manufacture of FSH. Meanwhile, LH production has reached its peak, the precise moment when ovulation occurs. *Ovulation is thus seen to be determined by the interplay of the concentrations of FSH, estrogen, and LH.* The high concentration of estrogen at ovulation has also further thickened the wall of the uterus and increased the activity of glands lining its inner wall. These effects prepare the uterus to receive the ovum as it migrates downward in the oviduct. Ovulation marks the end of the first stage in the female reproductive cycle.

The second stage in the cycle is regulated by the hormone progesterone. You will recall that this hormone is made by the corpus luteum, the yellow body formed after ovulation. Progesterone further increases the thickness of the inner lining of the uterus. With greater thickness, there is a further increase in the supply of blood and nutrients in the lining, all in prepara-

tion for the reception of the ovum. If the ovum has been fertilized in its transit of the oviduct, the secretion of progesterone is maintained. For this reason, progesterone is sometimes called the pregnancy hormone. If the ovum has not been fertilized, the secretion of progesterone ceases, and the corpus luteum degenerates. This marks the end of the second stage of the menstrual cycle.

A sudden drop in the amount of progesterone causes abrupt changes in the uterine lining. The capillaries in the thickened lining become damaged and rupture, releasing blood into the soft epithelial tissues. Most of the temporary lining tissue is now

39–4 THE OVARIAN-UTERINE CYCLE

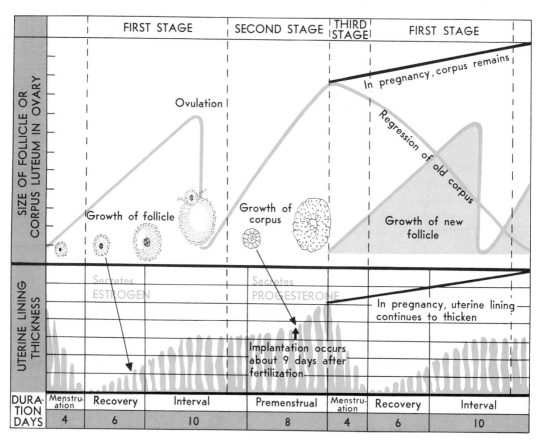

loosened. *Menstruation* is the monthly discharge of blood and lining tissues from the uterus.

THE FERTILE PERIOD. Now that we have compared the ovarian and uterine cycles, we can relate them by a timetable. The onset of menstruation is a convenient time to begin. During the four-day period of menstrual flow, increasing amounts of FSH are being sent to the ovaries. FSH stimulates follicle formation. As the follicle increases its production of estrogen, this hormone reduces the production of FSH by feedback to the pituitary gland. Meanwhile, the production of LH has been increasing. Ovulation occurs on about the fourteenth day following the onset of menstruation. Since no ovum was present in the oviduct for the first fourteen days of the cycle, fertilization could not take place.

Although the ovum usually remains in the oviduct and uterus for a period of four or five days, it is only fertile for about twenty-four hours. Unless active sperm cells are present in the female reproductive tract at this time, fertilization cannot occur. Sperm cells generally cannot live within the female system for more than forty-eight hours. The chance that fertilization may occur, therefore, depends upon copulation at or near the time of ovulation. Thus, the *fertile period,* or the period in which conception can occur, is believed to be about three days.

During the fourteen days following ovulation, increasing amounts of LH influence the growth of the corpus luteum. This yellow body in turn secretes progesterone, further preparing the uterus to receive the fertilized egg. If fertilization has not occurred, however, the progesterone level continues to increase. Now the elaborate hormone feedback system operates again. The high level of progesterone shuts off the LH from the pituitary, and this in turn causes the corpus luteum to stop functioning. On about the twenty-eight day, menstruation begins again. The events of the ovarian-uterine cycle are summarized in the table that follows.

EVENTS OF THE OVARIAN-UTERINE CYCLE

Days	Events
1	Menstruation begins. Uterine lining is shed. FSH stimulates follicle growth.
2–4	Uterine lining becomes thin. Menstruation ceases. FSH increases.
5–13	Estrogen is secreted by follicle. FSH tapers off. Uterine lining begins to thicken.
14	Ovulation occurs. Follicle bursts and releases egg. Estrogen level is high.
15–25	LH increases. Corpus luteum enlarges and secretes progesterone. Uterine lining becomes still thicker.
25–28	LH decreases as progesterone increases. Corpus luteum stops producing progesterone, triggering onset of menstruation.

FERTILIZATION AND THE PLACENTA. Suppose the ovum has been fertilized shortly after ovulation. Instead of being expelled within a day or two, the zygote moves slowly along the oviduct. As it moves, it begins to divide, forming a small clump of about a hundred cells. After several days, this clump of cells has reached the uterus. Within the next week, it becomes implanted in the soft, thickened lining of the inner wall. The maintenance of this lining is now of great importance to the tiny embryo. How can the normal shedding of the uterine lining be prevented?

Biologists believe that special cells of the embryo begin to assume an endocrine function within several days after fertilization. These special cells eventually form the membranes that surround the embryo. In this very early period of development, however, these special cells begin to make estrogen and progesterone. The effect of these hormones is to maintain the uterine lining and to keep the corpus luteum intact. In the pregnant female, therefore, neither menstruation nor ovulation occurs. Later, as the membranes of the embryo develop more fully, the outer membrane, the *chorion*, grows closely attached to the uterine wall, intertwining itself with the tissues of the uterus. The chorion and the uterine wall together form the *placenta*, an organ that brings the circulation of mother and embryo into close contact. The placenta continues to make large amounts of estrogen and progesterone. The placenta also secretes hormones that cause breast development and milk production.

Pregnancy and Childbirth

Life has always been a mystery to man, and despite his scientific advances, life still remains a mystery in many ways. If there is one aspect of life that intrigues man more than another, it is birth itself, for in birth man witnesses his own beginnings.

In the latter part of the seventeenth century, before the process of fertilization was understood, the most widely accepted theory was that of *preformation*. This theory stated that the sperm or the egg contained a complete, preformed individual in miniature.

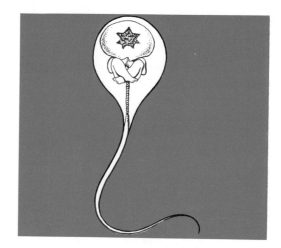

39–5   Spermists' conception of a homunculus, the preformed individual contained within each sperm.

There were two schools of preformationists —the *spermists* and the *ovists*. The spermists believed the sperm contained the miniature individual, called a *homunculus* (see Figure 39–5). The only function served by the female was to house the developing individual after its introduction into the uterus. The ovists, on the other hand, believed the miniature was contained within the egg. The sperm served only to stimulate the egg into growth.

The preformationists realized that if their theory was indeed correct, it followed that each miniature individual contained within itself all its descendants until the end of the human race. Despite the unlikelihood of this encasement concept, they tenaciously held to their respective theories.

Since the time of the preformationists, scientists have made great advances in attempting to understand human reproduction. Most of the earlier experiments were performed on the eggs of the sea urchin and the chicken. To this day, no man has observed directly the full patterns of human growth and development to be described in the next few pages. Except for the earliest stages, biologists have been unable to find ways to grow mammalian embryos outside the body of the mother. To attempt to obtain direct observation of the human embryo would probably result in its destruction. What we shall describe, then, has been inferred from many indirect bits of information painstakingly put together from many sources.

THE EARLY EMBRYO. As a result of copulation, as many as 400 million sperm cells are injected into the female reproductive system. If copulation has occurred near the time of ovulation, fertilization of an ovum in the oviduct is likely to result. The motile sperm cells, propelled by their flagella and aided by rhythmic contractions of the walls of the vagina and uterus, reach the upper portion of the oviduct in about an hour. Despite the large number of sperm cells, only one fertilizes the egg.

At the instant of fertilization, there may be hundreds of sperms surrounding the ovum. The combined enzyme activity of large numbers of sperm cells is believed to dissolve the protective coating surrounding the egg. Once the coating has been opened, a single sperm enters the egg. With the entry of this single sperm, another membrane forms about the egg and prevents the entry of others. The sperm tail now drops off, and the sperm nucleus moves toward the egg nucleus. Fertilization occurs when the two nuclei unite. The union of the two nuclei restores the diploid number of chromosomes to 46. The fertilized egg, now called a zygote, has not yet left the upper part of the oviduct.

The zygote now begins to divide, forming two, then four, then eight cells. This process of *cleavage* continues as the zygote moves down the oviduct. By the time it has reached the uterus, several days later, successive cleavages of the zygote have produced about a hundred cells arranged in a tiny sphere. Already some of these cells have been set aside as those which will form the membranes that will nourish the growing embryo. In a little more than a week after fertilization, the embryo will attach itself to the spongy, thickened lining of the uterus, a process called implantation. The arrival of the embryo in the uterus and its implantation sets hormone reactions in motion that suppress menstruation.

MEMBRANES OF THE EMBRYO. At the time of implantation the embryo consists of a hollow ball of cells called the *blastocyst*. During the early period of implantation, the embryo receives nourishment from the cells lining the uterus. Enzymes from the embryo break down the lining cells. Soon, however, a more lasting arrangement begins as the membranes of the embryo begin to develop. Some of the cells of the blastocyst begin to develop and enfold the remaining cells. The latter cells form the embryo. The outer membrane is the *chorion*. Immediately beneath it is the *amnion*. Both the chorion and the amnion

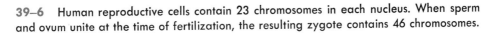

39–6   Human reproductive cells contain 23 chromosomes in each nucleus. When sperm and ovum unite at the time of fertilization, the resulting zygote contains 46 chromosomes.

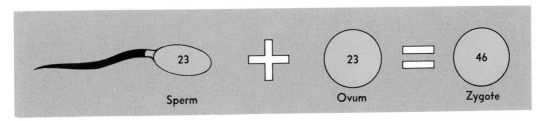

are formed by the outermost layer of cells, the ectoderm. A third membrane, the *allantois,* grows out of the center of the embryo from the digestive tract.

The chorion, being the outermost membrane, develops into a feathery mass that presses against the uterine wall. The membrane intermingles with the wall, forming finger-like projections that invade the uterine tissue. These projections, or villi, come into such intimate contact with the uterus that they are able to obtain oxygen and nutrients from the mother's circulation.

The amnion forms the amniotic cavity about the developing embryo. This cavity becomes filled with a fluid in which the embryo floats during its nine month period of development. The fluid protects the embryo from shock and mechanical injury.

THE PLACENTA AND UMBILICAL CORD. As development proceeds, the chorion extends out over the wall of the uterus, and flattens against it, bringing more nourishment to the embryo. The number of villi increases. Capillaries develop in the villi. Veins and arteries extend from the embryo to the chorion. The uterine lining tissue and the chorion are now indistinguishable. They have grown together so closely, they are now one. This pancake-like structure, consisting of uterine tissue and the chorion, is called the *placenta.*

Meanwhile, on the ventral surface of the developing embryo, the amnion and allantois have formed a tube. The tube is about the diameter of a pencil and is called the *umbilical cord.* The cord contains the arteries and veins that bring nourishment from the placenta. The cord, which reaches a length of several feet, is twisted about in the uterus. The umbilical cord is the connecting link between the embryo and the placenta.

One further fact should be stressed about the relationship between the placenta and the uterus: *the bloodstream in each re-mains separate.* Despite the proximity of the capillaries in the villi, the passage of nutrients and wastes from the placenta to the uterine wall is always controlled by membranes separating the two circulatory systems. The placenta can then be considered a protective barrier against the entry of harmful substances from the mother's circulation. The microbes of infectious diseases are usually not able to penetrate this barrier, although the virus of German measles is an exception. Other exceptionally small viruses are also suspected of being able to penetrate the membrane barrier.

Another indication that the barrier is not absolute is the appearance of birth defects attributable to specific drugs. A well publicized case occurred in West Germany in 1961. German physicians had noticed a high incidence of birth defects of the arms of babies born during 1959 and 1960. The defects were finally traced to the use of the tranquilizer thalidomide. The drug had been absorbed through the placenta of the pregnant mother during the early days of pregnancy. The effect was to interfere with the normal development of the limbs, especially the arms, so that they grew into misshapen flippers.

A TIMETABLE OF DEVELOPMENT. From the instant of fertilization until the time of birth about nine months later, the millions of cells that will form from the zygote follow a strict timetable of development. As we have learned from our study of genetics, the basic plans for this schedule of development are prescribed by the genes contained in the forty-six chromosomes. In the timetable on page 636, some of the more noteworthy stages of human development are mentioned. It is interesting to note that the single fertilized ovum has developed into 200 million differentiated cells by the time of birth about 266 days later.

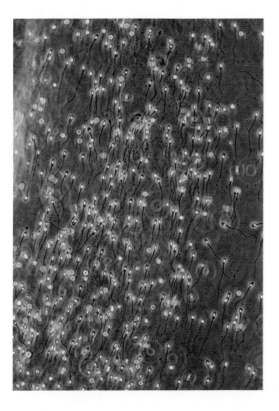

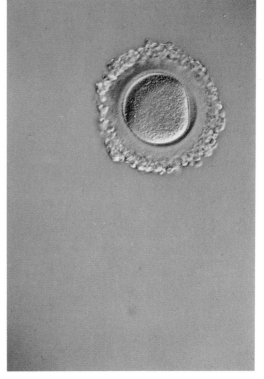

39—7A About 200 million sperm cells are released in one ejaculation. With their tails whipping them forward, they begin their long journey to the oviducts, where fertilization normally occurs. There are potential obstacles along the way, such as the chemical state of the vagina (may be too acidic) and the physical states of the cervix (may be compressed or crooked) and the oviducts (may be narrowed or occluded). The chances are, though, that some sperm—and it only takes one—will survive, still viable, to fertilize an awaiting ovum.

39—7B The ovum is surrounded by the translucent and noncellular zona pellucida and by the corona radiata, which consists of follicle cells. The ovum seems to start deteriorating as soon as it breaks out of the ovarian follicle, retaining its capacity to be fertilized for only about 24 hours. If the sperm cells are present and viable during that short time and fertilization occurs, then the deterioration stops, the process is reversed, and the egg starts to cleave. Food materials are contained within the mature ovum to nourish the embryo.

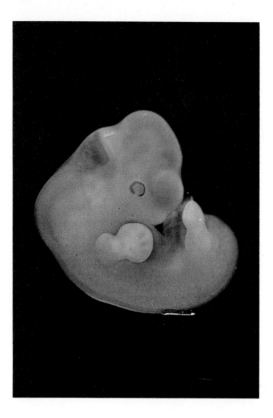

39–7C Entering its sixth week, the embryo has undergone remarkable development. The heart has been beating for several weeks. The thyroid gland, lungs, stomach, liver, kidneys, and intestine have formed, as have the limb buds, later to become the arms and legs. The five brain regions are well established and muscle differentiation has progressed greatly. For all this, the embryo measures only one inch. The bulge in front of the eye will become the nose. The tail, most obvious now, will soon begin to recede and finally disappear entirely.

39–7D The ear of this embryo, also in its sixth week, is visible as a thin light area just to the right (in the picture) of the eye. It will gradually work its way upward to its final position behind the eye. The skeleton is still composed of cartilage. The balloon-like yolk sac seen here produces red blood cells during the first two months and then ceases having any function at all. The fluffy-looking tissue is a piece of the placenta. Notice the fluid-filled amnionic sac that surrounds the embryo and protects it from physical shocks.

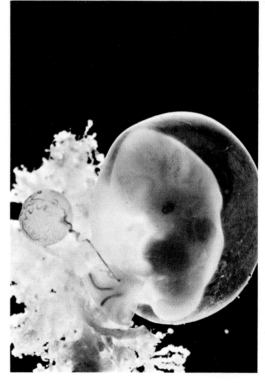

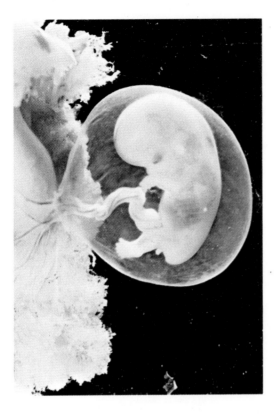

39-7E The tenth-week fetus is about two inches long. It has straightened considerably, and the tail has greatly diminished. The ears have reached their final position, the fingers and toes have formed, and eyelids now cover the eyes. The rib cage is noticeable through the skin, for bone has replaced much of the cartilage. In one week, the fetus will begin to move. Why will the mother not notice it? Clearly shown are the twisted umbilical cord and its blood vessels. Notice again the placenta, the amnionic sac, and now the absence of the yolk sac.

39-7F In the first months of development, energy was directed toward cell differentiation and then toward organ and system formation. Now, in the last few months, energy goes toward preparing the fetus for its entrance into the outside world. Now fat accumulates, providing insulation against the cold that will greet the fetus. Having acquired certain antibodies from the mother, there is protection from some infections for six months after birth. The digestive and respiratory systems are ready to begin. And so, hopefully, is the fetus.

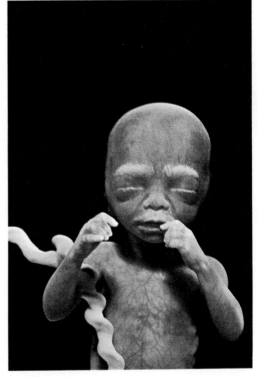

A TIMETABLE OF HUMAN DEVELOPMENT

Days	Events
	Fertilization. The zygote is formed.
2–7	Cleavage of the zygote.
7	Implantation of embryo in uterine lining.
18	Heart begins to beat.
26	Embryo is now one-tenth of an inch long and has eyes, spinal cord, thyroid gland, lungs, stomach, liver, kidneys, and intestine. Head is only a bulge.
28	Head now huge, proportionately nine times the size of the adult head.
35	Embryo is three-eighths of an inch long. The head is about one-third the length of the body. Arm and leg buds have formed. The skeleton is cartilage with a small, pointed tail. Embryo not yet human in appearance.
42	Fingers are beginning to develop, but facial features are still not human. Most organ systems are well established.
56	Arms and legs are well developed. Bone cells are being formed to replace cartilage. The embryo is now called a fetus.
70	Fetus is two inches long and human in appearance.
84	Fetus moves, kicks, and sucks thumb.
112	Fetus is five and a half inches long, well developed, and human in appearance.
126	Fetus is six inches long and very active, especially in kicking.
200	Fetus weighs more than two pounds and is about ten inches long. Hair begins to develop on head.
266	Birth. Fetus weighs about seven pounds and consists of 200 million cells.

BIRTH. During the nine months of pregnancy, the fetus has reached a large size. Weighing about seven pounds, the fetus measures about a foot in length with its tiny arms and legs tucked against the body. The amnion has provided a sac filled with amniotic fluid to protect the fetus from shock. The uterus has been stretched by the developing fetus. The placental hormones have also caused the breasts to develop further and the milk-producing cells to become active.

The early stages of birth are marked by strong rhythmic contractions of the uterus. These contractions force the head of the fetus through the cervix into the birth canal. The factors that cause the initial contractions are not known with any certainty. During the time when the fetal head is passing into the birth canal, the amnion is usually broken. Breaking the amnion releases the amniotic fluid.

The final stage of birth consists of two phases. In the first, the child passes through the birth canal to the outside. Meanwhile, the placenta has been loosened from the uterine wall. Shortly after the birth of the child, the second phase occurs. Further

39–8   Birth of the Child. Top left shows position before labor begins. Top right, baby's head in birth canal. Bottom left, baby's head emerges. Bottom right, doctor assists in the final phase of the delivery.

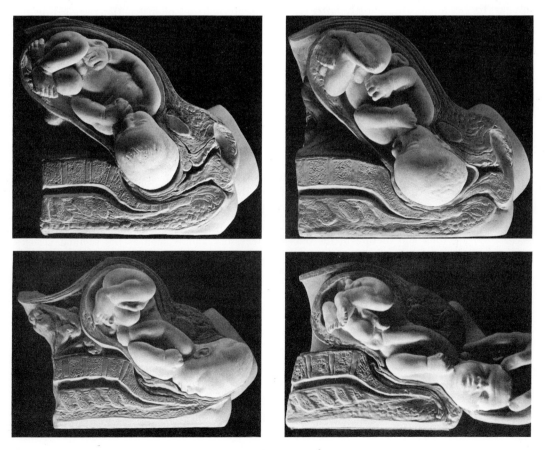

contractions of the uterus now expel the placenta. Severing the umbilical cord separates the infant from the placenta. With its first gasp of air, the infant begins its independent existence.

THE PROBLEM OF DEVELOPMENT. Ever since biologists discovered that the human body is composed of cells, they have been faced with an intriguing question: How do the cells of the body develop into different forms? The fully developed fetus is composed of over 200 million cells of many types, including muscle cells, nerve cells, bone cells, and blood cells. All of these cells are formed from the division of a single cell, the fertilized egg. How does the fertilized egg differentiate into cells of different types?

Early in the life of the embryo, all cells appear to be alike. But shortly after the embryo reaches the one hundred cell stage, the cells begin to differentiate. Marked for different roles in the design of life, some of these cells become part of the head, others become part of the arms or legs. The orderly plan of development is basic to the growth of the organism, whether it be man, frog, or fruit fly. Orderly development depends both upon the DNA in the nuclear genes and upon factors in the cytoplasm that interact with these genes.

The fertilized egg contains a complete set of instructions for the development of an organism. However, it is apparent that development requires a step by step activation of the genes that make up these detailed instructions. The head of the embryo, for example, begins to develop before the feet and hands. It has been suggested that some factors in the cytoplasm may act like switching devices in a push-button tuner on a radio. The radio is built so that many stations can be tuned in. Similarly, the DNA in the nucleus contains a complete set of instructions regarding the developing embryo. Pressing one button tunes one station. In a similar fashion, activating one gene or set of genes may begin the formation of a particular organ in the human body.

IMPORTANT POINTS

- At puberty, the male and female gonads become active when stimulated by hormones, called gonadotropins, from the pituitary gland.

- The male gonads, or testes, make the sperm cells and hormones called androgens. Sperm cells are stored in the epididymis and pass by means of the sperm duct and urethra to the outside. Accessory glands such as the seminal vesicles, prostate, and Cowper's glands make the seminal fluid in which the sperm cells move. A sperm cell consists of a head, containing the chromosomes, a neck, and a whiplike tail.

- The female gonads, or ovaries, produce the egg cells. The egg cell is made inside a follicle, which becomes the corpus luteum after the egg cell is released. Both the follicle and the corpus luteum produce female hormones.

- The female cycle of ovulation and menstruation is regulated by the interaction of hormones produced by the pituitary gland and the ovaries. These hormones effect the menstrual process, the monthly discharge of the uterine lining.

- During copulation, sperm cells are introduced into the female reproductive tract. Fertilization occurs when a sperm cell unites with an egg cell in the oviduct. The fertilized egg, or zygote, moves down the oviduct and becomes implanted in the lining of the uterus. Membranes form about the embryo, attach it firmly to the uterus, and provide its nourishment. After about 266 days, the fetus has become fully developed and birth occurs.

• Birth is begun by strong contractions of the uterus. These contractions force the fetus through the vagina, or birth canal, to the outside. Similar contractions expel the placenta shortly after birth has occurred.

REVIEW QUESTIONS

1. What is the role of the pituitary gland in sexual maturity?
2. List the main parts of the male reproductive system.
3. What is seminal fluid?
4. Why is the motility of sperm cells important in fertilization?
5. Describe briefly the events that lead to ovulation.
6. List the main parts of the female reproductive system.
7. How many chromosomes are found in the human sperm cell? How many are in the egg cell?
8. What hormones are formed by the follicle and by the corpus luteum?
9. How does estrogen affect the lining of the uterus?
10. What is the approximate length of the fertile period?
11. What are the functions of the embryonic membranes?
12. List the several stages that occur in birth.

CHECK YOUR UNDERSTANDING

13. Compare the functions of FSH and LH in the male and female reproductive systems.
14. What would be the effect of a decreased amount of LH upon the development of male secondary sexual characteristics?
15. What reason can you suggest for the introduction of huge numbers of sperm cells during copulation?
16. How does fertilization of the ovum delay the growth of other egg cells?
17. How is the corpus luteum maintained during pregnancy?
18. What is the relation between the chorion and the placenta?
19. What is the advantage of having the maternal circulation separated from the embryo's circulation?
20. From the Timetable of Human Development on page 636, select three dates you think are especially critical, then justify your selections.

RESEARCH PROJECTS AND REPORTS

1. Obtain information from your school or public library and prepare a report on one of the following topics:

Placental Mammals	Embryonic Membranes
Thalidomide	Preventing Birth Defects

2. *Female Reproductive System:* Obtain a female fetal pig about eight inches long from a biological supply house. Consult your teacher and obtain instructions to dissect the reproductive system. Locate the pair of small, yellow ovaries in the lower part of the abdominal cavity. Find the opening of the oviduct and trace the oviduct to the uterus. Locate the cervix and the vagina. Prepare a sketch of the dissected reproductive organs.

3. *Development of the Fetal Pig:* Your biology teacher may have a series of fetal pigs that show how the embryo develops. The early stages are often embedded in plastic so that they may be handled more easily. Prepare a series of sketches to scale showing how the embryo develops as it grows.

FURTHER READING

The First Nine Months of Life. Geraldin Lux Flanagan. Simon and Schuster, New York, N.Y. Written by a young mother with an excellent background in biology, this is a fascinating account of human development from conception to birth.

The Body. Anthony Smith. Walker and Co., New York, N.Y. An informative account of human reproduction is given in chapters 4 through 19.

Growth. James Tanner, Gordon Taylor and the Editors of LIFE. Time Inc., New York, N.Y. Chapters 2 and 3 are especially good because of their fine photographs of pre-natal development.

"Transplanted Nuclei and Cell Differentiation." J. B. Gordon. *Scientific American,* December, 1968, page 24. Describes experiments which seek to discover how the genes guide development.

CHAPTER

40

The Diseases of Man

Man's average life span has been lengthened many years by improvements in medical knowledge and treatment. In the early 1900's, an infant could be expected to live no more than 45 years. Today, the life expectancy of the newborn child exceeds 70 years. In some parts of the world, however, life expectancy is still very low because of unsanitary conditions and poor medical care.

Medical scientists have learned to control the communicable diseases, the principal cause of death in the past. This conquest has led to longer, fuller, more productive lives. No longer do we fear such great past killers as bubonic plague, cholera, smallpox, and diphtheria. We have identified the causes of these diseases and how they are transmitted from one victim to another. By knowing the causes, we are usually able to prevent their onset; by knowing the means of transmission, we can prevent epidemics if such diseases do appear.

Today the principal killers are diseases associated mainly with aging—heart disease and cancer. Perhaps you will see these conquered within your lifetime. Then, it may be that most people will live more than 100 years.

Communicable Diseases

The year 1347 was a terrifying one for the people of Europe. In that year the bubonic plague, brought to the ports of Italy by sailing men, swept across the continent. Millions died as a result of the disease that came to be known as the "black death." Its cause was unknown at that time. Even then, one factor was recognized that could protect a potential victim. Physicians advised people to avoid contact with the sick, to flee from the cities and find refuge in the country. The disease was communicable; that is, it could be transferred from person to person.

Most of the causes of communicable disease have now been identified. They are referred to as *pathogens,* or, more commonly, as germs or microbes. Usually, pathogens are microscopic organisms such as protozoans, bacteria, or viruses. It is small wonder that the conquest of disease is so recent a chapter in medical history. Before microscopes, people placed the blame for disease upon sinful living or evil-smelling air.

Spreading Disease. For over 500 years bubonic plague continued to terrify Euro-

SOME BACTERIAL DISEASES OF MAN

Disease	Bacterial Pathogen
Anthrax	Bacillus anthracis
Blood Poisoning	Staphylococcus aureus
Bubonic Plague	Pasteurella pestis
Cholera	Vibrio comma
Diphtheria	Bacillus diphtheriae
Meningitis	Meningococcus
Pneumonia	Diplococcus pneumoniae
Scarlet Fever	Streptococcus scarlatinae
Tetanus	Bacillus tetani
Tuberculosis	Bacillus tuberculosis
Typhoid Fever	Bacillus typhosis
Whooping Cough	Bacillus pertussis

peans. In 1665, Samuel Pepys, writing in his diary, mentioned that over 6000 persons had died of the plague in one week in the city of London. About 20 per cent of that city's population was killed by the plague in that year alone.

At that time a strong suspicion began to grow that rats were, in some way, associated with this disease. Through the years the suspicion was confirmed. Rats harbor the bacterium *Pasteurella pestis,* which causes the plague. The microorganism was named after the famous French chemist Louis Pasteur. But how did the rats infect people? The answer was—fleas. Fleas bit first the rat, then they bit humans. The transfer of the bacteria was effected by an insect so tiny that it escaped notice.

Today we recognize a number of ways in which diseases can be spread. Insects are just one means. Malaria and yellow fever are both carried by mosquitoes. The tsetse fly carries African sleeping sickness.

Snails carry liver flukes. Pigs and other animals spread tapeworms. These animal carriers are fairly easy to control once their connection with disease has been established. But some diseases are spread by water, food, and air. These are more difficult to check. Constant precautions must be taken to prevent water and food from transmitting disease. Safeguarding the air we breathe is a problem over which we can exercise no great control at present.

BACTERIAL DISEASES. Many of the illnesses of man are caused by bacteria. Among them are pneumonia, diphtheria, typhoid fever, tuberculosis, meningitis, septic sore throat (strep throat), and blood poisoning. Skin boils, too, are caused by bacteria.

How do these microorganisms get into the body? Any of the openings of the body can admit bacteria. Most commonly, however, the nose, mouth, and throat are the points of attack. Infections of the ear, the eye, and the reproductive organs are not unusual. Breaks in the surface of the skin also permit the entry of bacteria. Sometimes it isn't necessary that the skin be broken, for the bacteria can lodge in the ducts of the skin glands or at the root of the hair shaft. Then they grow into the skin and find a still more suitable place to reproduce.

Once inside the body, bacteria find excellent conditions for growth. There is food. There is moisture. There is just the right temperature. Attacking a particular site, the bacteria multiply rapidly during a period of incubation. Usually an inflammation occurs. Often there is an accompanying rise in body temperature.

It is not known why certain microbes attack particular areas or organs. The diphtheria bacillus attacks the throat. The tubercle bacillus thrives in the lungs, but also attacks the kidneys and bones. The cocci of meningitis multiply in the fluids of the central nervous system. Certain staphy-

Milestones in Biology

Louis Pasteur
(1822–1895)

ON July 6, 1885, a dramatic event occurred in Paris. A small boy who had been bitten 14 times by a mad dog was brought to Pasteur for treatment. Without help the boy would surely die a horrible death from hydrophobia. The boy's mother had learned of Pasteur's vaccine for the disease. Thus far, his vaccine had been tried only on dogs. She begged him to use it on her son. Two weeks later, nine-year-old Joseph Meister returned to his home, the first human being saved from rabies by a vaccine.

The man who saved the boy's life was not a physician but a trained chemist. Called "one of the greatest scientists of his century," Pasteur's achievements were twofold: he advanced biological theory by proving that microorganisms cause disease, and he gave physicians a powerful weapon in their fight against death by discovering how to make vaccines.

Born in Dole, a small village in eastern France, Pasteur attended the Ecole Normale (Normal School) and the University of Paris where he studied chemistry. In 1857, after a short career of teaching, he began investigations into the fermentation of wine. Wine, he proved, was fermented by yeasts but was spoiled when contaminated by other microorganisms. To prevent spoilage, he recommended that wines be gently heated to 140° F. for 30 minutes. This safeguarding procedure, known as "pasteurization," was later applied to milk.

In 1865, Pasteur became partially paralyzed. A semi-invalid at 43, he began research into the diseases of animals. While working with chicken cholera, he accidentally discovered that weakened disease organisms injected into an animal produced a lasting immunity. Years later, this knowledge was to achieve his greatest triumph, the conquest of hydrophobia.

lococci produce boils that are extremely painful and contagious. Occasionally they cause severe infections of the blood stream.

The invading bacteria may produce harmful effects in at least two ways. First, they may destroy tissues to an extent that normal body functions cease completely. This is the case in tuberculosis of the lungs. In advanced cases, the tissues of the lungs are completely destroyed. Second, they may produce waste products that are poisonous. These are called *toxins* (TOCK-sinz). Released into the blood, toxins can be swiftly fatal. In cases of diphtheria, for example, the death rate for very young children was 81 per cent just before 1900.

WONDER DRUGS. At the turn of the century, German chemist Paul Ehrlich was searching for a cure for syphilis. He sought a chemical that would kill the germ of syphilis without injuring the body cells. In 1909, after 605 failures, he found the chemical. He called it *salvarsan.*

In 1932, Gerhard Domagk, another German chemist, discovered the first of the "wonder drugs," sulfanilamide. The "sulfa drugs" were used with remarkable effect. Deaths from blood poisoning, pneumonia, and meningitis dropped dramatically.

Even more effective drugs were soon found. Penicillin, discovered by Alexander Fleming in 1928, was mass produced in World War II. This was the first of the *antibiotics,* compounds produced by living organisms that have been used to kill bacteria in man. Other antibiotics soon followed: tyrothricin, streptomycin, terramycin, and many others. Today penicillin still remains one of the most effective agents against disease. Although powerful, antibiotics have limitations: they cannot damage viruses.

VIRUSES AND DISEASE. Since the middle of the twentieth century, interest in the control of communicable disease has shifted from bacteria to viruses. Prior to the widespread use of the electron microscope as a research tool, viruses were unknown phantoms in the world of public health. Their small size had made it almost impossible to identify and study them. No matter how carefully medical researchers had searched for the microorganisms of certain diseases, they had been unable to find them. They had filtered the blood of diseased animals. Then they had examined the filtrate with extreme care, but had found no microorganisms. But when the filtrate had been injected into other animals, it produced the disease. Early in the twentieth century, the term "filterable viruses" was used to describe these mysterious pathogens. Today, the isolation and identification of viruses is one of the most important research problems in medicine. It has been estimated that 60 per cent of the world's illnesses are caused by viruses.

SOME VIRAL DISEASES OF MAN

Chicken pox
Common cold
Encephalitis
Hepatitis
Herpes (cold sore)
Influenza
Measles (rubeola)
Measles, German (rubella)
Meningitis
Pneumonia, viral
Poliomyelitis
Rabies
Smallpox
Typhus
Vaccinia (cowpox)
Yellow fever

Several hundred viruses are known to cause disease in man. Like the bacteria, the viruses appear to have certain preferences as infective sites in the body. The reasons for these preferences are not known. A common illustration is the Herpes virus, which infects the lips and causes "fever blisters." A very large group of viruses attacks the respiratory system. About 100 kinds of respiratory viruses have been associated with the common cold. The viruses of influenza also attack the nose, throat, and lungs.

Another large group of viruses attacks the intestinal tract. Some shift their attack to other sites later. Poliomyelitis, for example, attacks the intestinal tract first, then damages the nervous system. Still other viruses attack the nervous system, as in the case of encephalitis, or damage the liver, as in hepatitis. Two common childhood diseases, measles and smallpox, are caused by viruses. About 500 million people in the underdeveloped parts of the world suffer from a disease of the eyes called trachoma. Trachoma is caused by a virus-like microbe. Yellow fever is a serious health problem in the tropics of South America and Africa. Carried by the *Aedes aegypti* mosquito, yellow fever viruses are injected into the victim by the insect's bite. These viruses damage the kidney and the liver.

A common way of classifying viruses is on the basis of the nucleic acid they contain. You will recall that viruses contain either RNA or DNA inside a protein coat. (See Chapter 4.) The viruses of the common cold, for example, are largely of the RNA type, as are the viruses that cause mumps, influenza, and measles. The "fever blister" virus, on the other hand, contains DNA, as does the cowpox virus.

Despite major medical efforts to curb it, influenza continues to be a serious health problem in the world. Doctors have not forgotten the wave of this disease that swept across many nations in 1918, killing 25 million people. Named by Italian astrologers, influenza means influence and indicates the belief that the disease was caused by heavenly intervention or in-

fluence. This disease causes severe inflammation of the nose, throat, and lungs. Very often its victims have severe muscular pains and headache. The "flu," as it is more commonly called, has ravaged large populations for centuries, taking more than 5000 lives in London in 1847.

The flu virus exists in different varieties or strains. One strain, Asian flu, caused a major epidemic in the eastern United States in the winter of 1967–68. Asian flu also caused epidemics in Europe, Japan, South Africa, and Argentina that same winter. Commencing in July, 1968, a variant of the Asian strain caused a major outbreak of flu in Hong Kong. Nicknamed Hong Kong flu, the variant strain caused epidemics in Asian countries before it spread to the United States later in the year. Adequate supplies of vaccines to combat Hong Kong flu were not immediately available, and cases occurred in epidemic numbers before it was finally brought under control.

TISSUE CULTURE. There is an old saying to the effect that you must know your enemy's weaknesses in order to defeat him. In the case of viruses, biologists wanted to see them first. This was a problem in itself because of their size. Then, like the bacteriologists, they wanted to grow them in agar, perhaps in Petri dishes or test tubes. This proved impossible. The viruses would not grow outside living cells.

Virologists soon learned to grow viruses in chick embryos. This technique, developed in 1931 by Ernest W. Goodpasture, was successful for many types of virus. But some wouldn't grow in this medium. They had to be injected into living animals. Meanwhile, a few biologists had an idea that the best procedure might be to develop a way of growing cells in test tubes. Culture the cells, then inoculate them with the virus.

Many kinds of cells are grown in the laboratory. *Tissue culture* is an invaluable supporting technique that provides many more opportunities for growing and examining viruses. All kinds of cells have been tried—even human cells have been grown. A particularly good strain of human cells called HeLa cells has been grown very successfully. HeLa cells have been used for culturing many kinds of viruses.

One discouraging fact has emerged from the study of viruses. They are not destroyed by antibiotics. In each case it is necessary to produce a specific vaccine to hold them in check. This is another part of the story of how the body defends itself against disease.

CONQUERING POLIO. Poliomyelitis, or infantile paralysis, is a crippling disease of childhood. Although the polio virus attacks adults, its principal victims are children. The determined war against polio illustrates the many techniques science uses to combat disease.

Polio was found to be caused by three different strains of virus. All three are dangerous, and immunity to one does not provide immunity to the others. Their attack centers in the nervous system where they damage the motor nerves of the spinal cord. This is what causes paralysis of the arms and legs. One form of polio attacks the nerve centers at the base of the brain that control breathing.

Growing the polio virus proved especially difficult. It grew well in monkeys, but that was about all. These were expensive laboratory animals, so other methods were sought. Finally, a team of three scientists, headed by John F. Enders at the Harvard Medical School, succeeded in growing polio virus in human and monkey cells in tissue cultures. All three scientists received the Nobel Prize in 1954 for this work.

Meanwhile, Jonas Salk and his associates at the University of Pittsburgh had been working at the task of developing an effective vaccine. The three separate strains of

polio were grown in isolated tissue cultures that had been made from monkey kidney cells. Each infected tissue culture was then treated with a weak formaldehyde solution that killed the virus. The three types of killed virus were then combined into one vaccine. Extensive tests were subsequently performed upon monkeys during the year 1952. These tests provided proof that animals could be immunized with the vaccine.

In the spring of 1954, controlled experiments were conducted on large numbers of school children. The number of cases of polio among children who had received the vaccine was 75 per cent less than in the control group that had not received it. Some, however, did contract polio, but their cases were mild. Paralysis was reduced by 80 per cent. On April 12, 1955, the Salk vaccine was pronounced "safe, potent, and effective."

By 1959, still another weapon against polio had been forged. Albert B. Sabin of the University of Cincinnati had developed a "live" vaccine. The Salk vaccine consists of dead viruses. The Sabin vaccine contains "tamed" viruses that do not produce polio. However, it seems more effective in stimulating the body to produce its own protective substances. It has the further advantage of being taken by mouth in a pleasant-tasting syrup. During 1960, the Sabin vaccine was used to vaccinate over 80 million persons in the United States, Europe, the Soviet Union, and South America. Most of these were in the Soviet Union where the Salk vaccine had not been used previously.

The electron microscope, tissue cultures, and teams of medical researchers had won a great victory over an exceedingly stubborn and dangerous enemy. In 1967, only 47 cases of polio were reported in the United States and Canada.

THE BODY'S DEFENSES. Surrounded as we are by a world of unseen bacteria and viruses, you may wonder how we survive

DECLINE IN REPORTED CASES OF ACUTE POLIOMYELITIS (U.S.) 1952-1967

	0	10,000	20,000	30,000	40,000	50,000	60,000
1952						57,879	
1955			28,985				
1958	5,787						
1961	1,312						
1964	122						
1967	47						

Source: United States Statistical Abstract

at all. Yet serious illness is the exception rather than the rule. We stay healthy because the body maintains certain natural defenses against disease.

Several parts of the first line of defense have already been discussed. The skin acts as an effective barrier. Unless it is cut or punctured, microorganisms cannot usually get through. The mucous membranes of the nose and throat are also valuable defenders against air-borne invaders. The hairs of the nostrils and the cilia of living cells remove many of them before they can get very far. The tonsils, large lymph glands of the throat, destroy large numbers of microorganisms. Most bacteria on the food we eat are killed by the hydrochloric acid in the stomach.

Yet, similar to a persistent horde of attacking enemies, many microorganisms are still able to get through. These microorganisms invade the blood and tissue fluids only to be met by more defenders. (See Figure 40–1 on the following page.) In the blood, certain white corpuscles surround bacteria, engulf, and consume them. Sometimes, however, the bacteria are able to overwhelm these corpuscles, destroying many of them. The resulting mixture of bacteria and destroyed corpuscles is known as *pus*.

Physicians have long associated a rising temperature, or fever, with the body's struggle to rid itself of disease. Although not a certainty, it seems that the white corpuscles release a chemical agent in their fight with bacteria. This agent is carried by the blood to the brain centers that regulate the body temperature. The resulting rise in temperature retards the reproductive rate of the bacteria. As long as the fever does not rise too high or last too long, it is generally regarded as beneficial.

The most important defense against disease, however, is the chemical reaction that makes us *immune* to it. The body is stimulated by the presence of antigens, molecules found on the surface or coating of a microbe. As a result of this stimulation, the body forms *antibodies*, which combat the antigens. Antibodies help us recover from a disease and prevent future attacks by the same pathogens.

The Chemistry of Immunity

It has been known for centuries that persons who recovered from certain diseases rarely contracted them a second time. During the great plagues that ravaged Europe and America, such persons often

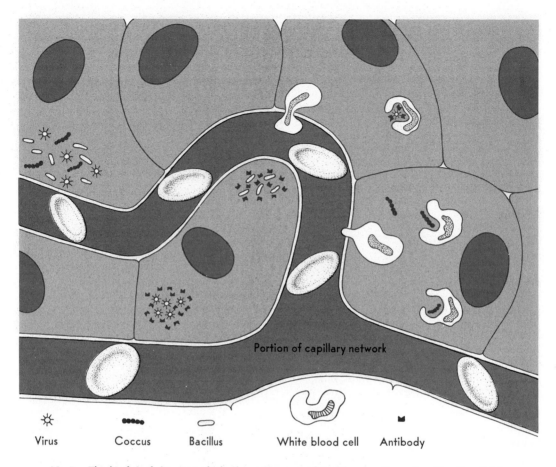

Virus   Coccus   Bacillus   White blood cell   Antibody

40-1 The body's defenses include the actions of white blood cells and antibodies. White blood cells escape through the capillary walls to engulf invading bacteria. Specific antibodies react to antigens on the viral surfaces, causing the viruses to clump together, thereby rendering them harmless. White blood cells then consume the clumped viruses.

volunteered to care for the sick while others fled in fear. Long before the causes of infectious disease were known, immunity to the disease was recognized. But how did immunity occur?

One of the first attempts to explain immunity came from the German bacteriologist Paul Ehrlich in 1895. He proposed that invading bacteria are masses of foreign proteins. Their amino acids are not linked in the same kinds of chains that characterize ours. Ehrlich reasoned

that the two kinds of proteins engage in a "war of proteins." The invaders try to link their protein chains with ours, making us ill when they succeed. Many physicians thought that Ehrlich was mad to suggest this kind of theory. Yet the basic ideas Ehrlich proposed still persist.

THE THYMUS GLAND. Situated in the center of the chest between the lungs and in front of the aorta is the thymus gland. In the adult, the thymus is much smaller than in the child. Until recently the role of the thymus was uncertain. In the last decade, however, the thymus has been closely linked with the immunity system of the body. Researchers have found that mice, rats, and rabbits that have had their thymus gland removed at birth lose most of their ability to produce antibodies.

In young mammals, including man, the thymus produces large numbers of special white blood corpuscles, called *lymphocytes* (LIM-fuh-sites). Of all the cells in the body, lymphocytes have the largest nuclei in proportion to the total cell size. The lymphocytes produced in the young animal are distributed in the blood to the lymph glands and the spleen. In these glands, the descendants of the original lymphocytes provide the entire immunity defense system of the body.

The thymus gland reaches its maximum size in the child at age ten and steadily diminishes in size after that. During these ten years of childhood, most of the antibodies that protect the human body are being formed. The antibodies are produced by special *plasma cells* derived from the lymphocytes found in the lymph nodes and spleen. (See Figure 40–3.)

PRODUCTION OF ANTIBODIES. Let us try to simplify the chemistry of the immunity reaction so that we can understand what is happening. The immunity reaction is brought about by the presence of antigens in the body. As mentioned in the previous section, antigens are molecules that project from the surface of a virus, bacterium, or any other cell foreign to the body. Like the features of the human face, antigens give a unique quality to the invading microbe or cell. The antigen of smallpox virus, for example, is recognized by the cells of the body as being different from the antigen of the influenza virus. One distinguished biologist has described the immunity reaction as a system the body uses to distinguish self from non-self. Invaders such as viruses and bacteria, or any foreign proteins, are recognized

as non-self particles and are attacked by the body's defenses. *Antibodies* are huge protein molecules composed of two interlocking chains of amino acids. Each end of the antibody contains an *active site* for receiving an antigen.

Although the analogy is crude, one might think of an antigen as a mold that is pressed into a claylike material. The mold makes an impression that exactly fits it. The clay is the antibody. The point of contact of the mold with the clay is the active site. The active site of the antibody is the end portion of the molecule where antigen and antibody fit together exactly.

How does this analogy help us to understand immunity? In the first place, it is the presence of the antigen that induces the immunity, for without the mold the clay cannot be shaped properly. In the second place, the antibody that is formed is designed to fit just one antigen—the antigen that formed it. Therefore, the immunity acquired is specific for one disease only. For instance, if you had measles in childhood, you are not likely to get measles later. But your immunity to measles will not protect you from being infected by smallpox. The

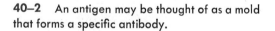

40–2 An antigen may be thought of as a mold that forms a specific antibody.

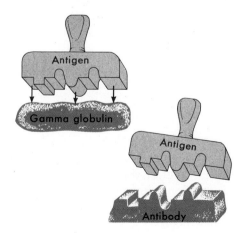

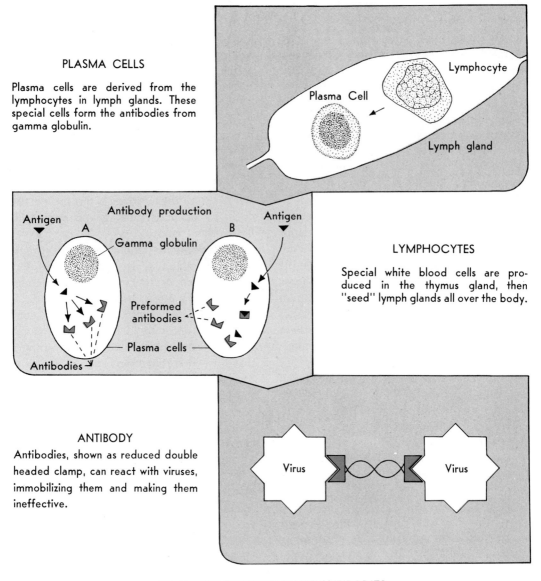

PLASMA CELLS

Plasma cells are derived from the lymphocytes in lymph glands. These special cells form the antibodies from gamma globulin.

Lymphocyte

Plasma Cell

Lymph gland

Antibody production

Antigen

A

Gamma globulin

Antigen

B

Preformed antibodies

Plasma cells

Antibodies

LYMPHOCYTES

Special white blood cells are produced in the thymus gland, then "seed" lymph glands all over the body.

ANTIBODY

Antibodies, shown as reduced double headed clamp, can react with viruses, immobilizing them and making them ineffective.

Virus

Virus

40–3   THE PRODUCTION OF ANTIBODIES

antibodies formed against the measles virus are entirely different from the antibodies formed to protect you against the smallpox virus. The antigen unique to each disease shapes the active site of antibodies to receive it alone.

Blood typing and transfusions involve the same principles of antigen-antibody reaction. We have seen, for example, that type *A* red corpuscles have an antigen on the cell surface that reacts with antibodies found in type *B* blood plasma. For this reason, type *A* blood cannot be transfused into a person having type *B* blood. (See also pages 561–562.) Just as blood cells are clumped by the proper antibody, so the proper antibody appears to join together the antigens of a virus. It is as though the invading virus soldiers were bound together and immobilized by the body's defenses. Viruses that are bound together cannot invade cells and cause disease. Bacteria that are bound together by the action of antibodies are captured and consumed more readily by the white blood cells called phagocytes.

GAMMA GLOBULIN. In 1951, two young boys were being treated in a Boston hospital. They seemed to lack the ability to resist bacterial disease. Something was wrong with the complicated chain of reactions that provides the final line of defense in the body. But what could it be? The doctors attending the boys had a thorough analysis of their blood made by expert chemists. In both boys one of the blood proteins, *gamma globulin,* was missing. The peculiar case of the two boys alerted doctors to the fact that chronic and repeated infections may be due to lowered amounts of gamma globulin in the blood plasma.

Let's go back for a moment to our mold-and-clay idea. The mold is the antigen, the germ. But what is the clay? It is the complex protein, gamma globulin.

Where is the raw material that is finally molded into the antibody? Special cells, the *plasma cells*, are produced in abundance by lymphocytes in the lymph glands scattered all over the body. These are the cells that produce antibodies from gamma globulin.

KINDS OF ANTIBODIES. The reaction of certain antibodies with antigens can be shown in the laboratory. One kind, the *precipitins*, cause the antigens to settle to the bottom of a tube in an insoluble form.

Another, the *agglutinins*, cause invading organisms to clump or stick together. In the body, this reaction permits the defending white cells to consume them in quantity.

The *antitoxins* are still another kind of antibody. Antitoxins neutralize the poisons, or toxins, that some antigens produce. One antitoxin of especial importance is that which combats the diphtheria toxin.

ACQUIRED IMMUNITY. Some individuals appear to be immune to certain diseases almost from birth. Their bodies have already formed antibodies to protect them. These people are said to have *natural immunity*. This resistance to disease may be genetically inherited, as in the case of sickle-cell anemia. (See page 160.) In many cases, however, immunity has been acquired at a very early age and has been assumed to be natural.

In most individuals, the immunity reaction is begun by the invasion of the body by antigens. Antigens in large numbers may overpower the body's defenses and cause death. If the attack is not too severe, antibodies are made by the plasma cells. During this initial attack, normal body functions are frequently upset. Fever, dizziness, headache, and loss of appetite often occur. A generally weakened condition is common. Having survived the attack, however, the body has erected a defense that lasts a long time. In some unknown way the body's immunity system is "instructed" or "remembers" the exact antigens that have caused the disease. The body keeps a supply of antibodies ready to attack specific antigens during any future invasion. The length of this period of *active immunity* varies with different diseases.

The fact that the body can acquire immunity by fighting a mild case of the disease led to an interesting idea. Why not give the person a mild case of the disease by inoculation? Inject germs that have been weakened or killed. In other

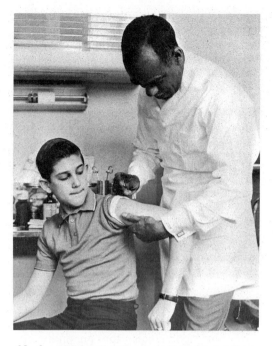

40–4 Child Being Vaccinated. The boy's body will produce antibodies specific for those antigens introduced by the vaccine. This results in an acquired immunity.

words, control the attack. This is the theory behind *vaccination,* which produces an *acquired immunity.*

Vaccines are produced in the laboratory. The disease germs are cultured very carefully. Then they are treated by heat or chemicals to reduce their ability to produce the disease. They may, in some cases, lose this ability completely. But when they are injected into the body, they can still stimulate the production of antibodies. The vaccinated person then becomes immune without any risk.

The widespread use of vaccines has almost eliminated certain diseases. In the United States smallpox is almost completely controlled by childhood vaccination. This is compulsory in most states. Other diseases of childhood, such as whooping cough,

mumps, and measles are also controlled by vaccines.

INTERFERON. Medical doctors have been impressed by the ability of certain patients who lack gamma globulin to ward off diseases caused by viruses. Does this ability mean that these patients have some alternate means to combat disease?

Research biologists have known for a long time that viruses interfere with each other when they attack cells. Exactly how the attack of one virus excluded the other virus was not known, however. In 1957, a protein was isolated from cells that had been subjected to viral attack. Named *interferon,* this protein protected cells against the attack of viruses. Interferon interferes with the normal ability of the virus to enter the cell and upset its metabolism. When chemists analyzed interferon, they found that it has almost the same molecular weight as hemoglobin. Interferon does not attack viruses directly; otherwise, it might have proved the greatest medical discovery in history. Furthermore, interferon does not confer immunity over a period of time.

What is the role of interferon in the body's defense plan? Biologists have wondered about the answer to this question. It appears that interferon production rises rapidly when viruses invade the body. This rapid rise of interferon protects the cells during the period of time when antibodies are being formed. Thus, interferon is the first line of defense to resist invading antigens while the second line of defense is being prepared. Biologists are seeking ways to increase the production of interferon in the body. Rapid mobilization of large amounts of interferon would be the most effective way of combating viral infection of any type.

IMMUNITY SUPPRESSION. The immunity reaction system of the body is also directly concerned with one of the most remarkable

TABLE OF ARTIFICIAL IMMUNIZATIONS

Disease	Immunizing Material	Type of Immunity	Duration of Immunity	When Recommended
Smallpox	Cowpox virus	Active	5 to 10 years	1st: 3 to 9 months of age 2nd: entrance to school Later: every 5 to 6 years
Diphtheria	1. Toxoid	Active	5 to 10 years	1st: 3 to 6 months of age 2nd: entrance to school and every 5 years to age 15
	2. Antitoxin	Passive	2 to 3 months	If exposed when not immunized
Whooping cough	Dead bacilli	Active	Several years	4 months of age
Measles	Weakened virus and gamma globulin	Active	Unknown	Infancy
Measles, German	Weakened virus	Active	Not yet known	Children and young women
Mumps	Weakened virus	Active	Not yet known	Children approaching puberty
Tetanus	1. Toxoid	Active	5 to 10 years	In infancy
	2. Antitoxin	Passive	Several weeks	After contaminated injury, if no toxoid was administered
Typhoid	Dead bacilli	Active	2 to 3 years	When exposed, or when traveling in foreign countries
Rabies	Weakened virus	Active	Unknown	When bitten by a suspected animal
Polio	Dead or weakened virus	Active	Not yet known	Infancy to age 40

developments of modern surgery, transplanting human organs. Before a heart transplant operation can be performed, the matching of the donor and receiver is made with utmost care. Both the red and the white blood cells are typed and matched to establish compatibility. Despite the great care which is exercised, the chief cause of failure in transplant surgery is due to rejection reactions that set in after the surgery has been performed.

How can the rejection reaction be prevented? Since the lymphocytes are the keystone of the body's defense system, their action must be stopped. Several drugs, such as cortisone, have been found to act in opposition to the production of antibodies. These drugs are called *immunosuppressive* for this reason. An antilymphocyte serum (ALS) has also been developed. Both ALS and the immunosuppressive drugs can slow down or stop the body's normal reaction to the "foreign" transplant. Meanwhile, the body's defense against disease has been reduced to almost nothing. Many transplant patients have died of disease after the surgery itself was successful.

Organic Disease

In 1900, the leading causes of death in the United States were pneumonia and influenza. Following closely in second place was tuberculosis. By 1958, the death rate from pneumonia and influenza had declined 85 per cent. In the corresponding period, the death rate from tuberculosis had dropped 97 per cent. The figures represent an impressive picture of man's control over communicable disease.

Meanwhile, other diseases emerged as the leading killers. Heart disease rose from fourth place in 1900 to first place in 1958. Today, 52 per cent of all deaths are due to heart conditions. Cancer, seventh in 1900, is now second. It causes one death out of every six.

DEATH RATE AND CAUSE PER 100,000 POPULATION IN THE UNITED STATES

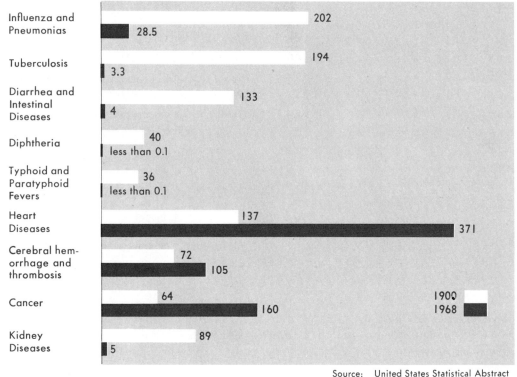

	1900	1968
Influenza and Pneumonias	202	28.5
Tuberculosis	194	3.3
Diarrhea and Intestinal Diseases	133	4
Diphtheria	40	less than 0.1
Typhoid and Paratyphoid Fevers	36	less than 0.1
Heart Diseases	137	371
Cerebral hemorrhage and thrombosis	72	105
Cancer	64	160
Kidney Diseases	89	5

Source: United States Statistical Abstract

How do we explain these facts? The answer seems to be tied in with one striking fact: More people live longer today than ever before. Control over communicable disease has prolonged life. But with advancing age we succumb to organic failure more easily.

CORONARY HEART DISEASE. What happens in a heart attack? There is sudden, sharp pain in the chest that radiates into the left shoulder and down the left arm. The blood supply in the coronary arteries has been suddenly reduced or shut off. These arteries supply blood to the heart muscle. Without an adequate supply of blood, it does not function properly. There are varying degrees of severity in heart attacks. They may be mild or fatal. If only a small branch of the coronary artery is affected, minor damage results. Blocking of the main course of the artery can cause death.

The conditions that lead to coronary defects develop over a long period of time. With advancing age, deposits of calcium and *cholesterol,* a fatty substance, are laid down in the inner walls. This condition is called *atherosclerosis* and is the commonest form of arteriosclerosis. The blood supply dwindles as the inner diameter of the arteries shrinks. The arteries lose their elasticity. Blood pressure rises. The heart increases in size. Sudden strain taxes the system and the heart fails.

Sometimes an internal blood clot is formed in the narrow, roughened arteries. This is a *thrombus.* If it grows so large that it lodges in an artery and cannot move, circulation stops. In the coronary arteries this is called *coronary thrombosis.* It can be swiftly fatal.

Heart specialists blame a number of factors for coronary heart disease. No one cause can be singled out. A high cholesterol level in the blood, excessive smoking, overweight, and lack of exercise all contribute to the condition. It tends to run in families,

too. The high standard of living Americans enjoy seems to make them especially prone to heart attack.

TREATMENT FOR HEART ATTACK. Immediate treatment consists of giving the patient drugs that cause the coronary arteries to widen so that blood can flow. When the pain is reduced, clot-reducing substances are often used. These are called *anticoagulants.* They dissolve clots in the blood and tend to prevent the formation of new ones.

Heart patients are required to rest as much as possible immediately after an attack. Then, after several weeks, they are encouraged to resume their former activities with moderation. During the patient's period of recovery, the physician checks heart function by using an instrument called an *electrocardiograph.* This instrument records changes in heart activity. These changes indicate to the physician the rate of healing of the damaged heart muscle. Heart attacks can occur at any age, but they are more common beyond the age of 60. For some unknown reason, most heart patients under 60 are men.

CANCER. What is cancer? Cancer may be defined as an uncontrolled new growth of tissue. About 330,000 Americans die of cancer each year. Vast amounts of money have been spent trying to seek out its causes. The recovery rate in certain forms of the disease is discouragingly low.

Cancer cells multiply in a wild, disorganized way. They interfere with normal cell growth and replacement. They invade normal tissue and disrupt normal function. Cancer cells often exhibit marked differences from normal ones. Generally, they are larger and have a proportionately larger nucleus. Sometimes there are numerous nuclei within one cell, or the nucleus is badly deformed. These are bits of evidence the physician seeks in order to diagnose cancerous tissue.

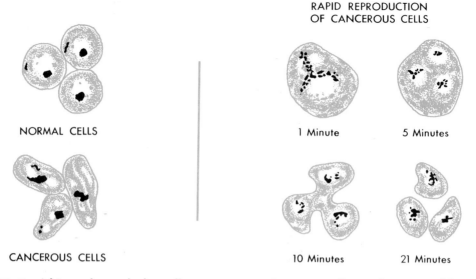

RAPID REPRODUCTION
OF CANCEROUS CELLS

NORMAL CELLS

CANCEROUS CELLS

1 Minute

5 Minutes

10 Minutes

21 Minutes

40–5 A biopsy shows whether cells are cancerous. Cancerous cells are characterized by their greater size, enlarged nuclei, and their rapid rate of growth.

The chief difficulty in treating cancer is that cancer cells often spread rapidly to other sites in the body. This spreading is called *metastasis*. Metastasis establishes secondary cancerous growths in other parts of the body.

Not all abnormal growths, or tumors, are cancerous. Noncancerous growths are called *benign*, or nonmalignant. How does the doctor determine whether the tissue is malignant? He examines a thin section of the suspected growth under the microscope. An examination of this type is called a *biopsy*. An experienced observer can identify cancerous cells by their appearance.

AGENTS THAT PRODUCE CANCER. Although the causes of cancer remain unknown, various means have been found to produce cancer in test animals. At first it was thought that if cancer could be produced, its cause could be determined. In 1915, two Japanese scientists produced cancer by painting rabbits' ears with coal tar. As early as 1775, certain types of cancer had been linked to chimney sweeps. One of the cancer-producing compounds that have since been discovered occurs in soot from chimneys. Thousands of substances have been tested since 1915. Quite a number have the ability to produce cancer. Many environmental factors have been linked with cancer. The most important example continues to be cigarette smoke, which is directly related to death from lung cancer.

Certain radiations also produce cancer. Precautions must be taken to protect workers in radiation areas. Some X-ray workers developed leukemia and bone cancer years ago before proper precautions were recognized and taken. Long exposure to intense sunlight may also lead to cancer. The farmers of the Southwest, for example, are far more susceptible to skin cancer than are those in other parts of the country. Miners of radioactive ores have a higher rate of lung cancer than do those who mine non-radioactive ores.

Is some virus the cause of cancer? None has yet been discovered in human beings. But poultry cancer was reported to be contagious in August, 1960, by researchers in the U.S. Department of Agriculture. Chickens that had been injected with the poultry cancer virus were able to transmit it to birds reared in the same pen.

CANCER TREATMENT. Two principal methods are used to treat cancer. The older is surgical removal of the cancerous tissue. This involves risk, particularly if the site of the disease is deep seated. The newer method uses chemicals or radiation. Anticancer chemicals have not had much success. Radiation treatment, using X rays or radioisotopes, has been helpful. But it must be carefully controlled, for radiation can also cause cancer when improperly used.

Cancer can be cured. Over a million Americans are alive today who had cancer that was treated promptly. Permanent cures are most likely when the cancer is diagnosed in its early stages. Although only one person in seven survived cancer less than 25 years ago, today one in three survives.

Watch for the seven danger signals described by the American Cancer Society.

1. Unusual bleeding or discharge.
2. A lump or thickening in the breast or elsewhere.
3. A sore that does not heal.
4. Change in bowel or bladder habits.
5. Hoarseness or cough.
6. Indigestion or difficulty in swallowing.
7. Change in a wart or mole.

CANCER RESEARCH. Cancer is the focal point of many questions about growth. What is normal growth? How does a cell control it? What destroys the pattern of normal growth in a cancer cell? What chemicals regulate growth? What is the effect of radiation? How do the viruses influence cell growth? Cancer researchers ask these questions, probing the basis of life itself.

Four active areas of cancer research can be identified. They are not separate and distinct. Frequently, the information areas overlap and interlock.

1. *Chemical Agents.* This area has two subdivisions. The first seeks to discover all chemicals that can produce cancer. These are called *carcinogens*. The second attempts to find those chemicals that can stop cancerous growth. Of more than 100,000 compounds tested, about 20 have some effect in arresting cancer. None can be considered a cure.

2. *Hormones.* There is some evidence that hormones, especially the sex hormones, are related to cancer. The treatment of certain cancers of men by injecting estrogens, or female hormones, has been beneficial in some cases. Similarly, cancer in women has been treated by administering androgens, or male hormones.

3. *Viruses.* We know that viruses produce cancerous growths in chickens, rabbits, and leopard frogs. But in spite of intensive search no one has reported viruses in human cancer. This does not rule them out as a possible cause, however. At least one cancer researcher, Chester M. Southam, thinks that most people are immune to the disease. He implanted cancer cells into 53 healthy volunteer prisoners. Result: no cancers. Then he tried it with cancer patients. The malignant cells "took" and had to be removed surgically.

4. *Enzymes and the Nucleus.* Cell growth is regulated by the nucleus, and cancer cells usually have an enlarged, deformed nucleus. This has led investigators to seek the chemical reasons for these unusual nuclei. In the chemistry of the nucleus and the control it exercises over cell enzymes, we may find the cause of cancer.

- With the aid of the microscope, man has learned that communicable diseases are caused by microorganisms such as protozoa, bacteria, and viruses. These microscopic pathogens are carried by insects, rodents, food, water, and air.

- Viruses as such were unknown before the development of the electron microscope. They have a noncellular structure, which may be described as a shell of protein containing either DNA or RNA.

- Better sanitation and the control of insects and other carriers have reduced the incidence of communicable diseases in many parts of the world.

- "Sulfa drugs" and antibiotics have greatly improved the treatment of many bacterial diseases. Through their use, a high percentage of recovery has been achieved in diseases that formerly had a high rate of mortality. Most drugs, however, are of little use against virus diseases. In these cases, recovery depends upon the immunity mechanism of the body.

- The body is capable of manufacturing antibodies that circulate in the blood. Invading microorganisms act as antigens that stimulate the production of antibodies. Antibodies are specific for each type of antigen. Antibodies sometimes remain in the blood for a long time, producing lasting immunity.

- Vaccines are dead or weakened pathogens injected into the body. Vaccines stimulate the production of antibodies and produce immunity without the risk of infection.

- With the conquest of communicable diseases, organic diseases are becoming more of a world health problem. Heart disease and cancer are now the principal causes of death in the United States.

- Heart and circulatory disease is due principally to atherosclerosis, a narrowing of the arteries as minerals and fatty substances accumulate on the inside walls.

- Cancer is a condition marked by uncontrolled cell growth. Carcinogens are capable of producing cancer, but the causes of cancer are not understood. Cancer often spreads rapidly and has a high mortality rate. Early diagnosis is essential. If cancer is removed by surgery before it has spread, the chances of recovery are very good. After metastasis, however, the chance of successful treatment is slim.

REVIEW QUESTIONS

1. List three pathogens and the diseases they cause.
2. Distinguish between the cause and the carrier of bubonic plague.
3. Why is tissue culture important in the fight against disease?
4. Describe four body defenses against disease.
5. Distinguish between antigen and antibody.
6. How are plasma cells involved in the immunity reaction?
7. What is the difference between a communicable and an organic disease?
8. How is a coronary thrombus formed?
9. List three factors to which physicians ascribe the increase in coronary heart disease in the United States.
10. Why is early diagnosis important in the treatment of cancer?

CHECK YOUR UNDERSTANDING

11. How do you account for the fact that the conquest of communicable disease is a rather recent chapter in medical history?
12. What two symptoms usually indicate the incubation of bacteria in the body?
13. Make a list of five important diseases caused by viruses.
14. Explain how an antibody is produced and why it is specific.
15. How was the role of gamma globulin in immunity discovered?
16. How is an anticoagulant useful in the treatment of heart patients?
17. What three characteristics are often typical of cancer cells?
18. In what four ways have cancers been produced?
19. About sixty years ago, pneumonia killed more persons than heart disease and cancer combined. Today, heart disease and cancer are the leading causes of death. How can these statistics be explained?
20. How might human cancer be treated if it were proved to be caused by viruses?
21. How will DNA research add to our understanding of cancer?

RESEARCH PROJECTS AND REPORTS

1. Obtain information from your school or public library and prepare a report on one of the following topics:

   The Black Plague   **Virus Cultures**

   The Conquest of Smallpox   **Cancer-Causing Factors**

2. *Table of Communicable Diseases:* Consulting medical and health references, make a table of at least ten communicable diseases. Divide it into four vertical columns with headings from left to right: Disease, Pathogen, Method of Transmission, and Prevention.

3. *Microscopic Examination of the Malarial Parasite:* Prepared slides of Plasmodium are available from a biological supply house. Examine and draw the parasite stage you find under the microscope. If possible, compare with a prepared slide of a human malarial blood smear and make other drawings. Do the two stages seem alike? Consult a textbook on the malarial protozoan and relate its life cycle inside man. (See also pages 245–246 in this book.)

FURTHER READING

Men of Medicine. Katherine B. Shippen. Viking Press, New York, N.Y. Biographies from ancient times to twentieth century; struggles to end human diseases.

"**The Thymus Hormone.**" Raphael H. Levy. *Scientific American,* July, 1964, page 66. For the advanced student, more about the mechanism of immunity.

"**Tetanus.**" W. E. van Heyingen. *Scientific American,* April, 1968, page 69. Soil bacteria cause this crippling disease by producing a paralytic toxin.

"**Plague Toxin.**" Solomon Kadis, Thomas Montie, and Samuel Ajl. *Scientific American,* March, 1969, page 93. How does this disease's toxin produce such lethal effects? If this question is answered, the plague may be better controlled.

The Web of Life

IT IS IMPOSSIBLE for a biologist to achieve a full understanding of a protist, a tree, or an insect by studying an isolated specimen. Each organism is a member of a population of similar organisms. Each interacts with its physical environment. Each interacts with members of its own species and other species in many ways. To study an organism in isolation is as difficult as studying a living fish removed from the stream in which it swims.

Biologically, a fish cannot be separated from its aquatic environment. The stream is the medium in which the fish moves. The stream is also the environment in which the fish seeks food and oxygen, escapes its enemies, grows to maturity, finds its mate, and reproduces. The stream also plays an important role in changing the characteristics of the species. The fish must adapt to changes in the conditions that are present in the stream in order for its species to survive. The stream provides the conditions in which the evolution of the species occurs. Thus, the fish is bound to its aquatic environment by hundreds of invisible threads.

What is true for fishes is true for all organisms. Bound inseparably to their environments, organisms live, grow, reproduce, and evolve as they interact with their physical and organic surroundings.

The environments of the planet Earth are many and varied, and it is this variety that affects the diversity and distribution of living things. The flat dry plains support large herds of grazing grass-feeders, but these animals cannot survive in the moist tropical rain forest. In the warm subtropical parts of the earth, many reptiles flourish, but these cold-blooded animals would freeze in the subpolar or polar regions. The Pacific islands favor the growth of coconut palms, yet these trees do not grow on the mountainous slopes of the northwestern United States. The distribution of a living thing is generally determined by the environment which is favorable to it.

An exception to this general rule is man himself. Less restricted than other species by the limitations imposed by his environment, man has become the most numerous and perhaps the most successful of all the large animals. There are few environments in which man cannot live. Seemingly unaffected by the limitations that control other species, **Homo sapiens** lives in practically all the regions of the earth. Man's unique status is due to the fact that he alone has the ability to alter his environment. Man's welfare and survival, however, are still inseparable from his environment, for man must breathe air, drink water, and grow the food he requires. Like every other species, man is dependent upon his environment for the basic necessities of life.

CHAPTER

41

The Organism
and Its Environment

THE STUDY of the complex interrelationships that exist between living things and their total environment is called *ecology.* Ecology is an important branch of biology. The ecologist seeks to understand the success or failure, not of individual organisms, but of whole populations of species.

The science of ecology has many practical applications. Because man alters his physical environment and uses other organisms for his own purpose, he sometimes overlooks the fact that he, too, is part of the vast web of life. Frequently, his activities upset the balance of nature to his own harm. He plants crops in closely spaced rows causing insect pests to overmultiply. He then dusts the pests with insecticides from an airplane, killing insects that pollinate useful plants. Further, the insecticides leave toxic residues in the soil that wash into lakes and streams and poison useful fish. In man's "control" of nature, which of his activities cause more harm than good? The ecologist can offer guidance and make practical suggestions.

The dictionary defines the term *environment* as "the aggregate of all external conditions and influences affecting the life and development of an organism." For convenience, we recognize two parts of the environment. One part is the *physical environment.* The physical environment can be described in terms of temperature, moisture, dryness, solar radiation, and so on. The other part is the living, or *biotic environment.* The biotic environment includes all the associated plants and animals that compete for food or provide it. In order to survive, an organism must be adapted to its total environment.

The Physical Environment

The physical environment is the source of components of which living things are made: oxygen and carbon dioxide from the air, water and minerals from the soil, energy from the sun. Using these ingredients, plants build food and tissues and set in motion the consumer transfers that support animal life.

Because of specific factors, all environments are not alike. The polar bear, for example, must endure the rigors of the

Arctic cold. The cactus must withstand the heat and dryness of the desert. Both the Arctic and the desert are sparsely populated. The jungle, on the other hand, teems with life. Its rich soil, plentiful moisture, and favorable temperatures encourage an abundance of living things.

From these examples we are aware that the physical factors in the environment such as air, water, light, and temperature favor or limit the existence of living things. Sometimes a single factor makes the difference. For example, the absence of light in deep caves means that plants cannot live there. The absence of warmth in the polar regions means that reptiles cannot live there. The absence of sufficient water in the desert means that many kinds of amphibians cannot find a home there.

The physical factors of the environment also play a role in determining the animals and plants that live there. Horses' hoofs are adapted to the hard, flat land, the long legs of wading birds to shallow streams, the streamlined shape of fishes to the water in which they swim.

AIR. We live at the bottom of the atmosphere, a huge air-ocean which extends several hundred miles above our heads. In terms of volume, it is the largest part of the physical environment. If it were stripped away, or its chemical content drastically altered, all life would cease.

The atmosphere supports life in a number of ways. It shields organisms from harmful radiation and is the medium of transport for birds, insects, pollen, and many microorganisms. It carries huge amounts of water vapor which later falls as rain, and is a reservoir of elements that are essential to life. Although it extends several hundred miles upward, most of its mass lies close to the earth in a dense, seven mile layer called the *troposphere*. It is in the troposphere that all weather and life supporting functions occur.

The atmosphere is a mixture of nitrogen (78%), oxygen (21%), plus carbon dioxide and certain rare gases (1%). All these components circulate through living things. Carbon dioxide is utilized by plants and green protists for photosynthesis, then returned to the atmosphere by the respiration of organisms. Nitrogen is combined with other elements by microorganisms in the soil, then absorbed by plants as nitrates, and later returned to the air by the bacteria of decay. Oxygen, essential for respiration, is continuously fed back to the air by photosynthesis. Thus, the proportion of gases in the atmosphere remains constant.

WATER. Water is a major component of all living things. Water is also the medium in which life's chemical reactions occur. Life would be impossible without water.

Over 70 per cent of the earth is covered with water, most of which makes up our vast oceans. (See Figure 2–1.) For millions of years the seas have been replenished by the rivers that empty into them. Rivers bring minute amounts of dissolved salts, which accumulate in the oceans. As a result, the *salinity*, or salt content, of sea water has continually increased. Organisms living in the sea must, therefore, become adapted to conditions of increasing salinity. On the other hand, organisms living in fresh water do not experience this problem. Generally, organisms living in salt or fresh water cannot exchange environments and survive.

All organisms that live on land still depend on water. As you have learned, the path of evolution led from the water to the land. The invasion of the land by living things was not possible, however, until they developed new ways of obtaining and conserving water. Plants developed vascular tissues, which aided the absorption and distribution of water. Animals developed thick coverings, which slowed the evaporation of their internal fluids. With adapted structures, life on land became possible even in regions where water is scarce.

The amount of water in the environment limits the kinds of organisms that can live there. Animals are less limited than plants since they can move about to seek water. Plants, however, are more dependent on soil water since they cannot seek it. Where rainfall is plentiful, a great variety of plants can survive. The plants, in turn, support the animals that depend on them for food. Where rainfall is scant, as in the desert, only a few hardy organisms can survive.

Sometimes humidity and even fog serve the functions of rainfall. For example, in humid tropical rain forests, *epiphytes*, plants that cling to other plants for support, use "air roots" to obtain moisture from the atmosphere. In the redwood forests of California, where there is little rain during the summer, ferns obtain water from the heavy fogs that are common in the region.

Soil. The formation of soil is an extremely slow process. It begins with the breaking down of rocks into tiny particles by the weathering action of wind, water, and temperature.

Pulverized rock, however, cannot support higher plant life. Only primitive organisms, such as bacteria, algae, and lichens, can establish themselves in the rock. As these primitive plants and protists die and decay, they leave a thin layer of organic materials, enabling the higher seed plants to gain a foothold. The decaying roots, stems, and leaves of the higher plants add to the slowly accumulating organic material.

The organic part of the soil is called *humus*. When added to the inorganic subsoil, humus forms the valuable layer of earth called *topsoil*. Topsoil is porous and is rich in nitrates and other mineral salts. The porous soil allows oxygen to enter and supply the respiratory needs of roots and necessary microorganisms. Only topsoil can support crops for food.

41–1   Heavy fog in California hills serves the same functions as an actual rainfall.

The rate of topsoil formation depends on many variables. On the average, about one inch is formed every 800 years. Thus, five inches of topsoil require about 50 lifetimes to build.

LIGHT. Biologists consider life a vast energy cycle powered by sunlight. Sunlight is the energy source for photosynthesis and therefore affects plants and green protists directly. Light affects animals indirectly since they are dependent on autotrophs for food.

Plants respond to light in a number of ways. Leaves and stems grow toward light; roots grow away from it. Leaves exposed to full sunlight tend to grow shorter and thicker. Partially shaded leaves develop thinner blades. In a dense forest, the tallest trees spread their crowns and utilize most of the available light. The shaded forest floor is sparsely populated with other plants. Only plants adapted to heavy shade can survive there.

Light affects the green protists of the sea. Algae grow in abundance at the surface where there is a maximum of sunlight. With increasing depth of water, however, their numbers decrease. Below 600 feet, where sunlight ceases to penetrate, autotrophic organisms disappear. Animals living below these depths are either carnivores or scavengers.

The behavior of birds and other animals is also influenced by light. Birds migrate by flying northward in response to the lengthening days of spring. When certain species were experimentally exposed to artificial light, they began their migrations earlier. Many birds begin to breed as the hours of daylight increase. Many mammals, on the other hand, begin to mate in the shorter days of fall.

TEMPERATURE. Most organisms live in temperatures ranging between the freezing and boiling points of water. Different organisms can tolerate temperatures at each

41–2 Tiny organisms flourish in the high temperatures of this mineral water at Yellowstone.

end of this broad range. Certain blue-green algae, for example, thrive in hot springs that approach 160° F, while some bacteria function at temperatures close to the freezing point of water.

The temperature range within which an organism functions best is called its *optimum*. For cold-blooded animals, the optimum is often very narrow. Reptiles and amphibia, for example, are abundant in the tropics, sparse in the temperate zones, and largely absent from polar regions. Even in temperate regions most reptiles must hibernate to survive the winter. On the other hand, warm-blooded animals are world wide in distribution. Their internal temperatures remain at optimum regardless of their external environment. Even so, some warm-blooded animals make special adjustments to cope with temperature extremes. Bears, for example, although they do not hibernate, become dormant during the winter. Their normal temperature of 100° F, drops to 50° or lower.

Plants do not have temperature regulating mechanisms. Observers have discovered, however, that during fall and winter they may have a slightly higher temperature than their surroundings as a result of respiration. During the heat of the summer, their temperature is often lowered by the evaporation of water from their leaves.

Temperature is the principal factor that accounts for certain life zones which the biologist identifies. Tropical plants and animals generally cannot live in temperate regions. Temperate species generally cannot live in polar latitudes. However, as temperatures fall with an increase in altitude, the biotic map is altered. As a result, temperate plants and animals may be found in the mountain highland of the tropics; arctic species occur in the mountains of the temperate zones.

The Biotic Environment

All organisms compete for food and space. As a result, every organism, directly or indirectly, affects every other organism. This total interaction of organisms makes up the biotic environment.

The largest effect of the biotic environment may be seen in the struggle for food (energy). Herbivores compete with herbivores for a limited supply of plants. Carnivores compete with carnivores for a limited supply of herbivores. Parasites attack living plants and animals. Scavengers find their food in dead and decaying organisms.

Plants, too, enter the struggle. Although they make food, they must still compete for energy and space. Forest trees that grow tall and slender will obtain sunlight. Larger plants deprive smaller plants of soil and water. Older plants limit the places where seedlings may take root.

Thus, the biotic environment, like the physical one, has its limiting factors. Often these limitations are indirect. A fungus parasite that destroys plants on which certain herbivores depend reduces the number of herbivores. If the herbivore is specialized in its diet and can eat no other food, and if the work of the fungus is complete, the plant-eater faces extinction.

COMPETITION. Since food and space are limited, competition is the rule in nature. Lions compete with hyenas for a zebra carcass. Birds compete with each other for nesting sites. Sometimes competition is not spectacular. A desert plant surrounded

41–3   Life zones change with increasing altitude as they change with increasing latitude. What environmental factors determine these changes?

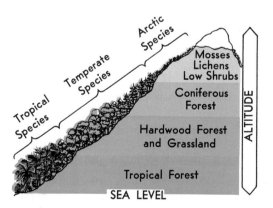

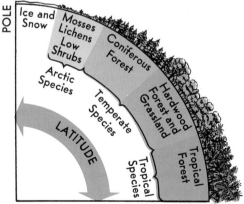

41–4 A desert plant surrounded by a bare zone has successfully competed with other plants for a limited supply of water.

eat their prey. Lions prey upon zebras and antelopes. Wolves prey upon deer, and occasionally upon sheep. Hawks prey upon small mammals, snakes, and other birds. Predators are adapted to their way of life in a number of ways. Some predators are strong and swift and have sharp teeth. Others have sharp claws and beaks for tearing flesh.

Biologically, predation is often considered a one-sided condition from which the predator alone benefits. This is not always the case. Predation is a biotic interaction affecting the population of both organisms. Although individual animals are killed, the population may benefit by having its weaker members weeded out. The predator may even be harmed when prey is abundant! Abundant prey increases the predator's own population. Now the larger predator population requires more prey to sustain it and may face starvation as a result.

SCAVENGING. Herbivores browse on living plants. Predators stalk and feed upon living animals. Unlike either of these, *scavengers* are organisms that feed upon dead organisms. Scavengers may eat what predators have left, or they may feed upon organisms that have died naturally. Scavengers in-

by a zone of bare soil has successfully outstripped its competitors in using the limited supply of water.

Competition can occur between members of the same species or different species. Competition among members of the same species dooms the weak and weeds them out of the species. This process regulates population size and induces evolutionary change through natural selection. Competition among organisms of different species may lead to other results. Two or more herbivore species competing for the same supply of food may increase the population of one species at the expense of the other. The extinction of many large mammals in the past may have resulted from this type of competition.

PREDATION. Predation is the devouring of one organism by another. The term *predator*, however, is more often used to describe carnivorous animals that kill and

41–5 Scavenger mushrooms, as other saprophytes, aid in the recycling of essential chemicals.

clude such diverse animals as vultures, jackals, and crayfish, as well as numerous kinds of insects. Saprophytic fungi and bacteria are also scavengers. The fungi and bacteria decompose the lifeless remains of many kinds of plants and animals.

Scavenging is of prime importance in the economy of nature. Scavengers consume the remains of billions of organisms, large as well as small. In so doing they make possible the reuse of chemicals essential for the growth of living things. Without scavengers these chemicals would remain bound in lifeless organisms, unavailable for the metabolism of the living.

PARASITISM. Parasitism is a condition in which one organism, the parasite, lives in or on another organism, the host. The parasite obtains its nourishment from the host. Parasitism is a common way of life in all kinds of environments. Nearly all organisms harbor one or more species of parasites. Furthermore, parasites may harbor parasites that live on them. Thus, the number of parasites far exceeds the number of free-living organisms.

Parasites are generally small and include most of the forms of life: viruses, monerans, protists, and many invertebrate animals. Flatworms and roundworms are often parasitic upon larger animals. Some roundworms even infest plants. Arthropods, such as lice and ticks, feed upon the blood of vertebrates. Many kinds of protozoa and bacteria cause disease in their hosts. Fungi, such as rusts, smuts, and blights, attack and destroy higher plants. Viruses are completely parasitic, living only inside living cells. A virus living in a pathogenic bacterium is really a parasite upon a parasite.

Although parasites harm the host, the degree of damage varies widely. Tapeworms may cause little harm in the intestine of the cow or horse. However, a heavy infection of hookworm in the human may cause severe anemia or even death. A parasite that kills its host loses its own source of food. On the other hand, a parasite that allows its host to survive insures its own survival. A long term parasite-host relationship may be considered an evolutionary adaptation. In sickle-cell anemia (see page 160), the sickling of red blood cells increases the individual's tolerance to the malarial parasites. This implies that sickle-cell anemia is a long-term parasitic relationship, which, in this case, is helpful.

SYMBIOSIS. One of the most intriguing relationships between organisms is symbiosis. *Symbiosis* is the close association between two unrelated species in which neither is harmed and one or both derive benefit. Examples of symbiosis abound in nature. In lichens, the fungus absorbs moisture, while the alga makes food for both. In a certain species of *Hydra*, green protists live in the cells and release oxygen, while the hydra's cells release carbon dioxide for the protists. In termites, intestinal flagellates digest wood, which serves as food for both insect and protist.

Mutualism is a symbiotic association in which both partners benefit. In most cases of mutualism, the dependence of the partners on each other is so great that neither can survive alone. Where a symbiotic relationship benefits only one partner, the association is called *commensalism*. One example of commensalism is the association between the shark and a smaller fish, the remora. The remora attaches itself to the shark by means of a suction disc on its head. Thus transported, the remora obtains scraps of food from the shark's kill. The shark receives no benefit from this association, but merely tolerates its "hitch hiker."

The Interrelationships of Living Things

The interrelationships among living things are frequently so complex that they may lead to some surprising conclusions. Charles

41–6 In their commensalistic relationship, the remora eats scraps of the shark's food, while the shark is neither benefited nor harmed.

Darwin, for example, once suggested that a relationship existed between cats and clover! Red clover, he explained, is pollinated solely by the actions of bumble bees. The underground nests of the bees are frequently destroyed by field mice. Likewise, the number of field mice is held in check by cats. More cats means fewer mice. Fewer mice means more bees. More bees means more clover seed. Keeping many cats, then, insures a good clover crop!

Darwin's amusing fable may have been facetious. Yet a more serious problem recently threatened the inhabitants of Borneo when complex interrelationships on that island were disturbed. In order to rid the rural interior of flies, health officials launched a drive to destroy them with the insecticide DDT. The DDT killed the flies, but small lizards feeding on the poisoned insects also sickened and died. Cats ate the lizards and also died of DDT poisoning. Soon the rats overmultiplied and threatened the island with plague spread by rat fleas. The situation became so serious that the same health officials ordered the emergency parachuting of cats into interior villages to restore the balance.

THE ECOSYSTEM. Although we have described the physical and biotic parts of the environment, this division of the environment is essentially artificial. The living and nonliving factors are so interconnected that it is difficult to separate them. The ecologist views the physical and biotic environments, plus the interaction between them, as a single unit called the *ecosystem.*

Within the ecosystem, materials circulate through food chains and chemical cycles. Energy, however, is continually lost as useless heat through the metabolism of organisms. New energy enters the ecosystem, replacing that which is lost. This is the main contribution of green plants and autotrophic protists. They trap the radiant energy of sunlight and store it in food.

The ecologist may study a limited ecosystem such as a lake, a meadow, or a desert. But each of these systems is influenced by a bordering system. Self-contained ecosystems are, therefore, difficult to establish.

FOOD CHAINS AND FOOD WEBS. The most common interrelationship among organisms is the *food chain.* A food chain may be thought of in terms of Jonathan Swift's satiric verse:

Great fleas have little fleas upon their
  backs to bite 'em.
And little fleas have lesser fleas, and so
  ad infinitum.
And great fleas themselves, in turn,
  have greater fleas to go on;
While these have greater still, and
  greater still, and so on.

Each organism is a link in a chain, transferring food (energy) to the next link. The first link in any food chain is a green plant or protist. They alone make food from inorganic materials. They alone store energy. Autotrophs, therefore, are called *producer organisms.* Since animals cannot make food, they depend on plants for their

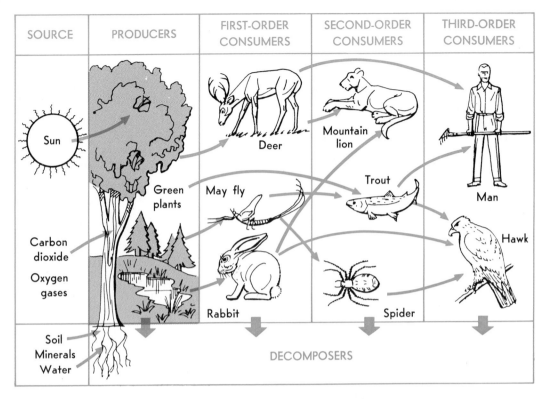

SOURCE	PRODUCERS	FIRST-ORDER CONSUMERS	SECOND-ORDER CONSUMERS	THIRD-ORDER CONSUMERS

Sun

Green plants

Carbon dioxide

Oxygen gases

Soil
Minerals
Water

Deer

May fly

Rabbit

Mountain lion

Trout

Spider

Man

Hawk

DECOMPOSERS

41–7 Food Web. In a food web, food energy is transferred from its primary source in green plants to other organisms linked together by their nutritional relationships.

nourishment. Animals, then, are referred to as *consumer organisms*. Depending on their habits, animals eat producers or other consumers, or both.

From the production base created by autotrophs, different food chains arise. For example, plant lice pierce the stems of plants and suck the sap. Carnivorous insects feed upon plant lice and are, in turn, eaten by spiders. Spiders are eaten by sparrows. Hawks devour sparrows.

Some food chains are long. Others are short. A chain can be long if the consumer links consist of small animals. Tiny insects, for example, can be eaten by those that are only slightly larger. The chain can then continue as the links gradually increase in size. When larger animals form

the consuming links, the chain is likely to be short. Western deer, for example, graze on plants. They are preyed upon by mountain lions, and there the food chain stops.

Food chains linking consuming animals in a straight line are not common in nature. This is so because few animals restrict themselves to only one type of food. Most predators eat several kinds of prey and have, in turn, several kinds of enemies. A rodent, for example, may occupy different positions in different food chains. He may eat several types of plants, or even smaller rodents. The same rodent may then be devoured by a hawk, a coyote, or even a cat. This means that food chains generally branch in several directions and crisscross into a nutritional fabric that biologists call *food webs.*

Food webs are exceedingly difficult to trace because they are subject to continual change. Certain consumers (rats, for example) eat plant as well as animal material. If one type of food becomes scarce, they switch to another. This temporarily alters the pattern of the food web.

FOOD AND POPULATION PYRAMIDS. Consuming animals convert the organisms they eat into their own body tissue. But this conversion results in a loss of mass. A herbivore eating ten pounds of grass cannot make ten pounds of herbivore tissue from it. Part is indigestable, part is water, and part is converted into energy. If a carnivore devours the herbivore, even further loss occurs. Ten pounds of herbivore will not make ten pounds of carnivore. These losses occur at every link in the chain. The longer the chain, the greater the total loss from producer to final consumer.

Because of this fundamental fact, *food pyramids* are formed in every community of organisms. The protoplasmic mass of the producing base constantly diminishes as more consumer links are added to the food chain. At the apex of the pyramid are the final consumers, the highest links in the chain. Their combined weight is only a fraction of that of the producer organisms that form the base of the pyramid. In the plant→cow→man food chain, one estimate indicates that approximately 4000 pounds of alfalfa are needed to produce one yearling weighing 550 pounds, and almost 5 such yearlings would be needed to feed one boy of 105 pounds at age 12.

Food pyramids are also *population pyramids* because of another fundamental fact: predatory animals are generally larger than the animals they consume. Thus, they require large numbers of prey to remain alive. A field of plants, for example, can support several thousand insects, but only

41–8 Simplified food pyramid of predatory animals begins with autotrophic plankton in the sea. Food energy loss from plankton to lion is indicated by pyramid shape.

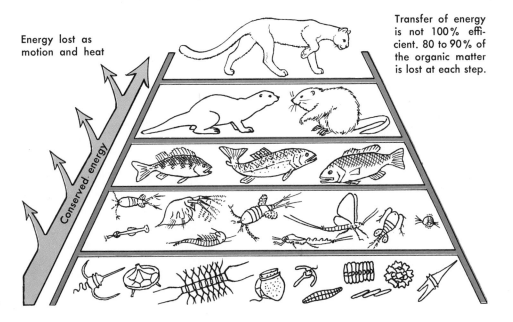

Energy lost as motion and heat

Conserved energy

Transfer of energy is not 100% efficient. 80 to 90% of the organic matter is lost at each step.

several dozen birds that feed upon the insects. A still smaller number of hawks can be supported by the insect-eating birds. Thus, as food chains lengthen, the consumers become larger and fewer in number until the apex of the pyramid is reached. Here the consumer population is the smallest. Consumers at every level in the pyramid act as checks on the population numbers of those below them. The importance of the population pyramid is this: it is one of the principal mechanisms by which a balance of species is achieved. Can you think of several population pyramids?

Chemical Cycles

All living things are composed of basic elements such as oxygen, nitrogen, carbon, hydrogen, calcium, and phosphorus. However, the total amount of these elements on our planet is fixed. This means that they must be used over and over again by successive generations of plants and animals. The use and reuse of these materials is an excellent illustration of interdependence on a vast scale. One significant feature of a food chain is that it is a series of transfers of these vital materials from one organism to another. Although consumers at the top of a pyramid do not transfer food to other consumers, the elements, nevertheless, do not become locked in. When the top consumers die, they are decomposed by bacteria and their elements are returned to the soil. This provides for new plant growth, which begins a new cycle of interdependence.

THE WATER CYCLE. Water is continuously circulated on earth between the oceans and the atmosphere. The sequence of events known as the *water cycle* begins with the evaporation of water from the oceans. The evaporated water becomes part of the atmosphere. When the atmosphere is chilled, its water vapor condenses. The condensed water falls to the earth as rain or snow. A small portion is also condensed in the form of dew. Of this water, some is described as *runoff*. Runoff flows into streams and rivers and is rapidly returned to the oceans. Some of the rain and snow soaks into the soil and is used by plants. The remainder of the water penetrates

41–9   Water Cycle. Movement of water to and from the air is powered by solar energy.

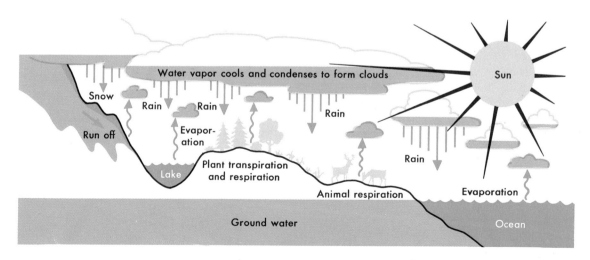

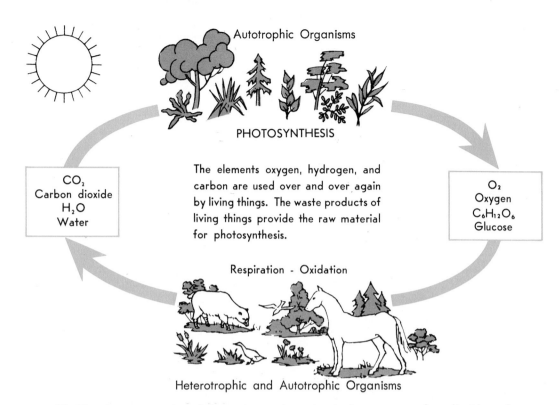

Autotrophic Organisms

PHOTOSYNTHESIS

| CO₂ | Carbon dioxide | H₂O | Water |

The elements oxygen, hydrogen, and carbon are used over and over again by living things. The waste products of living things provide the raw material for photosynthesis.

| O₂ | Oxygen | C₆H₁₂O₆ | Glucose |

Respiration - Oxidation

Heterotrophic and Autotrophic Organisms

41–10   A representation of the part organisms play in the oxygen-carbon dioxide cycle.

deeply into the ground and becomes *ground water*. Ground water may accumulate and remain deep in the earth for many years. Eventually, ground water also returns to the ocean.

The water cycle makes the land habitable for life. Without the continuous return of fresh water to the land, the earth would become a vast desert and life would perish. Plants absorb water from the soil. Animals obtain water either by drinking it directly or obtaining it from their foods. Furthermore, both plants and animals release water to the cycle. Plants transpire water from their leaves. Animals release water through their skin, their lungs, and through their excretory system. Even after the death of the organism, the return of water to the atmosphere continues through evaporation and decay.

THE OXYGEN-CARBON DIOXIDE CYCLE. A huge reservoir of oxygen exists in the earth's atmosphere. This oxygen is being continually used up by the respiration of all living things. Oxygen would disappear from our atmosphere if it were not somehow replaced. Autotrophic organisms constantly return oxygen to the air by the process of photosynthesis. Calculations indicate that without the work of the autotrophs, atmospheric oxygen would not last more than 2500 years. Similarly, the autotrophs consume the available supply of carbon dioxide as they use it to produce carbohydrates. However, carbon dioxide is replaced in the atmosphere by the respiration of organisms. This exchange of oxygen and carbon dioxide between living things through the medium of the atmosphere is called the *oxygen-carbon dioxide cycle*.

41–11 In a balanced aquarium, plants provide food and oxygen, fish and snails provide carbon dioxide and wastes. The wastes supply nitrogen and minerals to the plants.

THE NITROGEN CYCLE. Another illustration of the vast circular movement of key elements may be seen in the *nitrogen cycle*. (See Figure 12–5, page 206.) Although nitrogen makes up almost 80 per cent of the air, it is not useful to most organisms as free nitrogen. However, *nitrogen-fixing bacteria* living in the soil on the roots of plants like peas, clover, and beans change atmospheric nitrogen into nitrates. The green plants use the nitrates to build proteins. Food chains that begin with these green plants transfer the proteins to a succession of animal consumers.

Nitrogen is returned to the soil in the form of animal wastes, or when the plants and animals decay after death. In the soil, *ammonifying bacteria* decompose the nitrogen-rich material into ammonia. Ammonia is then converted into nitrates by *nitrifying bacteria,* or into free nitrogen in the air by *denitrifying* bacteria, thus completing the cycle.

THE BALANCED AQUARIUM. An excellent place to observe the different chemical cycles at work is in a balanced acquarium. A fish that is kept in an aquarium by itself will soon die from a lack of oxygen unless the water is changed at regular intervals. If aquatic plants are added, however, they replenish the oxygen supply. Then the water need not be changed.

A balanced aquarium can be established by careful trial. The right number of plants will supply food and oxygen for some fish and a few snails. The animals will, in turn, supply the plants with carbon dioxide. Their wastes will also supply the nitrogen and minerals that the plants need. Careful experiment with the number of plants will establish a balance. Then it will not be necessary to change the water or add food. The evaporation of water that will occur can be reduced by providing a glass cover over the aquarium.

The Carrying Capacity of the Environment

A single cow grazing in a small enclosed pasture may grow to full size, be well nourished, and yield a maximum of milk or meat. When a second cow grazes in the same pasture, however, the result might be that both animals are undernourished and scrawny. Obviously, a limited pasture that can support one cow well may support two cows poorly. Suppose a third cow is added to the same pasture. Again, it seems probable that this might result in starvation for all three animals. The pasture has a *carrying capacity* that is measured by the number of cattle it can support.

The term carrying capacity has a precise meaning for biologists. Before we can understand it exactly, we must learn more about another term used by biologists. You know that there are producers (autotrophs), consumers (heterotrophs), and decomposers (bacteria and molds) in any ecosystem. The combined weight of these three kinds of organisms in any ecosystem is termed its *biomass*. The size of the biomass varies and depends upon how efficiently materials and energy circulate in the ecosystem. We cannot expect the size of the biomass to increase indefinitely, for the ecosystem imposes limits upon it. This

would be somewhat like expecting a large oak tree to grow in a small flower pot. The carrying capacity of an ecosystem is the maximum biomass it can support. Thus, the carrying capacity is the upper limit of the biomass imposed by the environment.

THE ECOSPHERE: THE EARTH IN SPACE. Life on the planet Earth is confined to a thin shell of sea, land, and air. This shell extends from the bottom of the oceans, several miles deep, to the upper reaches of the atmosphere. Within this biotic shell exists an enormous variety of organisms: bacteria in the ooze of the sea bottoms, plankton and fish in the surface waters of the oceans, fungi and insects in the soil, flowering plants and vertebrates living on the land, and spores of microorganisms borne aloft by currents of air. The organisms inhabiting this planetary shell constitute the *biosphere*. The biosphere is thus a layer of living matter that covers and encircles the entire earth.

The habitable zone of the earth's surface is composed of many different environments. Each environment is characterized by the interaction of the living things it supports with the environment itself. Many different ecosystems are thus established. The total number of these ecosystems constitutes the *ecosphere*. The biosphere makes up the living part of the ecosphere. The different parts of the habitable zone of the earth's surface make up the physical environment of the ecosphere. All of the supplies of water, air, food, and energy circulate through the ecosphere on a worldwide scale to produce the earth's biomass. The ecosphere is thus the planet Earth's single ecosystem, completely self contained. Only radiant energy from the sun enters the ecosphere to provide the energy for the vast network of life.

POPULATION PRESSURE AND RESOURCES. One paramecium in a jar of stagnant water divides into two, then four, eight, and so on. As the number of paramecia increases, the supply of food acts as a control over the increase. The tendency of living things to increase faster than their food supply is called *population pressure*. In nature, it may mean starvation for many animals.

Long ago, Darwin pointed out that all organisms tend to overpopulate, but that certain fixed factors in their environment control their unlimited increase. Their populations, he believed, would be limited by three factors: available food, disease, and predators.

Modern ecological studies show that for many organisms this is not entirely the case. Populations of certain birds and mammals, for example, have been observed to increase rapidly, then to decline with equal suddenness. Often, these population buildups and die-offs occur in cycles that follow each other with regularity over the years. Lemmings, small woodchuck-like animals of the north countries, undergo periodic "mi-grations," about which there has been much speculation. Scandinavian arctic lemmings migrate between the lowlands and the highlands each year, but this seems to be merely a seasonal movement, not related to particular pressures. North American lemmings, however, during times of high population density, do undergo periods of random wandering (though not actual migrations).

Many scientists believe that, for certain species, space itself may be a limiting factor. As overcrowding occurs, interactions within the species probably retard further population growth.

POPULATION LIMITS. The giant puffball fungus can liberate 100 trillion spores when mature. If every spore developed into a new puffball, the volume of fungi would exceed 400 times the volume of the earth. Even a pair of elephants could, in a few centuries, leave enough descendants to overflow the earth. Obviously, neither fungi nor elephants can reproduce this rapidly. Nevertheless, the reproduction of more offspring than can survive is a fundamental characteristic of living things.

The tendency of an organism to fill the environment with its own kind is called its *biotic potential*. This potential is always greater than the environment can accommodate. Expanding populations soon run into environmental resistance. Their numbers are limited by the environment's carrying capacity. As the limits of food and space are reached, starvation, disease, and predation take their toll. The death rate increases. When the death rate equals the reproductive rate, population stabilization occurs. Some organisms are more successful than others in increasing their populations. Some successful organisms exploit their environments to a greater degree by adopting new food habits. Others invade new environments to the detriment of established species. Ultimately, however, new limits are reached and their populations stabilize.

41–12 Much speculation exists on what causes the wandering behavior of lemming populations.

IMPORTANT POINTS

● Living things can exist only in close association with their physical environment and with other living things. Ecology is the study of the complex interrelationships of organisms and their total environment.

● The physical environment contains certain limiting factors such as air, water, light, temperature, soil and climate. The limitations of the biotic environment are largely concerned with food relationships. Competition, predation, parasitism, scavenging, and symbiosis establish the organism's place in the total environment.

● The living and nonliving factors of the environment, plus the interactions among them, form the ecosystem. Within the ecosystem, materials circulate from one organism to another. Green plants and protists continually add new energy which they obtain from sunlight. The relationships between producer organisms (autotrophs) and consumer organisms (heterotrophs) are by way of food chains, webs, and pyramids.

● Chemical cycles illustrate the broad pattern of dependence among all organisms on earth. The use of oxygen in respiration is related to the consumption of carbon dioxide in photosynthesis. Nitrogen is converted from one compound to another as it is used by different forms of life. Water circulates continuously between organisms and the physical environment.

● An ecosystem has a limited carrying capacity in terms of the number of organisms it can support. Since the biotic potential of living things is toward greater and greater numbers, limitations of food and space help stabilize populations.

● All of the earth's ecosystems make up the ecosphere. The ecosphere is a closed, self contained system. Only the energy of sunlight enters to power the earth's network of life.

REVIEW QUESTIONS

1. List several limiting factors in the physical environment.
2. Why would life be impossible without the work of scavengers?
3. Distinguish between a food chain and a food web.
4. What is a food pyramid?
5. Why is the oxygen-carbon dioxide exchange between autotrophs and heterotrophs of fundamental importance to all living things?
6. List several types of bacteria associated with the nitrogen cycle and explain the function of each type.
7. Distinguish between the physical and the biotic environment.
8. What is the carrying capacity of the environment?
9. What is an ecosystem?
10. Distinguish between mutualism and commensalism.

CHECK YOUR UNDERSTANDING

11. How might a drought in Africa be responsible for a reduction in the number of leopards there?

12. Why are bacteria of decay necessary for the continuation of life?
13. Why are predatory animals valuable?
14. Where might arctic plants be found in the temperate zone?
15. What is meant by biotic potential?
16. Why cannot the population of an organism increase indefinitely?
17. What food chains may have produced a breakfast consisting of cereal and milk, bacon and eggs, and buttered toast?
18. Why is it that birds and mammals are more widely distributed than are reptiles and amphibians?
19. Explain why the number of parasites is greater than the number of free-living organisms.
20. What value might some parasites have?

RESEARCH PROJECTS AND REPORTS

1. Obtain information from your school or public library and prepare a report on one of the following topics:

The Water Cycle	**Scavengers**
Life in Caves	**The Science of Ecology**

2. *Nitrogen-fixing Bacteria:* On a field trip, collect some clover, bean, or alfalfa plants by removing them from the soil and carefully washing loose soil away from the roots. Examine the roots for swellings or nodules.

   Return to the classroom laboratory for further examination. Make slides of nitrogen-fixing bacteria for examination under the microscope. This may be done by crushing nodules between two slides, then staining the crushed material with methylene blue. Make a sketch of what you see. What is the importance of these bacteria?

3. *Mutualism in Lichens:* On a field trip, collect some lichens which may be found on tree barks, rocks, and even fence posts. Lichens are flat, papery, and pale green.

   Tease a small bit of lichen apart in a drop of water on a slide. Examine under a microscope. Can you find the algal cells enmeshed in the filaments of the fungi? What part does each partner play in their association? Can either partner survive independently? How do lichens reproduce?

4. *Overpopulation:* The number of offspring that is potentially possible in a few generations may surprise you. You may wish to make the following calculations:
   (a) Count the kernels on an ear of corn. Assume that each kernel will mature into a corn plant that will produce at least one ear with the same number of kernels. How many corn plants will there be in five generations?
   (b) A female frog lays 200 eggs. Suppose half this number hatches into females who lay the same number of eggs when they mature. How many descendents will there be in ten generations?
   (c) Under favorable conditions, a protozoan may divide every half hour. Assume this rate of division continues for one week. Calculate the number of organisms at the end of that time.

FURTHER READING

Ecology. Peter Farb and the Editors of LIFE. Time, Inc., New York, N.Y. A strikingly illustrated account of the world's environments and the interrelationships of species that inhabit them.

Basic Ecology. Ralph and Mildred Buchsbaum. Boxwood Press, Pittsburgh, Pa. A well written and well illustrated introduction to the science of ecology.

"**Toxic Substances and Ecological Cycles.**" George M. Woodwell. *Scientific American,* March, 1967, page 24. Such poisonous substances as radioactive isotopes and DDT, if released in the environment, may enter ecological cycles and become distributed on a world-wide basis.

"**Habitat Selection.**" Stanley C. Wecker. *Scientific American,* October, 1964, page 109. Experiments with mice indicate that both heredity and learning play a role in an animal's selection of its environment.

"**Life on the Human Skin.**" Mary J. Marples. *Scientific American,* January, 1969, page 108. The human skin is a distinct ecosystem. It is an environment inhabited by populations of microorganisms that interact with it and with each other.

CHAPTER

42

Life Communities

A LIFE COMMUNITY is a group of different organisms sharing a common environment. These organisms interact, particularly through their food (energy) relationships. If certain life communities contain both producer and consumer organisms, they are self-supporting. One of the simplest of the life communities may be found within a single drop of pond water. Algae make their own food. Some protozoa eat the algae. Still other protozoa feed upon the algae-feeders. Thus, the water drop community is a self-supporting community.

Since physical conditions on the land and in the water vary widely, life communties inhabiting these environments also vary. Each life community develops its own characteristics in relation to its environment and is called a *biome*. Thus, distinct biomes develop in deserts, grasslands, forests, oceans, and bodies of fresh water.

Biomes have a dynamic structure, subject to constant change. Physical changes in climate, rainfall, and the geology of a region alter the conditions under which certain species have survived. Organisms better adapted to the new conditions may arrive in the region and compete with the older species. The older species, unable to

compete with better adapted rivals, may perish. Thus, there is a succession of new organisms struggling to establish themselves in the new conditions of a changing environment. As change follows change, the biome is altered; the newer, better adapted organisms eventually dominate the biome.

Distribution of Species

Have you ever wondered why certain regions have characteristic organisms that reside in them? Polar bears live in the Arctic; penguins live in the Antarctic. Cacti are found only in the desert; kelps dwell in the surface waters of the sea. If organisms tend to scatter throughout the world, why do many of them inhabit certain limited zones?

What factors account for this uneven distribution of life? Why are polar bears not found in the antarctic regions where conditions are much like their arctic home? Why are the camels of the African and Asian deserts not found in the deserts of North America? One reason is that there must be some means of scattering or dispersing an animal or plant to the new environment. Large organisms tend to be less readily dispersed than very small ones. The monerans, smallest of all living things, are borne aloft by the wind or carried by water to almost every remote region of the earth. The large animals must walk or swim to new environments. Large plants are dispersed by special adaptations of their seeds. These adaptations enable plants to be scattered by wind, water, and animals. A second problem of dispersal is that an organism that reaches a new environment must be able to adapt itself to the new conditions of that environment. The organism must be able to compete successfully with established species. Many plants and animals have become too specialized in their established environment to become adapted to a new one; hence, they tend to remain in the regions where they first evolved.

42–1   Although they could live there, penguins are not found in the Arctic. Why?

The combination of two factors, then, effects the distribution of living things on the earth: dispersal and adaptability. Both must work together to enable an organism to establish itself in a new environment. The polar bear illustrates the point very well. Although apparently well adapted to the antarctic, the polar bear is not found there because he simply cannot get there.

METHODS OF DISPERSAL. How do organisms spread to new environments? Think about the organisms with which you are familiar. Among the animals are those that can crawl, run, swim, or fly. These creatures can move from one place to another. Even monerans and protists frequently have some means for moving from place to place. Many protists and nearly all the members of the plant kingdom have no means of locomotion whatsoever. Yet protists and plants are almost world-wide in their distribution. What methods of dispersal scattered them so widely?

Wind is a common agent that disperses many organisms. Small invertebrates, like spiders and insects, can be swept along by the wind. The spores of bacteria and some of the protists, as well as the seeds of many plants, all are dispersed by currents of air. In a similar manner, currents of water carry many organisms large distances from their native habitat. Small streams lead into larger streams. Larger streams merge into rivers. The rivers lead into the sea, sometimes carrying many forms of life into the ocean.

Animals also help to disperse many forms of life. Birds ingest seeds and eliminate them at a distance from the parent plant. Animals carry seeds attached to their fur and scatter them far afield. Man himself has been a principal factor in distributing all sorts of plants and animals to new regions of the earth. Sometimes man does this knowingly; at other times, however, he disperses organisms accidentally.

The dispersal of organisms sometimes leads to unusual results. In 1892, a tiny island with shrubs and several trees 30 feet tall was discovered in the Atlantic Ocean off the coast of North America.

But the "island" turned out to be a large man-made raft! Covered with a layer of soil and decaying matter, it supported a small life community. The raft had washed out to sea years before and was now a floating biome. Wind borne seeds, spores, bacteria, and protists had all reached the raft. Birds dropped large seeds, bits of debris, as well as soil that clung to their feet. The "island" was an unusual example of how an "open" environment becomes populated by the dispersion of organisms from other places.

PHYSICAL AND BIOTIC BARRIERS TO DISPERSAL. The most obvious barriers to the dispersal of an organism are the physical conditions that impede it. Geographic conditions often set the limits by which an organism is bound. The migration of a land animal may be halted by an ocean, a river, a mountain range, or a desert. A grassland herbivore cannot reach an adjacent grassland if a mountain range separates the two. A mountain goat cannot reach the next mountain if it is separated from it by a broad desert.

Even in the ocean, physical conditions impose barriers upon the free dispersal of living things. The existence of cool and warm currents in the ocean is well known. The Gulf Stream is one of the best known warm water currents. An organism that is a warm water dweller cannot cross a cold current and migrate to another warm region of the ocean. The temperature barrier is just as real as the desert barrier is to the mountain goat. Variations in the amount of salt (salinity) of areas in the ocean also act as barriers to the migration of marine forms.

Climate is an effective physical barrier to the distribution of organisms even after dispersal has occurred. Tropical plants, for example, generally will not survive in temperate zones because of reduced temperature and light. The seeds of warm region plants do not germinate when transported to the Arctic. Many cases have been found in which two similar species of mammals live on opposite sides of the same mountain, but do not interbreed. Each species is capable of scaling the range and thus migrating to the other side. But neither species, it appears, is able to adapt to the cold climate of the upper elevations. Hence, the barrier is the climate, and not the mountain's height.

Biotic factors also control the establishment of a species in a new environment. Birds must compete with other birds as well as predators in a new territory. Sometimes the competition is too keen for the newcomer. Wind borne seeds may be unable to germinate in a new environment because the soil is unsuitable, or because native herbivores eat the seedlings before they can become established.

Biomes of the World

The biomes established on the land are different from the biomes of the sea. Furthermore, there are varying conditions under which organisms grow and interact on the land itself. The kind of soil, the amount of rainfall, the amount of solar radiation, and the nearness of mountain ranges or large bodies of water all influence the kind of biome that will develop. The sea, too, has varying conditions that affect the growth of organisms. The temperature and depth of water are important factors. The intensity of the light filtered through is another. The salinity is not constant and may influence the growth of organisms. All these factors, the varying physical factors on land and sea, influence the biome that arises in a particular area or region.

There are no exact boundaries separating one biome from another. Adjacent biomes fade imperceptibly into each other. Imagine a motorist traveling toward the north from Florida. He soon becomes aware of the

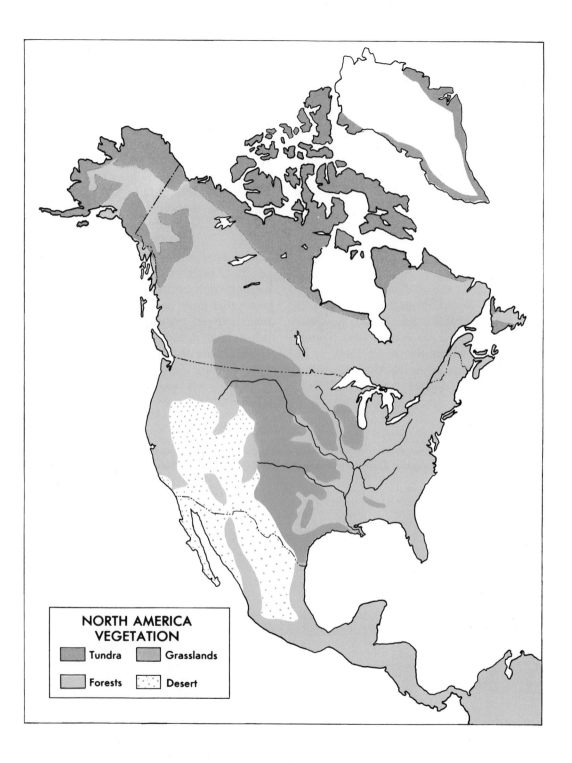

NORTH AMERICA VEGETATION

- Tundra
- Grasslands
- Forests
- Desert

42–2   The North American Biomes

changing landscapes as he proceeds to cooler latitudes. Palm trees become sparse and finally disappear. Spanish moss, so common in semitropical regions where it grows from trees, is soon left behind. Birds and insects of the semitropics become rarer. Then the broad-leaved maples and oaks appear. The pines and spruce become more numerous. The flora and fauna of Maine are different from Florida, but the transition has been gradual and not abrupt.

Ecologists have identified distinct biomes on the land and in the waters of the earth. Each biome is a product of its region with characteristic plants and animals. Land biomes include the tundras, deserts, grasslands, and forests. Water biomes exist in both fresh and salt water. Generally, water biomes are less variable than land biomes, since conditions in the water tend to be more constant than on the land. Nevertheless, there are distinct marine and fresh water biomes.

THE TUNDRA. The northernmost fringes of Asia, Europe, and North America encircle the polar region and the Arctic Ocean. In this extensive region, the earth remains permanently frozen a few feet below the surface. The surface soil thaws for only two months of the year, permitting plants to grow briefly in the rays of a summer sun that does not set. Biologists call this Arctic biome the *tundra*. Tundra is a Russian word that means timberline. A timberline is an imaginary line beyond which there are no trees.

The brief summer thaw of the tundra produces marshes and shallow ponds. The melting snow nourishes the few species of plants that grow in this forbidding land. Although dwarf conifers are fairly common, lichens and mosses are the main producer organisms on the barren land. Despite the brief growing season, a few flowers growing as dense mats lend their brilliance to an otherwise drab environment. Some grasses,

42–3   TUNDRA vegetation consists mostly of grasses, sedges, mosses, and lichens. The topsoil thaws during the short summer season, but the subsoil is frozen the year round.

adapted to the short summer, grow rapidly and cover wide areas. Producing their seeds quickly, the grasses provide food and cover for the animals that thrive in summer.

For the few short summer weeks, the tundra teems with active plant and animal life. During this period, the ever-present sun stimulates plant growth. Insects abound. Waterfowl nest and rear their young in the marshes and ponds. Predators, such as the Arctic fox, prey upon the birds and abundant rodents. Caribou and reindeer browse upon the increased vegetation and they, in turn, are preyed upon by wolves.

Abruptly, the summer ends and winter arrives. The water freezes. Food disappears. The birds and most of the larger mammals migrate to other regions. The animals that remain burrow under the snow for shelter. A few, like the musk ox, are able to endure the harsh winter. Generally, however, the tundra is almost devoid of animal life in winter.

The tundra biome is not found in the Southern Hemisphere for there are no land masses at corresponding southern latitudes. At high altitudes, a few tundra-like biomes exist in the United States. Rocky Mountain National Park in Colorado, for example, has an alpine tundra at an elevation of 11,000 feet.

THE DESERT. The limiting factor of the desert is its dryness. Most deserts receive fewer than ten inches of rainfall annually, far less than is necessary to support most plant life.

Many of the smaller desert plants are active only during the short periods of rain. Their seeds germinate quickly. Growth is rapid. The desert "blooms overnight" and its drabness is suddenly transformed into a thing of beauty. Seed production is speeded up before the next dry spell returns. The plants wither and die leaving only seeds that survive until the next period of rain.

42–4 **DESERT** communities are characterized by low precipitation and a high rate of evaporation. Desert plants grow far apart and do not compete for sunlight. Roots of plants, which spread out widely from the base, lie close to the surface of the soil. When rain falls, water is quickly absorbed and stored in the plants' thick stems. Because producers are scarce, there are few consumers, and animal life is sparse. Deserts are hot by day and cold by night.

Larger desert plants survive in other ways. The root system of the sagebrush extends deep into the soil for the water it requires. The large cacti store water in their thick, leathery stems. The leaves, which in most other plants are a source of water loss, are reduced to spines. The spines also protect the plant from animals.

Animals of the desert also adapt to their dry environment. Since daytime temperatures in some deserts may reach 150 degrees Fahrenheit, most of the animals are

42–5　GRASSLANDS develop where there is not enough water to support a forest. Organisms are exposed to a climate of harsh winds and great variations in temperature.

active only at night. During the day snakes and lizards seek the shade of plants and rocks. Small mammals remain in underground burrows. At night mammals venture forth to forage for plant materials. This is the time when snakes and other predators seek out their victims.

One of the best examples of desert adaptation is the kangaroo rat. It never drinks water, but obtains small amounts of it from the seeds it eats. Another source of water is provided by its own metabolism. The animal excretes little. Its kidneys recover most of the water and eliminate waste that is almost dry.

THE GRASSLANDS. Grasslands are found largely in temperate regions. The rainfall in these regions ranges from 10 to 35 inches annually, but is irregular and unevenly distributed. In North America, the grasslands are called plains or prairies. They form the grazing area for cattle and sheep, for the land is suited for the growth of grasses and shrubs. Much of the prairie is ideal for the growth of such cereal grasses as wheat, corn, barley, oats, and rye. Corresponding areas in other countries include the pampas of South America and the steppes of Asia.

Because of the richness of vegetation, grasslands support extensive and varied communities. Insects and spiders are abundant and provide food for many types of ground-nesting birds. Numerous small mammals such as mice, rats, and rabbits feed upon plants and are preyed upon by snakes and larger birds. Before North America was settled by Europeans, huge herds of bison and elk roamed the grasslands from Canada southward into Mexico. The American Indian used them for food and made clothing and shelter from their hides.

Grasslands support more large herbivores than do any other land biomes. On the African grasslands, huge herds of zebras and antelopes graze as primary consumers. All are swift runners, since they are preyed upon by secondary consumers such as lions and leopards. South American grasslands have few herbivores that graze in herds. As a result of this reduced competition, the world's largest rodents have developed in these areas.

A special type of grassland is the *savanna*. A savanna is a flat plain covered with coarse grass and sparsely dotted with trees. Although the grasses are drought resistant, the long dry spells limit the number of trees that can establish themselves. The savannas of Africa are the regions where the elephant, rhinoceros, giraffe, and buffalo are found.

THE TEMPERATE FORESTS. The heavier rainfall that occurs in the forest regions sustains the growth of trees as well as smaller plants. This growth provides food and shelter for a varied abundance of animal life. Depending on latitude and rainfall, different types of forests develop. Where precipitation is especially heavy, as in the tropics or the Pacific Northwest, rain forests develop. In the temperate regions, hardwood forests flourish. Farther north, evergreen forests are more common.

Hardwood forests consist of large stands of beech, maple, walnut, and oak trees. All are deciduous, shedding their leaves each winter. The leaves provide a rich source of organic matter that covers the for-

est floor. Fungi attack the leaves and fallen branches, creating a soft humus in which smaller plants flourish. Seeds provide food for a variety of animals. Woodpeckers drill into the bark seeking insect larvae that live there. Hawks prey upon songbirds and rodents. Deer browse near the forest's edge keeping a wary eye for the predators that stalk them.

North of the hardwood forests but below the tundra, the *taiga* (TIE-guh), or evergreen forest is found. The taiga con-

42–6 MIDDLE LATITUDE DECIDUOUS FOREST. In this forest community the primary producers are broad-leafed trees of many species. A canopy of leaves catches solar radiation. Smaller trees, shrubs, mosses, and ferns share the sunlight. Rainfall is ample at regular intervals. Climate is varied, but not extreme, and there are four well-defined seasons. In autumn, deciduous leaves change color from green to red and gold before falling.

42–7 The taiga's longer, milder summers attract moose and other animals from the tundra.

42–8 The great variety of mosses, vines, and creepers that grow in the tropical rain forest give this biome its rich green color.

sists of conifers, such as spruce, hemlock, fir, and pine trees, whose leaves are laden with the winter snows. Like the tundra to the north, the taiga is a unique biome. Its winters are just as severe but its longer, milder summers account for its larger trees and more varied animal populations. Large mammals, such as moose and bears, are common. Each fall, caribou arrive from the tundra. Lynxes and wolves prey upon the many birds and smaller mammals.

THE TROPICAL RAIN FORESTS. Of all the biomes mentioned, tropical rain forests have the greatest variety of life. Nowhere else on land is so complex a variety of living things seen. A temperate forest may support as many as ten species of trees, although the number is usually smaller. But rain forests of the tropics have a hundred or more. Clinging to them are the epiphytes, vines, and creepers that add to this lush growth.

The precipitation in the rain forest averages 120 inches annually, and temperatures are high the year round. Nurtured by rain and warmth, the trees often reach a height of 200 feet. Their upper branches merge with vines and creepers into a dense canopy that darkens the forest, even at noon. The canopy retards evaporation, thus keeping the forest warm and humid. Large numbers of fungi grow on the forest floor, but green plants, unable to overcome the lack of light, are sparse.

Animal species in the rain forest live both on the ground and in the trees. Wild pigs, small deer, and several species of ground rodents inhabit the forest floor. Squirrels, monkeys, and tree frogs, however, live high above the ground. The large carnivores, such as the leopards and jaguars, hunt their prey both on the ground and in the trees. Insects abound everywhere. Birds nest and find their food in the high matted cover of the trees.

THE MARINE BIOMES. Far removed from the inquiring eyes of man, the sea is the most densely populated pool of life. The oceans, covering two-thirds of the earth, nurture an astounding array of living things, many of them little known to man. For the seemingly endless stretches of the open sea, there appears to be no diversity. The vast stretches of water are interconnected, creating one vast biome that stretches from ocean to ocean encircling the earth. What appears to be uniform, however, is in fact subdivided into regions that are different. Depth is an important factor. Temperature, while not as variable as on the land, changes from the polar to the tropical seas. Along the shores, where land and water meet, still different conditions prevail. Despite a seeming uniformity, biologists usually study marine life by dividing the seas into three convenient regions: the open sea, the ocean deeps, and the shore. (See Figure 42–9 on pages 690–691.)

In the open sea billions of microscopic algae float near the sunlit surface. Protozoa and tiny crustacea find food abundant. The algae, protozoa, and small crustacea make up the *plankton*. Plankton is an important food for small fishes. The small fishes are consumed by larger fishes who are, in turn, eaten by larger fishes. Plankton is sometimes called "pasture of the sea," since it serves the same purpose for marine animals as pastures for land herbivores. One giant, the blue whale, feeds directly on plankton by straining sea water.

The ocean depths have very different forms of life. Since no plants can grow in the inky darkness, deep-sea fishes get their food from the constant stream of organic material that "rains" down from the surface. These strange fishes, frequently equipped with glowing lights, prey upon each other or seize unwary surface dwellers that venture down too far.

The shallow shore waters have a rich variety of life. The gentle slope of the continents provides a sunlit basin where plant life thrives. At the water's edge, ever-changing conditions must be met. The ebb of the tide leaves some organisms dry for several hours each day. Mussels and barnacles attached to tidal rocks close their shells tightly to prevent drying. Clams and marine worms burrow into the moist bottom until the tide returns.

Along the edge of the sea, saltwater marshes and tidal pools develop in the indentations of the coast. Seawater is washed into these low areas by the tide and then remains. Collecting in tidal pools, the seawater is diluted by the rain. During extended periods of drought, however, evaporation increases the salinity of the pool. Thus, an important factor in the tidal pool is the varying salt content of the water. This change in salinity creates problems for the organisms that live in coastal marshes and pools. The algae, grasses, protozoa, crustacea, worms, and mosquito larvae that live in such places can withstand these changes. Few larger animals live here. Herbivores may graze along the edge of the marsh. Waterfowl often feed in the marsh during their long migratory flights, but they are not permanent residents. Some migrant birds return each year to breed and nest in these coastal wetlands.

THE FRESH WATER BIOMES. Scattered over the continents of the earth are the thousands of ponds, lakes, streams, and rivers that make up the fresh water biomes. The major distinction between these biomes is that ponds and lakes are filled with standing water, whereas the water in streams and rivers flows. Such physical factors as temperature, light, depth, and speed of the current influence the kind and number of organisms that live there.

In lakes and ponds, plankton initiates the food chains, much as it does in the sea.

42–9   DISTRIBUTION OF LIFE IN THE OCEAN BIOME

Where the water is clear and the light plentiful, the food-making algae support large communities of consumer organisms: crayfish, insect larvae, snails, and fish. Although the algae are the principal autotrophs, pondweeds, duckweed, and water lilies also add to the food supply.

Depth is an important, limiting factor in standing water biomes. In ponds and lakes, for example, the exchange of essential gases with the atmosphere is confined to the higher water levels. No oxygen penetrates to the lower levels. As a result, the rich organic matter that has accumulated at the bottom is not available to most of the freshwater animals. This organic material can be used only by the bacteria of decay and some larger organisms, such as bloodworms, that respire anaerobically. During cold and windy weather, however, currents may cause bottom water to be brought to the top, which results in "overturn." Overturn temporarily redistributes oxygen and other important materials. However, a sudden freeze

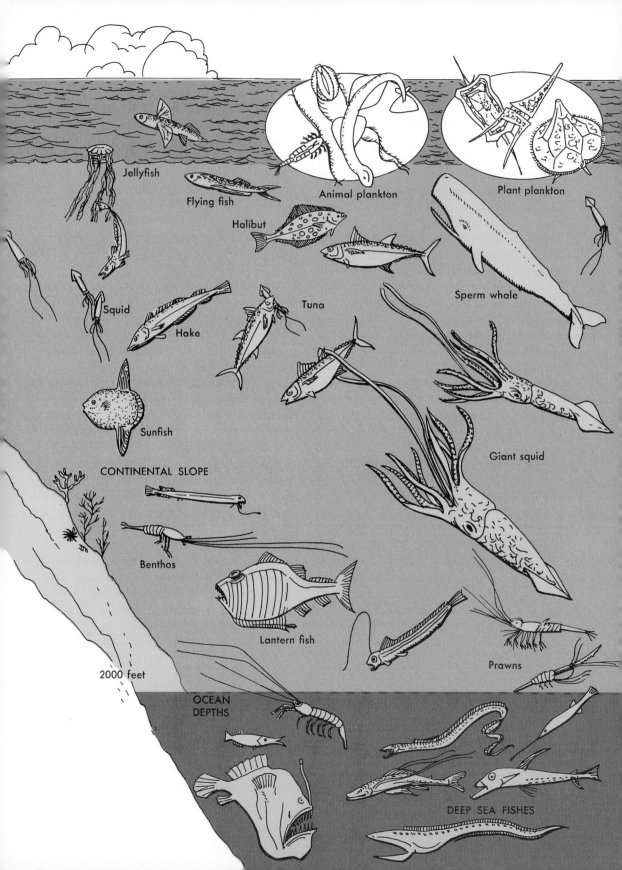

Jellyfish

Flying fish

Animal plankton

Plant plankton

Halibut

Sperm whale

Squid

Hake

Tuna

Sunfish

Giant squid

CONTINENTAL SLOPE

Benthos

Lantern fish

Prawns

2000 feet

OCEAN
DEPTHS

DEEP SEA FISHES

that covers a pond with ice before overturn has occurred may force fish to lower levels where many die of suffocation.

In running-water biomes the organisms must adapt to other conditions. Plankton is usually less dense, resulting in a lower food base for the rest of the community. In certain streams, however, mosses and liverworts grow along the margins. Animals in these biomes avoid being carried downstream and out to sea by a variety of means. Flatworms, leeches, and snails flatten themselves against stones at the bottom. The larvae of caddis flies build adhering tube houses in which they live. Tadpoles and fish cling to rocks with special sucking mouths. In swiftly running mountain streams, trout swim against the current and thus manage to stay in the same place.

42–10 Mountain stream autotrophs are found marginally and on rocks in the shallow water.

The Succession of Communities

The marsh you see today may well have been a lake fifty years ago. In another fifty years, the marsh may become a young forest. Life communities are rarely static, but undergo dynamic physical and biotic change. Changes in a life community may be slow or relatively rapid. A rain forest, for example, may have taken centuries to achieve its present state. On the other hand, a barren island, rising from the ocean floor, may become a flourishing biome within a few short years.

Complex biomes tend to be more stable than simpler ones. A pine forest, for example, may persist for a long time. A field of wheat, on the other hand, may soon turn to weeds if untended. Stable biomes, however, do not arise full blown; their development follows certain stages. Smaller plants appear first. These are succeeded by larger plants, which, in turn, give way to still larger ones. Corresponding changes also occur in the animal population. The succession of plants is accompanied by successive species of animals that feed on the plants and interact with each other. Each stage in the development of a complex biome is a temporary life community that is succeeded by still another. The succession of these temporary communities culminates in a biome that persists with little change. This final biome is the climax of the successive life communities that preceded it.

THE DYNAMICS OF SUCCESSION. Why do life communities follow each other in orderly succession? Many physical and biotic factors induce the changes that cause succession. A change in climate might begin the replacement of organisms in a region by other organisms better adapted to the new conditions. For example, suppose that the rainfall decreases and a pine forest becomes drier. Other trees now begin to supplant the pines. Junipers can survive in more arid conditions. With further drought, the junipers cannot survive and are succeeded by sage brush. Finally, only cactus might be able to survive the extreme conditions of drought.

More important than the physical conditions that initiate succession are those changes brought about by the life community that establishes itself. The new life community creates conditions that are more favorable for the growth of other organisms. These new organisms move in and begin to compete with the established species, thus continuing the process of succession. For example, algae and lichens change the pH (acidity) of barren soil. After a time the lichens and algae can no longer survive in the conditions they themselves created. Now better adapted newcomers move in. Mosses and ferns begin to flourish. In time, these newcomers may be supplanted by flowering plants and trees.

The succession of populations and the changing conditions they create may be seen in miniature in the laboratory. A jar of pond water is mixed with pieces of hay. Soon the jar of water teems with bacteria that have fallen into the water from the air and multiplied. Bacteria acidify the water, making it suitable for the growth of protozoans. Flagellated protozoa appear first and feed upon the bacteria. Later, ciliated protozoans appear and feed upon the flagellates. As the population of ciliates increases, the acidity of the water is reduced. Now conditions favorable for Paramecium have been produced. The population of paramecia increases until the supply of food diminishes. If no new food is added to the jar, the chain of succession comes to a halt in a few weeks. If algae are introduced, new food is synthesized and the succession continues. Rotifers and tiny crustacea may appear, feeding upon the paramecia and the algae.

The same dynamics are at work when a freshwater lake fills and is replaced by a forest. Except for differences in species related to latitude and climate, the replacement pattern is the same. First, silt washes into the lake from adjacent land, making it smaller and shallower. The edge of the lake turns to marsh land. In the muddy soil fringing the lake, different species of grasses, ferns, mosses, and small shrubs begin to grow. Then, the small plants die, enriching the soil with humus. In this enriched soil, alders and willows take root. Continued silting displaces the remaining open water. The aquatic organisms die and decay. These decaying organisms and humus further enrich the soil as it becomes drier. Oak seedlings sprout in the soil as trees begin to establish themselves. Maples and beeches follow the oaks. Competing more successfully for light, maples and beeches shade the smaller oaks. Soon the maples and beeches are the dominant trees in the newly established forest. (See Figure 42–11 on page 694.)

CLIMAX COMMUNITIES. The dynamics of succession eventually lead to a community that is more stable than those that preceded it. This stage is the *climax community.* Climax communities have achieved a dynamic equilibrium and often persist for centuries. The desert, the grassland, and the forest are all climax communities. Each is the end result of orderly succession. Each has reached a stage where dominant forms of plants and animals control the environment of the remaining species. Unless physical and biotic conditions are drastically altered, further succession is unlikely to occur.

Under certain conditions, a climax community may appear in a short time. A forest destroyed by fire can return in a few decades. Successions of secondary plants take root in the burned over soil and prepare the way for the climax species' return. In this case, the road back is short

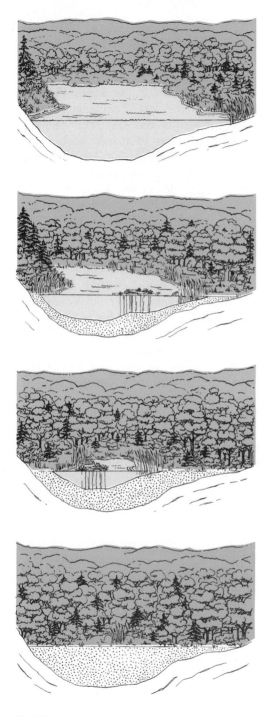

42–11 Lake to forest succession occurs as each stage sets up conditions that prepare the way for the next stage. (See discussion, page 693.)

because many necessary conditions, such as good soil, already exist. Seeds are carried in from nearby, undamaged areas. Larger animals follow as food becomes available again.

The transition from barren rock to the forest biome requires centuries. Many of our forests occupy land that was once covered by glaciers. As the glaciers retreated, they left a lifeless landscape. At first, only lichens were able to live on the bare rocks. Through centuries of slow action, the lichens changed the rocks to small fragments of soil. Weathering wore away large boulders. As the soil became mixed with organic matter, other vegetation could take hold. Mosses appeared. Thin layers of soil began to form in which seed plants could live. Insects and small invertebrates could inhabit the same thin layer. Ground-nesting birds and small mammals could now be supported as small shrubs gained a foothold. As soil continued to be formed, small trees appeared. These provided living quarters for birds, squirrels, and wood boring insects. Finally, climax trees took root. They overshadowed the smaller trees and shrubs and, in time, became the dominant species. Larger mammals appeared. Thus, over many centuries, the climax species replaced those that had preceded them.

THE STORY OF KRAKATOA. Occasionally nature provides a laboratory for the ecologist as he studies the succession of life communities. Such was the case of the island of Krakatoa, lying 25 miles off the coast of Java. In 1883, a series of volcanic eruptions literally blew the island apart. All that was left was a jagged peak covered with a layer of hot ashes. Every living thing, including 37,000 people, was destroyed.

Three years later an exploring Dutch botanist reported that the ashy soil was covered with blue-green algae and diatoms. Among them were some scattered mosses,

42-12 In the long transition period from a rock to a forest biome, the earlier trees have a gnarled shape due to the rocky terrain.

ferns, and a few flowering plants. There were no shrubs or trees. Ten years later there were 50 species of flowering plants.

Along the shore, coconut trees had begun to grow. Inland vegetation was still scarce.

By 1906, a rich variety of vegetation was growing on what had been rock and ashes less than a quarter of a century before. Fig trees and coconut palms lined the shore. Flowering plants and ferns filled the interior. The animals consisted mostly of flying forms, mosquitos, wasps, birds, and fruit bats. There were also a few lizards that had probably arrived on floating logs. By 1920, half the island was filled with trees. Ten years later, a forest of young trees covered the entire island. Thus, in less than 50 years, the dominant plants had returned.

The distance to the nearest island is twelve miles. The plants were able to return because many of their spores and seeds were wind- and water-borne. Few animals, however, have returned to the island and the life community is not yet stable. Occasionally rats, introduced by ships, overrun the island because there are no natural enemies to control them.

IMPORTANT POINTS

● A life community is a group of different organisms sharing a common environment. Life communities are not permanent. New organisms may be introduced. Older ones may die out.

● All organisms tend to invade and colonize new territories. Larger animals reach new environments through their own locomotion. Microorganisms, small invertebrates, and seeds are transported by wind, water, and larger organisms, including man.

● There are many barriers to the dispersal of organisms. Geographic obstacles, such as oceans, rivers, and mountains, limit the spread of larger animals. Biotic barriers limit the establishment of organisms that have arrived in new areas. Climatic differences are barriers to many plants and animals that cannot adapt to new temperatures.

● Life communities in different parts of the world develop unique characteristics and are identified as biomes. Different biomes appear in the desert, the grassland, the forest, the tundra, the ocean, and in rivers and lakes.

• Biomes that can persist a long time arise only after a succession of temporary communities has prepared the way. The succession of more complex communities finally leads to the formation of a climax community. Climax communities are generally stable. Changes in climate, rainfall, or soil, or the introduction of better adapted species of plants and animals can alter even a climax community.

REVIEW QUESTIONS

1. What is meant by a life community?
2. List several ways in which organisms may be dispersed.
3. List several barriers to the dispersal of plants and animals.
4. What physical factors in the tundra account for the sparseness of animal life?
5. Which biome supports the greatest variety of animals?
6. How does a savanna differ from a prairie?
7. What is the difference between a deciduous forest and a taiga?
8. Why are marine biomes not as clearly defined as land biomes?
9. List several ways in which fresh water biomes differ from marine biomes.
10. What are the outstanding features of the desert biome?

CHECK YOUR UNDERSTANDING

11. Why is a balanced aquarium considered to be a life community?
12. Why is depth an important factor in a lake biome?
13. Under what circumstances might a freshwater lake be transformed into a forest?
14. What is meant by the succession of communities?
15. What is a climax community?
16. Explain the statement, "Succession produces further succession."
17. Is it possible for certain stages in the succession of communities to be skipped? Explain your answer.
18. Why can a forest arise faster on a former lake bottom than on the land left by a retreating glacier?
19. Why is vegetation sparse on the tropical rain forest floor?
20. What physical changes can turn a forest's edge into a savanna?

RESEARCH PROJECTS AND REPORTS

1. Obtain information from your school or public library and prepare a report on one of the following topics:

    Ecological Succession   **Desert Plants and Animals**

    The Alpine Tundra   **The Tropical Rain Forest**

2. *Making a Terrarium:* A classroom is the best place to study a landlife community in miniature. Depending on the type of soil, moisture, temperature, plants and animals, terraria may represent life in the desert, woodland, bog, or

a semi-aquatic environment. Complete directions for their construction and maintenance may be obtained from biological supply houses.

The simplest type, requiring the least attention, is the desert terrarium. The bottom should be covered with coarse sand, then topped with real desert sand. A few stones and a half-buried pan of water should be added. A variety of small and large cacti may be planted after first moistening their roots. The animals included in the community may be "horned toads," small lizards and snakes. Because of the type of animal used, the terrarium should be covered with a wire screen. The grouping suggested should thrive with a minimum of attention if kept at temperatures ranging from 68 to 85 degrees F.

3. *Succession of Populations in a Jar of Pond Water:* Place some dried grass from the edge of a pond in a wide-mouthed glass jar that has been sterilized. Boil some pond water, allow it to cool, then add it to the grass in the jar. Cover the jar loosely and keep in a cool place.

Examine the water every day for about three weeks. Use both the low and high power of the compound microscope. Keep a record of the organisms you find, how numerous they appear to be, and the date of your observations.

During the first few days, the water will contain numerous bacteria. After the first week, flagellates, then ciliates will appear. The population of protozoa will increase from day to day, then decline toward the beginning of the third week. This is the time when you will begin to notice the appearance of rotifers and a reduction in the number of bacteria.

Why do the rotifers appear last, and the bacteria first? What accounts for the rise in the protozoan population followed by a decline? What food chains are at work in the jar? Are food and population pyramids formed in the pond water? What successions do you observe?

FURTHER READING

"The Nature of Oceanic Life." John D. Isaacs. *Scientific American,* September, 1969, page 147. Discusses the web of oceanic life and its ultimate dependence upon the green protists that live in the surface waters.

The Forest and the Sea. Marston Bates. Random House, Inc., New York, N.Y. A noted ecologist has written an exciting account of the world's major biomes.

Africa. Archie Carr and the Editors of LIFE. Time, Inc., New York, N.Y. A naturalist's illustrated descriptions of many unspoiled biomes on this large continent. The grassland and rain forest are especially well presented.

The Desert. A. Starker Leopold and the Editors of LIFE. Time, Inc., New York, N.Y. The deserts support an interesting variety of life patterns. Illustrated.

"The Migration of Polar Bears." Vagn Flyger and Marjorie R. Townsend. *Scientific American,* February, 1968, page 108. The dye marking of polar bears is used to determine the extent of their territory and their patterns of migration.

43

Man and the Balance of Nature

THE TIME AND PLACE of man's origins are uncertain. However obscure his origins, man has thrived and multiplied as he spread over the earth in increasing numbers. Today, man is the most numerous and successful of all the higher mammals. Man's success, however, has been detrimental to the rest of the biotic world. He has destroyed organisms that stood in his way and enslaved organisms he could use. Limited by his need for water, man established his cities on the banks of rivers. Here he built his homes, reared his children, and prospered. He has prospered to a point where his numbers have created problems that now threaten his supply of food and water.

Wherever man has settled he has produced biotic change. He has upset the delicate balance of nature and caused the extinction of plant and animal alike. His industries have poured forth wastes that have polluted streams. His factories have given off large amounts of soot and smoke that have contaminated the air that all life requires.

Man is part of the world's ecosphere. He cannot exist apart from it. If he has blindly destroyed productive elements in his environment in the past, he must now seek ways to remedy his mistakes. The biotic world supports man; without it he cannot survive.

Human Population and Resources

Although man is a relatively recent species, he now dominates the living world. Having learned to use tools, man has modified his environment to suit his own ends. By so doing, he has been able to colonize the entire earth. From his early beginning, man's population has increased rapidly. World population now exceeds three billion and is growing faster than ever.

To sustain his increasing numbers, man needs an ever greater supply of resources. Man's biological needs are for food and water. The problem of supplying sufficient food is already critical in those parts of the world where population has grown very rapidly. In the highly industrialized nations, the need for water is also becoming critical. As certain parts of the world become more densely populated, another problem appears to be created. This is the problem of space itself. For man, like other mammals, may need a minimum area in which he can live free from stress.

POPULATION CURVE

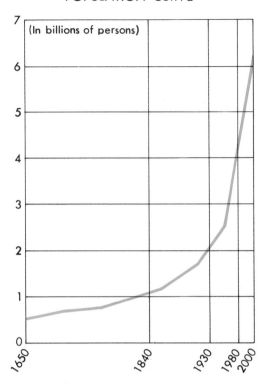

43–1 The chart shows that the recent rate of increase in world population will accelerate even more sharply in projection to the year 2000. The vertical lines indicate the progressive decrease in the time required for the population to double.

THE MALTHUS THEORY OF POPULATION. As early as 1798, the English clergyman Thomas Malthus summarized his views on population in his paper, *An Essay on the Principle of Population.* Malthus declared that man is subject to the same laws that regulate plant and animal populations. He predicted that the human population would increase by doubling every twenty-five years. Food supplies, he agreed, would also increase, but at a slower rate. Man's numbers would continually outrun his food supplies. This analysis led Malthus to the gloomy forecast that famine, disease, and war would haunt the human race. These would be the principal checks on population growth.

Few people accepted Malthus's predictions. For more than a century after his prediction, population grew faster than ever while many people were increasingly better fed. Let us examine the figures on world population growth.

THE RISE IN WORLD POPULATION. Americans are being added to our population at the rate of five per minute, 300 per hour, or 7200 per day. The daily net gains in world population are 100,000.

Human population has never been as large or risen as fast. There are now over 200 million in the United States. It is predicted that by the year 2000, there will be 300 million in our country and a world population of 6 billion!

Many factors are contributing to an increasing population. The conquest of disease through the use of vaccines and antibiotics, the control of disease-carrying insects, and the general improvement of sanitary conditions have caused the death rate to decline. The result is that births now greatly outnumber deaths. In the last 300 years alone, world population has risen almost sixfold: from one-half billion in 1650 to about three billion today.

The so-called population explosion has not yet caused any serious food problems in the United States, Canada, western Europe, and Australia where new lands are being farmed. Agricultural improvements have increased the yield per acre. The United States could probably support 600 million people without difficulty. At present we even raise surpluses that we share with others who are less fortunate.

Conditions are different in many parts of Latin America, Asia, and Africa. Starvation is a constant threat. To maintain health, the average adult requires about 2400 Cal-

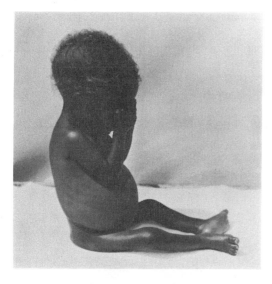

43–2 According to The Food and Agriculture Organization of the United Nations, every day 50 per cent of the world is hungry.

ories per day. In these parts of the world the daily consumption of food is about 1700 Calories, an amount that barely sustains life. Nor do Calories tell the entire story. About one-sixth of a minimum adequate diet should consist of proteins. This is especially true for children, who require amino acids for growth. Yet, it is in the regions where Calorie intake is already low that proteins are scarce.

THE RISE IN FOOD PRODUCTION. Since the time of Malthus, Europeans have colonized millions of square miles of new territories. Large areas of new land have been cultivated, increasing the world's food supply. Improved farming techniques have caused an agricultural revolution in the western nations. Chemical fertilizers, irrigation, the development of disease-resistant plants, and insecticides have combined to increase the farmer's yield. Farm machinery has replaced manual labor and horse power.

43–3 Percentages of World's Population Living at High and Low Caloric Intake

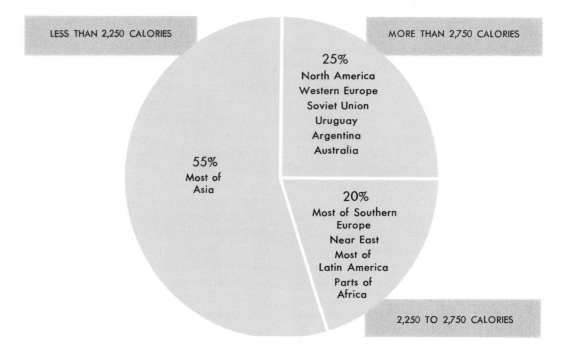

LESS THAN 2,250 CALORIES

MORE THAN 2,750 CALORIES

25%
North America
Western Europe
Soviet Union
Uruguay
Argentina
Australia

55%
Most of
Asia

20%
Most of Southern
Europe
Near East
Most of
Latin America
Parts of
Africa

2,250 TO 2,750 CALORIES

In 1850, one half of our nation's labor force worked on farms, but today less than nine per cent work on farms. This means that in 1850 the individual farmer raised only enough food to feed his family and one other. Today, he is able to support more than ten non-farm families besides his own. As the population grew, the standard of living increased. This does not mean, however, that we can expect this trend to continue indefinitely.

The people of Asia are not so fortunate. As their population increased, the available land per person decreased. In the United States the ratio is two acres per person. In most of Asia it is one-half acre per person.

Even intensive agriculture cannot close the gap between production and consumption completely. More than 100 million Japanese live on islands the size of California. They have about one-fifth of an acre per person. Each acre of Japanese soil is made to yield 13,000 Calories of food daily, far in excess of our daily yield of 4500 Calories.

WORLD POPULATION AND CARRYING CAPACITY. We have already defined the carrying capacity of an ecosystem as the upper limit of the biomass it can support. When man intrudes upon an established ecosystem, he alters its characteristics so that a greater number of human beings are supported by it. He rearranges the components of the system so that they become more favorable to him. It thus appears that he has increased the carrying capacity of the ecosystem. In reality, however, he has created a new ecosystem that supports more men. Take a desert biome, for example. Irrigation makes the barren desert fertile. The desert can now grow food to support man. Man can live where the desert once was. But it is no longer a desert biome. Consider a forest that is converted into a farm. Growing crops on the converted farmland permits men to live there. We must remember, though, that the forest biome is no longer in existence.

Alterations to existing ecosystems involve biotic risks. The forest, a climax community, is a stable ecosystem and can persist almost indefinitely. A corn or wheat field, however, is a simpler ecosystem, hence less stable. Unless constantly tended by man, the field can be destroyed by insects, flood, or drought. As man increases in number, he must alter more ecosystems to support larger human populations. Each ecosystem that is altered makes man more vulnerable to loss.

World population is expected to double by the end of this century. This means that more food will be required. Man, however, cannot continue to alter the ecosystems of the earth to feed more people indefinitely. There is a limit to the number of people the earth can support. Simple arithmetic forecasts this limit. At today's rate of growth (2 per cent annually), world population would reach 630,000 billion by the year 3500! Such a number would permit standing room only on every bit of available land, Antarctica included! By the year 5500, the human biomass would theoretically equal the weight of the earth itself.

POPULATION STABILIZATION. Is there some ideal population figure toward which the nations of the world should strive? Some figure like ten or even twenty billion? Whatever the figure, it would be one at which sufficient food, shelter, pure water, and other necessities of life would be available for all. If this sounds utopian, remember that many biologists believe that some such goal can be achieved with proper planning.

If world population were to be fixed at some agreed upon maximum, the birth rate would have to balance the death rate. The balancing of these two rates would achieve population stability. One factor that has increased world population has

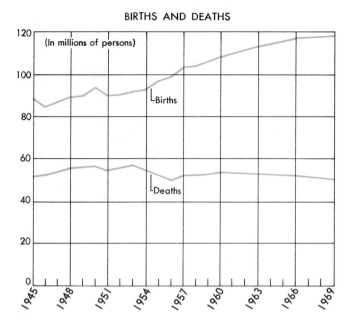

BIRTHS AND DEATHS

(In millions of persons)

43–4 A major reason for the recent increase in population is seen in the chart. The annual worldwide death rate has only changed slightly compared to a sharp increase in the worldwide birth rate. The United Nations estimates that world population is increasing at the rate of 1.8 per cent annually.

been the lengthening of the average life span. Modern science has enabled man to live longer. In terms of population stability, however, the increasing life span means that the birth rate must also be controlled. Population stability could not be maintained if either factor were uncontrolled. Realizing this, many nations have made strong efforts to disseminate birth control information among their people. These nations have offered their assistance to other countries desiring to establish programs of population control. Crowded Japan now enjoys the highest standard of living in Asia. One reason for this high standard may have been the success of its population program.

TERRITORIALITY. Ecologists believe that, for certain species, the limitation of space itself may act as a control on population. Each animal, apparently, has need for a certain area, which it defends against other members of its species. This need is called *territoriality*. As population density increases, individual animals no longer find

sufficient space to forage, hunt, mate, rear their young, or hide from enemies. Overcrowding causes many weaker members of the species to die, thus reducing population.

Laboratory experiments with rats seem to confirm the hypothesis of territoriality. In one instance, a small population of rats in an enclosure with ample food rose rapidly at first but eventually stabilized itself at about 150 rats. Stability was achieved when fertility declined and mortality among the young rose to 96 per cent.

Can we find a physiological explanation for the die-offs that accompany overcrowding? Many biologists agree that the "alarm reaction mechanism," a glandular upset, is the major cause. Acting through the sense of smell, overcrowding causes *stress*. Stress activates the adrenal glands, which, in turn, activate the flow of ACTH from the pituitary gland. Acting in a feedback cycle, the ACTH further stimulates adrenalin output until the animal enters a state of *shock*. Shock often leads to disordered behavior and finally to death. Usually, it is the young animals who are least able to tolerate stress and are killed by it.

An examination of 190 Sika deer, all victims of sudden death on James Island, Maryland, between 1958 and 1959, supports this idea. The deer carcasses were in good condition and showed no signs of starvation or disease. However, autopsies revealed adrenal glands that were much enlarged, indicating a period of great overactivity.

Little is known about man's territorial needs. Apparently, he can tolerate higher population densities than the lower vertebrates. His overcrowded cities seem to be proof of this. Also, since man's sense of smell is poorer than that of other mammals, he is probably less prone to the alarm of territoriality.

Man's Place in Nature

In most biomes, plant and animal populations tend to become stable. The physical and biotic elements of the environment tend to equate the reproductive rate of a species with the rate at which members are eliminated. Over a period of time, therefore, species numbers tend to become constant. By altering existing ecosystems, man changes this balance. By overhunting certain species, by transporting others to new regions, by indiscriminate use of insecticides, man alters the elements in the ecosystem. Once the natural pattern of balance is upset, other results may follow. Some species are killed off entirely and become extinct; other species may overrun new environments and become pests.

MAN'S EFFECT UPON PLANT AND ANIMAL POPULATIONS. In 1681, the last dodo died. The dodo was a flightless bird resembling a duck that lived on the island of Mauritius in the Indian Ocean. French settlers took their dogs and pigs with them to establish farms on the island. The dogs and pigs attacked the defenseless dodos sending them on their way to extinction.

The American passenger pigeon met the same fate as a result of man's intervention. In 1813, the American naturalist John Audubon wrote of one flock, "The air was literally filled with pigeons and the light of noon-day was obscured as by an eclipse . . ." In 1914, the last passenger pigeon died in a Cincinnati zoo. A century of overhunting caused the bird to disappear.

The American bison, or buffalo, almost followed the same path. In the 1860's, the

43–5 Studies of Sika deer on James Island indicate that glandular mechanisms, responding to the density of the deer population, are what control population.

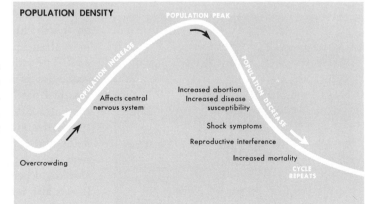

POPULATION DENSITY

POPULATION PEAK

POPULATION INCREASE

POPULATION DECREASE

Affects central nervous system

Increased abortion
Increased disease susceptibility

Shock symptoms

Reproductive interference

Increased mortality

Overcrowding

CYCLE REPEATS

43–6 Restoration of the Extinct Dodo Bird

animals were so numerous in this country that more than 200,000 were slaughtered in a two-month period in Kansas alone. Yet by 1906, not a single wild bison remained alive. Only a small, privately owned herd of 500 existed on a ranch in Mon-

43–7 Compared to the huge numbers that used to roam the prairies, very few bison remain. Man's uncontrolled desire for the bison's hide and meat almost brought extinction to the species.

tana. The buffalos you see in zoos today, plus the five to ten thousand protected animals on western ranges, are all descendents from the Montana herd.

In 1872, the mongoose was imported into Jamaica in the West Indies by sugar planters who wanted to rid their plantations of rats. The mongoose, a weasel-like native of Asia, not only killed rats but ate birds as well. With no enemies to keep it in check, it multiplied and became a first-rate pest. As a result of this experience, the importation of mongooses into the United States is strictly forbidden.

The history of the rabbit innocently imported into Australia illustrates the same mistake on a much greater scale. In 1788, an English settler imported a few to provide hunting sport for his friends. In the absence of rabbit-eating carnivores, the animals multiplied at a tremendous rate. In less than a century their population numbered in the hundreds of millions. The damage to crops and sheep pasturage ran to millions of dollars annually. At one time, the government even built a 1000-mile-long fence from north to south in an attempt to keep the pests from spreading westward. In 1950, a virus disease fatal to South American rabbits was introduced into Australia. In a few years, the rabbit population was reduced, and a balance was restored.

MAN UPSETS THE NATURAL BALANCE. In an effort to increase agricultural yields, man often upsets the natural balance of an area. The indiscriminate use of powerful insecticides is a case in point. When DDT was first used in the 1940's, it proved to be the most effective pest killer known. Widely spread from airplanes over the designated fields and forests, it destroyed harmful insects on a large scale. Unfortunately, DDT also killed beneficial insects and small birds. It was also learned that DDT contaminated soil, lakes, and rivers.

DDT is insoluble in water. It is also highly resistant to decomposition and therefore remains in the tissues of organisms that ingest it. Thus, it enters the food chains where its harm persists long after its original use. Two years after its use was discontinued in an area of Michigan, contaminated earthworms still caused the death of the birds who ate them. Today, large fish-eating birds such as the osprey and the bald eagle are suffering population declines. The contaminated fish in their diet cause them to lay eggs that do not hatch. Many ocean fish eaten by man have measurable residues of DDT. What effect these traces of DDT will have on humans is still unknown. Enough is known, however, so that indiscriminate spraying with DDT is now a prohibited practice in the United States.

MAN CAUSES REDISTRIBUTION. Although species are dispersed in a number of ways, man is the principal agent of redistribution. Man has successfully transplanted many of his food crops. Wheat was introduced to America by European colonists. The Europeans had previously received it from Asia. On their early voyages to America they discovered corn, which they took back with them. The Spanish conquerors of Peru brought back the potato to their homeland. From Spain, it spread to all of Europe and then back across the Atlantic to North America.

The importation of wild plants has on some occasions upset established ecosystems. In 1884, a Floridian imported the water hyacinth from South America for a lily pond on his estate. The plants did not thrive there, however, and were thrown into the St. John's river. Since that time, they have spread to practically every waterway in the state and have become a major hazard to navigation.

The importation of birds has seldom been successful, where man is concerned. The

43–8 These water hyacinths, descendants of the original few plants imported from Japan, have reproduced without control, choking many of the waterways in Florida.

ring neck pheasant seems to be an exception. Introduced into the United States from China in 1882, it has thrived and become an important game bird. The English sparrow and the starling, both brought to this country during the nineteenth century, have overmultiplied and become pests. The sparrow has interfered with the insect controlling activities of native birds. Starlings have become a nuisance in cities where they roost on the ledges of public buildings.

MAN REQUIRES NATURAL RESOURCES. The most important resources for man's survival are the natural resources that provide his food and shelter. The soil that grows his crops, the forests that preserve soil and provide timber, and the animals that provide food and recreation are termed renewable resources. These resources continually replenish themselves when they are not abused. If carefully managed, they can supply man's requirements indefinitely.

Water and air are also renewable resources. Until recently, little attention was paid to them because they were considered to be limitless. However, the growing problem of air and water pollution has made man realize that these "limitless" resources can also be diminished by abuse.

Man and His Physical Environment

Stone Age man made few demands on his environment. He was an efficient hunter, yet his numbers remained small. His prime needs were for shelter, access to water, and territory in which to hunt. With the discovery of agriculture about 10,000 years ago, more food was produced. Human population increased. Villages, towns, and cities were established. Now water and soil took on a new importance. Water and fertile soil limited the sites of man's cities.

The Industrial Revolution created entirely new problems. Crowded into cities, expanding populations increased the need for more food. Pollution became a serious byproduct of man's industry. Primitive man could solve the problem of accumulating wastes by moving to another site. But modern man cannot easily move to new sites in an increasingly crowded world. Technology has produced

43–9 In regions where rainfall is scarce and irrigation is not used, dust storms result in a considerable loss of fertile topsoil.

new and different kinds of wastes. Releasing these unwanted materials into the water or into the air creates still further problems. The wastes contaminate the environment on which man depends.

WATER CONSERVATION. Water is plentiful in the ecosphere. Although most of it is in the seas, some 900 million cubic miles of fresh water is available in streams, rivers, lakes, glaciers, underground accumulations, and as vapor in the atmosphere. Nevertheless, man sometimes finds water scarce. Some people live in regions that suffer periodic drought. Agriculture, industry, and large populations also tax existing supplies of water. Without canals, irrigation ditches, dams, and reservoirs to conserve and deliver water, man may suffer severely from fluctuations in the water cycle. In the 1930's, for example, drought forced more than half a million farm dwellers to leave their "dust bowl" areas of Texas and Oklahoma.

Man's increased need for water has made scarcity more frequent. Hardly a large city in the world today has not experienced a water shortage. Man's need for water may spell further trouble in the future. In the arid southwestern United States, for example, wells must be drilled to considerable depths to obtain groundwater. Since groundwater requires centuries to accumulate, its removal is equivalent to mining. When ground supplies of water are exhausted, other water may have to be brought in by pipeline.

WATER POLLUTION. Each year our rivers and lakes yield fewer fish. Each year our coastal waters yield fewer lobsters, clams, and oysters. In both cases the reason is the same: water pollution. Man causes many kinds of water pollution. Farms release silt from eroding land, factories release chemical wastes, mills and nuclear reactors release heat, and the cities release sewage from homes.

43–10 In 1963, such a high detergent level was reached in one part of Lake Erie that this suds area resulted, measuring 300 feet long and one foot deep.

Silt is eroded topsoil and contains organic matter. Bacterial decomposition of this organic matter reduces the amount of oxygen in lakes and rivers. Fish die from lack of oxygen. Silt also interferes with the penetration of light into the water. Without light, aquatic autotrophs cannot make food and perish. The decline in producer organisms reduces the carrying capacity of the lake or river.

Industrial wastes also kill many organisms that live in water. Coal mines poison streams with sulphuric acid. Paper mills release toxic amounts of calcium salts. Oil wells coat water with thick layers of crude oil that smother all life. Steel mills and nuclear reactors heat large quantities of water through their cooling operations. The heated water then raises the temperature of rivers. Higher river temperatures reduce the amount of oxygen dissolved in water and many fish are thus destroyed by *thermal pollution.*

The greatest source of pollution is sewage. All types of human wastes are potential sources of water-borne disease. These wastes are highly organic and therefore decrease the amount of dissolved oxygen. In the 1940's, soon after household detergents were introduced, new pollution problems occurred. The detergents did not rapidly decompose and accumulated in streams and rivers, killing many organisms. In the mid-1960's, new detergents were developed that decompose in water. Unfortunately, their decomposition liberates phosphates, which are nutrients for many algae. These algae increase so rapidly that they overtax water purification systems.

CLEANING UP OUR WATER. Polluted water from one city is often poured into a river and carried downstream for use by the next city. Since the re-use of water is a feature of our urban environment, water purification and sewage treatment systems become necessary. Water from a river is made safe for drinking through a number of steps. Pumped into large basins where solid particles settle out, it is then filtered through sand and gravel beds. Finally, it is treated with chlorine or chlorine dioxide to kill bacteria.

Sewage treatment plants receive raw sewage before it is poured into the river. The sewage is allowed to stand in tanks where its solids settle out as *sludge*. The desludged water is then chemically treated and returned to the river. The sludge is piped into drying beds and converted by bacteria into fertilizer, or a fuel that is later burned.

Industrial wastes also require processing before reaching rivers and lakes. For many industries, more research is needed. An example of what can be accomplished may be seen in the paper industry. Research has found new uses for pulp fibers that were previously a serious pollutant when poured into waterways.

AIR POLLUTION. Air pollution probably began with the growth of large cities. Soot from household fuels and industrial wastes were released into the air. With the increase of modern industrial plants, air pollution has become steadily worse. Manufacturing and oil refining wastes, home heating, trash burning, and motor vehicle exhaust gases have all polluted the air. According to a recent estimate, more than 145 million tons of "aerial garbage" are released into the atmosphere by the United States each year. Air pollutants may be dusts, unburned fuel particles, toxic gases, or radioactive materials from nuclear ex-

43–11 Weather greatly affects city air pollution. When the air is becalmed, car exhaust and other pollutants are trapped, becoming not only obvious but also far more dangerous.

plosions. Each has a deteriorating effect on our total environment. Each is injurious to health.

Unusual combinations of weather and air pollution sometimes cause disasters. In the fall of 1948, a stagnant air mass remained over Donora, Pennsylvania, for five days. The air over the town became so filled with pollutants from a nearby zinc refinery that several thousand people became ill. Twenty died. In 1952, a similar set of circumstances in London killed 4000 people.

Perhaps the most deadly pollutants are the radioactive elements that constitute the "fall out" from atomic explosions. Many of these radioisotopes cease to be radioactive in a few days. But the activity of strontium-90 and cesium-137 persists for decades. These radioisotopes contaminate the soil and are absorbed by plants. In this manner they become part of the food chains to which man belongs.

One long-term effect of air pollution cannot yet be measured. By burning coal and oil, man increases the amount of carbon dioxide in the atmosphere. Carbon dioxide lies close to the surface and produces the earth's "greenhouse effect" by blocking the return of solar energy to outer space. The increase of carbon dioxide in the atmosphere may thus be warming the earth's climate. Since 1890, the small amount of atmospheric carbon dioxide has increased by eight per cent. A continuing increase could ultimately melt the polar ice caps and flood the coastal cities.

CONTROLLING AIR POLLUTION. Many industries have tried to control air pollution. Steel mills, for example, install devices that trap solid particles in their chimneys and keep them from the air. Increasingly, railroads have switched from coal and oil burning engines to electric locomotives. Sometimes government regulation is required. In the Los Angeles area, for ex-

ample, the oil refineries are among the cleanest in the nation. Most of the sulphur dioxide previously released into the air by these refineries is now converted to useful sulphuric acid. Trash burning in many cities is also regulated.

The greatest source of air pollution is the automobile. Before long, automobiles will be required to be equipped with afterburners. Afterburners circulate unburned waste gases back to the engine for complete combustion. Much interest exists in steam and electric automobiles that produce practically no pollutants.

Conservation of Natural Resources

Man's renewable resources provide him with his biological income. They may be compared with his bank account. As capital on deposit, they generate the interest on which he lives. Both his livelihood and his future depend on how he manages this capital. If he withdraws more from his account than he replaces, bankruptcy will eventually result. If his capital is conserved and increased, his income will be assured.

Conservation is the wise use of our natural resources. Soil, forests, and wildlife need to be maintained not only for the present but also for the future. Although many of these resources have been recklessly abused in the past, growing population makes conservation a necessity today.

SOIL DETERIORATION AND EROSION. Soil is a precious natural resource. The pressure for more food has forced man to commit more land to agriculture. Poor management of land, however, can reduce its value. Growing the same crops for too many seasons may remove the needed minerals from the soil. On the other hand, land may be over-mineralized and ruined. A farm, for example, may be established that depends on runoff water for irrigation.

43–12 These two fields were equally gullied. The owner of the field at the left used fertilizers to produce a cover crop that halted erosion and permitted livestock to feed.

Unlike rainwater, runoff water contains dissolved minerals. In time, the minerals accumulate and turn the farm into a "salt desert."

Topsoil may be lost by erosion. Under natural conditions, the rate of soil formation exceeds the rate of soil erosion. Erosion increases, however, when farm management is poor. The early settlers of our country had little understanding of how to care for the soil. Within a few hundred years after America was settled, almost one-third of the country's soil had been ruined. Plains had been stripped of their grassy cover in order to create farms. Cattle and sheep had overgrazed their pastures. With no plants left to hold the topsoil, heavy rains washed that topsoil away. And during periods of drought, winds blew it away.

Clearing hillsides of trees and shrubs had the same effect. Gulleys formed when there were no more plant roots to slow rainwater runoff. As the gulleys became deeper and wider, once-fertile hillsides became barren patches.

Ruined land sent early settlers westward in search of new farmland. But as population increased and new land became scarce,

the practice of soil conservation became a vital need.

SOIL CONSERVATION. Several methods of soil conservation are practiced in the United States today.

Contour plowing is used to conserve soil on sloping land. The farmer plows his furrows across the slope rather than up and down it. This arrangement of furrows impedes the runoff of rainwater. Each furrow acts as a small dam. Instead of creating gulleys, rainwater is absorbed by the soil.

Terracing is especially valuble in regions of heavy rainfall. Dividing ditches, several feet in width, are plowed among the regular crop furrows. These deeper ditches catch most of the runoff water and guide it into grassy areas at the edge of the field.

Strip cropping is used along with contour plowing. Crops providing dense cover, such as cereal grasses, are planted in alternate strips with "loose" growers such as cotton or potatoes. In this arrangement, the fibrous roots of the grasses impede the runoff by absorbing excess water.

Where wind is an erosion factor, fields are plowed at right angles to the prevailing winds. Also, shelter belts of trees often are planted at the edges of fields to slow the wind.

Complete soil conservation includes soil fertility. The same crop grown year after year soon depletes the soil of certain minerals. To preserve the mineral content of the soil, fertilizers must be added each season. Rotation of crops is another method of avoiding the depletion of minerals.

FOREST MANAGEMENT. Forests provide one of our largest crops, wood, and are the home of much wildlife. Primarily, however, forests make and conserve soil. The large root systems of trees hold soil together and slow the runoff of rainwater. Decaying leaves, twigs, branches, and trunks, along with the remains of animals, form the rich humus of the forest floor. Conserving forests, therefore, conserves wood, wildlife, and soil.

Often, man has failed to understand the role of forests. Climax forests, requiring thousands of years to form, have been cut down in a short time. The birds and mammals that lived there have either migrated or died. Rains have washed over the forest floor, destroying soil and flooding the valleys below.

The once-vast forests of the eastern United States now have almost disappeared. By the end of the 19th century, many millions of acres of valuable timberland had been cut. Finally, as population spread westward, conservation of our remaining forests became a necessity.

The Forestry Act of 1897 set aside "forest reserves" in the West. By 1907, these reserves, called National Forests, were placed under the supervision of the National Forest Service. Today, some 150 National Forests, covering approximately 180 million acres, are set aside for recreation and as a source of timber. Limited lumbering is permitted if it is conducted under sound methods of conservation.

43–13   Forest Management. Pulpwood and saw-logs are the crops taken from this managed loblolly pine forest. In a few years the stand will be ready for another harvest.

The main difference between lumber and a crop such as wheat is the time required to grow each one. Some trees are not ready for the sawmill before they are 30, or even 100 years old.

Rotation is the key to good forest usage. As trees are cut, new trees are planted to replace them. Older trees are harvested as new trees grow to maturity, insuring a perpetual crop.

Forests suffer many agents of destruction besides man. Insects, disease, and fire reduce our annual timber crop by about 20 per cent. Finding ways to control these natural enemies is one duty of the U.S. Forest Service.

Fire is the greatest danger to forests, especially during late summer and early fall when forests are dry. The camper who leaves his fire burning, the driver who tosses a lighted cigarette from his car, the lumberman whose drag chains cause sparks, all can cause extensive damage. Preventing forest fires is the responsibility of all.

43–14 Draining a marsh affects all organisms adapted to the conditions set up by that marsh.

RESTORATION OF WILDLIFE. Overhunting endangers wildlife, but the alteration of biomes is an even greater threat. The destruction of a forest deprives animals of a home. The draining of a marsh leaves waterfowl without nesting sites. The pollution of a stream kills fish. The effects of this destruction can be overcome by applying sound ecological principles. Hunting can be regulated. Unspoiled habitats can be allowed to remain.

Many once scarce species are protected by state game laws. Deer hunters, for example, are licensed. Limits are placed on the age, sex, and number of animals they may kill in a season. This practice allows the animals to maintain their numbers and yield annual "harvests." Unharvested deer overmultiply. During a hard winter, many die of starvation. Thus, regulated hunting is a form of conservation. In some western states, bounties encourage the hunting of wolves, coyotes, and mountain lions. Conservationists oppose these laws. The reduction of predators may save occasional sheep or cattle, but it allows deer to overmultiply and destroy valuable vegetation.

For ducks, geese, and other waterfowl, preservation of the natural environment is essential. The United States Fish and Wildlife service maintains refuges as breeding grounds. Since waterfowl are migratory, hunting is regulated on a national rather than a state basis.

The preservation of ocean dwelling mammals requires international agreements. The seal population of the Pribilof Islands near Alaska was reduced from four million in 1786 to less than 150,000 in 1910. A treaty signed by Japan, Canada, and the United States regulating these herds resulted in rapid improvement. By 1950, there were more than three million seals, providing 50,000 to 75,000 skins annually. The history of whaling in the Antarctic Ocean followed the same pattern. As the efficiency of whale hunting increased, these valuable giants were threatened with extinction. International agreements among twenty-five nations came into being. The United States and other whaling nations now share in the enforcement of whaling regulations.

The New Technology of Food and Water

By the year 2000, we expect to have six billion people in the world. If they are to be well nourished, the present rate of food production must be greatly expanded. This means that our technology faces a formidable new challenge. It means that our present resources must be not only conserved but greatly increased. New land areas must be made productive through irrigation. New sources of water must be found. Agriculture must be made more productive. Additional food, perhaps from new sources, must somehow become available.

NEW SOURCES OF WATER. Despite growing industrial demand, the prime need for water is in agriculture. Successful farming depends on the amount of available water. Where rainfall is insufficient, irrigation is required. Irrigation consists of bringing water to the crops that need it. One of the oldest methods of making water available is through the erection of dams. Dams back up rivers and create lakes above them. The lake acts as a reservoir. With today's soaring water needs, many new dams are built each year.

Other means of obtaining water are also being tried. In one scheme, clouds are "seeded" from airplanes with silver iodide crystals. Seeding causes clouds to drop their moisture as rain. Since the right type of cloud must be present in the right place, the technique is still experimental. Another rain making scheme proposes that large areas of water-short regions be coated with a black surface. In theory, the dark surface will absorb solar heat and cause updrafts that will be followed by rain.

The most promising source of new water is the sea. Water-short countries such as Kuwait and Israel already resort to *desalination* of seawater. Desalination is the removal of salts from seawater by large scale distillation. At present, construction and power requirements have kept the cost of water relatively high. Engineers state, however, that as desalination technology improves, costs will drop.

INTENSIFIED AGRICULTURE. Mechanization, chemical fertilizers, weed killers, and closer spacing of crops have all worked well in the United States. They have enabled smaller and smaller fractions of our population to raise food for our expanding cities. These methods have allowed food exportation to the overpopulated and underdeveloped regions of the world.

The need for a superior insecticide that will not damage the food chains still remains. Recently isolated *juvenile hormone* holds promise of becoming the most useful pest killer known. The hormone, produced by insect larvae, controls their transformation into adults. When applied to the egg, it prevents hatching. When applied to the adult, it prevents reproduction. Calculations indicate that one gram of juvenile hormone is sufficient to destroy one billion insects! At present, only experimental quantities are available. Hopefully, when practical amounts are extracted or synthesized, world agriculture will benefit without penalizing the rest of the environment.

NEW SOURCES OF FOOD. Proposals for increasing food production include: (1) the irrigation of new lands for agriculture, (2) the creation of superior crops through plant genetics, (3) more intensive exploitation of the sea, (4) the production of proteins from petroleum, and (5) artificial photosynthesis. These proposals are discussed in more detail on the next page.

1. At least a billion acres of land are classified as arid because they receive less than eight inches of rain annually. These acres can be made productive through irrigation. Vast stretches of Australia, Africa, Asia, and our own Southwest can be made to increase world food substantially. The reduction in the cost of desalinated water, perhaps by the use of solar or nuclear power, can make this possible.

2. Superior crops will also narrow the gap between food and people. About 30 years ago, scientists developed new varieties of corn and wheat for Mexico. At that time, the country's per capita diet averaged 1700 Calories daily. Now, it averages 2700 Calories daily, even though her population has since doubled. Plant geneticists have recently created a new rice, called IR8, that may confer the same benefits in Asia. It is a shorter, sturdier plant with heavier grains. Introduced into the Philippines where Calories per acre rose dramatically, it is now being raised in India and Pakistan. A new type of hybrid corn, rich in protein, has also been created. It is being experimentally grown in the protein-poor nations of Colombia and Kenya.

3. The sea is a vast storehouse of food. Until now, however, the sea was used the way Stone Age man used the land: to hunt and gather food. Just as man made the land more productive through agriculture, scientists today seek ways to make the sea more productive. But before this can be done, our basic knowledge of this vast area of the earth's surface must be increased. This is the main reason many governments now support the study of *oceanography,* or ocean science.

   Some progress has been made. Undesirable fish, previously discarded, are now converted into a tasteless fish flour, which is 80 per cent protein. Added to starchy foods, it has proved a practical way to fight protein malnutrition in food-short countries.

   One ingenious scheme proposes to increase the sea's fish yield through the management of plankton. Ocean scientists have learned that plankton, the surface "soup" that supports fish life, is enriched by nutrients that upwell from the sea's lower layers. They suggest that nuclear reactors on the ocean floor could generate convection currents, carrying nutrients from below to the plankton above. Richer plankton would yield more fish.

4. Food from petroleum may be another weapon against hunger. Certain bacteria multiply rapidly on petroleum and produce colonies rich in proteins and vitamins. Converted into a tasteless powder, this bacterial product contains more protein, pound for pound, than does beef. Experiments in which *single cell protein,* the name given the new food, was fed to livestock have been successful. Its direct use by humans would probably be as an additive rather than as a whole food.

5. The achievement of artificial photosynthesis would be of tremendous significance to man. In 1961, Melvin Calvin was awarded a Nobel prize for identifying the complicated steps by which autotrophs convert water and carbon dioxide into carbohydrates. Scientists, however, cannot yet apply this knowledge in a practical way. One biologist stated, "We are in the position of a watchmaker who is asked to fix a watch with Stone Age tools." Should feasible techniques be developed to perform photosynthesis on an industrial basis, man's struggle for food might be brought to a sudden end.

IMPORTANT POINTS

• Man occupies a unique place in nature. He modifies his environment extensively, increases his numbers, yet is subject to the same laws that regulate other organisms. To sustain his large numbers, he alters the ecosystems of many regions so that they become more productive in terms of his own species.

• Alteration of ecosystems in order to support large populations cannot be continued indefinitely. At some point, human population must be stabilized. World population is now growing faster than ever and there is real danger that there may not be enough food and other resources in the future.

• Man upsets natural balance wherever he establishes his farms and cities. By doing so, man may bring about the redistribution of plants and animals, the extinction of certain species, the overmultiplication of others, and the introduction of poisonous substances into the food chains.

• Man has contaminated his environment with many kinds of pollutants. Silt from eroding farms, heat and chemical wastes from industry, and sewage from homes have all polluted water. Toxic gases and incompletely burned fuels from factories and motor vehicles, and radioactive materials from nuclear explosions have polluted air, soil, and food. Water and air pollutants are all hazardous to health, and methods of controlling pollution must be strengthened.

• Man's survival depends upon his resources. Water, air, topsoil, forests, and wildlife are renewable resources. When not abused, they can replenish themselves. With proper methods of conservation, their yield can be maintained and even increased. As population increases, conservation becomes more important than ever.

• World population is expected to double by the end of this century. This means that man's technology must develop new sources of food, and new sources of water for agriculture.

REVIEW QUESTIONS

1. List several ways in which man upsets the balance of nature.
2. What is meant by territoriality? Give one example.
3. What is the Malthus theory of population?
4. Describe several causes of soil erosion.
5. How has it been possible for America and western Europe to improve living standards despite rising populations?
6. Why is the importation of the mongoose into the United States prohibited?
7. Why are soil, forests, and wildlife called renewable resources?
8. Describe two methods of farming that conserve soil.
9. List the principal pollutants of water and air.
10. List four ways by which scientists can increase food production.

CHECK YOUR UNDERSTANDING

11. What are the principal dangers of the indiscriminate use of DDT?
12. How might low cost desalination of seawater increase food production?

13. Why do some biologists argue that conservation alone is insufficient for the future?
14. How is it possible for a nation to increase agricultural yield each year and have less food per capita than before?
15. Why do ecologists insist that because man has altered his environment, he must continue to do so in order to survive?
16. The philosopher Francis Bacon wrote, "We cannot command Nature except by obeying her." How do you interpret this observation?
17. Some people are of the opinion that overpopulation is a concern only of the underdeveloped nations. What is your opinion?
18. Conservationists argue that regulated hunting can be as beneficial to deer populations as a total ban on hunting. Explain this point of view.
19. How has man been able to increase productivity, when the carrying capacities of ecosystems are limited?

RESEARCH PROJECTS AND REPORTS

1. Obtain information from your school or public library and prepare a report on one of the following topics:

Thomas Malthus	**Food From the Sea**
Air Pollution in the United States	**World Population**

2. *Erosion:* Place one or two handfulls of loose soil in a tray that has a drain tube at the far end. Incline the tray under a tap, with the drain tube arranged to flow into the sink. Allow a slow stream of tap water to flow over the soil, down the tray, and out the drain tube.

   Observe the changes that take place on the soil's surface. Also observe the changes in the stream and in the shallow "pond" that will form at the far end of the tray. Try to relate what you see to natural processes.

3. *Air Pollution:* Working in teams, place several wide-mouthed gallon jars in widely separated and undisturbed locations, such as an industrial site, a park, the school yard, and a country location. Place 4 inches of distilled water in each jar and top the jar with wire mesh cover. Allow the jars to stand undisturbed for one month, adding distilled water from time to time.

   Return the jars to the laboratory and allow water to evaporate. Wash down sides and bottom of each jar with distilled water, then transfer water and suspended particles to an evaporating dish of known weight. Evaporate water in the dish, then weigh the dish plus its residue. How many milligrams of solid material were deposited at each station? By knowing the area of the jar's mouth and the weight of the particles deposited, can you calculate the weight of solid pollution on one square mile of the earth's surface?

FURTHER READING

The Challenge of Man's Future. Harrison Brown. Viking Press, New York, N.Y. A discussion of the problems of increased population and dwindling resources.

Silent Spring. Rachel Carson. Houghton Mifflin, Boston, Mass. The indiscriminate overuse of powerful insecticides is storing up severe problems for the future.

The Alien Animals. George Laycock. Natural History Press, Garden City, New York. Most attempts by man to rearrange natural animal distribution have ended in failure. Some have led to outright disaster.

"**Population Density and Social Pathology.**" John B. Calhoun. *Scientific American,* February, 1962, page 139. Even when food and water are ample in a rat population, limited space leads to abnormal behavior and an increase in the death rate.

"**Thermal Pollution and Aquatic Life.**" John R. Clark. *Scientific American,* March, 1969, page 19. The disposal of heated industrial waste in rivers and lakes is a threat to fish and other organisms.

Glossary

Many of the terms used in this text are briefly defined on this and the following pages. More can and should be learned about many of the terms by checking them in the *Index* to see their use in other contexts. The pronunciation for some terms is supplied by phonetic respelling. In such cases, the syllabic accent is indicated by the use of SMALL CAPITAL LETTERS.

A

abscission (ab-SIZH-un) **layer:** where leaf petiole separates from stem in leaf fall.

absorption: the passage of water and other fluids through cell membranes.

acquired character: character acquired by an organism as the result of use or disuse.

acquired immunity: protection gained by vaccination against specific disease.

ACTH: a pituitary hormone that controls the activity of the adrenal cortex.

activating center: the brain stem portion believed to control cerebral activity.

active transport: movement of materials through cell membrane in direction opposite to concentration or electrical gradient.

adaptation: a modification of an organism that better fits it for living in its environment.

adaptive radiation: process by which one species gives rise to two or more species.

adductor muscle: muscle that draws toward the median line or draws together.

ADP: adenosine diphosphate, the energy-poor compound in cells.

adrenal gland: an endocrine gland attached to the kidney.

adrenalin: adrenal medulla hormone.

aerobe (AY-er-ohb): an organism requiring atmospheric oxygen to survive.

agar (AH-gahr): a gelatine extracted from certain seaweeds.

agglutinate: to clump together or adhere.

air bladder: a gas-containing organ in bony fish used to regulate their specific gravity.

air sac: a structure, found in birds and insects, important in respiration.

albino: an organism lacking pigmentation.

allele: one of a pair of genes occupying parallel sites on homologous chromosomes and controlling the same hereditary trait.

allergy: excessive sensitivity to certain substances that are harmless to most people.

alpha ray: a stream of positively charged helium atoms.

alternate host: one of two or more hosts on which a parasite lives.

alternation of generations: alternation of a generation having sexual reproduction with a generation having asexual reproduction.

alveolus (al-VEE-oh-lus): a sac or cavity, such as in the vertebrate lung.

amino (ah-MEE-noh) **acid:** an organic nitrogen compound that is a fundamental unit in protein construction.

ammonifying bacteria: bacteria that convert nitrogen compounds into ammonia.

amnion: the innermost membrane that encloses some vertebrate embryos.

amylase (AM-i-lays): an enzyme that splits starch into maltose.

anaerobe (AN-uh-robe): an organism that can survive in the absence of free oxygen.

analogous organ: organ having function similar to another organ.

androgen: the general name of male hormones.

anemia: a condition in which the red corpuscles of the blood are reduced in number or are deficient in hemoglobin.

angiosperm (AN-jee-uh-spurm): a plant that has seeds in a closed ovary.

angstrom (ANG-strum): a unit of length, equal to one hundred-millionth of a centimeter, used to measure light waves.

annual: a plant that lives one year or one growing season only.

annual ring: a layer of woody tissue deposited each year by the cambium in stems and roots.

annulus (AN-u-lus): a ringlike structure.

antenna: much-jointed, sensory organ on the head of many arthropods.

antennule: a short antenna.

anther: terminal portion of a stamen, containing pollen.

antheridium (an-ther-ID-ee-um): the male sex organ in such primitive plants as algae, fungi, liverworts, mosses, and ferns.

antibiotic: substance extracted from a fungus that kills or stops bacterial growth.

antibody: a substance in the blood and body fluids that protects the body against pathogens and other foreign substances.

anticoagulant: a substance that reduces the blood's ability to clot.

antigen: a substance that stimulates the body to produce antibodies.

antitoxin: an antibody antagonistic to a specific toxin.

anus: the posterior external opening of the digestive tract.

aorta: a large artery leading from the heart to the rest of the body.

appendicular skeleton: the shoulders, arms, hips, and legs of a vertebrate skeleton.

arachnoid membrane: the membrane between the dura mater and pia mater of the brain and spinal cord.

archegonium (aar-keh-GOH-ni-um): the female sex organ in mosses, liverworts, ferns, and some gymnosperms.

arteriole: artery with very fine diameter.

arteriosclerosis: abnormal thickening and hardening of the walls of arteries.

artery: blood vessel that carries blood away from the heart.

ascorbic acid: vitamin C.

asexual (ay-SEK-shoo-al): lacking specialized sexual cells.

assimilation: conversion of simple food materials into more complex living material.

associative neuron: a nerve cell connecting a sensory neuron and a motor neuron.

atherosclerosis: arteriosclerosis in which a fatty deposit accumulates on inner wall of artery, thereby reducing its diameter.

atoll (AT-ol): a reef surrounding a central lagoon.

ATP: adenosine triphosphate, the energy-storing compound in cells.

atrium: one of the thin-walled chambers of the heart.

autonomic nervous system: the nervous system controlling the involuntary activities of the body.

autotrophic (aw-tuh-TROF-ik): capable of making food; obtaining nourishment from inorganic matter.

auxins (AWK-sins): plant hormones that promote or inhibit plant growth.

axial skeleton: the skull and backbone of a vertebrate skeleton.

axon: the part of a neuron carrying nerve impulses away from the cell body.

B

bacillus (bah-SIL-us): bacterium having a straight rod shape.

bacteriophage: a bacteria-destroying agent.

ball and socket joint: a joint, as the hip, permitting great freedom of motion in many directions.

barb: a lateral extension from the shaft of a feather.

barbule: a lateral branch of a feather barb.

barrier reef: a reef parallel to the shore but at a considerable distance.

basal disc: the portion of a coelenterate attached to the substratum.

beta ray: a stream of high-speed electrons.

biennial: a plant whose life cycle extends over two years.

bilateral symmetry: a condition whereby a structure can be halved in only one way so that the two halves are mirror images of one another.

bile: a secretion of the liver of vertebrates.

binomial system of nomenclature: the system for classifying organisms with a genus and a species name.

biology: the science of living things.

biome: a distinctive life community such as a desert, grassland, or forest.

biopsy: the removal and examination of a piece of living tissue.

blade: expanded part of a leaf.

blastocoele: the cavity within the blastula.

blastoderm: the sheet of cells formed as a result of cleavage of a yolky egg.

blastodisc: the disklike area of the blastoderm in which the embryo first appears.

blastula (BLAS-tyoo-lah): the embryonic stage at the end of cleavage, usually in the form of a hollow ball.

blind spot: the place, devoid of rod and cone cells, where the optic nerve enters the eye.

Bowman's capsule: a small sac surrounding each glomerulus of the kidney.

bronchiole: a fine branch of a bronchus.

bronchus: the branch of the trachea leading to each lung.

budding: an asexual reproductive process in which a small outgrowth of the parent produces a new organism.

C

caecum (SEE-kum): the sac into which the small intestine opens at the beginning of the large intestine.

calyx (KAY-liks): collective term for the sepals.

cambium: plant stem and root tissue that produces new cells for growth in diameter.

canine teeth: sharp, pointed teeth characteristic of carnivorous mammals.

capillarity (kap-ih-LAR-ih-tee): the tendency of a liquid to rise in a narrow tube.

capillary: a microscopic blood vessel forming networks intermediate between arterioles and venules.

capsomere: unit of protein that makes up the outer coat of viruses.

capsule: protective layer around some bacteria.

carapace: a bony or horny case covering the back of certain animals.

carbohydrate: a compound of carbon, hydrogen, and oxygen in which the ratio of hydrogen to oxygen is two to one.

carcinogen (kahr-SIN-oh-jen): a cancer-producing agent.

cardiac muscle: the heart muscle.

carnivorous (kahr-NIV-uh-rus): flesh-eating.

carotene (KAR-oh-teen): a yellow-orange pigment in some plants.

carrier: a chemical that actively transports another chemical across a cell membrane.

cartilage: a flexible, firm connective tissue.

catalyst: a chemical substance that promotes chemical change without being altered in the process.

cell membrane: boundary of a living cell.

cellulose (SELL-yuh-lohs): a complex, largely insoluble compound peculiar to plants.

cell wall: non-living, cellulose, outer wall of plant cells.

central nervous system: the brain and spinal cord.

centriole: a cell structure that functions in cell division by duplicating itself before mitosis and forming spindle fibers.

cephalothorax (sef-uh-loh-THOR-aks): body region in which head and thorax are fused.

cerebellum (ser-eh-BEL-um): the part of the brain that regulates muscle coordination.

cerebrum (SER-eh-brum): the part of the brain controlling voluntary activities.

chemical change: a change during which the chemical properties of a substance are altered.

chemosynthesis (kem-oh-SIN-the-sis): synthesis of organic compounds by energy derived from chemical reactions.

chlorophyll (KLOR-uh-fil): the green pigment in plants.

chloroplast (KLOR-uh-plast): green oval body containing chlorophyll in plant cells.

cholesterol: a white, fatty alcohol found in all animal fats.

chordate (KOR-dayt): a member of the phylum Chordata, an animal having a notochord, gill slits, and a dorsal tubular nerve cord at some stage of its life.

chromatid (KROH-muh-tid): one half of a chromosome that has doubled during cell division.

chromatin (KROH-muh-tin): the dark-staining material that makes the chromosomes visible.

chromatography (kroh-muh-TOG-rah-fee): the process of separating chemical compounds in an adsorbent column.

chromatophore: concentrations of pigment in the skin of some animals, primarily fish and amphibians.

chromosomes (KROH-muh-sohms): structures within the nucleus that transmit hereditary characters.

chrysalis: a hard case that encloses the pupal stage of the butterfly.

chyme (kym): partly digested food that enters the small intestine from the stomach.

cilia (SIL-ee-uh): short hairlike processes of some cells, often used for locomotion.

circulation: the movement of blood from the heart to the parts of the body and back to the heart.

cleavage (KLEE-vij): the repeated subdivision of an embryo, usually ending in a blastula.

climax community: a community with a stable composition.

clitellum (kli-TEL-um): the swollen region of earthworms and leeches, which secretes a slime tube during copulation.

cloaca (kloh-AY-kah): the terminal part of the gut into which kidney and reproductive ducts open.

coacervate: protein droplets held together by a layer of liquid such as water; a hypothetical pre-cellular condition.

coagulation: the state of becoming thick or jellylike as in the clotting of blood.

coccus (KOK-us): bacterium having a spherical shape.

cochlea (KOK-lee-uh): the spiral structure of the inner ear associated with hearing.

cocoon: protective covering of some embryonic stages, such as the eggs of annelids or the pupae of insects.

codon: a group of three adjacent nucleotides specific for coding a single amino acid.

coelom (SEE-lom): the main body cavity of an animal with three germ layers.

cohesion (koh-HEE-zhun): the molecular attraction of similar particles for one another.

cold-blooded: having a body temperature that varies as the temperature of the environment varies.

colon: the principal part of the large intestine of vertebrates.

color blindness: the inability to distinguish certain colors.

communicable disease: a disease that can be transmitted from one person to another.

complete flower: having all the parts of a typical flower, including calyx, corolla, stamens, and pistil.

complete metamorphosis: insect metamorphosis involving four stages: egg, larva, pupa, and adult.

composite family: a plant family in which many small flowers are borne together in one head resembling a single flower.

compound eye: an eye composed of many small sensory units, or ommatidia.

compound fracture: a fracture in which the bone pierces the skin.

conditioned reflex: a reflex modified by experience.

cone cell: a cell in the retina that is responsible for color vision.

conjugation: sexual reproduction in some protists, such as Paramecium.

conjugation tube: the tube formed between two conjugating organisms.

consumer organism: an organism that cannot make its own food.

contour feather: a feather that forms the outline of the bird's body.

contour plowing: plowing parallel to the contours of the land.

copulation: the sexual union of animals.

cork cambium: the layer of cells that produces the cork cells of the bark.

corm: a short, underground stem with thin, dry, leaf scales.

cornea: the transparent covering of the eye.

corolla (koh-ROL-ah): collective term used for the petals.

coronary thrombosis: the formation of a clot within the coronary arteries.

cortex: outer region of cerebrum and adrenal glands; in plant stems and roots, a storage tissue.

cortisone: adrenal cortex hormone.

cotyledon (kot-ih-LEE-dun): a primitive seed leaf or a leaf forming part of the embryo of seeds.

cranium: the cavity that contains the brain.

crop: an enlargement of the digestive tract used for storage or digestion.

crossing over: the mutual exchange of parts of homologous chromosomes.

cross-pollination: the transfer of pollen from the anther of one flower to the stigma of another flower of the same species.

culture: the cultivation or growth of microorganisms or cells in prepared nutrient media.

cuticle: waxy, noncellular coating on leaf surface.

cyst: in some protists, an inactive stage within a protective covering.

cytochrome: an enzyme that functions in cell respiration as an electron carrier.

cytoplasm (SY-toh-plazm): the substance of the cell outside the nucleus.

D

deciduous (de-SID-u-us): lost at maturity or at certain seasons, as teeth or leaves.

dehydration: the loss of water.

dendrite: the part of a neuron carrying nerve impulses into the cell body.

denitrifying bacteria (de-NY-tri-fy-ing): bacteria that convert nitrogen compounds in the soil into free nitrogen.

dentine: bone-like material found in teeth and shark scales.

dermis: the thick, deeper layer of the skin.

diaphragm: the muscular partition between the chest cavity and abdomen in mammals.

diastole (dy-AS-toh-lee): phase of heartbeat when heart muscle relaxes.

dicotyledon (dy-kot-ih-LEE-dun): an angiosperm with two seed leaves or cotyledons.

diffusion (dih-FYU-zhun): the spreading out of a substance due to molecular motion.

digestion: the physical and chemical breakdown of foods into basic components that can be absorbed and assimilated.

dihybrid: the offspring of parents with two dissimilar traits.

diploid (DIP-loid) number: the number of chromosomes found in all cells produced by the body (except gametes, which have half the diploid number of chromosomes).

DNA: Deoxyribonucleic acid, found in chromosomes and believed to be the primary hereditary material.

dominant trait: a trait that seems to conceal or hide another trait.

dormancy: a state of rest or sleep.

dorsal: pertaining to the back of an animal.

down feather: the soft feather found beneath the contour feathers.

drone bee: the male.

duodenum (doo-oh-DEE-num): the first part of the vertebrate small intestine.

dura mater (DOO-rah MAY-tur): the thick outer membrane covering the spinal cord and brain.

E

ecology: the study of the interrelations between living things and their physical and biotic environments.

ecosystem: the total biotic and physical environment and their interactions.

ectoderm: the outermost embryonic layer, which develops into the epidermis and nervous tissue.

egg cell: (see ovum)

embryo: the pre-birth or pre-hatching developmental phase of an organism.

embryo sac: the area within the plant ovule where fertilization of the egg occurs.

enamel: the extremely hard, outer layer of a tooth.

endocrine (EN-doh-kryn) gland: a ductless gland, whose secretion is passed directly into the blood.

endoderm: the innermost embryonic layer, which develops into the intestine and associated glands.

endosperm (EN-doh-spurm): the food nourishing the embryo in the seed.

environment: the conditions in which an organism lives.

enzyme: an organic catalyst that accelerates a particular chemical process.

epidermis: the outermost layer of cells of a plant or animal.

epiglottis: the small flap of tissue that covers the opening to the trachea.

epiphyte (EP-ih-fyt): non-parasitic plant that grows upon another plant.

erythrocyte (eh-RITH-roh-syt): the red blood corpuscle.

esophagus: the part of the intestine that leads from the pharynx to the stomach.

estrogen: the general name of female hormones.

eugenics: the science of human improvement through heredity.

evolution: the changes in characteristics of organisms occurring through descent.

exoskeleton: an external skeleton or body covering.

extensor: a muscle that extends the bones at a joint.

F

fatty acid: a molecular sub-unit of lipids.

feces: solid intestinal wastes.

fermentation: decomposition of organic compounds, usually by microorganisms, such as yeast acting upon sugar to produce alcohol and carbon dioxide.

fertilization: the union of two sex cells, egg and sperm, to form a diploid cell.

fetus: the developing young of a mammal in the later stages prior to birth.

fibrin: a white, insoluble protein formed from fibrinogen, causing blood to clot.

fibrinogen (fy-BRIN-oh-jen): the blood protein that forms fibrin, the blood-clotting fiber.

fission (FISH-un): the division of an organism into equal parts.

fistula (FIS-chuh-lah): an abnormal opening in a hollow organ.

flagellum (flah-JEL-um): a long, whiplike process of a cell, used for locomotion.

flame cell: a cell that functions in excretion in some simple multicellular animals.

flexor: a muscle that bends the bones at a joint.

fluoridation: the process of treating water with fluorides.

food chain: series of organisms dependent upon one another for food.

food web: interwoven food chains.

fossil: the remains or impression of an organism that lived in an earlier geological period.

fragmentation: breaking or splitting into parts, sometimes as a means of reproduction.

fraternal twins: twins that develop from two different fertilized eggs.

fringing reef: a reef that is close to the shore.

fruit: the ripened ovary, and its contents, of a seed plant.

G

gall bladder: the small sac that receives and stores bile.

gamete: a mature sex cell.

gametophyte (gah-MEE-toh-fyt): the haploid plant generation, which produces sex cells.

ganglion (GANG-glee-un): a cluster of nervous tissue.

gastrula (GAS-troo-lah): the embryonic stage during which two, then three cell layers are formed.

gemmule: in sponges, a mass of cells that develop into an adult sponge.

gene (jeen): section of a chromosome believed to carry a hereditary trait.

genotype: the genetic makeup of an organism.

geotropism (jee-AH-tro-pizm): the response of an organism to the force of gravity.

germination (jur-mih-NAY-shun): the sprouting of a spore or seed.

gestation (jes-TAY-shun): the period of carrying young in the uterus.

gills: respiratory structures of marine and aquatic organisms; function by absorbing dissolved oxygen directly from the water.

gizzard: the very muscular portion of a digestive tract in which food is broken up.

gliding joint: a joint permitting the bones to slide over each other, as in the wrist.

globulin: a blood protein important in immunity reactions.

glomerulus (gloh-MER-u-lus): in vertebrate kidneys, a small group of capillaries that projects into a Bowman's capsule.

glottis: the opening to the trachea.

glycogen: a starch found in animals and fungi.

glycolysis: the steps of cell respiration that result in the breaking down of glucose to pyruvic acid.

Golgi apparatus: a cell structure that functions in secretion of various cell products and in synthesis of large carbohydrate molecules.

gonad: a reproductive organ and endocrine gland.

gonadotropins (go-nad-uh-TROH-pins): pituitary hormones controlling gonadal activity.

grafting: the permanent union of one part of an organism to another part of the same, or another, organism.

grain: the seedlike fruit of cereal grasses.

grana: the layers of a chloroplast.

guard cell: in leaves, one of two cells that form a stoma.

gymnosperm: a plant that has naked seeds, or seeds not enclosed in an ovary.

H

haploid (HAP-loid) **number:** the number of chromosomes found in gametes, which is half the diploid number of chromosomes.

heartwood: the center, dark-colored wood of a tree, composed of dead cells.

helix: a spiral-like, curved line traced around a cylinder at a constant distance and oblique angle.

hemoglobin: the respiratory pigment in red corpuscles of vertebrates.

hemophilia: a hereditary disease, characterized by a severe reduction in the blood's ability to clot.

hemotoxin: a poison that attacks the blood.

herbaceous (hur-BAY-shus): a plant without woody tissue, thus soft and succulent.

herbivorous (hur-BIV-uh-rus): plant-eating.

hermaphrodite: any animal that has both male and female reproductive organs.

heterocyst: thick-walled, empty cell in Nostoc that is a breaking point of the filament.

heterotrophic (het-er-oh-TROF-ik): not capable of making own food; obtaining nourishment from organic matter.

heterozygous: having non-identical genes in parallel areas on a pair of chromosomes.

hinge joint: a joint permitting motion in only one plane, as the elbow.

homologous chromosomes: chromosomes, similar in size and shape, one from the sperm cell and one from the egg cell, controlling similar developmental processes.

homologous organ: an organ having the same basic embryonic structural plan as another organ.

homozygous: having identical genes in parallel areas on a pair of chromosomes.

homunculus: the name given to the "little man" that early microscopists claimed to see in spermatozoa.

hormone (HOR-mohn): product of cells in one part of an organism, transported by body fluid or sap, and affecting cells in another part.

host: an organism upon which another organism exists as a parasite.

hybrid: the offspring of parents with dissimilar traits.

hydrotropism (hy-DRO-troh-pizm): the response of an organism to water.

hyphae: basic filamentous structure of fungi.

hypocotyl (hy-poh-KOT-il): the embryonic stem of a seed.

hypothalamus (hy-poh-THAL-uh-mus): a section of the brain at the base of the cerebrum closely related to the pituitary gland in function.

I

icosahedron (eye-koh-suh-HEE-drun): twenty-sided figure that is a structural characteristic of many viruses.

immovable joint: a joint that permits no motion, as the sutures of the skull.

immune: the state of resisting the development of a disease.

imperfect flower: a flower lacking either stamens or pistil.

inbreeding: the breeding of closely related individuals.

incisor: a tooth adapted for cutting.

incomplete flower: a flower lacking any of the parts of a complete flower, such as the calyx, corolla, stamens or pistil.

incomplete metamorphosis: insect metamorphosis involving the egg, several nymph stages, and adult, and in which the nymph stages greatly resemble the adult.

incus: the second in the chain of bones connecting the outer ear to the inner ear.

Independent Assortment: the principle that traits are sorted independently of one another during sex cell formation.

ingestion: the taking-in of food.

insectivorous: insect-eating.

insertion: the point of attachment of a muscle on the bone that is moved by that muscle.

insulin: the pancreatic hormone that controls the amount of glucose in the blood.

invertebrate (in-VUR-tuh-brate): a collective term for animals that are not chordates.

ion: an electrically charged atom or group of atoms.

iris: the structure, usually pigmented, controlling the amount of light admitted to the vertebrate eye.

islets of Langerhans: groups of pancreatic cells that secrete insulin.

K

Krebs cycle: the series of chemical changes by which the energy of food is made available to cells.

L

lacteal: a branch of the lymphatic system in a villus.

larva: the usually free-living, immature form of some animals; generally very different in appearance from the parents.

larynx: enlarged region of the upper part of the trachea in most vertebrates.

lateral line: a system of sense organs along each side of the body of fishes.

lens: in man, the part of the eye that is responsible for focusing.

lenticel (LEN-ti-sel): a small opening in the bark of twigs and stems that allows for an exchange of gases.

lethal gene: a gene that results in death.

leucocyte (LYOO-koh-syt): a white corpuscle.

leukemia: a condition in which the number of white blood corpuscles is enormously increased.

ligament: a strong connective band holding bones together at a joint.

linkage: the location of certain genes on the same chromosome and the consequent tendency for the genes to be inherited together.

litmus paper: a red or blue paper used to distinguish acids from bases by color changes.

lymph: the colorless fluid contained in the lymph vessels.

lysosome: a cell structure that contains various lytic enzymes.

M

macronucleus (mak-roh-NU-klee-us): the largest nucleus of ciliate protozoa.

malleus: the outermost of three bones connecting the outer ear to the inner ear.

Malpighian (mal-PIG-ee-an) **tubule:** glandular excretory tube opening into the digestive tract of insects.

maltase (MAWL-tays): an enzyme that splits one maltose molecule into two glucose molecules.

mammary gland: a milk-producing gland in female mammals.

mandible: in vertebrates, the lower jaw; in invertebrates, a biting or crushing mouth part.

mantle: in mollusks, a thin fold of skin covering the body, which secretes the shell and protects internal organs.

maxilla (mak-SIL-ah): in vertebrates, the upper jaw; in invertebrates, the mouth part behind the mandibles.

maxilliped (mak-SIL-ih-ped): in arthropods, the first thoracic appendage, used to manipulate food.

medulla oblongata (muh-DUL-uh ob-long-GAH-tuh): the widened part of the extension of the spinal cord in the brain.

medusa: the sexual, jellyfish form of a coelenterate animal.

meiosis: the sequence of cell divisions that results in sexual reproductive cells, which have the haploid number of chromosomes.

mesoderm (MES-oh-durm): the middle embryonic tissue layer, which develops into muscle, blood, and connective tissue.

mesophyll (MES-oh-fil): portion of leaf between upper and lower epidermis.

mesothorax (mes-uh-THOR-aks): the middle segment of the insect thorax.

metabolism (meh-TAB-oh-lizm): the total of chemical reactions in a living system.

metamorphosis (met-ah-MOR-foh-sis): the transformation from larval to adult form involving marked changes in structure.

metathorax (met-ah-THOR-aks): the posterior segment of the insect thorax.

metazoan (met-ah-ZOH-an): an animal that is composed of numerous cells when adult.

micron: unit of length in the metric system equal to one-millionth of a meter or one twenty-five-thousandth of an inch.

micronucleus (my-kroh-NU-klee-us): the smaller nucleus of ciliate protoza.

micropyle: the opening in the ovule through which the pollen tube enters.

microtome: a device that cuts thin sections of tissue for microscopic examination.

milt: the seminal fluid and spermatozoa of fish.

mitochondria (my-toh-KON-dree-ah): oval or rodlike structures in cytoplasm that are the sites of energy production.

mitosis (my-TOH-sis): the process by which a cell and a nucleus divide in two.

mitral valve: the valve between the left atrium and the left ventricle.

monocotyledon: an angiosperm with one seed leaf, or one cotyledon.

motor neuron: a nerve cell that conducts a nerve impulse away from the central nervous system and to the organ to be activated.

mucus: slimy secretion of some epithelial cells that protects epithelial tissues.

mutation: an inheritable change in genetic material.

mutualism: a close relationship between two species from which both species benefit, such as the alga and fungus in a lichen.

mycelium (my-SEE-lee-um): mass of interwoven hyphae of a fungus.

N

nares (NAR-eez): openings from the olfactory organ.

natural selection: the theory that variations in organisms might give them an advantage in the struggle for existence.

natural immunity: the protection against specific diseases that some people appear to have at birth.

nematocyst (neh-MAT-uh-sist): a stinging structure, as in coelenterates.

nephridium (neh-FRID-ee-um): excretory organ, as in earthworms and mollusks.

nephron: the excretory unit of the vertebrate kidney.

nerve: a bundle of nerve fibers, connective tissue, and blood vessels in a sheath of connective tissue.

nerve impulse: electrochemical energy traveling along a nerve cell.

netted venation: a network arrangement of the veins in a leaf.

neural tube: a longitudinal tube of nervous tissue in vertebrate embryos from which the brain and nervous system develop.

neuron: a nerve cell.

neurosis: a functional nervous disorder of the central nervous system.

neurotoxin: a poisonous protein complex, present in various snake venoms, that attacks the nervous system.

nitrifying (NY-tri-fy-ing) **bacteria:** bacteria that convert ammonia into nitrates.

nitrogen-fixing bacteria: bacteria, living in the soil or in the nodules of legumes, that convert atmospheric nitrogen into nitrogen compounds.

nodule (NAWJ-ewl): a small swelling found on leguminous roots that contains nitrogen-fixing bacteria.

notochord (NOH-toh-kord): a flexible rod present in some stage of development of all chordates.

nuclear membrane: the selectively-permeable membrane that contains the nucleus and affords communication with the rest of the cell.

nucleic acid: a compound composed of groups of 5-carbon sugars, phosphates, and nitrogenous bases.

nucleolus (nu-KLEE-oh-lus): a spherical or oval body that is found in the nucleus of some cells.

nucleoprotein (nu-klee-oh-PROH-teen): a compound consisting of a protein and a nucleic acid, either RNA or DNA.

nucleotide: the basic building unit of nucleic acids; a 5-carbon sugar, a phosphate group(s), and a nitrogenous base.

nucleus: the cell structure that ultimately directs most of the cell's activities.

nutrition (nu-TRISH-un): the processes by which an organism takes in and uses food.

nymph (nimf): immature insect form that undergoes incomplete metamorphosis.

olfactory: pertaining to the sense of smell.

omnivorous (om-NIV-oh-rus): plant- and flesh-eating.

oogenesis: production of female sex cells.

operculum: the cover that protects the gills in bony fishes.

optic nerve: a nerve leading from the eye to the brain.

organ: a structure composed of different tissues with a common function.

organic compound: a chemical compound containing carbon.

organism: a living thing.

origin: the point of attachment of a muscle to a bone at the end that does not move when the muscle contracts.

osculum: the opening to the internal cavity in some sponges.

osmosis (os-MOH-sis): the movement of water through a semipermeable membrane.

osmotic (os-MOT-ik) pressure: the pressure that results from the accumulation of water inside a container bounded by a semipermeable membrane.

ossification (os-i-fi-KAY-shun): to change into or form bone.

osteoblast (os-tee-uh-blast): a bone-forming cell.

ovary: the female organ in which eggs are produced.

oviduct: the tube that carries egg cells toward the outside of an animal.

oviparous: producing eggs that hatch outside the maternal body.

ovipositor (oh-vi-POZ-ih-tur): the egg-laying organ of an insect.

ovoviviparous (oh-voh-vy-VIP-ah-rus): producing living young from eggs that are incubated and hatched within the maternal body.

ovule: the structure of a flower that develops into a seed after fertilization.

ovum: the female gamete.

oxidation: the combining of a substance with oxygen or the loss of hydrogen with subsequent release of energy.

oxyhemoglobin: the compound formed by the union of oxygen with hemoglobin.

pacemaker: a tissue in the heart that regulates the rate of heartbeat.

palisade layer: cell layer in leaf between upper epidermis and spongy layer.

pancreas: a digestive and hormonal gland located near the stomach and liver.

parallel venation: arrangement of veins in a leaf in such a way that main veins are parallel to each other.

parasite: an organism that derives its nourishment from another living thing.

parasympathetic nervous system: that part of the autonomic nervous system not connected to the sympathetic ganglia.

parathormone: the secretion of the parathyroid glands.

parathyroid gland: a ductless gland controlling calcium metabolism.

parenchyma (pah-RENG-ki-mah): a thin-walled, living plant tissue.

passive transport: the movement of materials through a membrane in the direction of a concentration or electrical gradient.

pasteurization (pas-chuh-ruh-ZAY-shun): partial sterilization of fluids by heat treatment, destroying some pathogenic organisms.

pathogen (PATH-oh-jehn): a disease-producing organism.

pathogenic (path-oh-JEN-ik): capable of producing disease.

pectoral (PEK-toh-ral) fins: the anterior paired fins of fish.

pectoral girdle: the bony or cartilaginous arch supporting the forelimbs.

pelvic fins: the posterior paired fins of fish.

pelvic girdle: the bony or cartilaginous arch supporting the hind limbs.

peptide bond: the linkage joining two amino acids.

perennial: a plant that continues to live from year to year.

perfect flower: a flower having both stamens and pistil.

pericardial (per-ih-KAHR-dee-al) cavity: the cavity within which the heart lies.

peristalsis (per-i-STAL-sis): the wavelike contractions of tubular organs, such as the digestive tract.

petal: one of the innermost leaflike parts of a flower, generally not green.

petiole (PET-i-ohl): the stalk of a leaf.

pharynx: the area between the mouth and the esophagus in vertebrates.

phenotype: the physical appearance of an organism.

phloem (FLOH-em): a tissue in higher plants with tubes that conduct food materials.

phloem vessels: the tubes in the phloem that conduct food to all parts of a plant.

photoperiodism: the response of an organism to varying periods of light.

photosynthesis (foh-toh-SIN-the-sis): the chemical reaction by which green plants make organic compounds from inorganic materials.

phototropism (fuh-TAH-truh-pizm): the response of an organism to light.

pH value: an assigned numerical value indicating the relative acidic or basic qualities of a substance.

phycocyanin: bluish pigment in certain algae.

pia mater (PY-ah MAY-tur): the delicate, thin membrane closely attached to the brain and spinal cord.

pinocytosis: the taking in of particles by the pinching off of indentations in the cell membrane.

pistil: female reproductive organ of a flower.

pistillate flower: a flower having a pistil but lacking stamens.

pith ray: extensions of the pith between vascular bundles of herbaceous stems.

pituitary gland: the ductless gland located at the base of the brain.

pivotal joint: a joint permitting a twisting motion, as of the head.

placenta (plah-SEN-tah): mammalian structure that nourishes the developing fetus.

placoid (PLAK-oid) **scale:** a scale present in many fish, similar to vertebrate teeth.

plankton: the floating collection of organisms, many microscopic, in a body of water.

plasma: the liquid portion of blood.

plasma cells: the special cells of the lymph glands that produce gamma globulin.

plasmodium (plaz-MOH-dee-um): nonreproductive stage of slime mold; multinucleate and without definite size or shape.

plastron: ventral part of the turtle's shell.

platelets (PLAYT-lets): minute structures in mammalian blood believed to be associated with the clotting reaction.

pleura: the protective membrane lining the lung cavity and covering the lung.

plumule (PLOO-mule): the part of the seed that grows into the first upward shoot.

polar body: tiny cellular unit produced during oogenesis; non-functioning, but with the same haploid chromosome number as ovum.

pollen basket: an adaptation of the hind leg of the honeybee for carrying pollen.

pollen grain: the male reproductive structure of flowering plants.

pollen tube: tube formed, after pollination, as pollen grows down style to ovary.

pollination (pol-ih-NAY-shun): the transfer of pollen from an anther to a stigma.

polyp (POL-ip): the form of a coelenterate having a hollow cylindrical body with tentacles surrounding the mouth.

population: a group of individuals of a species.

population pressure: the tendency of organisms to outstrip the food supply.

prehensile (pre-HEN-sil) **tail:** a tail that is adapted for seizing or grasping.

primitive streak: longitudinal thickening during gastrulation in some embryos, determining the center line of the body.

proboscis (proh-BOS-is): a tubelike process of the head of some animals.

producer organism: an organism that can make its own foods.

proglottid (proh-GLOT-id): one of the segments of a tapeworm.

prolactin: in mammals, a pituitary hormone that induces the secretion of milk.

prop root: a root growing above the ground that supports or props a plant.

protein (PROH-teen): a class of organic compounds consisting of amino acid units.

prothallus (proh-THAL-us): a heart-shaped structure, the fern gametophyte, on which the sex organs develop.

prothorax (proh-THOR-aks): the anterior segment of the insect thorax.

prothrombin: a blood protein that forms thrombin.

provitamin: a compound from which a vitamin is made.

pseudopod (SU-doh-pod): a temporary extension of the cytoplasm of a cell used for feeding or movement.

psychosis: any serious mental disease.

pulp cavity: the inner portion of the tooth, containing blood vessels and nerves.

pupa (PEW-pah): the stage between larva and adult in insects undergoing complete metamorphosis.

pupil: the opening in the iris of the eye.

pylorus (py-LOH-rus): in vertebrates, muscular valve between stomach and intestines.

pyrenoid (PY-ruh-noid): a starch-making center in many algae.

Q

queen bee: the reproductive female.

R

radial symmetry: a condition whereby a structure can be halved in two or more ways so that the halves are mirror images of one another.

radicle: rootlike structure of seed plant embryos.

radioautograph: picture produced by reaction of radiation with photographic film.

radioisotope: radioactive form of an element.

radula: the strip of horny teeth in the mouth of mollusks.

Recapitulation Theory: the development of the embryo summarizes the evolutionary history of the organism.

receptacle: in Fucus, the swollen area containing the reproductive cells.

recessive trait: a trait that appears to be concealed or hidden by another trait.

reflex arc: the chain of three neurons, sensory, associative, and motor, involved in an involuntary response.

replication: the process by which the DNA molecule makes an exact copy of itself.

resin: a yellow, sticky fluid found in many conifers such as the pines.

respiration: externally, the intake of oxygen and the expulsion of carbon dioxide; internally, the oxidative breakdown of food molecules with a release of energy.

retina: the light-sensitive inner layer of the eye.

Rh factor or **Rhesus factor:** how antigens in red blood corpuscles compare with those found in the Rhesus monkey; may affect child bearing.

rhizoid (RY-zoid): a rootlike growth of certain plants, such as fungi, liverworts, and mosses.

rhizome (RY-zohm): a modified underground stem, frequently rootlike.

Rh negative: the condition in which the antigens of blood cells of an individual are not identical to those of the Rhesus monkey.

Rh positive: the condition in which the antigens of blood cells of an individual are identical to those of the Rhesus monkey.

ribosome (RY-boh-sohm): small granule, found in the cytoplasm, that is the center of protein formation.

rickettsia (rik-ET-see-ah): a microorganism intermediate between viruses and bacteria.

RNA: ribonucleic acid, found in the nucleolus and ribosomes of the cell, believed to be essential in the formation of proteins.

rod cell: the cell in the retina that is responsible for black and white vision.

roentgen: a unit of measurement of X rays.

root cap: the protective group of cells at the tip of a root.

root hair: a projection of root epidermis that absorbs water and mineral salts.

royal jelly: a secretion of the pharyngeal glands of worker bees that is used to feed the larvae.

ruminant (ROO-mi-nant): an even-toed mammal that chews a cud.

S

saprophyte (SAP-roh-fyte): an organism that lives upon nonliving organic matter.

sapwood: the outer, light-colored wood of a tree, composed of living cells.

scion (SY-un): in grafting, the plant part that is used as the cutting.

scolex (SKOH-leks): the anterior, or head, region of a tapeworm.

scute: an external horny or bony plate.

sebaceous (seh-BAY-shus) **gland:** skin gland of mammals, usually opening into a hair follicle, that secretes a fatty substance.

secretin: a hormone that stimulates the pancreas and liver to produce digestive juices.

segregation: the hereditary principle that predicts the segregation of a recessive trait when hybrids are crossed.

self-pollination: the transfer of pollen from anther to stigma of the same flower or another flower on the same plant.

semen: the male reproductive fluid containing spermatozoa.

semicell: one of the two parts of a desmid.

semicircular canal: one of three canals in the inner ear that regulate sense of balance.

semilunar valves: valves between the aorta and the heart and between the pulmonary artery and the heart.

seminal vesicle (SEM-ih-nal VES-ih-kl): male organ that stores sperm.

semipermeable (sem-ih-PUR-mee-uh-bl): permeable to some substances but not to others.

sensitivity: the ability of an organism to respond to stimuli.

sensory neuron: a nerve cell that conducts a nerve impulse from a sense organ to the central nervous system.

sepal (SEE-pal): one of the outermost leaflike parts of a flower, generally green.

septum: a partition, as in the heart.

serum albumin: the chief protein fraction in blood plasma.

sex-linked trait: a trait controlled by a gene located on a sex chromosome.

sinus: a cavity or open space.

smooth muscle: involuntary muscle.

somatoplasm: the term used by Weismann for the body cells as distinguished from reproductive cells.

somite (SOH-myt): a block of mesoderm in vertebrate embryos from which arise the vertebrae and many muscles.

species (SPEE-sheez): the smallest group of related organisms, in the system of classification, that have the ability to interbreed.

spermatogenesis: the production of male sex cells.

spermatozoa: male gametes (sperm cells).

spicule (SPIK-yule): one of the minute, calcareous or siliceous structures supporting the tissue of such animals as sponges and sea cucumbers.

spinal nerve: a nerve emerging from the spinal cord.

spindle cell: blood cell in the frog that releases a clotting agent.

spinneret: an organ for producing a thread of silk, as in spiders or caterpillars.

spiracle (SPY-rah-kl): in insects, a breathing pore.

spirillum (spy-RIL-um): bacterium having the shape of a spiral rod.

spirochete (SPY-ruh-keet): a spinal-shaped bacterium lacking a cell wall.

spongin (SPON-jin): tough, flexible material forming the skeleton of some sponges.

spongy layer: cell layer in leaf between palisade layer and lower epidermis.

sporangiophore (spoh-RAN-jee-oh-fohr): a structure that bears a sporangium.

sporangium (spoh-RAN-jee-um): a spore case or the chamber in which spores are produced.

spore: an asexual reproductive body, or a resistant resting cell.

sporophyte (SPOR-uh-fyt): the diploid plant generation that produces spores.

stamen (STAY-men): male reproductive organ of a flower.

staminate flower: a flower having stamens but lacking a pistil.

stapes: the innermost of the three bones connecting the outer ear to the inner ear.

starch: a complex polysaccharide that is the major form of stored food in most plants.

sternum: in vertebrates, the breast bone.

stigma: the terminal portion of a pistil of a flower, which receives pollen.

stimulus (STIM-u-lus): a change in the environment that produces a response in an organism.

stipe: a short stalk, as the mushroom stem.

stock: in grafting, the rooted plant part that receives the cutting.

stolon: a horizontal stem with roots at nodes, or a horizontal hypha of a fungus.

stoma (STOH-mah): small opening, as in the lower epidermis of a leaf.

striated (STRY-ate-ed) **muscle:** voluntary muscle.

strip cropping: planting of alternate strips of dense-rooted and loose-rooted crops.

style: the stalk of the pistil of a flower.

suture: line of junction, as in skull bones.

swarming: the movement of a large group of organisms, such as occurs when honeybees form a new hive.

swimmeret: a small abdominal appendage found on some crustaceans.

symbiosis (sim-by-OH-sis): biological association of two dissimilar organisms in which one or both organisms benefit.

sympathetic nervous system: that part of the autonomic system that is connected to sympathetic ganglia.

synapse (SIN-aps): a gap between an axon of one neuron and dendrites of another neuron, over which nerve impulses travel.

synapsis: the pairing of homologous chromosomes during meiosis.

system: a group of organs with a common function.

systole (SIS-toh-lee): phase of heartbeat when heart muscle contracts.

T

taproot: the long, main root of a plant.

taste bud: a receptor organ for taste.

taxonomy (taks-ON-oh-mee): the science of classification of organisms.

telson: the broadened terminal segment of the abdomen of arthropods.

tendon: a band of connective tissue joining a muscle to bone.

tendril: a slender, modified stem or leaf used by climbing plants for attachment.

territoriality: the need of an animal for a certain amount of space, which it defends against other members of its species.

testis (TES-tis): the organ in male animals that produces sperm.

testosterone: the principal male hormone secreted by the testes.

tetanus (TET-ah-nus): the state of a muscle undergoing continued contraction; also, a disease in which muscle spasms occur.

thallus (THAL-us): the plant body of plant-like protists, having no roots, stems or leaves.

thiamine: vitamin B_1.

thigmotropism (thig-MO-truh-pizm): the response of an organism to contact.

thorax: the chest region in terrestrial vertebrates; also, the three segments behind the head in insects.

thrombin: the enzyme responsible for the formation of fibrin in blood clotting.

thyroid gland: a ductless gland located in the neck region.

thyroxine: the secretion of the thyroid gland.

tissue: a group of similar cells with a common function.

tonsils: a pair of lymph glands on either side of the pharynx.

tonus (TOH-nus): mild, steady activity characterizing muscle cells.

topsoil: the surface layer of soil.

toxin: a poisonous substance produced by living organisms.

toxoid: a harmless, chemically treated toxin capable of stimulating antibody formation.

trace element: an element necessary to metabolism, but only in minute amounts.

tracer element: radioactive element used to trace biological processes.

trachea: a xylem water-conducting tube with no cross walls; the tube leading from the pharnyx to the lungs in air-breathing vertebrates; tube leading from spiracle of insects.

tracheid (TRAY-kee-id): a cell that fits end to end with another similar cell to form a xylem water-conducting tube with cross walls.

tracheole (TRAY-kee-ohl): the finest branch of a trachea of an insect.

transpiration: the elimination of vapor through the external surface, as water vapor from a leaf.

trichinosis (trik-i-NOH-sis): disease caused by infection with the trichina worm.

trichocyst (TRIK-oh-sist): minute lassoing or stinging organelle of some protozoa.

tricuspid valve: the valve between the right atrium and the right ventricle.

tropism (TROH-pizm): response to a stimulus by growth curvature or movement.

tube feet: in echinoderms, tiny hollow appendages connected to the water vascular system, used in locomotion and feeding.

tuber: an enlarged, underground stem, with buds, containing stored food.

tympanic (tim-PAN-ik) **membrane:** the eardrum.

U

umbilical (um-BIL-ih-kuhl) **cord:** the cord that connects the fetus to the placenta.

uniformitarianism: geological principle that the forces changing the earth today are the same forces that changed it in the past.

urea: the major product of protein breakdown that is excreted by the kidney of some vertebrates.

ureter: the duct that carries urine away from the kidney.

urethra: the tube leading from the urinary bladder of mammals to the exterior.

urinary bladder: a sac storing urine.

urine: the kidney excretion.

uterus: in female mammals, the organ for containing and usually nourishing the young prior to birth.

V

vaccination: the inoculation with weakened or killed disease-producing organisms to induce immunity.

vacuole (VAK-u-ohl): fluid-filled space within the cytoplasm of a cell.

vagus: a parasympathetic and sensory nerve of the heart and many other internal organs.

vane: the expanded flat part of a feather.

vascular bundle: any bundle of conducting tissue consisting mainly of xylem and phloem.

vascular cylinder: vascular bundle in the center of roots and some stems, with xylem, phloem, and other tissues.

vegetative propagation: asexual reproduction in plants by complete plant development from a part of the plant body, such as a stem, leaf, or tuber.

vein: a blood vessel carrying blood toward the heart.

ventral: pertaining to the belly, or undersurface, of an animal.

ventricle: a cavity of an organ, such as the thick-walled chamber of the heart.

venule: a vein of very small diameter.

vertebra: one of a series of small bones or cartilages surrounding the spinal cord in vertebrate animals.

vertebrate: an animal belonging to the subphylum Vertebrata, having a backbone and a brain case.

vestigial organ: a degenerate remnant of an organ.

villus: a tiny projection, such as found in the small intestine.

virus: a noncellular "organism" composed of a nucleic acid core and a protein shell; reproduces only in a host cell.

viviparous (vy-VIP-ah-rus): producing living young from eggs within the mother's body and nourished by her blood stream.

vocal cords: elastic cords in the larynx, capable of producing sound.

W

warm-blooded: having a constant body temperature not affected by variances in environmental temperature.

water cycle: the cycle of water between the earth and the atmosphere.

wood ray: a thin-walled row of cells extending radially in woody tissue.

worker bee: the sterile female.

X

X rays: a form of radiation having a short wavelength and high energy value.

xylem (ZY-lem): plant vascular tissue responsible for most water conduction; major constituent of wood.

xylem vessels: the tubes in the xylem that conduct water upward in the plant.

Y

yeast: a single-celled fungus that causes fermentation.

yolk: the part of some eggs, as in the bird and frog, from which the egg cell obtains nourishment.

Z

zoospore (ZOE-uh-spor): produced by certain algae, flagellated cell that develops into new organism.

zygospore: a spore formed by the fusion of cytoplasmic elements in certain protists; has a tough, protective coating.

zygote: a fertilized ovum.

Index

Numbers in **boldface type** refer to pages on which the subject is illustrated. Book titles and the scientific names of genera and species are printed in *italics*.

blood bank, 563
blood types, 560
    and antigens, 560–561, 650–651
    inheritance of, 144
    and race, 501
bone,
    bird, 458–459
    fish, 411
bone, human, 506–512
    formation of, 508
    fracture, 512
    marrow, 508–509, 558
    specific bones, 509, 510
    (*see also* skeleton)
BONNET, CHARLES, 182
BORRIES, VON, 59
botany, defined, 2
botulism, 205
Bowman's capsule, 579–**580**
box turtle, **451**
BOYSEN-JENSEN, PETER, 311
BRACONNET, HENRI, 90
brain, frog, 441–**442**
brain, human, **596–597**
    activating center of, 609
    and central nervous system, 594
    and hearing, 590
    and learning, 597–598
    and nerve impulses, 591, 594
    and sense organs, 586–587
    and smell, 590
    and spinal cord, 594–595
    structure of, **596**
    and vision, 588–589
    (*see also* specific part of brain)
brain, vertebrate, 406
brainwaves, 598
brake fern, 256–257
bread mold, **18**, 227–228
breathing,
    capacity and rate, 577–578
    control of, 595
    (*see also* respiration)
breeding, plant and animal, 160–161
BRIDGES, CALVIN, 137
brittle star, **24, 354**
bronchi, 575, **576**, 578
bronchioles, 575, **576**, 578
bronchitis, 578
    and smoking, 619

Brontosaurus, 174, **447–448**
BROOM, ROBERT, 493
BROWN, ROBERT, 75
Bryophyta, 11, 20, 252–253
bubonic plague, 641
BUCKLAND, WILLIAM, 446
budding, 324, 327
bullfrog, 433
bursa, 512
bursitis, 512
butterfly, **26**, 385–388, *386, 387*

C

caecum, 551
Calamites, 259
calcium, 85, 526
    and blood clotting, 526, 560–561
    in diet, 526
    in earth's crust, 85
    in human body, 85
    and parathyroid, 604
    and tetany, 517
Calorie, 522
    body requirements for, 522, **523, 524**
calorimeter, **522**
CALVIN, MELVIN, 714
    biography, 289
calyx, 293
cambium, 267–268, 277, 278, 281
Cambrian Period, 171
camel, 165, **166**, 482
cancer, 641, 655–657
    causes of, 656–657
    cells, 655, **656**
    research, 657
    and smoking, 617–620
    treatment, 657
Cannabis sativa, 615
canning, of foods, 209
capillaries,
    blood, 564–565
    lymph, 566
capillarity, 282
capsomere, 62, 63
capsule,
    bacteria, 203
    fruit, 302, 303
    moss, 255
carbohydrates, 88–90, 521–524
    digestion of, 546–548
    synthesis of, 111, 287

    and tooth decay, 543
carbon,
    atom, **86**
    in body, 85
    on earth, 33
carbon dioxide, 87–88
    in atmosphere, 663
    and breathing rate, 577–578
    and cell wastes, 565
    and greenhouse effect, 709
    and muscle contraction, 516–517
    and photosynthesis, 105–107, 109–111
    and respiration, 113–116, 575–577
Carboniferous Period, 171–173, 259
carboxyl group, 91
carnivores (*Carnivora*), 104, 479–481
carotene, 528
carrier, in active transport, 97, 272
carrying capacity, and population, 701
Carteria, **218**
cartilage,
    fish, 410–411
    human, 508
catalyst,
    in digestion, 537
    magnesium as, 527
    in photosynthesis, 108
caterpillar, 385, **386**, 387
catfish, **27**
cats, 480
cattle, 481–482
Caucasoid, 499
Cecropia moth, **26**
cell,
    animal, 76
    blood, formation of, 508–509
    cancerous, 655, **656**
    ciliated, 626
    collar, 323
    cone, 588
    cytoplasm of, 73
    egg, 122, 623, 625, **633**
    (*see also* egg cell)
    guard, **285–286**
    membrane of, **76**
    model of, 72
    nerve, 591–592

ovate, 283
petiole, 282
shape of, 282–283
structure, 285–287, **286**
venation, 283
(*see also* leaves)
LEAKEY, DR. and MRS. LOUIS,
493–495
learning,
and conditioned reflex, 610–
612
and memory, 597
and motivation, 612–614
trial and error, 612
leaves, 276, 282–290
color changes, 283–285
fall of, 283–285
pigmentation of, 285
unusual, 288–290
varieties of, **284**
(*see also* leaf)
Lecanora, 234
leech, **23**, 346–347
LEEUWENHOEK, ANTON VAN,
45, 71
biography, 49
legumes, 206–207, 302, 303
lemming, **676**
lemur, 484
lens,
eye, 588
microscope, 45
leopard frog, 433–**434**
leucocytes, **559**
Leucosolenia, **323**–324
leukemia, 559–560
LH (*see* luteinizing hormone)
lichen, 233–**234**
life,
age of, 40
beginnings on earth, 36–40
characteristics of, 33–35
in space, 40–41
life community (*see* community, life)
life expectancy, and disease,
641
life zones, **666**
ligaments, 510
light,
and environment, 664–665
and plant growth, 309–310,
311, 316, 317
spectrum, 309–310
lignin, 277

lignite, 256
lily, **21**
linkage, genes, 135
LINNAEUS, CAROLUS, 6–7, 11,
165
lion, **29**, 480
liquid state of matter, 92
litmus,
paper, 50
source of, 234
liver, frog, 439
liver, human, 524, 547–548,
550
liverwort, **20**, 252–254
living standard, and population, 700–701
living things, naming, 3–5
lizards, 451–452
(*see also* dinosaurs and specific lizard)
llama, **166**
lobefin, 424
lobster, **24**, 367, 376
petrified, **170**
lockjaw, 204
locust, 385
LOHMAN, KARL, 120
long-horned beetle, **26**
Lophophora, 608
LSD (*see* lysergic acid diethylamide)
lungfishes, 423–424
lungs, human, 575–577
(*see also* human, respiratory
system)
luteinizing hormone (LH), 627
Lycopodium, 257–258
lymph, 556
lumph glands, 566, 651
lymph nodes, 649
lymphatic system, 556, 564,
566
and fats, 550–551
lymphocytes, 559, 649
lysergic acid diethylamide
(LSD), 608, 609, 610
lysosomes, 73–75

M

MACLEOD, COLIN, 149
macronucleus, in *Paramecium*,
242
magnesium,
as a catalyst, 527
in diet, 526–527

magnification, calculation of,
47
magnolia, **21**
MAGOUN, HORACE W., 609
malaria, 232, 245–246, 642
malnutrition, 533
MALPIGHI, MARCELLO, 383,
488, 555
MALTHUS, THOMAS R., 188,
699
Malthus, theory of population,
699
maltose, digestion of, 538–539
mammals, 468–486
appearance of, 175
characteristics of, 469
flesh-eating (carnivorous),
479–481
flying, 477–478
gnawing, 482–483
hoofed, 481–482
intelligence of, 469
ocean dwelling, 478–479,
481
orders of, 475–486
placental, 469, 474–475
pouched, 472–474
reproduction of, 472–475
rise of, 468–471
toothless, 476–477
trunk-bearing, 483
(*see also* specific mammal)
mammary glands, 469
mammoth, 469, **483**
man,
appearance on earth, 177
diseases of, 641–657
and dispersal of organisms,
681
modern, **494**, 498–502
as a primate, 484, 486, 490
races of, 499–502
(*see also* Homo sapiens and
human)
manatee, **479**
mandibles,
crayfish, 372
grasshopper, 379, 381
mange mite, 370
manta ray, **27**
maples, leaves of, **5**
Marchantia, 253–254
marihuana, **615**
marine biome, 689, **690**–691
marlin, **27**

organ, 81
  homologous, 166–167
  vestigial, 167
  (*see also* specific organ)
organ of Corti, **589**
organ systems,
  arthropod, 366
  vertebrate, formation of, 405–406
  (*see also* specific system)
organelles, 73
organism, 81
  consumer, 670
origin of life, 169
Origin of Species, 7, 185–186, 188, 195
Oscillatoria, **16, 201**–202
osculum, 323
osmosis, 95–97, 270–271, 282
osmotic pressure, 95
ossification, 508
Osteichthyes, 401, 403
osteoblasts, 509
Ostracoderm, 410
ostrich, **28**
ovarian-uterine cycle, 626–629
ovary,
  flower, 294, 295, 299
  human, 606, 625–626, **627**
  mammalian, placental, 474
overpopulation,
  and birth control, 701–702
  human, 698–703
  and natural selection, 185
  and pressure, 675–676
overweight, and heart disease, 655
oviducts, 625–626, 628, 631
ovipositor, grasshopper, 384
ovists, 630
ovulation, 626–629, 631
ovule, flower, 294, 295
  development of, 299–300
ovum, human (*see* egg cell, human)
oxidation, and respiration, 112–116
oxygen,
  and alveolus, diffusion in, 575–577
  in atmosphere, 84, 116
  and autotrophs, 116
  and capillaries, 565
  in earth's crust, 84, 85
  in human body, 84, 85

  and contraction of muscle, 516–517
  and photosynthesis, 105–107, 109
  and red corpuscles, 558
  and respiration, 112–116
  and water depth, 690–691
  and water pollution, 707
oxygen-carbon dioxide cycle, **673**
oxyhemoglobin, 558
oxytocin, 607
oyster, **23**

P

pacemaker, 569, 599
Pacific salamander, **27**
paired fins and limbs, 413
Paleocene Epoch, 176
paleontologist, 164–165
paleontology, 2, 396
Paleozoic Era, 171–173
palisade layer, 286
palm, date, 294
palps, 356–357
pampas, 686
pancreas, frog, 439
pancreas, human,
  and digestion, 548
  as endocrine gland, **604**–605
panspermia, theory of, 36
Paramecium caudatum, **18, 242**–244
parasites, 668
  flatworms as, 336–338
  protozoans as, 244–246
  roundworms as, 338–341
  (*see also* specific parasite)
parasitism, 668
parasympathetic nerves, 599
parathyroid gland, **604**
parenchyma cells, 267, 276
parrot fish, **27**
passive transport, 97
PASTEUR, LOUIS, 121, 209, 642–643
  biography, 643
pasteurization, 209, 643
pathogens, 641 (*see also* specific pathogen)
PAULING, LINUS, 168
PAVLOV, IVAN, 610–613
  biography, 611

pearl, formation of, **357**–359
peat, 256
pedipalps, 368
Peking Man, **494,** 495–496
Pelecypoda, 359
PENFIELD, WILDER, 598
penguin, **461,** 464, **681**
  king, **28**
penicillin, 210, 234, 236, 644
Penicillium, **18,** 234, 236
Pennsylvanian Period, 171–173
pepsin, 546
pepsinogen, 546
peptide bond, 91
PEPYS, SAMUEL, 642
perennials, 256, 278
perianth, 293
pericardial cavity,
  crayfish, 373
  fish, 417
periosteum, human, 510
Peripatus, **24, 366**
peristalsis, 545
Permian Period, 173
perspiration, 582
petal, 293, 295
petiole, 282
Petri dish, 209, 210
petrified forest, 250
petroleum, conversion to human food, 714
pH value, 50
Phaeophyta, 9, 19
phagocyte, 559, 651
phalanges, 166, 510
pharyngitis, 578
pharynx, 545, 574–575
  Planaria, 335
pheasant, **461**
  ring-necked, **28**
phenotype, 129
phenylalanine, 92, **153**
phenylketonuria, 156
phloem, 256, 267, 270, 277, 278
phlox, **21**
phosphate, in ADP and ATP, 102–103
phosphorescent, 221
phosphoric acid, 38
phosphorus, 85
  and ATP, 526
  in diet, 526
  and parathyroid gland, 604

photography, 47–50
  microscopic, 48–50
  time-lapse, 47–48
photoperiodism, 310
photosynthesis, 104–112, **105**, 287, 289, 665
  artificial, 714
  and oxygen-carbon dioxide cycle, 673
phototropism, 316, 317
phycocyanin, 200
phylum, defined, 8
Physalia, **329**
Physarum, **18**
physics, defined, 3
physiology, 2
  and modern races, 501
pia mater, 595, 597
pigeon, passenger, 703
pill bug, **376**
pine, **21**
pinnae, 256
pinnules, 256
pinocytosis, 73, **272**
Pisces, 403
pistil, 293–295
pitch, and hearing, 590
pitcher plant, 288, **290**
pith cells, 277
Pithecanthropus erectus, 495
pituitary gland, 604, 606–607, 626, 627, 629
  and stress, 702
placenta, 469, 474–475, 630, 632, **634, 635**, 637
placoid scales, 413–**414**
Planaria, 334–336
  digestion, **335**
  excretion, 336
  nervous system, **335**–336
  regeneration, 336
  reproduction, 336
plankton, 376, 689, 692
  and new technology, 714
plant growth, 262, 268–269, 309–317
  contact and, 315–316
  gravity and, 314–315
  hormones and, 311–314
  light and, 309–310, **311**, 316
  moisture and, 310, 316–317
  temperature and, 311
Plant Kingdom, 11, 20–21
plants,
  ancient land, 252

fungal diseases of, 230–232
insectivorous, 288–290
non-vascular, 11
parts of, 266–267
tissues of, 267
vascular, 11, 256
(*see also* plant growth and specific plant)
plasma, 556, 557
plasma proteins, 557–558
  and electrophoresis, 51
plasmodium, 232
Plasmodium, **17**, 245–246
platelets, 560–561
Platyhelminthes, 22, 334–338
platypus, **28, 472**
Pleistocene Epoch, **177**
Plesiosaurus, 448
pleura, 577
pleural cavity, 577
Pliocene Epoch, 177
Pliohippus, 471
plover, golden, 464
plumule, 264, 266
pneumonia, 578, 644
polar bodies, 124–126
poliomyelitis, 140, 645, 646
  virus particles of, **57**
pollen, 297, 388
pollen basket, 388
pollen sac, 297
pollen tube, 299
pollination, **296**, 297–299
  agents of, 298–299
  self- and cross-, **298**
pollution,
  air, 708–709
  thermal, 707
  water, 706–708
polyp, 325
  feeding, 328
  reproductive, 328
polypeptide, 91
  and digestion, 540
polysaccharide, 523
Polysiphonia, **19**
pome, 302, 303
PONNAMPERUMA, CYRIL, 38
population,
  and birth control, 701–702
  changes in, 160
  and food, 671–672
  and human resources, 698–703
  limits of, 676

rise in world, 699–700
  stabilization of, 701–702
Population, An Essay on the Principle of, 188, 699
population pressure, 188, 676
population pyramid, 671–672
porcupine, 483
porcupine fish, **27**
pore,
  genital, 336
  incurrent, 323
Porifera, 22, 323
porkworm, 340
Porphyra, 223
porpoise, **29**, 478–479
portal vein, 550
Portuguese man-of-war, 22, **329**
posture, human, 491–492
"pot," 615
potassium,
  in diet, 526–527
  and sodium balance, 527
potential energy, 100
potter's wasp, **26**
PREBUS, ALBERT, 59
precipitins, 651
predation, 667
predator, 667
preformation, theory of, 630
pregnancy, human, 630–637
PRIESTLEY, JOSEPH, 106
primates, 484–486
  divergent lines of development, 492
  probable development of, 484
  (*see also* specific primate)
primitive streak, 406
Proboscidea, 483
proboscis,
  elephant, 483
  moth, **387**
Proconsul, 492–493
progesterone, 626, 628–630
proglottids, 337–338
prolactin, 607
prophase, 77–78
prostate gland, 624
proteinoids, 37–38, **39**
proteins, 37, 90, 521, 525
  and digestion, **539**, 540, 546–548
  formation of, 111–112, 152–156, **153, 154, 155**

bacteria, 205
bird, **460**
clam, 356
crayfish, 373
earthworm, 343
fish, bony, **418**
frog, **440**–441
grasshopper, **382**, 383
Hydra, 326–327
plant, 287
respiratory system, human, 574–578, **576**
disorders of, 578
response, inborn, 594
rest, and heart disease, 655
reticulum, endoplasmic, 73
retina, 588
retting, 208
Rh (Rhesus) factor, 144–145, 562
rhizoids, 227, 235, 239
rhizome, 256
Rhizopoda, 17
Rhizopus nigricans, **18**, 227
Rhodophyta, 9, 19
rhodopsin, 588–589
rib, human, 509
riboflavin, 529
ribonucleic acid (RNA), 39, 80, 89–90, 151–156
in bacteriophage, 65–68
and leukemia, 560
in nucleolus, 76
in ribosomes, 73, 80, 152
in tobacco mosaic virus, 61–65
in viruses, 61–68, 645
ribose, 38, 89, 102–103
ribosomes, 73, 80, 152
rickets, 530, **532**
ring-necked pheasant, **28**
RNA (*see* ribonucleic acid)
rock,
sedimentary, 170
stratification of, 170
rockweed, 222
Rocky Mountain spotted fever, 371
rodent, and food chain, 670
Rodentia, 482–483
Roentgen, Wilhelm, 51
roentgen rays, 51
root, 268–273
cap, 269
hairs, 268, **270**–271

pressure, 262
regions of growth in, **268**–269
tip, 268
tissues, 269–270
rotifers (*Rotifera*), **23**
roundworms, 338–341
royal jelly, 390
Royal Society of London, 71
Ruben, Samuel, 107
ruminants, 482
runoff, 672
Ruska, Ernst, 59
Russell, Louis B., 571
rusts, 226
on wheat, **231**–232

S

Sagan, Carl, 38
St. Martin, Alex, 537
salinity, 663, 689
barrier to dispersal of organisms, 682
saliva, 540–541
salivary glands, **540**–541
Salk, Jonas, 646
Salk vaccine, 646
salmon, 419–420
salt, as essential nutrient, 526
salvarsan, 644
samara, 302, 303
sand dollar, **24, 354**
sand shark, **27**
sandworm, **23**, 345–346
saprophytes, 204
(*see also* bacteria)
sapwood, 280
Sargasso Sea, 222
Sargassum, **19**, 222
savanna, 687
sawfish, 414
scalariform vessels, 278
scales,
placoid, 413–**414**
reptile, 449
scallop, **23**
scarlet fever, and kidney, 518
scavengers, 667–668
schizophrenia, 140–141
Schizophyta, 9, 16, 202–210
Schleiden, Matthias, 72
Schleiden-Schwann cell theory, 72
Schmidt, Johannes, 420

Schwann, Theodor, 72
Schwann sheath, 592
Schwenderer, Simon, 233
scion, 305
scolex, 337
scorpion, **24**, 367, 370
scrotum, 624
Scudder, John, 563
scurvy, 530
Scypha, **22**
sea anemone, **22, 330**, 331
sea cow, **479**
sea cucumber, **24, 351**, 354
sea horse, **27**
sea lettuce, **223**
sea lion, 481
sea squirt, **26, 400**–402
sea urchin, **24, 351**, 353–354
seal, 481
sebaceous gland, 583
secretin, 548
seed coat, 263
seeds, 262–267
dispersal of, **304**
formation of, 299–300
segmentation, arthropod, 365
segregation, principle of, 130, **131**
Selaginella, 257–258
selection, 194 (*see also* natural selection)
self-pollination, **298**
semen, 624
semicells, 219
semicircular canal, 590
seminal receptacles, in earthworm, 344
seminal vesicles, earthworm, 344
sense organs,
crayfish, 374
fish, bony, 419
frog, 441–442
grasshopper, 383–384
human, 586–591
sensitivity, 33, 35
sepal, 293, 295
septa, earthworm, 342
Sequoia, **21**, 250
Sequoia National Park, 250
serotonin, 609
seta, moss, 255
setae, crayfish, 374
sewage, and water pollution, 707

tracheid, 278
Tracheophyta, 11, 20–21, 256
trachoma, 645
trait,
    continuous, 139
    discontinuous, 139
    dominant, 129
    recessive, 129
    sex-linked, 136–137
tranquilizers, 609–610
transfusion, blood, 561–562, 650–651
transpiration, 287–288
transport, active, 95–97, **96**, 271–272
transport, passive, 97
tree,
    deciduous, 285
    evergreen, 285
tree frog, **27**, **433**
trepang, 354
Triassic Period, 173–174
Triceratops, 175
trichina, 340
trichinosis, 340
trichocysts, 244
trilobite, 364–**365**
tropical rain forest, **688**
tropisms, plant, 314–317
troposphere, 663
TROTTER, THOMAS, 616
truffles, 230
trunk, 483
trypanosome, **17**, 244
trypsin, 548, 549
TSCHERMAK, ERICH, 128
tsetse fly, 244, 642
Tuatara, 449, **450**
tube feet, 351
tuberculosis, 140, 578, 644
tumors, 656
tundra, **684–685**
tunicates, 402
turkey, 461
turtle, 450–451
    box, **451**
    hawksbill, **28**
twins, **140**
tympanic membrane, 589
Tyrannosaurus, **28**, 175, 448
tyrant lizard, 448

U

Uakari monkey, **30**

ulcer, peptic, 546, **547**
Ulothrix, **216**, **217**
umbilical cord, 475, 632, **634**, **635**, 638
ungulate, 481–482
United Nations, Food and Agricultural Organization, 700
United States Fish and Wildlife Service, 712
univalve, 359
uracil, 152
urea, 88, 525, 579, 580
uredospores, 231
ureter, 579
urethra, 579, 624
uric acid, 579
urinalysis, 581
urine, 526, 579–581
uropods, 372
use and disuse, theory of, 183
uterine cycle (*see* ovarian-uterine cycle)
uterus, 474–475, 625–626, 628–632, 637–638

V

vaccine, 643, 646, 652
vacuoles, 76
    contractile, 240, 241
    food, 240
vagina, 474, 626, 631
valves,
    clam, 355
    heart, 567–569
    vein, **565**
variations, in species, 188
vascular bundle, 277
vascular cylinder, 270
vegetative propagation, **305–306**
veins,
    human, 564, 565, 570, 579
    leaf, 283, 286–287
venation, leaf,
    netted, 283
    parallel, 283
venom,
    black widow spider, 368
    snake, 453–454
ventricle,
    fish, 417
    human, 567–569
venules, 565

Venus, atmosphere of, 40
Venus flower basket, **22**
Venus's flytrap, **35**, 288, **290**
vertebrate, 10–11, 320, 396–397
    characteristics of, 402
    classes of, 402–403
    development of (*see* vertebrate development)
    embryonic stages of, **402**
    (*see also* specific vertebrate)
vertebrate development, 403–407
    blastula, 405
    chromosome numbers, 404
    cleavage, 404–405
    fertilization, 404
    gastrula, 405
    organ formation, 405–406
    zygote, 404–405
VESALIUS, ANDREAS, 488
vibrio, 203
VICTORIA, QUEEN, 143–144
villi,
    of chorion, 632
    of intestine, 549, **550**
viper, 454
viper fish, **27**
VIRCHOW, RUDOLF, 72
virology, 58
viruses, 56–69
    and cancer, 657
    crystals, **58–59**
    and disease, 60–61, 644–647
    and DNA, 61, 66–68
    filterable, 56, 644
    history of, 57–60
    hosts of, 60–61
    and leukemia, 560
    nature of, 56–57
    and pregnancy, 632
    and RNA, 61, 62–65
    shapes of, 61
    sizes of, 61
    staining, 59
    and tissue cultures, 645–646
    (*see also* specific virus)
vision, human, 587–588
vitamin A, 421, 528, 531
    deficiency in, **528**
vitamin B complex, 528–530, 531
    deficiency in, **529**
vitamin B$_{12}$, and anemia, 558

vitamin C, 530, 531
  deficiency in, **530**
vitamin D, 421, 530–532
  deficiency in, **532**
vitamin K, 205, 531, 532, 551
vitamins, 521, 527–533
  classification of, 532
  as co-enzymes, 528
  and the deficiency diseases,
    528, 531
  discovery of, 527–528
  functions of, 531
  in pills, 533
  sources of, 531
  table of essential, 531
  (*see also* specific vitamin)
vocal cords, 578
voice box, 578
Volvox, **18**, **217**, **220**
Vorticella, **18**

W

WAKSMAN, SELMAN, 236
WALLACE, RUSSELL, 188–189
walrus, 481
warblers, European, 464
water,
  conservation of, 706
  and digestion, 539–540
  and dispersal of organisms,
    681
  on earth, 31–32
  and environment, 663–664
  fluoridation of, 543–544
  in human body, 521, 525–
    526, 555, 578–579, 582
  new sources of, 713
  and plants, 268, 310

pollution of, 706–708
and seed dispersal, 304
in stems, 281–282
and technology, 713–714
water cycle, 288, **672**–673
water flea, 375–376
water moccasin, 454–**455**
water vascular system, 351,
  352
WATSON, JAMES P., 80
weapons, and human development, 502
weasels, 480–481
web, spider, **369**–370
WEIDENREICH, FRANK, 496
WEINBERG, WILHELM, 159
WEISMANN, AUGUST, 78, 184–
  185
WEIZSAKER, CARL VON, 36
WENT, FRITS, 311–312
whale, 478–479
  blue, 469, **478**, 689
wheat, **21**
wildlife, restoration of, 712–
  713
wilting, 288
wind,
  and dispersal of organisms,
    681
  and seed dispersal, 304
  and soil erosion, 710–711
wing, structure of, **458**
winter skate, **27**
WOEHLER, FRIEDRICH, 88
wolf, 480
  grey, **480**
  Tasmanian, 473
womb, 625
wonder drugs, 644

wood,
  spring, 279
  summer, 279
wood duck, **28**
woodpecker, 461–462
World Health Organization,
  and malaria, 245
worms, flat, round, segmented,
  334–347
wriggler, 388

X

X rays, 51–52
  and cancer, 656
xerophthalmia, 528
XX (female chromosomes),
  136
XY (male chromosomes), 137
xylem, 267, 277
  vessels, 256, 270–271

Y

yaws, 203
yeast, 114
yellow fever, 642
yolk, 404, 406

Z

Zinjanthropus, 493–495
zoology, defined, 2
Zoological Philosophy, 183
zoospore, 215
ZWORYKIN, VLADIMIR, 48
zygospore, 219, 228
zygote, 122
  (*see also* reproduction)

CDEFGH 076543
PRINTED IN THE UNITED STATES OF AMERICA